TECHNICAL COMMUNICATION
A Practical Approach

William S. Pfeiffer

Jan Boogerd

Custom Edition for
the University of British Columbia

Taken from:
Technical Communication: A Practical Approach, Fourth Canadian Edition
by William S. Pfeiffer and Jan Boogerd

Technical Writing: A Practical Approach, Third Canadian Edition
by William S. Pfeiffer and Jan Boogerd

D1418469

Taken from:

Technical Communication: A Practical Approach, Fourth Canadian Edition
by William S. Pfeiffer and Jan Boogerd
Copyright © 2007, 2004, 2000, 1997 by Pearson Education Canada
A division of Pearson Canada, Inc.
Toronto, Ontario

Technical Writing: A Practical Approach, Third Canadian Edition
by William S. Pfeiffer and Jan Boogerd
Copyright © 2004 by Pearson Education Canada
A division of Pearson Canada, Inc.

This special edition published in cooperation with Pearson Custom Publishing.

Printed and bound in Canada

10 9 8 7 6 5 4 3 2

ISBN 0-536-48968-8

2007360558

SB

Please visit our web site at *www.pearsoncustom.com*

PEARSON CUSTOM PUBLISHING
501 Boylston Street, Suite 900, Boston, MA 02116
A Pearson Education Company

Contents

Chapter 13 Oral Communication **350**

Chapter 14 Technical Research **373**

This content is taken from *Technical Writing: A Practical Approach*, Third Edition, by William S. Pfeiffer and Jan Boogerd

Communication Challenge 1
  "There Ain't No Justice"
Communication Challenge 2
  "M&K's Moscow Buyout: Global Dilemmas"
Communication Challenge 3
  "Telecommuting: The Last Frontier?"
Communication Challenge 4
  "The Montreal Format Guide: Trouble in River City"

Preface

Every student who plans to work in business and industry must master the art of technical communication. Indeed, your ability to communicate effectively in print, in presentations, and in electronic media will play a major role in your success in your chosen profession. *Technical Communication: A Practical Approach* is grounded in the principle that you will learn to communicate more effectively by writing early and as much as possible in a course. It contains a wealth of guidelines, examples, and models to help you become a competent professional writer.

When students are asked to describe their professional goals for the next 10 years, their comments often suggest that they hope to rise to important positions in the workplace and make genuine contributions to their professions. Such long-term thinking is crucial, keeping you on course in your life. Yet, ultimately, the way you handle the small details of daily life most influences the real contribution you will make in the long run. If you do good work, believe in what you do, and communicate well with others—both interpersonally and in writing—success will come your way. This book tries to show that clear, concise, and honest writing is one of the most powerful tools at your disposal.

KEY FEATURES

The core features of the text include the following:

Focus on process and product: Students begin writing in Chapter 1, Process in Technical Communication. The text immerses students in the process of technical communication while teaching practical formats for getting the job done.

A simple ABC pattern for all documents: The "ABC format"—Abstract, Body, and Conclusion—will guide students' work in this course and throughout their careers. This underlying three-part structure provides a convenient handle for designing almost every technical document.

Numbered guidelines: Many sets of short, numbered guidelines make this book easy to use to complete class projects. Each set of guidelines will take students through the process of finishing assignments, such as writing a proposal, doing research on the Internet, constructing a bar chart, and preparing an oral presentation.

Martin & Koffman, a fictional company: Martin & Koffman is a fictional diversified engineering consulting firm working in a variety of technical and nontechnical areas. This company was created to provide a context for the many students who do not have experience working in a professional or technical organization. Martin & Koffman provides a realistic setting for many of the book's examples and assignments.

Annotated models: The text contains models grouped at the end of chapters on grey-edged pages for easy reference. Annotations in the margins show exactly how the sample documents illustrate the guidelines set forth in the chapters.

Assignments: Practical assignments, both individual writing projects and collaborative work, provide opportunities for students to build their portfolio of communication skills and practise all forms of technical communication.

Writing handbook: This book provides an alphabetized handbook on grammar, mechanics, and usage. The writing handbook gives quick access to rules for eliminating editing errors during the revision process.

NEW IN THIS EDITION

Key changes for the fourth Canadian edition include the following:

Employability skills exercises: The Conference Board of Canada has developed *Employability Skills 2000+*, a list of the skills, attitudes, and behaviours needed for success in today's working world. At the end of each chapter, an exercise highlights some of these skills and shows how they can be applied to the tasks of technical communications.

Expanded coverage of e-mail: Chapter 8, E-mail and Memos, has a new, stronger focus on the use of e-mail and guidelines for its appropriate use.

New coverage of web design: Chapter 4, Page Design and Web Design, includes examples and guidelines for designing effective web pages. Further information on writing for the web can be found in a bonus chapter on the Text Enrichment Site that accompanies this text.

Updated coverage of graphics: The chapter on graphics (Chapter 5) directly follows the chapter on page and web design. The coverage has been expanded and updated.

Updated coverage of documentation: Chapter 14, Technical Research, offers updated information on using APA, MLA, and CBE styles. The model report at the end of the chapter uses APA style.

SUPPLEMENTS

Text Enrichment Site (**www.pearsoned.ca/text/pfeiffer**)*:* This website provides the following resources to support the text:

- Sample documents: A variety of documents that supplement the models given at the end of chapters in the text.
- Grammar tests: Two tests of 20 questions each that focus on punctuation, subject–verb agreement, use of numbers, misplaced modifiers, dangling modifiers, unclear antecedents, and active voice.
- Internet exercises: Assignments that involve looking at external websites to assess their effectiveness as examples of technical communication or to use them as research sources on topics related to the text.
- Communication challenges: Cases that present realistic problems related to the chapter material, such as an ethical dilemma to address or a communication problem to solve.

- Weblinks: Links to additional information and guidance on the topics presented in the text.
- Bonus chapter: A full chapter on developing websites, including the planning of content, structure, and design (written by Craig Baehr of Texas Tech University).

Instructors can download the following supplements from a password-protected section of Pearson Education Canada's online catalogue (vig.pearsoned.ca). Navigate to your book's catalogue page to view a list of those supplements that are available. See your local sales representative for details and access.

Instructor's Manual: This manual offers chapter overviews, teaching suggestions, additional assignments, and transparency masters.

Test Item File: Provided in Microsoft Word format, this testbank provides 15 multiple-choice and 20 true/false questions per chapter, as well as editing revision questions for Chapter 16.

ACKNOWLEDGMENTS FOR THE SIXTH U.S. EDITION

I would like to thank the following reviewers of the sixth edition textbook for helping with the revision of the textbook:

Brian Ballentine, Case Western Reserve University
Jay Goldberg, Marquette University
Linda Grace, Southern Illinois University
Darlene Hollon, Northern Kentucky University
John Puckett, Oregon Institute of Technology
Kirk Swortzel, Mississippi State University
Catharine Schauer, Visiting Professor, Embry Riddle University

A special thanks goes to Craig Baehr, from Texas Tech University, for contributing the new Chapter 11, Web Pages and Writing for the Web.

The book also greatly benefited from the help of Shawn Tonner, who revised Chapter 13, as she has done in three previous editions, with the help of her husband, Mark Stevens. Other friends and colleagues who contributed to this edition and/or other editions include Saul Carliner, George Ferguson, Alan Gabrielli, Bob Harbort, Mike Hughes, Dory Ingram, Becky Kelly, Chuck Keller, Jo Lundy, Minoru Moriguchi, Randy Nipp, Jeff Orr, Ken Rainey, Lisa A. Rossbacher, Betty Oliver Seabolt, Hattie Schumaker, John Sloan, Herb Smith, Lavern Smith, James Stephens, John Ulrich, Steven Vincent, and Tom Wiseman.

Four companies allowed me to use written material gathered during my consulting work: Fugro-McClelland, Law Engineering and Environmental Services, McBride-Ratcliff and Associates, and Westinghouse Environmental and Geotechnical Services. Although this book's fictional firm, McDuff, Inc., does have features of the world I observed as a consultant, I want to emphasize that McDuff is truly an invention.

I also appreciate the help of the following students for allowing me to adapt their written work for use in the book: Michael Alban, Becky Austin, Corey Baird, Natalie Birnbaum, Cedric Bowden, Gregory Braxton, Ishmael Chigumira, Bill Darden, Jeffrey Daxon, Rob Duggan, William English, Joseph Fritz, Jon Guffey, Sam

Harkness, Gary Harvey, Lee Harvey, Hammond Hill, Sudhir Kapoor, Steven Knapp, Wes Matthews, Kim Meyer, James Moore, Chris Owen, Scott Lewis, James Porter, James Roberts, Mort Rolleston, Chris Ruda, Barbara Serkedakis, Tom Skywark, Tom Smith, DaTonja Stanley, James Stephens, Chris Swift, and Jeff Woodward.

For all six editions, it has been my good fortune to have the same extraordinary developmental editor, my friend and colleague Monica Ohlinger. Many of the ideas that have made this book successful for over a decade were hers. Also, I want to give special thanks to my Prentice Hall editor, Gary Bauer, for his continuing faith in my book. Gary has developed deep knowledge of the field of technical communication that greatly enhanced the sixth edition. Other Prentice Hall people who contributed significantly to the project include Kevin Happell, production editor, and Kristina Holmes, design coordinator.

Finally, deepest thanks go to my family—Evelyn, Zachary, and Katie—for their love and support throughout this and every writing project I take on.

William Sanborn Pfeiffer

ACKNOWLEDGMENTS FOR THE FOURTH CANADIAN EDITION

The formal technical report used in Chapter 11 of this text is a slightly modified version of the actual report prepared by Jacques Whitford Consulting Engineers and Environmental Scientists for Lundy Construction Limited. In particular I would like to thank Fred Griffiths of Jacques Whitford, Enzo DiChiara of Lundy Construction, and Barry Padolsky of Barry Padolsky Architect Limited for providing material for the book. I would especially like to thank Fred Griffiths at Jacques Whitford for allowing me to transform their original material into a Martin & Koffman product for the purposes of this text. Also, I would like to thank the International Energy Agency (IEA) for their permission to use an excerpt from *Energy Technology and Climate Change*.

I would like to thank the reviewers who provided feedback on the previous edition and the manuscript, including the following:

Jim Catton, Algonquin College of Applied Arts and Technology
Carole Clark, Nova Scotia Community College (Marconi Campus)
Erick Desjardins, Fanshawe College
Michelle Flanagan, Nova Scotia Community College (Akerley Campus)
Nirdosh Ganske, Red River College
Ian Hartley, University of Northern British Columbia
Barry McKinnon, College of New Caledonia

Jan Boogerd

Process in Technical Writing

Good communication skills are essential in any career you choose. Jobs, promotions, raises, and professional prestige result from your ability to write and speak effectively. With so much at stake, you need a simple road map to direct you toward writing excellence. *Technical Communication: A Practical Approach* is such a map.

Chapters 1–5 give you an overview of technical writing and prepare you to complete the assignments in this book:

Chapter 1: Defines technical writing and describes the writing process. As shown in Figure 1-1, the technical writing process has three main parts: planning, drafting, and revising. Careful completion of this process is the best guarantee of a successful product—the final document.

Chapter 2: Introduces you to life in the corporate world via Martin & Koffman. This organization will provide the framework for most examples and assignments in this book.

Chapter 3: Focuses on organizing information for diverse readers, who are often busy and who may be unfamiliar with a particular project.

Chapter 4: Describes techniques for using the best elements of page and Web design in the writing process.

Chapter 5: Explains the principles behind effective graphics.

We have kept preliminaries to a minimum so that you can begin writing early in the course. Now let's take a closer look at the nature of technical writing.

GETTING FROM HERE TO THERE

Many of you will already have had some experience writing in the workplace or will have learned how to write short essays in previous writing courses. This book helps you transfer basic knowledge of writing to the kind of writing done on the job. In the process, you will discover that learning technical writing is a bit like studying a foreign language, in that you face a new set of rules. Yet career writing is so practical, so well grounded in common sense that your writing should develop smoothly from your work. This section highlights features of both traditional academic writing and job-related technical writing.

Features of Academic Writing

Writing you have done in school probably has had the following characteristics:

- **Purpose:** To demonstrate what you know about the topic, in a way that justifies a high grade
- **Your knowledge of the topic:** Less than the teacher who evaluates the writing.
- **Audience:** Teacher, who requests the assignment and then reads it from beginning to end
- **Criteria for evaluation:** Depth, logic, clarity, unity, and grammar

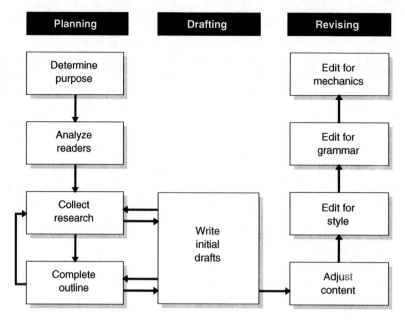

Figure 1-1   Flow chart for the technical writing process

Academic writing requires you to display your learning to someone who knows more about the subject than you do. Because this person's job is to evaluate your work, you have what might be called a "captive audience." Following are two common situations in which academic writing would be appropriate, along with brief examples:

Example 1: Essays for English Class

In a typical high school, college, or university writing class, you write short essays based on your experience or readings. Instructors expect you to (1) state the topic, purpose, and main points in the introduction; (2) develop the supporting points in the body; and (3) wrap up the paper in the conclusion. Your reader wants a coherent, unified, grammatically sound, and interesting piece of writing. What follows is the first paragraph from one such essay. The student was asked to attend and then comment on a local cultural event.

> "Prairie Painters," a recent exhibit at the National Gallery of Canada, offers viewers a glimpse of the land that confronted the early settlers, of the struggles those early settlers endured, and of the reconciliation that was achieved between the settlers and the land. This paper will describe how these aspects of settlement are reflected in three contemporary works—Gerard's *Open Sky*, Fagan's *Warmth in Winter*, and Schumacker's *A Lonely Triumph*.

Example 2: Exams and Papers in General Studies Courses

Courses such as history and science often require you to write analytical papers and exam answers. As with essays for a writing class, these papers should start with a topic statement that outlines the main points and then proceed with supporting paragraphs. For example, you may be asked to describe both the immediate and long-term reasons for a particular event. Following is the first paragraph of a cause–effect essay in environmental science. The writer must define and give causes for the "greenhouse effect."

> The term *greenhouse effect* refers to the global warming trend of the earth. It occurs when the sun's reflected heat is unable to escape the earth's atmosphere into space, because of a buildup of carbon dioxide and other gases in the atmosphere. This essay will describe these main reasons for the dramatic increase in the greenhouse effect: the burning of rain forests in the Amazon, worsening auto pollution around the world, and the increased use of coal-fired plants.

In both examples, the **purpose** is to demonstrate knowledge, and the **audience** is someone already familiar with the subject or approach. In this sense, academic writing shows your command of information to someone more knowledgeable about the subject than you are. The next section examines a different kind of writing—the kind you will be doing in this course and in your career. The purpose and audience differ considerably from those of academic writing.

Features of Technical Writing

The ground rules for writing shift somewhat when you begin your career. Those unprepared for this change often flounder for years, never quite understanding the new rules. *Technical writing* is a generic term for all written communications done on the job, whether in business, industry, or other professions. Technical writing is particularly identified with jobs in technology, engineering, science, the health professions, and other fields with specialized vocabularies. The terms *technical writing*, *professional writing*, *business writing*, and *occupational writing* all mean essentially the same thing—writing done in your career. Following are the main characteristics of technical writing:

- **Purpose:** Getting something done within an organization (for example, completing a project, persuading a customer, pleasing your boss)
- **Your knowledge of the topic:** Usually greater than that of the reader
- **Audience:** Often several people, with differing technical backgrounds
- **Criteria for evaluation:** Delivery of the information that the audience needs, with clear and simple organization, in a format that meets the needs of busy readers

Contrast the following features with those of academic writing, which were listed earlier:

1. Technical writing has a practical role on the job; academic writing aims only to display your knowledge.
2. In technical writing, an informed writer conveys needed information to an uninformed reader; academic writing is done by a student (the learner) for a teacher (the source of knowledge).
3. Technical writing often is read by many readers; academic writing aims to satisfy only one person—the teacher.

Technical writing places greater emphasis on organization and format, to help readers find important information as quickly as possible.

Figure 1-2 lists some typical on-the-job writing assignments. While not exhaustive, the list does include many of the writing projects you will encounter. Also, Figure 1-3 gives an example of a short technical document.

Besides projects that involve writing, you will also have speaking responsibilities during your career—for example, formal speeches at conferences and informal presentations at meetings. **Technical communication** includes both the writing and the speaking tasks involved with any job.

Although technical communication plays a key role in the success of all technical professionals and managers, the amount of time you devote to it will depend on your job. A 1989 American survey of technical managers, however, gives some idea of the time involved. Conducted by the National Aeronautics and Space Administration (NASA), this survey canvassed managers in profit-making and nonprofit organizations in the field of aeronautics. As Figure 1-4 shows, 100 percent of the profit managers and 98 percent of the nonprofit managers in the study considered technical communication a "somewhat important" or "very important" part of their work.

Even more telling is the amount of time the NASA survey respondents spend communicating. Figure 1-4 indicates that they used (1) over one-third of their work time conveying information *to* others, and (2) another one-third working with technical information sent to them *by* others. In other words, both groups spent roughly two-thirds of their working time on duties associated with technical communication.

Now you know the nature and importance of technical writing. The next section examines the first part of the planning stage: determining a document's purpose.

Correspondence: In-house or External
- memo to your boss and to your subordinates
- routine letter to customers, vendors, etc.
- "good news" letter to customers
- "bad news" letter to customers
- sales letter to potential customers
- email message to co-workers or customers over a computer network

Short Reports: In-house or External
- analysis of a problem
- recommendation
- equipment evaluation
- progress report on project or routine periodic report
- report on the results of laboratory or fieldwork
- description of the results of a company trip

Long Reports: In-house or External
- complex problem analysis, recommendation, or equipment evaluation
- project report on field or laboratory work
- feasibility study

Other Documents
- proposal to boss for new product line
- proposal to boss for change in procedures
- proposal to customer to sell a product, service, or idea
- proposal to funding agency for support of research project
- abstract or summary of technical article
- technical article or presentation
- operation manual or other manual

Figure 1-2   Examples of technical writing

DISCOVERING YOUR PURPOSE

Kate Paulsen works as a training supervisor for the Vancouver office of Martin & Koffman, a firm described in more detail in Chapter 2. The company is growing so quickly that its major goals include hiring, training, and retraining employees. Kate recently flew to San Francisco to attend a workshop sponsored by a major professional training organization. The workshop emphasized a new in-house procedure

MEMORANDUM

DATE: December 6, 2005
TO: Angela Koffman (Montreal)
FROM: Michael Allen (Toronto) *MA*
SUBJECT: Printer Recommendation

Introductory Summary

Recently you asked for my evaluation of the Hemphill LaserFast printer currently used in my department. Having analyzed the printer's features, print quality, and costs, I am quite satisfied with its performance.

Features

Among the LaserFast's features, I have found these five to be most useful:
1. Portrait and landscape print modes
2. Compatibility with Adobe PostScript (level 3), providing a wide variety of fonts
3. 32 megabytes of print-buffer memory
4. Selectable paper sizes (letter, legal, half-letter)
5. Print speed of 22 pages per minute
In addition, the LaserFast printer is equipped with 2 built-in fonts, and additional fonts may be downloaded into the buffer. This combination of features makes the LaserFast a most versatile printer.

Print Quality

The Hemphill LaserFast printer produces laser-sharp clarity that rivals professional typeset quality. The print resolution is an amazing 1200 x 1200 dots per inch, among the highest attainable in current desktop printers. This memo was printed on LaserFast, and as you can see, the quality speaks for itself.

Costs

Considering the features and quality, the LaserFast is an excellent printer for the money. At a retail price of $1,200, it is one of the lowest-priced laser printers of its class.

Conclusion

On the basis of my observations, I strongly recommend that our firm continue to use and purchase the LaserFast printer. Please call me at ext. 204 if you want further information about this excellent machine.

Figure 1-3 Short report

for surveying the training needs of a company's employees. After returning to Vancouver, Kate must write her manager a trip report that describes the survey technique. She ponders three different approaches for the report:

- **Giving an overview** of the survey procedure she studied during the three-day workshop, stressing a few key points so that her manager can decide whether to inquire further
- **Providing details** of the survey procedure, with enough specifics for her manager to see exactly how the survey can be used at M&K
- **Proposing** that M&K use the survey procedure, in language that argues strongly for adoption

Purpose Statements

Kate's first step is to decide what she wants to accomplish. Likewise, every piece of *your* writing should have a specific reason for being. Either you or someone else may dictate the purpose, but, in either case, you must have a firm understanding of the

Figure 1-4 Data from NASA aeronautics survey

Source: Thomas E. Pinelli et al., *Technical Communications in Aeronautics: Results of an Exploratory Study—An Analysis of Profit Managers' and Nonprofit Managers' Responses* (Washington, DC: National Aeronautics and Space Administration, NASA TM-101626, October 1989), p. 71.

TABLE 1 Importance of Technical Communications

How Important	Profit Managers		Nonprofit Managers	
	No.	%	No.	%
Very	86	92.5	43	84.3
Somewhat	7	7.5	7	13.7
Not at all	0	0.0	1	2.0
	93	100.0	51	100.0

TABLE 2 Time Spent Communicating Technical Information to Others

Time Spent per Week (hours)	Profit Managers		Nonprofit Managers	
	No.	%	No.	%
5 or less	13	14.3	9	18.0
6 to 10	33	36.2	16	30.0
11 to 20	37	40.7	21	42.0
21 or more	8	8.8	5	10.0
	91	100.0	51	100.0
Mean	13.5		13.9	

TABLE 3 Time Spent Working with Technical Information Received from Others

Time Spent per Week (hours)	Profit Managers		Nonprofit Managers	
	No.	%	No.	%
5 or less	8	8.7	6	12.0
6 to 10	42	46.2	23	46.0
11 to 20	36	39.6	18	36.0
21 or more	5	5.5	3	6.0
	91	100.0	50	100.0
Mean	13.0		13.0	

purpose before you start writing. **Purpose statements** guide every decision you make while you plan, draft, and revise.

When preparing to write, therefore, you need to ask yourself two related questions about your purpose:

Question 1: Why Am I Writing This Document?

This question should be answered in one sentence, even in complicated projects. Often the resulting purpose statement can be moved "as is" to the beginning of your outline and later to the first draft.

For example, Kate Paulsen finally decides on the following purpose statement, which becomes the first passage in her trip report: "Several training applications, discussed at the training needs survey workshop in San Francisco, may be of use at Martin & Koffman." Though she will not be strongly advocating M&K's use of the survey, she will be giving information that suggests the company might benefit by using it.

Question 2: What Response Do I Want from Readers?

The first question about purpose leads inevitably to the second about results. Again, your response should be only one or two sentences long. Though brief, it should pinpoint exactly what you want to happen as a result of your document. Are you just giving data for the file? Will the information you provide help others to do their jobs? Will your document recommend a major change?

Kate Paulsen decides on this **results statement:** "Though I'm not yet sure if this training survey is worth purchasing for M&K, I want my boss to consider it." Unlike the purpose statement, the results statement may not go directly into your document. Kate's statement, written for her own use, becomes an essential part of her planning. It is a concrete goal for her to keep in mind as she writes.

The answers to these two questions about purpose and results are included on the Planning Form that your instructor may ask you to use for assignments. Figure 1-5 on pages 8 and 9 includes a copy of the form, along with instructions for using it. You may duplicate this form for use with assignments.

Having established your purpose, you are now ready to consider the next part of the writing process: **audience analysis.**

ANALYZING YOUR READERS

One cardinal rule governs all on-the-job writing:

> Write for your reader, not for yourself.

This rule applies especially to science and technology because many readers may know little about your field. In fact, experts on writing agree that most technical writing assumes too much knowledge on the part of the reader. The key to preventing this problem is to examine the main obstacles readers face, and adopt a strategy for overcoming those obstacles. In short, *your job is not to write so that you can be understood, but to write so that no one in your audience can possibly* misunderstand.

This section (1) highlights readers' problems with understanding technical writing, (2) suggests techniques to prevent these problems, and (3) describes some main

PLANNING FORM

NAME: _____   ASSIGNMENT: _____

I. Purpose: Answer each question in one or two sentences.

A. Why are you writing this document? _____

_____

B. What response do you want from readers? _____

_____

II. Reader Matrix: Fill in names and positions of people who may read the document.

	Decision makers	Advisers	Receivers
Managers	_____ _____ _____	_____ _____ _____	_____ _____ _____
Experts	_____ _____ _____	_____ _____ _____	_____ _____ _____
Operators	_____ _____ _____	_____ _____ _____	_____ _____ _____
General readers	_____ _____ _____	_____ _____ _____	_____ _____ _____

III. Information on Individual Readers: Answer these questions about selected members of your audience. Attach additional sheets as necessary.

1. What is this reader's technical or educational background?

_____

2. What main question does this person need answered?

_____

3. What main action do you want this person to take?

_____

4. What features of this person's personality might affect his or her reading?

_____

5. What features does this person prefer in

Format? _____

Style? _____

Organization? _____

IV. Outline: Attach an outline (topic) to use in drafting the **BODY** of this document.

continues

Figure 1-5 Planning Form for technical documents

Instructions for Completing "Planning Form"

The Planning Form is for your use in preparing assignments in your technical writing course. It focuses only on the planning stage of writing. Complete it *before* you begin your first draft.

1. Use the Planning Form to help plan your strategy for all writing assignments. Your instructor may or may not require that it be submitted with assignments.

2. Photocopy the form on the last page of this book or write the answers to questions on separate sheets of paper—whichever option your instructor prefers. (Your instructor may hand out enlarged, letter-size copies of the form, which are included in the Instructor's Manual.)

3. Answer the two purpose questions in one or two sentences each. Be as specific as possible about the purpose of the document and the response you want—especially from the decision makers.

4. Note that the reader matrix classifies each reader by two criteria: (a) technical levels (shown on the vertical axis) and (b) relationship to the decision-making process (shown on the horizontal axis). Some of the boxes will be filled with one or more names; others may be blank. How you fill out the form depends on the complexity of your audience and, of course, on the directions of your instructor.

5. Refer to Chapter 2 for any Martin & Koffman positions and titles you may want to use in the reader matrix, if your paper is based on a simulated case from Martin & Koffman.

6. Note that questions in the "Information on Individual Readers" section can be filled out for one or more readers, depending on your instructor. But you should answer all five questions for each reader you choose.

7. Complete the topic outline after you have collected whatever information or research your document requires. The outline should be specific and should include two or three levels (see Figure 1-8 and Figure 1-9).

Figure 1-5 *continued*

classifications of technical readers. At first, analyzing your audience might seem awkward and even unproductive. You are forced out of your own world to consider your reader's world, before you even put pen to paper. The payoff, however, will be a document that has clear direction and gives the audience what it wants.

Obstacles for Readers

As purchasing agent for Martin & Koffman, Nizar Bhindi must recommend one automobile sedan for fleet purchase by the firm's sales force and executives. First, he will conduct some research—interviewing car firm representatives, reading car evaluations in consumer magazines, and inquiring about the needs of his firm's salespeople. Then he will submit a recommendation report to the selection committee, which consists of the company president, the accounting manager, several salespeople, and the supervisor of company maintenance. As Nizar will discover, readers of all backgrounds often have the following four problems when reading any technical document:

1. Constant interruptions
2. Impatience in finding information that they need
3. A technical background that differs from the writer's
4. Shared decision-making authority with others

If you think about these obstacles every time you write, you will be better able to understand and respond to your readers.

Obstacle 1: Readers Are Always Interrupted

As a professional, how often will you have the chance to read a report or other document without interruption? Such times are rare. Usually, your reading time will be interrupted by meetings and phone calls, so a report often gets read in several sittings. And by the time you are able to get back to the report, you may have forgotten details of the project.

Obstacle 2: Readers Are Impatient

Readers lose patience with vague or unorganized writing. They think "What's the point?" or "So what?" as they plod through memos, letters, reports, and proposals. They want to grasp the document's significance right away.

Obstacle 3: Readers Lack Your Technical Knowledge

In college and university courses, the readers of your writing are professors who usually have knowledge of the subject that you are writing about. In your career, however, you will be writing for readers who lack your information and background. They expect a technically sophisticated document but in language they can understand—if you write over their heads, you will not accomplish your purpose. Think of yourself as an educator: if readers do not learn from your reports, then you have failed in your objective.

Obstacle 4: Most Documents Have More Than One Reader

If you always wrote to only one person, technical writing would be much easier than it is. Each document could be tailored to the background, interests, and technical education of just that individual. In the business world, however, readers usually share decision-making authority with others, who may read all or just part of the text. Thus, you must respond to the needs of many individuals, most of whom have a hectic schedule, are impatient, and have a background different from yours.

Ways to Understand Readers

Obstacles to communication can be frustrating. Yet there are techniques for overcoming them. First, you must try to find out exactly what information each reader needs. Think of the problem this way: would you give a speech without learning about your audience's background? Technical writing depends just as much, if not more, on such analysis. Follow the these four steps to determine your readers' needs:

Audience Analysis Step 1: Write Down What You Know about Your Reader

To build a framework for analyzing your audience, you need to write down—not just casually think about—the answers to the following questions for each reader:

1. What is this reader's technical or educational background?
2. What main question does this person need answered?
3. What main action do you want this person to take?
4. What features of this person's personality might affect his or her reading?
5. What features does this reader prefer in
    Format?
    Style?
    Organization?

   The Planning Form in Figure 1-5 includes these five questions.

Audience Analysis Step 2: Talk with Colleagues Who Have Written to the Same Readers

Often your best source of information about your readers is a colleague where you work. Ask around the office or check company files to discover who else may have written to the same audience. Useful information could be as close as the next office.

Audience Analysis Step 3: Find Out Who Makes Decisions

Almost every document requires action of some kind. Identify decision makers ahead of time so that you can design the document with them in mind. Know the needs of your *most important* reader.

Audience Analysis Step 4: Remember That All Readers Prefer Simplicity

Even if you uncover little specific information about your readers, you can always rely on one basic fact: readers of all technical backgrounds prefer concise, simple writing. Remember that "for every word you lose, you gain a reader."

Types of Readers: Technical Levels

You have learned about some typical problems readers face and some general solutions to those problems. To complete the audience-analysis stage, this section shows you how to classify readers by two main criteria: knowledge and influence. Specifically, you must answer two questions about every potential reader:

1. How much does this reader already know about the subject?
2. What part will this reader play in making decisions?

Then use the answers to these questions to plan your document. Figure 1-6 (adapted from the Planning Form in Figure 1-5 on page 8) provides a reader matrix that you can use to quickly view the technical levels and decision-making roles of all your readers. If the document is complex, your audience may include many of the 12 categories shown on the matrix. Also, you may have more than one person in each box—that is, there may be more than one reader with the same background and decision-making role.

On-the-job writing normally requires that you translate technical ideas into language that nontechnical people can understand. This task can be complicated because you often have several readers, each with a different level of knowledge about the topic. If you are to "write for your reader, not for yourself," you must identify each reader's technical background. The following four categories will help you classify each reader's knowledge of the topic:

Reader Group 1: Managers

Many technical professionals aspire to become managers. Once in management, they may be removed from the hands-on technical details of their profession. Instead, they manage people, set budgets, and make decisions of all kinds. Thus, you should assume that management readers will not be familiar with fine technical points, or will have forgotten details of your project, or both. These managers often need the following:

- Background information
- Definitions of technical terms
- Lists and other format devices that highlight points
- Clear statements about what is supposed to happen next

Technical Level	Decision-Making Level		
	Decision makers	Advisers	Receivers
Managers			
Experts			
Operators			
General readers			

Figure 1-6 Reader matrix

In Chapter 3, we will discuss an all-purpose ABC format for organization that responds to managers' needs.

Reader Group 2: Experts

Experts include anyone with a good understanding of your topic. They may be well educated—for example, engineers and scientists—but not necessarily. In the example mentioned earlier, a maintenance supervisor with no college or university training could be considered an "expert" about selecting a new automobile for fleet purchase. That supervisor will understand any technical information about car models and features. Whatever their educational level, most experts in your audience need the following:

- Thorough explanations of technical details
- Data placed in tables and figures
- References to outside sources used in writing the report
- Clearly labelled appendices for supporting information

Reader Group 3: Operators

Because decision makers are often managers or technical experts, they tend to get most attention. Many documents, however, also have readers who are operators. They may be technicians in a field crew, workers on an assembly line, salespeople in a department store, or drivers for a trucking firm—anyone who puts the ideas in your document into practice. These readers expect the following:

- A clear table of contents for locating sections that relate to them
- Easy-to-read listings for procedures or instructions
- Definitions of technical terms
- A clear statement of exactly how the document affects their work

Reader Group 4: General Readers

General readers, also called "laypersons," often have the least amount of information about your topic or field. For example, a report on the environmental impact of a toxic waste dump might be read by general readers who are homeowners in the surrounding area. Most will have little technical understanding of toxic waste and its associated environmental hazards. These general readers often need the following:

- Definitions of technical terms
- Frequent use of graphics, such as charts and photographs
- A clear distinction between facts and opinions

Like managers, general readers need to be assured that (1) all implications of the document have been put down on paper, and (2) important information has not been buried in overly technical language.

Types of Readers: Decision-Making Levels

Figure 1-6 shows that your readers, whatever their technical level, also can be classified by the weight they carry in making decisions based on your document. Pay special attention to those most likely to use your report to create change. Use the following three levels to classify your audience during the planning process.

First-Level Audience: Decision Makers

The first-level audience must act on the information. If you are proposing a new fax machine for your office, for example, first-level readers will decide whether to accept or reject the idea. If you are comparing two computer systems for storing records at a hospital, the first-level audience will decide which unit to purchase. If you are describing electrical work your firm completed in a new office building, the first-level audience will decide whether the project has fulfilled agreed-upon guidelines.

In other words, decision makers translate information into action. They are usually, but not always, managers within the organization. One exception occurs in highly technical companies, where decision makers may be technical experts with advanced degrees in science or engineering. Another exception occurs when decision-making committees consist of a combined audience. For example, a board of education—with disparate levels of understanding of construction costing—may be charged with the task of choosing a firm to build a new addition to the board of education office.

Second-Level Audience: Advisers

This second group could also be called *influencers*. Although these advisers don't make decisions themselves, they read the document and give advice to those who will decide. Often, the second-level audience comprises experts, such as engineers and accountants, who are asked to comment on technical matters. As well, after reading the summary, a decision-making manager may refer the rest of the document to advisers for their comments.

Third-Level Audience: Receivers

Some readers do not take part in the decision-making process. They only receive the information contained in the document. For example, a report recommending changes in the hiring of fast-food workers may go to the store managers *after* it has been approved, just so they can put the changes into effect. This third-level audience usually includes readers defined as *operators* in the previous section—that is, those who may be asked to follow guidelines or instructions contained in a report.

Using all this information about technical and decision-making levels, you can analyze each reader's (1) technical background with respect to your document, and (2) potential for making decisions after reading what you present. Then you can move on to the research and outline stages of writing.

COLLECTING INFORMATION

Having established a clear sense of purpose and of your readers' needs, you're ready to collect information for writing. Although you may want to use a scratch outline to guide the research process, you would normally write a detailed outline *after* you have collected the research necessary to support your document.

Research Steps

This section lays out a general strategy for research. Details about research are included in Chapter 14 ("Technical Research").

Research Step 1: Decide What Kind of Information You Need

There are two types of research: primary and secondary. You conduct primary research first hand, whereas secondary information is generated by others and found in periodicals, online, or in other sources. Figure 1-7 gives examples of both types. Use the kind of research that will be most helpful in supporting the goals of your project. Following are two examples:

- **Report context for using primary research:** A recommendation report to purchase new drafting software for the drafting department is supported by your survey of the office drafters: all of them recommend the brand of software you have selected.
- **Report context for using secondary research:** Your report on software depends on data found in several written sources, such as an article in a mechanical engineering journal that contrasts features of three types of software. On the basis of this article, you recommend a particular brand.

Research Step 2: Devise a Research Strategy

Before you start searching for information or conducting interviews, you need a plan. In its simplest form, this plan may list the questions that you expect to answer in your quest for information. For example, a research strategy for a report on office chairs for word-processing operators might pose the following questions:

- What kind of chair design do experts in the field of workplace environment recommend for word processors?
- Are there any data that connect the design of chairs with the efficiency of operators?
- Have any specific chair brands been recommended by experts?
- Is there information that suggests a connection between poor chair design and specific health problems?

Research Step 3: Record Notes Carefully

Once you have located the information you need, you must exercise care as you incorporate that information into your own document. You must clearly distinguish direct quotations, paraphrases, and summaries in your notes. (Chapter 14, "Technical Research," explains this process.) Then, when you are ready to translate these notes into a first draft, you will know exactly how much borrowed information you have used and in what form.

Research Step 4: Acknowledge Your Sources

The care that you took in step 3 must be accompanied by thorough acknowledgment of the specific sources. Chapter 14 demonstrates three citation systems.

Research Step 5: Keep a Bibliography for Future Use

Consider any research you do for a writing project as an investment in later efforts. Even after your research for a project is complete and you have submitted the report, keep active files on any subjects that relate to your work. Update these files every time you complete a research-related project, such as the one mentioned previously on drafting software. If you or a colleague wants to examine the subject later, you will have developed your own database from which to start.

Primary	Secondary
1. **Interviews** 2. **Surveys** 3. **Laboratory work** 4. **Field work** 5. **Personal observation**	1. **Online services** (including access to the Internet) 2. **Periodical indexes** (journal and magazine articles, by subject, in print, or on computer databases) 3. **Newspaper indexes** 4. **Journals** 5. **Newspapers** 6. **Government reports** 7. **Company reports** 8. **Reference books** (encyclopedias, dictionaries, directories, etc.) 9. **Books** 10. **Bibliographies** (possible sources— in print or on computer databases)

Figure 1-7 Research sources

WRITING AN OUTLINE

After determining purpose and audience and completing your research, you are ready to write an outline. Making an outline is the best method for planning any piece of writing, especially a long document. The outline does not have to be pretty; it just has to guide your writing of the draft. If you conscientiously use outlines now, you will find it easier to organize and write documents of all kinds throughout your career.

Outline Steps

Refer to the following steps in preparing a functional outline. Figures 1-8 and 1-9 show the outlining process in action.

Outline Step 1: Record Your Random Ideas Quickly

At first, you need not place ideas in a pattern. Just jot down as many major and minor points as possible. For this exercise, try to use only one piece of paper, even if it is oversized. Putting points on one page helps prepare the way for the next step, in which you begin to connect those points.

Outline Step 2: Show Relationships

Next you need to connect related ideas. Using your brainstorming sheet, follow these three steps:

1. Circle or otherwise mark the points that will become main sections.
2. Connect each main point with its supporting ideas, using lines or arrows.
3. Delete material that seems irrelevant to your purpose.

Figure 1-8 shows the results of applying steps 1 and 2 to a writing project at Martin & Koffman, a company used throughout this book. Diane Simmons, office services manager at the Toronto office, plans to recommend a change in food service. She uses the brainstorming technique to record her major and minor points. First, she circles the six main ideas. As it happens, these ideas include three main problems and three possible solutions, so she labels them P #1 through P #3 (problems) and S #1 through S #3 (solutions). Second, she draws arrows between each main point and its related minor points. In this case, there is no material to be deleted. Although the result is messy, it prepares her for the next step, which is writing the formal outline.

Like Diane Simmons, you will face one main question as you plan your outline: what pattern of organization best serves the material? Chapter 3 presents an ABC format that applies to overall structure. Each document should start with an **A**bstract (summary), move to the **B**ody (discussion), and end with a **C**onclusion. Outlines, however, usually cover only the *body* of a document. Here are some common patterns to consider in outlining the middle part, or body, of a report or proposal. The examples all relate to a decision by M&K to revamp its photocopying system.

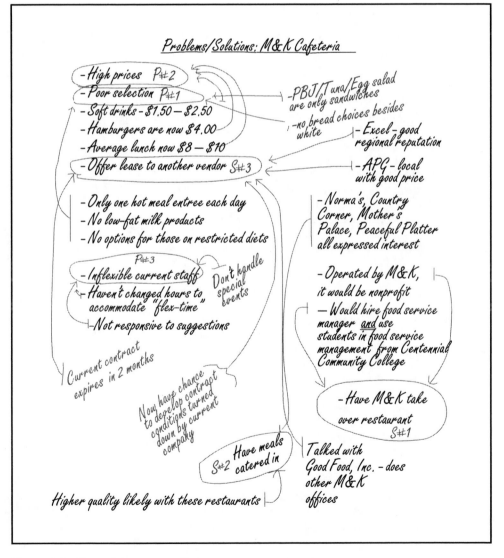

Figure 1-8   The outlining process: Early stage

- **Chronological:** The writer wants to describe the step-by-step procedures for completing a major photocopying project, from receiving copy at the copy centre to sending it out the next day.
- **Parts of an object:** The writer wants to provide a part-by-part description of the current photocopying machine, along with a list of parts that have been replaced in three years of service calls.
- **Simple to complex or vice versa:** The writer wants to describe problems associated with the current photocopying procedure, working from minor to major problems or vice versa.
- **Specific to general (inductive):** The writer wants to begin by listing about 20 specific complaints about the present photocopying machine and then place those complaints into three general groupings.
- **General to specific (deductive):** The writer wants to lead off with some generalizations about photocopying problems at M&K and then describe specific incidents related to poor copies, missed deadlines, and high service bills.

PROBLEMS AND SOLUTIONS: CURRENT CAFETERIA IN BUILDING

I.   Problem #1: Poor selection
   A. Only one hot meal entrée each day
   B. Only three sandwiches—PBJ, egg salad, and tuna
   C. Only one bread—white
   D. No low-fat milk products (milk, yogourt, LF cheeses, etc.)
   E. No options for those with restricted diets
II. Problem #2: High prices
   A. Soft drinks from $1.50 to $2.50 each
   B. Hamburgers now $4.00
   C. Average lunch now $8 to $10
III. Problem #3: Inflexible staff
   A. Unwilling to change hours to meet M&K's flexible work schedule
   B. Have not acted on suggestions
   C. Not willing to cater special events in building
IV. Solution #1: End lease and make food service an M&K department
   A. Hire food service manager
   B. Use students enrolled in food service management program at Centennial Community College
   C. Operate as nonprofit operation—just cover expenses
V.   Solution #2: Hire outside restaurant to cater meals into building
   A. Higher quality likely
   B. Initial interest by four nearby restaurants
      1. Norma's
      2. Country Corner
      3. Mother's Palace
      4. Peaceful Platter
VI. Solution #3: Continue leasing space but change companies
   A. Initial interest by three vendors
      1. Excel—good regional reputation for quality
      2. APG—local, with best price
      3. Good Food, Inc.—used by other M&K offices with good results
   B. Current contract over in two months
   C. Chance to develop contract conditions turned down by current company

---

Figure 1-9 The outlining process: Later stage

Outline Step 3: Draft a Final Outline

Once related points are clustered, it is time to transform what you have done into a somewhat ordered outline. (See Figure 1-9, which continues with the report context used in Figure 1-8.) This step allows you to (1) refine the wording of your points, and (2) organize them in preparation for writing the draft. Although you need not produce the traditional outline with Roman numerals, and so on, some structure is definitely needed. Abide by the following basic rules:

- **Depth:** Make sure every main point has enough subpoints that it can be developed thoroughly in your draft.
- **Balance:** When you decide to subdivide a point, have at least two breakdowns (because any object that is divided will have at least two parts). This same rule applies to headings and subheadings in the final document. (In fact, a good outline will provide you with the wording for headings and subheadings. The outline even becomes the basis for a table of contents in formal documents.)
- **Parallel form:** For the sake of consistency, phrase each of your points in either topic or sentence form. Sentences give you a head start on the draft, but they may lock you into wording that needs revision later. Most writers prefer the topic approach. Topics take up less space on the page and are easier to revise as you proceed through the draft.

WRITING AN INITIAL DRAFT

With your research and outline completed, you are ready to begin the draft. This stage in the writing process should go quickly if you have planned well. Yet many writers have trouble getting started. The problem is so widespread that it has its own name—"writer's block." If you suffer from it, you are in good company; some of the best and most productive writers often face the "block."

Drafting Steps

In business and industry, the worst effect of writer's block is that it makes people delay the start of writing projects, especially proposals. These delays can lead to rushed final drafts and editing errors. Outlining and other planning steps are wasted if you fail to complete drafting on time. The suggestions that follow can help you start writing and keep the words flowing:

Drafting Step 1: Schedule at Least a One-Hour Block of Drafting Time

Most writers can keep the creative juices flowing for at least an hour if distractions are removed. Rather than writing for three or four hours with your door open and thus with constant interruptions, schedule an hour or two of uninterrupted writing time. Most other business can wait an hour, especially considering how import good writing is to your success. Colleagues and staff members will adjust to your new strategy for drafting reports. They may even adopt it themselves.

Drafting Step 2: Do Not Stop to Edit

Later on, you will have time to revise your writing; that time is not now. Instead, force yourself to write down ideas from the outline as quickly as possible. Most writers have trouble getting back into their writing pace once they have switched gears from drafting to revising.

Drafting Step 3: Begin with the Easiest Section

In writing the body of the document, you need not move chronologically from beginning to end. Because the goal is to write the first draft quickly, you may want to start with the section that flows best for you. Later, you can piece together sections and adjust content.

Drafting Step 4: Write Summaries Last

As already noted, the outline used for drafting covers only the body sections of the document. Only after you have drafted the body should you write overview sections such as summaries. You cannot summarize a report until you have actually completed it. Because most writers have trouble with the summary—a section that is geared mainly for decision makers in the audience—they may get bogged down if they begin writing it prematurely.

REVISING THE DRAFT

You may have heard the old saw, "There is no writing, only rewriting." In technical writing, as in other types of communication, careful revision breeds success. Errors, no matter how minor, give the reader an excuse not to accept the entire report. Revision encompasses four tasks that transform early drafts into final copy:

1. Adjusting and reorganizing content
2. Editing for style
3. Editing for grammar
4. Editing for mechanics

Revision Steps

Following are some broad-based suggestions for revising your technical prose. For more details, consult Chapter 16, "Style in Technical Writing," or the Handbook at the end of the book.

Revision Step 1: Adjust and Reorganize Content

In this step, go back through your draft to (1) expand sections that deserve more attention, (2) shorten sections that deserve less, and (3) change the location of sentences, paragraphs, or entire sections. The use of word processors has made this step considerably easier than it used to be.

Revision Step 2: Edit for Style

The term *style* refers to changes that make writing more engaging, more interesting, more readable. Such changes are usually matters of choice, not correctness. For example, you might want to do the following:

- Shorten paragraphs
- Rearrange a paragraph to place the main point first

- Change passive-voice sentences to the active voice
- Shorten sentences
- Define technical terms
- Add headings, lists, or graphics

One stylistic error deserves special mention because of its frequency: long, convoluted sentences. As a rule, you should simplify a sentence if its meaning cannot easily be understood in one reading. Also, be wary of sentences that are so long you must take a breath before you complete them.

Revision Step 3: Edit for Grammar

You probably know your main grammatical weaknesses. Perhaps comma placement or subject–verb agreement gives you problems. Or maybe you have trouble distinguishing couplets, such as imply/infer, effect/affect, or complementary/complimentary. In editing the document for grammar, focus on the particular errors that have given you problems in the past.

Revision Step 4: Edit for Mechanics

Your last revision pass should be for mechanical errors, such as misspelled words, misplaced pages, incorrect page numbers, missing illustrations, and errors in numbers (especially cost figures). Word-processing software can help prevent some of these errors, such as most misspellings, but computer technology has not eliminated the need for at least one final proofing check.

This four-stage revision process will produce final drafts that reflect well on you, the writer. Here are two final suggestions that apply to all stages of the process:

1. **Depend on another set of eyes besides your own.** One strategy is to form a partnership with another colleague, whether in a technical writing class or on the job. In this arrangement, you both agree that you will carefully review each other's writing. This "buddy system" works better than simply asking favours of friends and colleagues. Choose a colleague in whom you have some confidence and from whom you can expect consistent editing quality. However, never make changes suggested by another person unless you fully understand the reasons for doing so. After all, it is *your* writing.
2. **Remember the importance of completing each step separately.** Revising in stages yields the best results.

WRITING IN GROUPS

Group writing (also called collaborative writing) can be defined in the following way:

> **Group writing:** the effort by two or more people to produce one document, with each member *sharing* in the writing process. The term assumes that all members actually help with the drafting process, as opposed to (1) one person writing the document after all group members have met to discuss the project, or (2) the group editing something written by one person. The team must have clear goals and effective leadership to achieve results. Group work can be done in person, over the phone, or through email.

This section further defines group writing, highlighting benefits of the strategy and noting some pitfalls to avoid. It then provides you with guidelines for using group writing in your classes and on the job.

Benefits and Drawbacks of Group Writing

Most organizations rely on people working together throughout the writing process to produce documents. The success of writing projects depends on the information and skills contributed by varied employees. For example, a report-writing team may include technical specialists, marketing experts, graphic designers, word processors, and technical editors. The company depends on all these individuals working together to produce the final product—a first-rate report.

In group writing, however, the whole is greater than the sum of the parts. In other words, there are benefits beyond those provided by the collective experience of the group members. Participants create *new* knowledge as they plan, draft, and edit their work together. They become better contributors and faster learners simply by being a part of the social process of a team. Discussion with fellow participants moves them toward new ways of thinking and inspires them to contribute their best. This collaborative effort yields ideas, writing strategies, and editorial decisions that result from the mixing of many perspectives.

Of course, group writing does have drawbacks. Most notably, the group must make decisions without falling into time traps that slow down the process. There must be procedures for getting everyone's ideas on the table and for reaching decisions on time. A leader with good interpersonal skills will help the group reach its potential, whereas an indecisive or autocratic leader will be an obstacle to progress. Good leadership rests at the core of every effective writing team.

In addition to good leadership, shared decision making is at the heart of every successful writing team. Group writing is not one writer simply getting information from many people before he or she writes a draft. Nor is it one person writing a draft for the editorial red pen of individuals at higher levels. These two models may have their place in some types of company writing, but they do not constitute group writing. Instead, participants in a group must work together during the planning, drafting, and revising stages of writing. Although the degree of collaboration may vary, all forms of group writing differ considerably from the model of one person writing with only occasional help from others.

Guidelines for Group Writing

This section offers six pointers for group writing, to be used in this course and throughout your career. The suggestions concern the writing process as well as interpersonal communication.

Group Guideline 1: Get to Know Your Group

Most people are sensitive about strangers evaluating their writing. Before collaborating on a writing project, therefore, learn as much as you can about those with whom you will be working. Drop by their offices before your first meeting, or talk informally as a group before the writing process begins. In other words, first establish a personal relationship. This familiarity will help set the stage for the spirited dialogue, group criticism, and collaborative writing to follow.

Group Guideline 2: Set Clear Goals and Ground Rules

Every writing group needs a common understanding of its objectives and procedures for doing business. Either before or during the first meeting, these questions should be answered:

1. What is the group's main objective?
2. Who will serve as team leader?
3. What exactly will be the leader's role in the group?
4. How will the group's activities be recorded?
5. How will responsibilities be distributed?
6. How will conflicts be resolved?
7. What will the schedule be?
8. What procedures will be followed for planning, drafting, and revising?

The guidelines that follow offer suggestions for answering the preceding questions.

Group Guideline 3: Use Brainstorming Techniques for Planning

The term **brainstorming** means pooling ideas in a nonjudgmental fashion. In this early stage, participants should feel free to suggest ideas without criticism by colleagues in the group. This nonjudgmental approach does not come naturally to most people. Thus, the leader may have to establish ground rules for brainstorming before the group proceeds.

Here is one possible approach to brainstorming:

Step 1: The group recorder takes down ideas as quickly as possible.
Step 2: Ideas are written on large pieces of paper affixed to walls around the meeting room so all participants can see how major ideas fit together.
Step 3: Members use ideas as springboards for suggesting others.
Step 4: Before meeting again, the group takes some time to digest the ideas generated during the first session.

The results of a brainstorming session might look much like a nonlinear outline produced during a solo writing project (see Figure 1-8 on page 17). The goal of both is to generate as many ideas as possible. These ideas can be culled and organized later.

Group Guideline 4: Use Storyboarding Techniques for Drafting

Storyboarding, a technique that originated in the screenwriting trade in Hollywood, helps propel participants from the brainstorming stage toward completion of a first draft. It also makes visuals an integral part of the document. A storyboard is a sheet of paper that contains (1) one draft-quality illustration and (2) a series of sentences about one topic (see Figure 1-10). As applied to technical writing, the technique involves six main steps:

Step 1: The group or its leader assembles a topic outline from ideas brought forth during the brainstorming session.
Step 2: All group members are given one or more topics to develop on storyboard forms.
Step 3: Each member works independently, creating an illustration and a series of subtopics for each board (see Figure 1-10).

Step 4: Members meet again to review all completed storyboards, modifying them where necessary and agreeing on key sentences.

Step 5: Individual members develop draft text and related graphics from their own storyboards.

Step 6: The group leader or the entire group assembles the draft from the various storyboards.

Group Guideline 5: Agree on a Thorough Revision Process

As with drafting, all members usually help with revision. Team editing can be difficult, however, as members strive to reach consensus on matters of style. Following are some suggestions for keeping the editing process on track:

- Avoid making changes merely for the sake of individual preference.
- Search for areas of agreement among group members, rather than areas of disagreement.
- Make only those changes that can be supported by accepted rules of style, grammar, and usage.
- Ask the group's best all-round stylist to do a final edit.

This review will help produce a uniform document, no matter how many people work on the draft.

Group Guideline 6: Use Computers to Communicate

When team members are at different locations, computer technology can be used to complete some or all of the project. This section describes three specific types of computer application that can improve communication among members of a group-writing project: email, computer conference, and groupware.

- **Email:** Individuals can send and receive messages from their office computers or from remote locations. Like written memos, email messages usually include the date, sender, receiver, and subject. Messages are sent at a time convenient for the sender and saved until a time when readers check their mail.
- **Computer conference:** Members of a group can make their own comments and respond to comments of others on a specific topic or project. Computer conferences may be open to all interested users or only to a particular group. For the purposes of group writing, the conference probably would be open only to members of the writing team. A leader may be chosen to monitor the contributions and keep the discussion focused. Contributions may be made over a long period as opposed to a short period, as with conventional face-to-face meetings, for which all team members must be present at the same time. Accumulated comments in the conference can be organized or indexed by topic. The conference may be used to brainstorm and thus to generate ideas for a project, or it may be used for comments at a later stage of the writing project.
- **Groupware:** Team members using this software can work at the same time, or at different times, on any part of a specific document. Groupware that permits contributions at the same time is called *synchronous;* that which permits contributions at different times is called *asynchronous.* Because team members are at different locations, with synchronous groupware they may also be speaking on the phone at the same time they are writing or editing. Such sophisticated software gives writers a much greater capability than if they simply sent a document

DOCUMENT TITLE: M&K's Training Needs
STORYBOARD TOPIC: Results of employee survey
STORYBOARD WRITER: Susan Hernandez

1. In one sentence, summarize this section of the document.

The recent survey of employees showed a strong preference for nontechnical over technical training.

2. In sentence form, include the key points to be developed in this document section. Use the same order that points will appear in the document.

A. The greatest interest was in the area of sales and marketing training—engineers, in particular, feel deficient here.

B. Many employees also wanted further training in project management—with emphasis on scheduling, accounting practices, and basic management.

C. The third most called-for training area was communication skills—that is, report writing, grammar, and oral presentations.

D. Many employees want training in stress management, to reduce or manage on-the-job pressures and make work more enjoyable.

E. The fifth area of interest was technical training in the respondents' own area of expertise.

3. Include an illustration that supports the text in this document section.

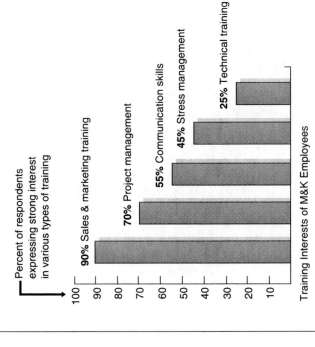

Percent of respondents expressing strong interest in various types of training

90% Sales & marketing training

70% Project management

55% Communication skills

45% Stress management

25% Technical training

Training Interests of M&K Employees

(The 5 most popular training topics, according to company-wide employee survey)

Figure 1-10 Completed storyboard

over a network for editing or comment. They can collaborate with team members on a document at the same time, almost as if they were in the same room. With several windows on the screen, they can view the document itself on one screen and make comments and changes on another screen.

Computers can be used to overcome many obstacles for writers and editors in different locations. Indeed, electronic communication can help meet all the guidelines noted earlier. Specifically, (1) email can be used by group members to get to know each other; (2) email or a computer conference can be used to establish goals and ground rules; (3) synchronous, or real-time, groupware can help a team brainstorm about approaches to the project (and may, in fact, encourage more openness than a face-to-face brainstorming session); (4) computer conferences combined with groupware can approximate the storyboard process; and (5) either synchronous or asynchronous groupware can be used to approximate the editing process.

Granted, such techniques make impossible the body language used in face-to-face meetings. Yet when personal meetings are not possible, computerized communication allows writers in different locations to work together.

Of course, computers can create problems during a group writing project unless care is taken. When different parts of a document have been written and stored by different writers, the group must be vigilant during the final editing and proofreading stages. Before the document is submitted, it must be reviewed for consistency and correctness.

Team writing may play an important part in your career, particularly in producing formal reports. If you use the preceding techniques, you and your team members will build on each other's strengths to produce top-quality writing.

Employability Skills

The Conference Board of Canada has developed *Employability Skills 2000+,* a list of "the employability skills, attitudes and behaviours that you need to participate and work." *

At the end of each chapter in this text, you will find an exercise that highlights some of these skills and shows you how they can be applied to the tasks of technical communications. Figure 1-11 is the complete Employability Skills 2000+ list, to which you can refer while working on these exercises.

Visit The Conference Board of Canada's Web site at **www.conferenceboard.ca** for additional information.

* *Employability Skills 2000+* Brochure 2000 E/F (Ottawa: The Conference Board of Canada, 2000).

Employability Skills 2000+

The skills you need to enter, stay in, and progress in the world of work—whether you work on your own or as a part of a team.

These skills can also be applied and used beyond the workplace in a range of daily activities.

Fundamental Skills
The skills needed as a base for further development

Personal Management Skills
The personal skills, attitudes and behaviours that drive one's potential for growth

Teamwork Skills
The skills and attributes needed to contribute productively

You will be better prepared to progress in the world of work when you can:

Communicate

- read and understand information presented in a variety of forms (e.g., words, graphs, charts, diagrams)
- write and speak so others pay attention and understand
- listen and ask questions to understand and appreciate the points of view of others
- share information using a range of information and communications technologies (e.g., voice, e-mail, computers)
- use relevant scientific, technological and mathematical knowledge and skills to explain or clarify ideas

Manage Information

- locate, gather and organize information using appropriate technology and information systems
- access, analyze and apply knowledge and skills from various disciplines (e.g., the arts, languages, science, technology, mathematics, social sciences, and the humanities)

Use Numbers

- decide what needs to be measured or calculated
- observe and record data using appropriate methods, tools and technology
- make estimates and verify calculations

Think & Solve Problems

- assess situations and identify problems
- seek different points of view and evaluate them based on facts
- recognize the human, interpersonal, technical, scientific and mathematical dimensions of a problem
- identify the root cause of a problem
- be creative and innovative in exploring possible solutions
- readily use science, technology and mathematics as ways to think, gain and share knowledge, solve problems and make decisions
- evaluate solutions to make recommendations or decisions
- implement solutions
- check to see if a solution works, and act on opportunities for improvement

You will be able to offer yourself greater possibilities for achievement when you can:

Demonstrate Positive Attitudes & Behaviours

- feel good about yourself and be confident
- deal with people, problems and situations with honesty, integrity and personal ethics
- recognize your own and other people's good efforts
- take care of your personal health
- show interest, initiative and effort

Be Responsible

- set goals and priorities balancing work and personal life
- plan and manage time, money and other resources to achieve goals
- assess, weigh and manage risk
- be accountable for your actions and the actions of your group
- be socially responsible and contribute to your community

Be Adaptable

- work independently or as a part of a team
- carry out multiple tasks or projects
- be innovative and resourceful: identify and suggest alternative ways to achieve goals and get the job done
- be open and respond constructively to change
- learn from your mistakes and accept feedback
- cope with uncertainty

Learn Continuously

- be willing to continuously learn and grow
- assess personal strengths and areas for development
- set your own learning goals
- identify and access learning sources and opportunities
- plan for and achieve your learning goals

Work Safely

- be aware of personal and group health and safety practices and procedures, and act in accordance with these

You will be better prepared to add value to the outcomes of a task, project or team when you can:

Work with Others

- understand and work within the dynamics of a group
- ensure that a team's purpose and objectives are clear
- be flexible: respect, be open to and supportive of the thoughts, opinions and contributions of others in a group
- recognize and respect people's diversity, individual differences and perspectives
- accept and provide feedback in a constructive and considerate manner
- contribute to a team by sharing information and expertise
- lead or support when appropriate, motivating a group for high performance
- understand the role of conflict in a group to reach solutions
- manage and resolve conflict when appropriate

Participate in Projects & Tasks

- plan, design or carry out a project or task from start to finish with well-defined objectives and outcomes
- develop a plan, seek feedback, test, revise and implement
- work to agreed quality standards and specifications
- select and use appropriate tools and technology for a task or project
- adapt to changing requirements and information
- continuously monitor the success of a project or task and identify ways to improve

The Conference Board of Canada

255 Smyth Road, Ottawa
ON K1H 8M7 Canada
Tel. (613) 526-3280
Fax (613) 526-4857
Internet: www.conferenceboard.ca/education

Figure 1-11 *Employability Skills 2000+*
Source: The Conference Board of Canada.

C H A P T E R   S U M M A R Y

Technical writing refers to the many kinds of writing you will do in your career. In contrast to most academic writing, technical writing aims to get something done (not just to demonstrate knowledge), relays information from someone more knowledgeable about the topic (you) to someone less knowledgeable about it (the reader), and is read by people from mixed technical and decision-making levels.

For each writing project, you should complete a three-stage process of planning, drafting, and revising. Planning involves understanding your purpose, knowing the readers' needs, collecting information, and outlining major and minor points. In the drafting stage, you use the outline to write a first draft as quickly as possible—without stopping to make changes. Finally, the revision process requires that you adjust content and then edit for style, grammar, and mechanics.

Technical writing can be completed by you alone or by you as a member of a writing team. The latter approach is common in companies, for it exploits the strengths of the various professionals within an organization. In group writing, you work closely with your team during the planning, drafting, and revising processes.

A S S I G N M E N T S

Your instructor will indicate whether assignments 1 through 6 should serve as the basis for class discussion, or a written exercise, or both. Assignment 7 requires a written response.

1. Features of academic writing.

Option A: Select an example of writing that you did for a high school course, or a college or university course other than this one. Then prepare a brief analysis in which you explain (1) the purpose for which it was written, (2) the audience for which it was intended, and (3) the ways in which it differs from technical writing as defined in this chapter.

Option B: As an alternative to using your own example, complete the assignment by using the following example. Assume that the passage was written as homework or as an in-class essay in an environmental science class.

There are many different responses that are possible in the event that toxic waste contamination is suspected or discovered at a site. First, you can simply monitor the site by periodically taking soil and/or water samples to check for contamination. This approach doesn't solve the problem and may not prove politically acceptable when contamination is obvious to the community, but it does help determine the extent of the problem. A second approach—useful when contamination is likely or proven—is to contain the toxic waste by sealing off the site in some fashion, such as by building barriers between it and the surrounding area or by "capping" it in some manner (as in the case of a toxic waste pit). Basically, this alternative depends on the ability to isolate the toxic substances effectively. A third strategy, useful when the contamination is liquefied (as with toxic groundwater), is to pump the water from under the ground or from surface ponds and then transport it to treatment systems.

A fourth method is appropriate when toxic substances need to be treated on-site, in which case they can be incinerated or they can be solidified at the site in some way. Then the the toxic substances can be placed in a landfill at the site. Fifth, waste can be hauled to another location where it can be incinerated or placed in some kind of secure landfill—when an off-site disposal approach is needed.

---

2. Features of technical writing.

Option A:	Locate an example of technical writing (by borrowing it from a family member or an acquaintance who works in a technical profession). Then prepare a brief analysis in which you explain (1) the purpose for which the piece was written, (2) the apparent readers and their needs, (3) the way in which the example differs from typical academic writing, and (4) the relative success with which the piece satisfies the objectives of technical writing.
Option B:	Using the following brief example of technical writing, prepare the analysis requested in Option A.

DATE: June 15, 2006
TO: Pat Jones, Office Coordinator
FROM: Sean Parker, Word-Processing Operator
SUBJECT: New Word-Processing Software

Introductory Summary

As you requested, I have examined the WordWonder word-processing software we are considering. On the basis of my observations, I recommend we secure one copy of WordWonder and test it in our office for two months. Then after comparing it to the other two packages we have tested, we can choose one of the three word-processing packages to use throughout the office.

Features of WordWonder

As we agreed, my quick survey of WordWonder involved reading the user's manual, completing the orientation disk, and meeting with a salesperson from the company. Here are the five features of the package that seemed most relevant to our needs:

1. **Formatting Flexibility:** WordWonder includes diverse "style sheets" to meet our needs in producing reports, proposals, letters, memos, articles, and even brochures.
   By engaging just one command on the keyboard, the user can change style sheets—whereby the program will automatically place text in a specified format.
2. **Mailers:** For large mailings, we can take advantage of WordWonder's "Mail Out" feature that automatically places names from mailing lists on form letters.
3. **Documentation:** To accommodate our staff's research needs, WordWonder has the capacity to renumber and rearrange footnotes as text is being edited.
4. **Page Review:** This package's "PagePeek" feature permits the user to view an entire written page on the screen. Without having to print the document, he or she can then see how every page of text will actually look on the page.
5. **Tables of Contents:** WordWonder can create and insert page numbers on tables of contents, created from the headings and subheadings in the text.

Conclusion

Though I gave WordWonder only a brief look, my survey suggests that it may be a strong contender for use in our office. If you wish to move to the next step of starting a two-month office test, just let me know. Then I will make arrangements with the manufacturer for us to receive a complimentary trial copy.

---

3. Purpose and audience. The following examples deal with the same topic in four different ways. Using this chapter's guidelines on purpose and audience, determine the main reason each excerpt was written and the technical level of the intended readers.

A. You can determine the magnitude of current flowing through a resistor by use of the following process:
- Connect the circuit (power supply, resistor, ammeter, voltmeter).
- Set the resistor knob to a setting of "1."
- Turn the voltage adjusting knob to the left until it stops rotating.
- Switch the voltmeter to "on" and make sure it reads 0.00 volts.
- Switch the power supply to "on."
- Slowly increase the voltage on the voltmeter from 0 to 10 volts.
- Take the reading from the ammeter to determine the amount of current flowing through the resistor.

B. After careful evaluation of several testers, I strongly recommend that Langston Electronics Institute purchase 100 Mantra Multitesters for use in our laboratories in Belleville, Kingston, and Cornwall.

C. Selected specifications for the Ames Multitester are as follows:
- Rangers 43
- DC Voltage . . . . .0–125–250 mV 1.25–2.5–10–5–125–500–1000 V
- AC Voltage . . . . .0–5–25–125–250–500–1000 V
- DC Current . . . . .0–25–50 μA–2.5–5–25–50–250–500 mA–10 amperes
- Resistance . . . . .0–2 K–20 K–200 K–20 Mega ohms
- Decibels . . . . .220 to 162 in db 8 ranges
- Accuracy . . . .±3% on DC measurements
  ±4% on AC measurements
  ±3% on scale length on resistance
- Batteries . . . . .one type AA penlight cell
- Fuse . . . . .0.75 A at 250 V

Note that the accuracy rate for the Ames is within our requirements of ±6%, and is considerably lower than the three other types of testers currently used by our staff.

D. Having used the Ames Multitester in my own home laboratory for the last few months, I found it extremely reliable during every experiment. In addition, it is quite simple to operate and includes clear instructions. As a demonstration of this operational ease, my 10-year-old son was able to follow the instructions that came with the device to set up a functioning circuit.

---

4. **Interview.** Interview a friend, relative, or recent graduate who works as a technical professional or manager. Gather specific information on these topics:
   - The percentage of the workweek spent on writing
   - Types of documents that are written and their purpose
   - Specific types of readers of these documents

5. **Contrasting styles.** Find two articles on the same topic in a professional field that interests you. One article should be taken from a newspaper or magazine of general interest, such as one you would find on a newsstand. The other should be from a magazine or journal written mainly for professionals in the field you have chosen. Now contrast the two articles according to purpose, intended audience, and level of technicality.

6. **Contrasting audiences.** Photocopy three articles from the same Saturday issue of a local or national newspaper. Choose each article from a different section of the paper—for example, you could use the sections on automobiles, business, travel, personal computers, national political events, local events, arts, editorials, or employment. Describe the intended audience for each article. Then explain why you think the author has been successful, or unsuccessful, in reaching that particular audience.

7. **Rewriting for a different audience.** Locate an excerpt from a technical article or textbook, preferably on a topic that interests you because of your background or school major. Rewrite all or part of the selection so that it can be understood by readers who have no previous knowledge of the topic.

CHAPTER 2

Corporate Culture Today

Chapter 1 defined technical writing and outlined the writing process. This second chapter introduces you to a fictional company, Martin & Koffman, which has a number of subsidiaries. The company is used in examples and assignments throughout this book. Then Chapters 3 and 4 cover organization and page and Web design, while Chapter 5 explains the use of effective graphics. This five-chapter package provides the foundation for your work in the rest of the book.

The use of M&K is intended to yield two main benefits for you as a student:

- **Real-world context:** The company provides you with an extended case study in modern technical communication. By placing you in actual working roles, the text prepares you for the writing and speaking tasks ahead in your career.

- **Continuity:** Using this material will lend continuity to class assignments and discussions throughout the term. Your frequent use of this international organization in assignments and in class will emphasize the connections among all on-the-job assignments.

Thus, M&K gives you a window into an international organization similar to one where you may soon work. This chapter begins with a look at corporate culture in the new millennium and then covers three main topics related specifically to M&K and its subsidiaries: (1) the background of the companies and the work they do, (2) the activities and positions at the corporate and branch offices, and (3) typical writing tasks that employees perform. The chapter ends with a discussion of ethical guidelines for work and writing.

CONTEMPORARY CORPORATE CULTURE

As a preface to information about Martin & Koffman, the first part of this section presents three features common to the culture of any organization that may employ you.

Elements of a Company's Culture

Unless you become self-employed, you will work for some sort of business enterprise or nonprofit organization after you graduate. For simplicity, we'll use the terms *company* or *firm* to refer to any organization where you may work. As noted in Chapter 1, writing for a company differs greatly from writing for college or university. Writing will directly influence your performance evaluations, your professional reputation, and your company's productivity and success in the marketplace. Given these high stakes, let's look at typical features of the organizations wherein you may spend your career.

Starting a job is exciting and sometimes a bit intimidating. Although you look forward to practising the skills you learned in this course and related ones, you also wonder just how you will fare in new surroundings. Soon you will discover that any organization you join has its own personality. This personality, or "culture," can be defined as follows:

> **Company culture:** term for the main features of life at a particular company. A company's culture is influenced by the firm's history, type of business, management style, values, attitude toward customers, and attitude toward its own employees. Taken together, all features of a particular company's culture create a definable quality of life within the working world of that company.

Let's look more closely at three features mentioned in the preceding definition: a firm's history, its type of business, and its management style.

Feature 1: Company History

A firm's origin often is central to its culture. The culture of a 100-year-old steel firm will depend on accumulated traditions that most employees are accustomed to. The culture of a recently established home electronics firm, for example, may depend more on the entrepreneurial spirit of its founders. Thus the facts, and even the mythology, of a company's origin may be central to its culture, especially if the person starting the firm remained at the helm for a long time. Magna International Inc., for instance, possesses a culture very much connected to the dreams, aspirations, and open management style of its founder, Frank Stronach. And Spar Aerospace Ltd. still reflects its strong research-and-development orientation.

Feature 2: Type of Business

Culture is also greatly influenced by a company's type of business. Many computer software firms, for example, are known for their flexible, nontraditional, and sometimes chaotic culture. Such firms encourage constant change and innovation. The software industry's well-known competitiveness probably inspires this cultural trait. Some of the large computer hardware firms, however, have a culture focused more on tradition, formality, and custom. Yet both hardware and software companies share the same cultural trait of a high level of customer service.

Feature 3: Management Style

A major component of a company's culture is its style of leadership. Some companies run according to a rigid hierarchy, with all decisions coming from the top. Other companies have fewer top-down pronouncements from upper management. Instead, they involve a wide range of employees in the decision-making process. As you might expect, most firms have a decision-making culture that lies somewhere between these two extremes.

These three features give you some idea of what makes up the culture of any company. A company's culture influences who is hired and promoted at the firm, how decisions are made, and even how company documents are written and reviewed.

The Global Workplace

Very possibly, you will work for an organization that does some business beyond the borders of its home country, one that may even have international offices, as does M&K. Such organizations face opportunities and challenges of diversity among both employees and customers. As a result, these companies seek employees who can view issues from the perspective of people outside their culture. This section examines work in the global marketplace by posing 10 questions to ask when you communicate with someone from another country or culture. Asking and answering these questions may ensure your personal success and that of your organization.

Let's start with the most important point, one that seems obvious and yet is often forgotten:

> People in different cultures have different ways of thinking, different ways of acting, and different expectations in communication.

To be sure, there are a few basic ethical guidelines common to most cultures that you will do business with. But, in addition to these core values, differences abound, which employees of multinational firms should study and then reflect in their communication with colleagues, vendors, and customers. At the close of their excellent text, *Intercultural Communication in the Global Workplace* (1994), Iris Varner and Linda Beamer list five recommendations to help organizations with *intercultural* business communication:

1. "Train employees in intercultural business communication skills and distribute this training . . . to . . . employees at all levels . . .
2. "Send more people to foreign subsidiaries and don't restrict travel to top executives. Foreign travel should not be a perk but [instead] should meet specific business goals . . .
3. "Train employees in intercultural communication skills early in their careers. At this point employees are less costly and more flexible . . .
4. "Carefully evaluate employees as they are hired . . . Interpersonal skills, language ability, a sense of adventure, and an open attitude may be much more important than specific technical skills . . .
5. "Above all, encourage a climate of excitement and adventure."[1]

Perhaps you will work for a firm that shares Varner and Beamer's enlightened view of interculturalism. To prepare you for that possibility, this section includes some questions to ask about those whom you communicate with outside your own culture. Consider these questions a starting point for your journey toward understanding communication in the global workplace.

Question 1 — *Work:* What are their views about work and work rules?

Question 2 — *Time:* What is their approach to time, especially with regard to starting and ending times for meetings, being on time for appointments, expected response time for action requests, hours of the regular workday, and so on?

Question 3 — *Beliefs:* What are the dominant religious and philosophical belief systems in their culture, and how do these belief systems affect the workplace?

---

[1] Iris Varner and Linda Beamer, *Intercultural Communication in the Global Workplace* (Chicago: Irwin, 1994), pp. 306–8. The following 10 questions in this section are gleaned from information in two excellent sources for the student of international communication: the Varner/Beamer text and David A. Victor, *International Business Communication* (New York: HarperCollins, 1992).

Question 4 — *Gender:* What are their views on equality of men and women in the workplace, and how do these views affect their actions?

Question 5 — *Personal Relationships:* What degree of value is placed on close personal relationships among people doing business with each other?

Question 6 — *Teams:* What part does teamwork play in their business and, accordingly, how do they view individual initiative?

Question 7 — *Communication Preferences:* What types of business communication are valued most—formal writing, informal writing, formal presentations, casual meetings, email, phone conversations?

Question 8 — *Negotiating:* What are their expectations for the negotiation process, and, more specifically, how do they convey negative information?

Question 9 — *Body Language:* What types of body language are most common in the culture, and how do these types differ from your own?

Question 10 — *Writing Options:* What writing conventions are most important to them, especially in prose style and the organization of information? How important is a document's design relative to content and organization?

To be sure, asking these questions does not mean we bow to attitudes that conflict with our own ethical values, as in the equal treatment of women in the workplace. It only means that we first seek to comprehend the cultures we are dealing with before we operate within them. Intercultural knowledge translates into power in the international workplace. If we are aware of diversity, then we will be best prepared to act.

It might help to see how Sarah Logan, a marketing specialist who transferred to M&K's Tokyo office three years ago, addressed some of these issues. In her effort to find new clients for M&K's services, she discovered much about the Japanese culture that helped her and her colleagues do business in Japan. For example, she learned that Japanese workers at all levels depend more on their identification with a group than on their individual identity. Thus, Sarah's prospective clients in Japan felt most comfortable discussing their work in a corporate department or team, rather than their individual interests or accomplishments—at least until a personal relationship was established.

Sarah learned that an essential goal of Japanese employees is what they call *Wa*—harmony among members of a group and, for that matter, between the firm and those doing business with it. Accordingly, her negotiations with the prospective Japanese clients often took an indirect path. Usually, she established personal relationships and observed social customs before initiating any business dealings. A notable exception, she discovered, occurred among the smaller, more entrepreneurial Japanese firms, where employees often displayed a "Western" predisposition toward getting right down to business.

She also discovered that, more than in her own culture, Japanese business is dominated by men and that there tends to be more separation of men and women in social contexts. Although this cultural feature occasionally frustrated her, she tried to focus on understanding behaviour rather than judging it from her own perspective. Moreover, she knew the roles of women in Japan are changing. Indeed, her own considerable success in getting business for M&K suggested that the Japanese value ability and hard work most of all.

Like Sarah Logan, you should enter every intercultural experience with your mind open to learning about those with whom you will work. Adjust your communication strategies so that you have the best chance of succeeding in the international marketplace. Intercultural awareness does not require that you jettison your own ethics, customs, or standards. Rather, such awareness provides you with a wonderful opportunity to learn about, empathize with, and show respect for the views of others.

M&K BACKGROUND AND TYPES OF PROJECTS

Today Martin & Koffman is trying hard to develop company cultures that are based on concerns about quality and intercultural awareness. Managers at M&K as well as those at its subsidiaries believe that such an effort is crucial to success. This section examines the company—its history and the work it performs.

History of Martin & Koffman

In 1974, two students from Concordia University founded Martin & Koffman. Jacques Martin was a computer science graduate and Angela Koffman had completed part of a business administration degree. The company undertook to advise clients on how to best use new technology in their offices. Over the next few years the company developed an excellent reputation and won a number of contracts for integrating new technologies into existing work environments.

In 1979 Martin & Koffman decided that the company should diversify so that it would not be so dramatically affected by downturns in the IT industry. M&K successfully bought controlling interest in an American engineering firm based in Baltimore that had expanded into the environmental field. M&K felt that the acquisition enabled M&K to diversify and provided opportunities to become a good corporate citizen.

In 1983, when M&K decided to bid on environmental and construction contracts in Canada, the company decided to enlarge M&K rather than operate two corporations in Canada. At that point M&K's head office was transferred to Toronto. The Montreal office became a branch, and the company added branches in Calgary and Vancouver, as well as internationally, including San Francisco, Tokyo, Caracas, and Saudi Arabia.

Jacques Martin moved to Toronto to become president of the company; Angela Koffman chose to remain in Montreal as branch manager. In Baltimore, Janice Kowalski became M&K's president of American operations, of which the larger part was the engineering firm.

Projects

Every company must improve its products and services to stay in business. M&K is no exception. If it had stayed with just its IT consulting work, the company would be stagnant today—periodic slowdowns would have taken their toll. Fortunately, the company diversified. Following are the kinds of services that M&K offers to its clients:

1. Information systems implementation
2. Corporate training
3. Soils work on land
4. Soils work at sea
5. Equipment development

WRITING AT MARTIN & KOFFMAN

Good writing is crucial to M&K's work. First, one of its main products is the written report. After the company completes a technical project, the project report stands as a permanent statement about, and reflection of, the quality of the company's work. Second, many of the company's projects begin as written proposals. Third, most routine activities within the firm are preceded or followed by memos, reports, in-house proposals, and manuals. As an employee of M&K, you would be writing to readers in the following groups:

- Superiors at your own branch
- Subordinates at your branch
- Employees at other branches or at the corporate office
- Clients
- Subcontractors and vendors

As we pointed out in Chapter 1, you will often write to a mixed group of readers, all of whom have different needs and backgrounds. Likewise, at M&K, readers of a given document could come from more than one of the groups just listed. For example, assume that the training coordinator at M&K's Toronto office needs to send out a memo to 20 people confirming their attendance at an upcoming training seminar. Coming to Toronto from various locations across Canada, the participants will need a seminar schedule and information about lodging close to the site, as well as information about the course. The training coordinator would have to send copies of the memo to (1) the participants' managers, who need to be reminded that they will be minus an employee for three days, (2) the vice president for research and training in Toronto, who likes to be aware of every training activity, and (3) the instructor hired to deliver the course.

And this memo is not unique. Most documents are read by persons from different levels. Listed next are more examples of M&K writing directed to diverse readers. Some of these projects resemble the examples and assignments you will encounter in later chapters.

Examples of Internal Writing

1. Memo about changes in benefits—from a manager of human resources at a branch to all employees at that branch
2. Memo about changes in procedures for removing asbestos from buildings—from a project manager to field engineers and technicians
3. Orientation booklet on M&K—from the manager of employment to all new employees at the firm
4. Internal proposal for funds to develop a new piece of equipment—from a technician to the equipment development lab manager
5. Draft of a project report—from a project manager for review by a department manager (before being submitted to the client)
6. Long report on future markets for M&K—from the vice president of business and marketing to all employees, including those working in the United States and overseas

7. Memo on new procedures for compensating domestic employees who work on overseas projects—from the corporate manager of compensation to all branch managers

8. Manual on new accounting procedures—from the corporate manager of computer operations to all branch managers

9. Article on an interesting environmental project at a national park—from a project manager to all employees who read the company's monthly newsletter

10. Trip report on a professional conference—from a biologist in the environmental science area to the corporate manager of training

Examples of External Writing

1. Sales letter—to potential client
2. M&K brochure describing technical services—to potential client
3. Proposal—to potential client
4. Progress report—to client
5. Final project report—to client
6. Refresher letter—to previous client
7. Complaint letter—to supplier
8. Article on technical subject—for technical periodical
9. Training manual—for client
10. Affirmative action report—for government

Writing and speaking tasks can present ethical dilemmas. The next section of this chapter describes an ethical framework within which technical work—and technical writing in particular—can be completed at organizations where you may work.

ETHICS ON THE JOB

This section outlines the ethical context in which all workers, including those at M&K, do their jobs. The goals here are (1) to present one main ethical principle and four related guidelines for the workplace and (2) to show how ethical guidelines can be applied to a specific activity—writing. Following the chapter summary, and throughout this book, you will find assignments in which your own ethical decisions play an important role.

Ethical Guidelines for Work

Like your personal life, your professional life will hold many opportunities for demonstrating your views of what is right or wrong. There is, in fact, no way to escape these ethical challenges, most of which occur daily, without much fanfare. And how you respond to these ethical dilemmas will reflect your personal belief systems.

Obviously, not everyone in the same company—let alone in the same industry or profession—has the same ethical beliefs. Nor should they. After all, each person's understanding of right and wrong flows from individual experiences, upbringing, religious beliefs, and cultural values. Some "ethical relativists" even argue that ethics only makes sense as a descriptive study of what people *do* believe, not a prescriptive study of what they *should* believe. Yet there are some basic ethical guidelines that, in our view, should be part of the decision-making process in every organization. These guidelines apply to small employers just as they apply to large multinational organizations. And, although such guidelines may be displayed in different ways in different cultures, they should transcend national identity, cultural background, and family beliefs. In other words, these guidelines represent what should, ideally, be the core values for employees at international companies like M&K.

The guidelines in this section flow from one main tenet, which Peter Singer, author of *Practical Ethics* (1979), calls the principle of Equal Consideration of Interests (ECI):

> **ECI:** You should make judgments and act in ways that treat the interests and well-being of others as no less important than your own.[2]

Note that the ECI principle resembles similar principles espoused by religions and philosophies worldwide. That fact makes ECI especially useful as a bedrock principle for multinational organizations. Now let's examine four guidelines that flow from this principle.

Ethics Guideline 1: Be Honest

First, you should relate information accurately and on time—to your colleagues, to customers, and to outside parties such as government regulators. This guideline also means you should not mislead listeners or readers by leaving out important information that relates to a situation, product, or service. In other words, give those with whom you communicate the same information that you would want presented to you.

This guideline does not prescribe the manner or form in which information will be delivered. Indeed, issues such as format, organization, and presentation will change from culture to culture. The need for accurate and timely information, however, will not change.

Ethics Guideline 2: Do No Harm

The healthiest, most productive, and enjoyable workplaces are those with a positive, constructive atmosphere. One way to achieve such a working environment is to avoid words or actions calculated to harm others. For example, avoid negative, rumour-laden conversations that hurt feelings, spread unsupported information, or waste time.

Of course, different cultures and countries differ in the degree to which personal, familiar chatting takes place at work. But this cultural difference does not change the fact that you should consider the impact words and deeds have on colleagues, clients, and competitors. Our ideal goal should be to make the working world a better place at the end of each day; our minimum goal should be to leave the world at least as good as we found it.

---

[2] This definition is a slightly condensed form of the one in Singer's *Practical Ethics* (Cambridge, UK: Cambridge University Press, 1979), p. 19, as included in Raymond S. Pfeiffer and Ralph P. Forsberg, *Ethics on the Job* (Belmont, CA: Wadsworth, 1993), p. 4. The four guidelines that follow are paraphrased from six rules included in *Ethics on the Job*, pp. 12–17.

Ethics Guideline 3: Keep Your Commitments

People expect that you will keep your word. Be careful about the commitments you make to superiors, subordinates, customers, and others. When you do make a legitimate commitment, follow through on it. *Legitimate* means a commitment wherein you do not violate other ethical guidelines, such as being honest and doing no harm.

Cultural guidelines differ as to what makes up a commitment, and you should be sensitive to such variations. In one country, for example, a comment in a meeting may seal an agreement from the perspective of some participants. In another, multiple legal contracts are required. Make sure you know what constitutes a commitment with your audience, and then make sure you abide by it.

Ethics Guideline 4: Be Independent

Make no mistake—teamwork will be crucial to the success of organizations for which you work. Group efforts, however, do not relieve you of personal responsibility for making decisions that come with your job and then accepting the resulting blame or credit. We cannot simply go along with group decisions if we have ethical reservations. This phenomenon of excessive conformity within teams has its own name—"groupthink"—and it can be dangerous. Effective teamwork is more important than ever, but it is only as valid as the strength of individual contributors.

If you do business in non-Western countries, such as Japan, you will learn that some cultures emphasize teamwork to the point where individuals seem to be absorbed into the fabric of the group. If you are part of such a team, you may need to alter your style to adapt to a pattern of decision making that is highly consensual. Yet such cultural adjustments don't change the importance of being assertive when appropriate, and taking individual responsibility. Although you should be cooperative in teamwork, you cannot sacrifice your own values on the altar of group consensus. Be clear and direct, while still listening and adjusting to others' views.

Now let's examine the manner in which ethical considerations play a part in the writing responsibilities at companies such as M&K.

Ethics in Writing

In your career you should develop and apply your own code of ethics, making certain it follows the four guidelines already noted. Writing—whether on paper, for audiotape, for videotape, or on computer screen—presents a special challenge when it comes to demonstrating your personal ethics. During your career, there may be no more important ways for you to display your beliefs than through speaking and writing. The following section will (1) list some ethical questions related to specific documents and (2) provide responses based on the ethical guidelines noted earlier.

Being honest, doing no harm, keeping commitments, showing independence of thought and action—all four of these ethical guidelines apply to written communication. Here are some typical examples from the working world:

Lab report: *Should you mention that a small, possibly insignificant percentage of the data you collected did not support your conclusions?*

Answer: Yes. Readers deserve to see *all* the data—even (and perhaps especially) any information that doesn't support your conclusion. They need a true picture of the lab study so that they can draw their own conclusions.

Trip report: Should you mention that one client you visited expressed dissatisfaction with the service he received from your group?

Answer: Yes. Assuming that your report is supposed to present an accurate reflection of your activities, your reader deserves to hear about *all* your client contacts—both good news and bad. You can counter any critical comments by indicating how your group plans to remedy the problem.

Proposal: Should you include cost information, even though cost is not a strong point in your proposal?

Answer: Almost certainly yes. Most clients expect complete and clear cost data in a proposal. It is best to be forthright about costs, even if they are not your selling point. Then you should highlight features that are exemplary about your firm so that the customer is encouraged to look beyond costs to matters of quality, qualifications, scheduling, experience, and so on.

Feasibility study: Should you list all the criteria you used in comparing three products, even though one criterion could not be applied adequately in your study?

Answer: Yes. It is unethical to adjust criteria after the fact to accommodate your inability to apply them consistently. Besides, information about a project's dead end may be useful to the reader.

Technical article: Should you acknowledge ideas you derived from another article, even though you quoted no information from the piece?

Answer: Yes. Your reliance on *all* borrowed ideas should be noted, whether the ideas are quoted, paraphrased, or summarized. The exception is "common knowledge," which is general information that is found in many sources. Such common knowledge need not be footnoted.

Statement of Qualifications (SOQ): Should you feel obligated to mention technical areas in which your firm does not have extensive experience?

Answer: Probably not, as long as you believe the customer is not expecting such information in the Statement of Qualifications. Ethical guidelines do not require you to reveal everything about your firm, especially in a marketing document like an SOQ. They only require that you provide the information the client requests or expects.

Of course, many other types of technical writing require careful ethical evaluation. You might even consider performing an "ethical review" during the final process of drafting a document. Other parts of this book cover topics that apply to specific stages of such an ethical review, as well as to ethics in spoken communication. For ethics in the use of graphics, see Chapter 5; for ethics in argumentation, see Chapter 6; for ethics in instructions, see Chapter 7; for ethics in the research process, see Chapter 14; and for ethics in negotiation, see Chapter 15.

In the final analysis, acting ethically on the job means thinking constantly about the ways people will be influenced by what you do, say, and write. Peter Singer's ECI principle embodies this approach perfectly: "Make judgments and act in ways that treat the interests and well-being of others as no less important than your own." These "others" can include your colleagues, your customers, your employers, or the general public. Always show them your very best self.

Employability Skills

The Conference Board of Canada's *Employability Skills 2000+* has determined that those who have successful and productive careers must have the flexibility and tolerance to work with others. Teamwork and adaptability skills include the following:

- Understand and work within the dynamics of a group.
- Ensure that a team's purpose and objectives are clear.
- Be flexible: respect, be open to and supportive of the thoughts, opinions, and contributions of others in a group.
- Recognize and respect people's diversity, individual differences, and perspectives.
- Accept and provide feedback in a constructive and considerate manner.
- Contribute to a team by sharing information and expertise.

- Lead or support when appropriate, motivating a group for high performance.
- Understand the role of conflict in a group to reach solutions.
- Manage and resolve conflict when appropriate.
- Be innovative and resourceful: identify and suggest alternative ways to achieve goals and get the job done.
- Be open and respond constructively to change.*

Write the speech that your employer may give on the day of your retirement. In the speech, mention those parts of your character and behaviour that allowed you to function effectively in a group environment. Attempt to be honest in your assessment of what characteristics you will have demonstrated. Do make reference to the skills identified by *Employability Skills 2000+*.

* *Employability Skills 2000+* Brochure 2000 E/F (Ottawa: The Conference Board of Canada, 2000).

CHAPTER SUMMARY

This book will use the fictional firm of Martin & Koffman to lend realism to your study of technical writing. The many M&K examples and assignments will give you a purpose, an audience, and an organizational context that simulate what you will face in your career.

Like other organizations where you might work, M&K has developed its own personality or culture. A company's culture can be influenced by its own features, including its history, its type of business, and its management style. Two particular features that many organizations have in common today are (1) an interest in improving the quality of their services and products and (2) a need to operate in a global environment.

This chapter looks specifically at the culture of Martin & Koffman. Though started as a consulting firm with a narrow focus, M&K is now an international company with 2,500 employees, 15 branches, and a corporate office. The project sheets at the end of this chapter give summary information about specific projects in five areas.

M&K employees at all levels do a good deal of writing, both to superiors and subordinates within the organization and to clients and other outside readers. Documents often have multiple readers with different backgrounds, making writing even more challenging. Employees who meet this challenge will have the best chance of doing valuable work for the company and succeeding in their careers.

Another major concern at M&K—and at all organizations—is ethical behaviour in the workplace. Companies and their employees should follow some basic ethical guidelines in all their work, including communication with colleagues and customers.

ASSIGNMENTS

1. **Intercultural communication.** Refer to the 10 questions in "The Global Workplace" section of this chapter. Using them as the basis for your investigation, conduct your own research on the cultural features of employees in a specific country. Consider using some or all of the following sources: campus library, travel agencies, consulate offices, the international students' office on your campus, or individuals who have worked in or visited the country. Your instructor will indicate whether you should present your report orally or in writing.

2. **Company profile.** Having read the information in this chapter about M&K, create your own profile of a multinational company in your region. Collect information from sources such as the following: corporate annual reports, newspaper and magazine articles, and personal contacts. Consider some or all of the following subtopics: company history, types of projects, corporate structure, common types of writing produced, and special features of the company (such as an international market or workforce). Your instructor will indicate whether you should present your report orally or in writing.

3. **Group project: ethics.** This is a group assignment.

   Option A: Your group is to investigate the ethical climate in various organizations that are in the same type of business. You may decide to (a) collect company codes of ethics, (b) do research on ethical guidelines issued by professional associations to which the organizations belong, (c) interview employees about ethical decisions they face on the job, and/or (d) read any available information on ethics related to the companies or to the profession.

   Option B: For this option your group will select (or be assigned) one of the five project sheets at the end of the chapter. Perform a "brainstorming" session in your group to arrive at numerous potential ethical dilemmas related to your project. For example, you may want to consider some of these concerns: (a) decisions to be made by and about employees on the job, (b) technical questions related to the project, (c) interaction with clients, and (d) communication with any parties or agencies that are not directly connected with the project but that may be influenced by it.

   Assignments 4 through 7 can be completed by individuals or by groups, as your instructor directs. Prepare a response that can be delivered as an oral presentation for discussion in class.

   Analyze the context of each case by considering what you learned in Chapter 1 about the context of technical writing and what you learned in this chapter about M&K. In particular, answer these five questions:

   - What is the purpose of the document to be written?
   - What result do you hope to achieve by writing it?
   - Who will your readers be, and what will they want from your document?
   - What method of organization will be most useful?
   - What tone and choice of language will be most effective?

4. **Analysis: memo changing supplies policy.** As the office services manager at M&K's Calgary office, you have a problem. In the past fiscal year, the office has used significantly more bond paper, computer paper, pens, mechanical pencils, eraser fluid, and file folders than in previous years. After going back through the year's projects, you can find no business-related reason why the office has spent $12,000 more on these items. Given that everyone has easy access to the supplies, you have concluded that some employees are taking them home. Putting the best face on it, you assume they may be "borrowing" supplies to complete company business they take home with them, then just keeping items at home. Putting the worst face on it, you wonder whether some employees are stealing from the company.

   After consulting with the branch manager and some other managers, you decide to restrict access to office supplies. Starting next month, these supplies must be signed out through secretaries in the various departments. First, you plan to meet with the secretaries to explain how to make the system work. Following that meeting, you will send a memo explaining the change to all employees.

   Would you change your approach in this memo if it were to be sent to a specific audience in the office? Explain.

5. **Analysis: letter requesting testimonials.** As a writer in the corporate marketing department, you spend a good deal of your time preparing materials to be used in sales letters, brochures, and company proposals. Yesterday you were assigned the task of asking 20 customers if they will write "testimonial letters" about their satisfaction with M&K's work. In all cases, these clients have used M&K for many projects and have informally expressed satisfaction with the work. Now you are going to ask them to express their satisfaction in the form of a letter, which M&K could use as a testimonial to secure other business.

   Your strategy is to write a "personalized" form letter to the 20 clients and then follow it up with phone calls.

6. **Analysis: memo on inventory control.** For five years, you have supervised the supply warehouse at M&K's Calgary office. Your main job is to maintain equipment and see that it is returned after jobs are completed. When checking out equipment, each project manager is supposed to fill out part of a project equipment form that lists all equipment used on the job and the date of checkout. On returning the equipment, the project manager should complete the form by listing the date of return and any damage, no matter how small, that needs to be repaired before the equipment is used again. This equipment ranges from front-end loaders and pickup trucks to simple tools, such as hammers, wrenches, and power drills.

   Lately you have noticed that many of the forms you are receiving are incomplete. In particular, project managers are failing to record fully any equipment damage that occurred on the job. Thus, if, for example, someone fails to report that a truck's alignment is out, the truck will not be in acceptable shape for the next project for which it could be used.

   Your oral comments to project managers have not done much good. Because the project managers do not seem to take the warehouse problem seriously, you believe it is time to put your concerns in writing. The goal is to inform all technical professionals who manage projects that from now on the forms must be correctly filled out. You have no "authority," as such, over the managers; however, you know that their boss would be very concerned about this problem if you chose to bring it to his or her attention.

   At this point, you have decided to ask nicely one more time—but this time in writing. You want your memo to emphasize issues of safety and profitability, as well as the need to follow a procedure that has helped you maintain a first-rate warehouse.

7. **Analysis: memo report on flex-time.** As manager of M&K's Vancouver office, you have always tried to give employees as much flexibility as possible—as long as the work

gets done. Recently you have had many requests to adopt flex-time. In this arrangement, the office would end its standard 8:00 a.m. to 4:30 p.m. workday (with a half-hour lunch break). Instead, employees would fit their eight-hour day within the following framework: 7:00 a.m. to 8:30 a.m. arrival, a half hour or full hour for lunch, and 3:30 p.m. to 5:30 p.m. departure.

Two conditions would prevail, however, if flex-time were adopted. First, each employee's supervisor would have to agree on the hours chosen, since the supervisor would need to make sure that departmental responsibilities were covered. Second, each employee would "lock in" a specific flex-time schedule until another was negotiated with the supervisor. In other words, an employee's hours would not change from day to day.

Before you spend any more time considering this change, you want to get the views of employees. You decide to write a short memo report that (1) explains the changes being considered and the conditions (see previous paragraph), (2) solicits their views in writing, by a certain date, and (3) asks what particular work hours they would prefer, if given the choice. Also, you want your short report to indicate that, later on, there may be department meetings and, finally, a general office meeting on the subject, depending on the degree of interest expressed by employees in their memos to you.

Brief Project Description

During the spring of 2005, M&K used its drillship *Dolphin* to examine the ocean floor over a 96-kilometre stretch off the coast of Nova Scotia. We collected data on-site and then tested and analyzed samples at our labs. After sending the client our report on the study, we met with the client to discuss final conclusions and recommendations for further offshore use of the coastline.

Main Technical Tasks

- Kept *Dolphin* on-site for two months to map the sea floor, to drill borings, and to observe ocean habitats
- Used sonar to develop a profile of the surface of the ocean floor and its near-surface geology (return time of sound waves helped gauge the depth to the floor and to sediments below the floor)
- Drilled successfully for samples from *Dolphin's* drilling platform, often in difficult weather
- Analyzed samples from the borings to estimate geological age and stability of the ocean floor
- Viewed ocean life and geology first-hand at some locations, using a small, submersible craft with a one-person crew

Main Findings or Benefits

- Concluded that most of the zone was too environmentally sensitive to be used for offshore drilling of oil and gas
- Found two locations where a pipeline might be safely placed, with minimum damage to ocean life and minimum risk of geological disturbance (such as ocean avalanche)

Project 2: Evaluated Soil Conditions at a Construction Site

Client: City of Ottawa, Ontario

Source: Barry Padolsky Architect Ltd.

Brief Project Description

The City of Ottawa planned to build a new library on a piece of publicly owned land. At that location the land is composed of a layer of topsoil over silty clay. There were concerns about placing a structure there. Martin & Koffman was hired to recommend a method of construction that would ensure the stability of the foundation.

Main Technical Tasks

- Drilled boreholes to determine the soil's depth and composition
- Tested samples
- Recorded groundwater levels

Main Findings or Benefits

- Established that there are a number of options that will guarantee the building's stability
- Concluded that there was a more solid layer at the top of the clay that, if not ruptured, would support the building securely
- Since the footings have to be located in the lower (softer) layer, recommended that surcharge (fill) be placed on the site in order to consolidate the silt clay prior to the construction of the building
- Determined that proposed technique would minimize the settlement of the building after construction

Brief Project Description

The Maritime Canning Company has its head office in Halifax. It operates canning plants in Halifax, Yarmouth, Digby, and Shediac. The company formerly communicated internally by messenger and with its various plants by mail, courier, and telephone. The company decided that it could reduce costs, improve efficiency, and clarify communication by utilizing modern technology. Martin & Koffman's Montreal branch office sent a computer science technologist to evaluate the client's needs and to recommend ways to satisfy those needs. The technologist submitted a report of the findings to the Maritime Canning Company.

Main Technical Tasks

- Took inventory of existing hardware and software
- Consulted with clerical and managerial staff about the nature and frequency of communication requirements
- Determined the annual cost of existing communication methods
- Surveyed clerical and managerial staff to determine the level of computer literacy

Main Findings or Benefits

- Concluded that the efficiency of office personnel could be dramatically improved
- Concluded that communications between plants, and between the plants and head office, could be faster and more accurate
- Concluded that the company could respond more quickly to changing market conditions
- Recommended LANs (Local Area Networks) be installed at each of the firm's locations
- Recommended that Internet access be used at each of the firm's locations
- Recommended that computer training be offered to interested employees

Brief Project Description

Since the breakup of the old Soviet Union, some individual republics have sought Western assistance in updating their nuclear plants. The government of Russia hired safety experts and mechanical engineers from M&K to design a new control panel and to retrofit it into an existing plant. M&K designed, manufactured, installed, and tested the panel—with the help of several subcontractors.

Main Technical Tasks

- Spent one week at site observing operators using old panel
- Hired ergonometric and nuclear power experts to help evaluate old panel design and to suggest features of new design
- Designed and manufactured panel
- Installed panel at Russian plant and observed one full week of testing, when panel was used at plant under simulated conditions
- Remained on-site for three days after full power was resumed so we could continue training operators on use of new panel

Main Findings or Benefits

- Designed panel that international experts considered to be as safe as any currently in use
- Stayed on schedule, keeping the plant out of use only two weeks

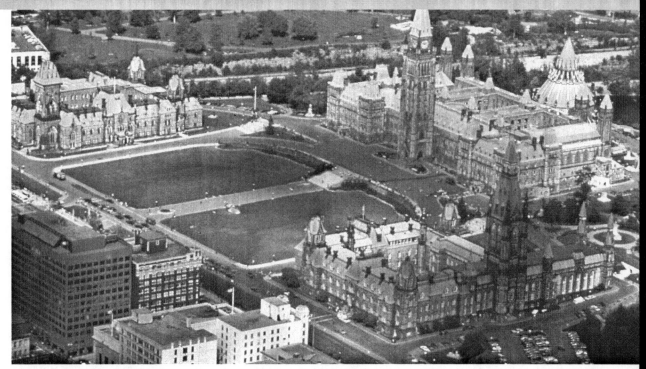

Brief Project Description

The government of Canada has dramatically increased the number of technical experts in departments in Ottawa. Martin & Koffman's Montreal office was selected to design and teach in-house technical writing seminars in both official languages. Seminars are offered on an ongoing basis to participants from the ministries of agriculture, energy, mines and resources, and health and welfare.

Main Technical Tasks

- Met with representatives from the ministries to determine each group's needs
- Examined sample reports from all participants
- Studied the government's style guidelines
- Designed and taught a three-day seminar, using a manual of guidelines and in-house samples tailored for the group
- Evaluated actual on-the-job reports written by participants after the seminar

Main Findings or Benefits

- Received "very good" to "excellent" ratings from the initial group of participants on the written critiques completed on the last day of the course
- Wrote a final report to client that documented improvement shown in participants' reports written after the seminar, compared with those written before the seminar

CHAPTER 3

Organizing Information

Tom Kent asks the department secretary to hold his calls. Closing his door, he reaches for the report draft written by one of his staff members and sits down to read it. As an M&K manager for 10 years, he has reviewed and signed off on every major report written by members of his department. Of all the problems that plague the drafts he reads, poor organization bothers him the most.

This problem is especially annoying at the beginning of a document and the beginning of individual sections. Sometimes he has no idea where the writer is going. His people don't seem to understand that they are supposed to be "telling a story," even in a technical report. Grammar and style errors are annoying to him, but organization problems are much more troublesome. They require extensive rewriting and time-consuming meetings with the report writer. Reaching for his red pen, Tom hopes for the best as he begins to read yet another report.

You, too, will face internal reviewers like Tom Kent when you write on the job. To help you avoid organization problems, this chapter offers strategies for organizing information as you plan, draft, and revise your writing. It builds on the discussion of the three stages of writing covered in Chapter 1. The next two chapters will complete your introduction to technical writing by showing you how to use effective page and Web design as well as effective graphics to keep your readers' attention.

IMPORTANCE OF ORGANIZATION

In a survey of engineering professionals, respondents named "organizing information" the most important topic for any undergraduate technical writing course. This research[1] is backed up by the experience of many communication consultants—including one of the authors of this textbook, who for many years has helped companies improve their employees' writing. Overwhelmingly, these firms have cited poor organization as the main writing problem among both new and experienced employees. That concern underlies the suggestions in this chapter.

As you learned in Chapter 1, your documents will be read by varied readers with diverse technical backgrounds. Chapter 2 displayed this technical range within Martin & Koffman and referred to an even broader technical spectrum among the company's clients. Given this diversity of readers, this chapter aims to answer one essential question: how can you best organize information to satisfy so many different people?

Figure 3-1 shows you three possible options for organizing information for a mixed technical audience, but only one is recommended in this book. Some writers, usually those with technical backgrounds themselves, choose Option A. They direct their writing to the *most* technical people. Other writers choose Option B. They respond to the dilemma of a mixed technical audience by finding the lowest com-

---

[1] T.E. Pinelli, M. Glassman, R.O. Barclay, and W.E. Oliu, *Technical Communications in Aeronautics: Results of an Exploratory Study—An Analysis of Profit Managers' and Nonprofit Managers' Responses,* NASA TM–101626 (Washington, DC: National Aeronautics and Space Administration, 1989), p. 28.

mon denominator—that is, they write to the level of the *least* technical person. Options A and B each satisfy one segment of readers at the expense of the others.

Option C is preferred in technical writing for mixed readers. It encourages you to organize documents so that *all* readers—both technical and nontechnical—get what they need. The rest of this chapter provides strategies for developing this option. It describes general principles of organization and guidelines for organizing entire documents, individual document sections, and paragraphs.

Three Principles of Organization

Good organization starts with a careful analysis of your audience. Most readers are impatient and skip around as they read. Think about how you examine a weekly newsmagazine or an airline magazine. You are likely to take a quick look at articles of special interest to you; then you might read them more thoroughly, if there is time. That approach also resembles how your audience treats technical reports and other work-related documents. If important points are buried in long paragraphs or sections, busy readers may miss them. The following three principles respond realistically to the needs of your readers.

Principle 1: Write Different Parts for Different Readers

The longer the document, the less likely it is that any of your readers will read it from beginning to end. As shown in Figure 3-2, they use a "speed-read" approach that includes the following steps:

Step 1: **Quick scan.** Readers often scan easy-to-read sections, such as executive summaries, introductory summaries, introductions, tables of contents, conclusions, and recommendations. They pay special attention to beginning and ending sections, especially in documents longer than a page or two, and to illustrations.

Step 2: **Focused search.** Readers go directly to parts of the document body that will give them what they need at the moment. To find information quickly, they search for format devices such as subheadings, listings, and white space in margins to guide their reading. (See Chapter 4 for a discussion of page and Web design.)

Step 3: **Short follow-ups.** Readers return to the document, when time permits, to read or reread important sections.

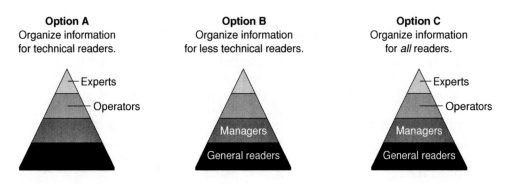

Figure 3-1 Options for organizing information

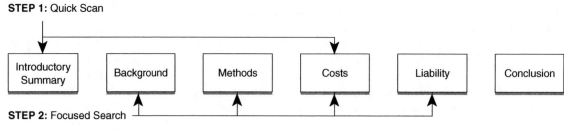

STEP 1: Quick Scan

STEP 2: Focused Search

STEP 3: Short Follow-Ups
Can involve any section, especially the Introductory Summary

Figure 3-2   Sample speed-read approach to short proposal

Your job is to write in a way that responds to the nonlinear, episodic reading processes of your audience. Most important, you should direct each section to those in the audience most likely to read that particular section. Shift the level of technicality as you move from section to section within the document, to meet the needs of each section's specific readers. Managers and general readers favour less technical language and depend most heavily on overviews at the beginning of documents; experts and operators expect more technical jargon and pay more attention than others to the body sections of documents.

Of course, you walk a fine line in designing different parts of the document for different readers. Although technical language and other stylistic features may change from section to section, your document must hang together as one piece of work. Common threads of organization, theme, and tone must keep it from appearing fragmented or pieced together.

This approach breaks the rules of nontechnical writing, which strives for dogged consistency throughout the same document. However, the goals of technical writing differ from those of nontechnical writing and often so too does the approach.

Principle 2: Emphasize Beginnings and Endings

Suspense fiction relies on readers' interest and patience to piece together important information. The writer usually drops hints throughout the narrative before finally revealing who did what to whom. Technical writing operates differently. Busy readers expect to find information in predictable locations. Their first-choice locations for important information are as follows:

- The beginning of the entire document
- The beginnings of report sections
- The beginnings of paragraphs

The reader interest curve in Figure 3-3 reflects this focus on beginnings. But the curve also shows that the reader's second choice for reading is the *end* of documents, sections, and paragraphs. That is, most readers tend to remember best the first and last things they read. The ending is a slightly less desirable location than the beginning because it is less accessible, especially in long sections or documents.

Of course, some readers inevitably will read the last part of a document first, for they may have the habit of fanning pages when first seeing a document—that is, their thumb first locks on the last section of the report. Thus, although there is no guarantee that the first document section will be read first, you can be fairly sure that either the beginning or the ending will get first attention.

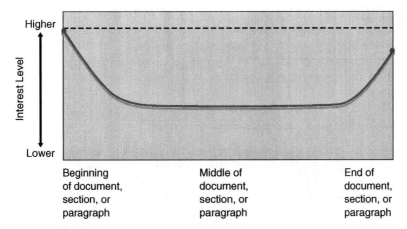

Figure 3-3 Reader interest curve

Emphasizing beginnings and endings responds to readers' reading habits and psychological needs. At the beginning, readers want to know where you're heading. They need a simple "road map" for the rest of the passage. In fact, if you don't provide something important at the beginnings of paragraphs, sections, and documents, readers will start guessing the main point themselves. It is in your best interests to direct the reader to what *you* consider most important in what they are about to read, instead of making them guess at the passage's importance. At the ending, readers expect some sort of wrap-up or transition, so your writing shouldn't simply drop off. The following paragraph begins and ends with such information:

> *The proposed word-processing software has two other features that will help our writers: a dictionary and a thesaurus.* When the built-in dictionary is engaged, it compares each word in a document with the same word in the system's dictionary. Differences are then highlighted so that the word can be corrected. The thesaurus also can help our writers by offering alternative word selections. When the writer is having difficulty pinpointing just the right word, he or she can trigger the system to provide a list of related words or synonyms. *Both the dictionary and thesaurus features are quick and thus far superior to their book counterparts.*

The first sentence gives readers an immediate impression of the two topics to be covered in the paragraph. The paragraph body explores details of both topics. The last sentence flows smoothly from the paragraph body by reinforcing the main point about features of the dictionary and thesaurus.

Why is this top-down pattern, which seems so logical from the reader's perspective, frequently ignored in technical writing? The answer has to do with the difference between the way you complete your research or fieldwork and the way busy readers expect you to convey results of your work in a report. Figure 3-4 illustrates this difference. Having moved logically from data to conclusions and recommendations in technical work, many writers assume that they should take this same approach in their report. They reason that the reader wants and needs all the supporting details before being confronted with the conclusions and recommendations that arise from these data.

Such reasoning, however, is wrong. Readers want to see the results first, followed by details that support your main points. Of course, you must be careful not to give detailed conclusions and recommendations at the beginning; most readers want and expect only a brief summary. Such an overview should provide a framework within which readers can place the details presented later. In other words, readers of technical documents want the "whodunit" answer at the beginning. Recall the motto in Chapter 1: Write for your reader, not for yourself. Now you can see that this rule governs the manner in which you organize information in everything you write.

Principle 3: Repeat Key Points

You have learned that different people focus on different sections of a document. Sometimes no one reads the entire report in detail. For example, managers may only have time to read the summary, whereas technical experts may skip the lead-off sections and go directly to "meaty" technical sections with supporting information. These varied reading patterns require a *redundant* approach to organization—you must repeat important information in different sections for different readers.

For example, assume that you are an M&K employee in Calgary and are writing a report to the University of Manitoba on prospective sites for several athletic fields. Having examined five alternatives, your report recommends one site for final consideration. Your 25-page report compares and contrasts all five alternatives according to the following criteria: land cost, proximity to other athletic locations, and the relative difficulty of grading the site and building the required facilities. Given this context, where will your recommendation appear in the report? Here are five likely spots:

1. Executive summary
2. Cost section in the body
3. Location section in the body
4. Grading/construction section in the body
5. Concluding section

Our assumption, you will recall, is that few readers move straight through a report. Because they often skip to the section most interesting to them, you need to

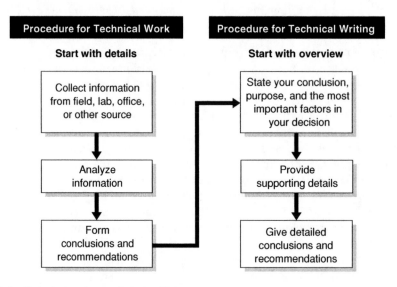

Figure 3-4   Technical *work* vs. technical *writing*

make main sections somewhat self-contained. In the University of Manitoba report, therefore, you would place the main recommendation at the beginning, at the end, and at one or more points within each main section. In that way, readers of all sections would encounter your main point.

What about the occasional readers who read the entire report, word for word? Will they be put off by the restatement of main points? No, they won't. Your strategic repetition of a major finding, conclusion, or recommendation gives helpful reinforcement to readers, who are always searching for an answer to the "So what?" question as they read. Fiction and nonfiction may be alike in this respect—writers in both genres are "telling a story." The theme of this story must periodically reappear to keep readers on track.

Now we're ready to be more specific about how the three general principles of organization apply to documents, document sections, and paragraphs.

ABC FORMAT FOR DOCUMENTS

You have learned the three principles of organization: (1) write different parts of the document for different readers, (2) emphasize beginnings and endings, and (3) repeat key points. Now let's move from principles to practice. Here we will develop an all-purpose pattern of organization for writing entire documents. (The next major section covers document sections and paragraphs.)

Technical documents should assume a three-part structure that consists of a beginning, a middle, and an end. This book labels this structure the "ABC format" (for **A**bstract, **B**ody, and **C**onclusion). Visually, think of this pattern as a three-part diamond structure, as shown in Figure 3-5 and as demonstrated in the memo report in Model 3-1 at the end of this chapter.

- **Abstract:** A brief beginning component is represented by the narrow top of the diamond, which leads into the body.
- **Body:** The longer middle component is represented by the broad, expansive portion of the diamond figure.
- **Conclusion:** A brief ending component is represented by the narrow bottom of the diamond, which leads away from the body.

The following sections discuss the three ABC components in detail.

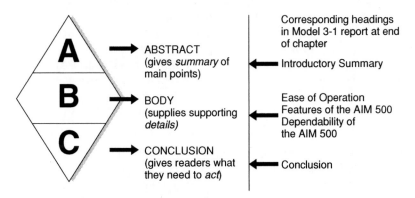

Figure 3-5 ABC format for all documents

Document Abstract: The "Big Picture" for Decision Makers

Every document should begin with an overview. As used in this text, abstract is defined as follows:

> **Abstract:** brief summary of a document's main points. Although its makeup varies with the type and length of the document, an abstract always includes (1) your conclusion, (2) a clear purpose statement for the document, and (3) the most important points for decision makers. It may also note the main document sections that follow. As a capsule version of the entire document, the abstract should answer readers' typical mental questions, such as the following: "How does this document concern me? What's the bottom line? So what?"

Abstract information is provided under one of several different headings, depending on the document's length and degree of formality. Some common headings are Summary, Executive Summary, Introductory Summary, and Overview. The abstract may vary in length from a short paragraph to a page or so. Its purpose, however, is always the same: to provide decision makers with the document's highlights.

For example, assume you are an engineer who has evaluated environmental hazards for the potential purchaser of a shopping mall site. The abstract information in your report should include (1) a brief project summary, (2) a statement of findings, and (3) the most important points and an indication of sections to follow. In effect, this summary should answer three questions:

- What are the major risks at the site?
- Are these risks great enough to warrant not buying the land?
- What major sections does the rest of the report contain?

Here is how the summary might read:

> Examination of the site being considered for the new Klinesburg Mall reveals that the possibility of environmental contamination is negligible. Our field exploration revealed two locations with deposits of household trash, which can be easily cleaned up. Another spot has a more serious deposit problem of 10 barrels of industrial waste. However, our inspection of the containers and soil tests revealed no leaks. Given these limited observations and tests, we conclude that the site poses no major environmental risks and recommend development of the mall. The rest of this report details our field activities, test analyses, conclusions, and recommendations.

This general abstract, or overview, is mainly for decision makers. Highlights must be brief, yet free of any possible misunderstandings. On some occasions you may need to state that further clarification is included in the text, even though that point may seem obvious. For example, if your report concerns matters of safety, the overview may not be detailed enough to prevent or eliminate risks. In this case, state this point clearly so that the reader will not misunderstand or exaggerate the abstract's purpose.

Later chapters in this book contain guidelines for writing the following specific types of abstracts:

- Introductory summaries for informal reports (Chapter 10)
- Executive summaries for formal reports (Chapter 11)
- Introductory summaries for informal proposals (Chapter 12)
- Executive summaries for formal proposals (Chapter 12)
- Abstracts of technical articles (Chapter 14)

Document Body: Details for All Readers

The longest part of any document is the body. As used in this book, the body is defined as follows:

> **Body:** the middle section(s) of the document providing supporting information to readers, especially those with a technical background. Unlike the abstract and conclusion, the body component allows you to write expansively about items such as (1) the project's background; (2) field-, lab-, office-, or any other work on which the document is based; and (3) details of any conclusions, recommendations, or proposals that might be highlighted at the beginning or end of the document. The body answers the following main reader question: "What support is there for points put forth in the abstract at the beginning of the document?"

Managers may read much of the body, especially if they have a technical background and if the document is short. Yet the more likely readers are technical specialists who (1) verify technical information for the decision makers or (2) use your document to do their work. In writing the body, use the following guidelines:

- **Separate fact from opinion.** Never leave the reader confused about where opinions begin and end. Body sections usually move from facts to facts-based opinions. To make a clear distinction, preface opinions with phrases such as "We believe that," "I feel that," "It is our opinion that," and the like. Such wording gives readers clear signals that you are presenting judgments, conclusions, and other nonfactual statements.
- **Adopt a format that reveals much structure.** Use frequent headings and subheadings to help busy readers locate important information immediately. (Chapter 4 covers these and other elements of page and Web design.)
- **Use graphics whenever possible.** Use graphics to draw attention to important points. Today more than ever, readers expect visual reinforcement of your text, particularly in more persuasive documents such as proposals. (Chapter 5 deals with graphical elements in technical documents.)
- **Don't interrupt the flow of information.** The body should not include raw data. Mention and discuss the results of surveys, testing, and research. Raw data and discussions of methodology must be placed in appendices.

By following these guidelines, which apply to any document, you will make detailed body sections as readable as possible. The guidelines keep ideas from becoming buried in text and show readers what to do with the information they find.

Document Conclusion: Wrap-up Leading to Next Step

Your conclusion deserves special attention, for readers often recall first what they have read last. We define the conclusion component as follows:

> **Conclusion:** the final section(s) of the document bringing readers—especially decision makers—back to one or more central points already mentioned in the body. Occasionally, the conclusion may include one or more points not previously mentioned. In any case, the conclusion provides closure to the document and often leads to the next step in the writer's relationship with the reader.

The conclusion component may have any one of several headings, depending on the type and length of the document. Possibilities include Conclusion, Closing, Closing Remarks, and Conclusions and Recommendations. Later chapters of this book describe the options for informal and formal documents of many kinds. In general, however, a conclusion component answers the following sorts of questions:

- What major points have you made?
- What problem have you tried to solve?
- What should the reader do next?
- What will you do next?
- What single idea do you want to leave with the reader?

Because readers focus on beginnings and endings of documents, you want to exploit the opportunity to drive home your message, just as you did in the abstract. Format can greatly affect the impact you make on decision makers. Although specific formats vary, most conclusions take one of the following two forms:

- **Listings:** This format is especially useful when you are pulling together points mentioned throughout the document. Whereas the abstract often gives readers the big picture in narrative format, the conclusion may instead depend on listings of findings, conclusions, and/or recommendations. (Chapter 4 gives suggestions on using bulleted and numbered listings.)
- **Summary paragraph(s):** When a listing is not appropriate, you may want to write a concluding paragraph or two. Here you can leave readers with an important piece of information and make clear the next step to be taken.

Whichever alternative you choose, your goal is to return to the main concerns of the most important readers—the decision makers. Both the abstract and the conclusion, in slightly different ways, should respond to the needs of this primary audience.

TIPS FOR ORGANIZING SECTIONS AND PARAGRAPHS

First and foremost, the ABC format pertains to the organization of entire documents. Yet the same "beginning-middle-end" strategy applies to the next smaller units of discourse—document sections and paragraphs. In fact, you can view the entire document as a series of interlocking units, each responding to reader expectations, as illustrated by the reader interest curve in Figure 3-3 on page 53.

Document Sections

As mentioned earlier, readers often move from the document abstract to the specific body sections they need to solve their problem or answer their immediate question. Just as they need abstracts and conclusions in the whole document, they need "mini-abstracts" at the start and brief wrap-ups at the end of each major section.

To see how a section abstract works, we must first understand readers' dilemmas. Refer to Model 3-2 on page 67, which contains one section from a long report. Some readers may read it from beginning to end, but others might not have the time or interest to do so in one sitting. Instead, they would look to the section's beginning for an abstract, and then move around within that section at will. Thus the beginning must provide them with a map of what's ahead. Here are the two items that should be part of every section abstract:

1. **Interest grabber:** a sentence or more that captures the reader's attention. Your grabber may be one sentence or an entire paragraph, depending on the document's overall length. Avoid asking a question. Make your grabber a positive statement.
2. **Lead-in:** a list, in sentence or bullet format, that indicates the main topics to follow in the section. If the section contains subheadings, your lead-in may include the same wording as the subheadings and be in the same order.

The first part of the section gives readers everything they need to encourage them to read on. First, you get their attention with a grabber. Then you give them an outline of the main points to follow so they can move to the part of the section that interests them most. As in Model 3-2, the section abstract immediately precedes the first subheading when subheads are used.

Sections also should end with some sort of closing thought, instead of just dropping off after the last supporting point has been stated. For example, you can (1) briefly restate the importance of the information in the section or (2) provide a transition to the section that follows. Model 3-2 takes the latter approach by suggesting the main topic for the next section. Whereas the section lead-in provides a map to help readers navigate through the section, the closing gives a sense of conclusion so that readers will be ready to move on.

Paragraphs

Paragraphs represent the basic building blocks of any document. Organizing them is not much different in technical writing than it is in nontechnical prose. Most paragraphs contain the following elements:

1. **Topic sentence:** This sentence states the main idea to be developed in the paragraph. Usually it appears first. Do not delay or bury the main point, for busy readers may read only the beginnings of paragraphs. If you fail to put the main point there, they may miss it entirely.
2. **Development of the main idea:** Sentences that follow the topic sentence develop the main idea with examples, narrative, explanation, and/or other details. Give the reader concrete supporting details, not generalizations.
3. **Transitional elements:** Structural transitions help the paragraph flow smoothly. Use transitions in the form of repeated nouns and pronouns, contrasting conjunctions, and introductory phrases.
4. **Closing sentence:** Most paragraphs, like sections and documents, need closure. Use the last sentence for a concluding point about the topic or for a transitional point that links the paragraph with the one following it.

Model 3-3 on page 68 shows two paragraphs that follow this pattern of organization. The paragraphs are from an M&K recommendation report. M&K was hired to suggest ways for a hospital to modernize its physical plant. Each paragraph is a self-contained unit addressing a specific topic, while being linked to surrounding paragraphs (not shown) by theme and transitional elements.

This suggested format applies to many but not all paragraphs included in technical documents. In one common exception, you may choose to delay statement of a topic sentence until you engage the reader's attention with the first few sentences. In other cases, the paragraph may be short and serve only as an attention grabber or a transitional device between several longer paragraphs. Still, for most paragraphs in technical writing, the beginning-middle-end model described here will serve you well. Remember the following points as well, as you organize paragraphs in technical writing:

- **Length:** Keep the paragraphs six to ten lines long. Many readers won't read long blocks of text, no matter how well organized the information is. If you see that your topic requires more than ten lines for its development, split the topic and develop it in two or more paragraphs.
- **Listings:** Use short listings of three or four items to break up long paragraphs. Readers lose patience when they realize that the information could have been more clearly presented in listings. Chapter 4 offers detailed suggestions on using lists.
- **Use of numbers:** Paragraphs are the worst format for presenting technical data of any kind, especially numbers that describe costs. Readers may ignore or miss data that are packed into paragraphs. Tables or figures are a clearer and more appropriate format. Also, be aware that some readers may think that cost data couched in paragraph form represent an attempt to hide important information.

This chapter mostly concerns the ordering of ideas within paragraphs, sections, and whole documents. Good organization helps make your writing successful. However, organization alone will not win the day. Readers also expect a visually appealing document. The next chapter will describe technical devices for creating the best possible page and Web design.

Employability Skills

The Conference Board of Canada's *Employability Skills 2000+* suggests that the ability to manage and organize information is critical to success in the workplace. Relevant communication and information management skills include the following:

- Read and understand information presented in a variety of forms (e.g., words, graphs, charts, diagrams).
- Write and speak so others pay attention and understand.

- Locate, gather, and organize information using appropriate technology and information systems.*

In groups, develop an information package to be given to potential applicants to your program of study. Show how the skills that will be learned and demonstrated as a student will be useful in a working career.

* *Employability Skills 2000+* Brochure 2000 E/F (Ottawa: The Conference Board of Canada, 2000).

CHAPTER SUMMARY

Good technical writing calls on special skills, especially in organization. Writers should follow three guidelines for organizing information: (1) write different parts of the document for different readers, (2) place important information at the beginnings and endings, and (3) repeat key points throughout the document.

This chapter recommends the "ABC format" for organizing technical documents. This format includes an **A**bstract (summary), a **B**ody (supporting details), and a **C**onclusion (wrap-up and transition to next step). The abstract section is particularly important because most readers give special attention to the start of a document.

Individual sections and paragraphs also require attention to organization. Sections need overviews and closing passages so that busy readers can find information quickly. Most paragraphs should contain a topic sentence, supporting details, transitional words and phrases, and a closing sentence that leads into the next paragraph.

A S S I G N M E N T S

1. **Overall organization.** Find an example of technical writing directed to more than one reader. Prepare a written or an oral report (your instructor's choice) that explains how well the excerpt follows this chapter's guidelines for organization.

2. **Evaluating an abstract.** Read the following abstract and evaluate the degree to which it follows the guidelines in this chapter.

I recommend that we adopt the new Blaupunkt BMA5350B into our line of car audio products. As one of the buyers for Randall Auto Parts, I constantly search for new products that I feel can increase our sales. I recently attended an electronics convention to see what new products were available. One product that caught my eye was the new amplifier.
This proposal supports my recommendation and includes the following sections:

1. Features of the Blaupunkt BMA5350B
2. Customer Benefits
3. Cost
4. Conclusions

---

3. **Section organization.** As a graphics specialist at M&K, you have written a recommendation report on ways to upgrade the firm's graphics capabilities. One section of the report describes a new desktop publishing system, which you believe will make M&K's proposals and reports much more professional looking. Your report section describes the system's technical features, the free training that comes with purchase, and the cost.

   Write a lead-in paragraph for this section of your report. If necessary, invent additional information for writing the paragraph.

4. **Paragraph organization: analysis.** Select a paragraph from each of four different articles taken from periodicals in your campus library. Choose one from a nationally known newspaper (like the *Globe and Mail*), one from a popular magazine (like *Maclean's* or *Canadian Geographic*), one from a business magazine (like *Report on Business* or *Canadian Business*), and one from a technical journal (like *IEEE Transactions on Professional Communication*). Explain in writing how each of the paragraphs does or does not follow the top-down pattern of organization discussed in this chapter. If a paragraph does not follow the top-down pattern, indicate whether you believe the writer made the right or wrong decision in organizing the paragraph. In other words, was there a legitimate reason to depart from the ABC format? If so, what was the reason? If not, how would you revise the paragraph to make it fit the ABC format?

5. **Paragraph organization: writing.** With the following list of related information, write a paragraph that follows the organizational guidelines in this chapter. Use all the information, change any of the wording when necessary, and add appropriate transitions.

Assume that this paragraph is part of an internal M&K document suggesting ways to improve work schedules.

- Four-day weeks may lower job stress—employees have long weekends with families and may avoid the worst part of rush hour.
- A four-day, 10-hour-a-day workweek may not work for some service firms, where projects and clients need five days of attention.
- Standard five-day, eight-hour-a-day workweeks increase on-the-job stress, especially as this relates to commuter time and family obligations.
- M&K is considering a pilot program for one office, whereby the office would depart from the standard 40-hour workweek.
- M&K is also considering other strategies to improve employees' work schedules.
- The 40-hour workweek came into being when many more families had one parent at home while the other worked.
- Some firms have gone completely to a four-day week (with 10-hour days).
- M&K's pilot program would be for one year, after which it would be evaluated.

6. Writing an abstract: individual work. The following short report lacks an abstract that states the purpose and provides the main conclusion or recommendation from the body of the report. Write a brief abstract for this report.

DATE: June 13, 2006
TO: Ed Simpson
FROM: Jeff Radner
SUBJECT: Creation of an Operator Preventive Maintenance Program

THE PROBLEM

The lack of operator involvement in the equipment maintenance program has caused the reliability of equipment to decline. Here are a few examples:

- A tractor was operated without adequate oil in the crankcase, resulting in a $15,000 repair bill after the engine locked.
- Operators have received fines from police officers because safety lights were not operating. The bulbs were burned out and had not been replaced. Brake lights and turn-signal malfunctions have been cited as having caused rear-end collisions.
- A small grass fire erupted at a construction site. When the operator of the vehicle nearest to the fire attempted to extinguish the blaze, he discovered that the fire extinguisher had already been discharged.

When the operator fails to report deficiencies to the mechanics, dangerous consequences may result.

THE SOLUTION

The goal of any maintenance program is to maintain the company equipment so that the daily tasks can be performed safely and on schedule. Since the operator is using the equipment on a regular basis, he or she is in the position to spot potential problems before they become serious. For a successful maintenance program, the following recommendations should be implemented:

- Hold a mandatory four-hour equipment maintenance training class conducted by mechanics in the motor pool. This training would consist of a hands-on approach to preventive maintenance checks and services at the operator level.
- Require operators to perform certain checks on a vehicle before checking it out of the motor pool. A vehicle checklist would be turned in to maintenance personnel.

The attached checklist would require five to ten minutes to complete.

Fleet Maintenance Division
Vehicle Checklist
Pretrip Inspection

Inspected by: _____   Date: _____

Vehicle #: _____   Odometer: _____

Fluid Levels, Full/Low   Comments

_____   Engine Oil   _____

_____   Transmission Fluid   _____

_____   Brake Fluid   _____

_____   Power Steering   _____

_____   Radiator Level   _____

Before Cranking Vehicle

_____   Tire Condition   _____

_____   Battery Terminals   _____

_____   Fan Belts   _____

_____   Bumper and Hitch   _____

_____   Trailer Plug-in   _____

_____   Safety Chains   _____

After Cranking Vehicle

_____   Parking Brakes   _____

_____   Lights   _____

_____   All Gauges   _____

_____   Seat Belts   _____

_____   Mirrors/Windows/Wipers   _____

_____   Clutch   _____

_____   Fire Ext. Mounted and Charged _____

_____   Two-Way Radio Working   _____

Additional Comments:_____

_____

CONCLUSION

I believe the cost of maintaining the vehicle fleet will be reduced when potential problems are detected and corrected before they become serious. Operator training and the vehicle pretrip inspection checklist will ensure that preventable accidents are avoided. I will call you this week to answer any questions you may have about this proposal.

7. **Writing an abstract: conventional group work.** For this assignment your instructor will divide the class into groups. Using one of the project sheets at the end of Chapter 2, your group will write a generic abstract for a report of the completed project. Follow the guidelines in this chapter.

8. **Writing an abstract: group work using computer communication.** As in assignment 7, for this assignment you will (a) work in groups established by your instructor, (b) write a generic abstract for a report on one of the project sheets, and (c) follow the abstract guidelines included in this chapter. In addition, you are to conduct at least part

of your team business by email. The degree to which your team uses email will depend on the technical resources of team members and the campus. At a minimum, you should plan for each member to send a message to every other member concerning, for example, the drafting or editing process. At a maximum, and if computer resources permit, you may develop onscreen "windows" whereby you conduct a conversation with each fellow member in one window and make changes in text in another window. The point of this assignment, in other words, is for team members to use email in a substantive way to communicate with one another for group projects.

MEMORANDUM

DATE: September 5, 2006
TO: Danielle Firestein
FROM: Barbara Ralston *BR*
SUBJECT: Recommendation for AIM 500 Fax

INTRODUCTORY SUMMARY

This memo presents my evaluation of the AIM 500 facsimile (fax) machine by Simko, Inc. The AIM 500 has served our department well for the past two years. If other departments need a fax machine, I highly recommend this model because it is easy to operate, has many useful features, and has been quite dependable.

EASE OF OPERATION

The AIM 500 is so easy to operate that a novice can learn to transmit a document to another location in about two minutes. Here's the basic procedure:

1. Press the button marked TEL on the face of the fax machine. You then hear a dial tone.
2. Key in the telephone number of the person receiving the fax on the number pad on the face of the machine.
3. Lay the document face down on the tray at the back of the machine.

At this point, just wait for the document to be transmitted—about 18 seconds per page to transmit. The fax machine will even signal the user with a beep and a message on its LCD display when the document has been transmitted. Other more advanced operations are equally simple to use and require little training. Provided with the machine are two different charts that illustrate the machine's main functions.

The size of the AIM 500 makes it easy to set up almost anywhere in an office. The dimensions are 33 cm in width, 38 cm in length, and 13 cm in height. The narrow width, in particular, allows the machine to fit on most desks, file cabinets, or shelves.

FEATURES OF THE AIM 500

The AIM 500 has many features that will be beneficial to our employees. In the two years of use in our department, the following features were found to be most helpful:

Automatic redial
Last number redial memory
LCD display

continues

Model 3-1 ABC format in whole document

Ralston to Firestein, 2

Preset dialing
Group dialing
Use as a phone

Automatic Redial. Often when sending a fax, the sender finds the receiving line busy. The redial feature will automatically redial the busy number at 30-second intervals until the busy line is reached, saving the sender considerable time.

Last Number Redial Memory. Occasionally there may be interference on the telephone line or some other technical problem with the transmissions. The last number memory feature allows the user to press one button to automatically trigger the machine to retry the number.

LCD Display. This display feature clearly shows pertinent information, such as error messages that tell a user exactly why a transmission was not completed.

Preset Dialing. The AIM 500 can store 16 preset numbers that can be engaged with one-touch dialing. This feature makes the unit as fast and efficient as a sophisticated telephone.

Group Dialing. Upon selecting two or more of the preset telephone numbers, the user can transmit a document to all of the preset numbers at once.

Use as a Phone. The AIM 500 can also be used as a telephone, providing the user with more flexibility and convenience.

DEPENDABILITY OF THE AIM 500

Over the entire two years our department has used this machine, there have been no complaints. We always receive clear copies from the machine, and we never hear complaints about the documents we send out. This record is all the more impressive in light of the fact that we average 32 outgoing and 15 incoming transmissions a day. Obviously, we depend heavily on this machine.

So far, the only required maintenance has been to change the paper and the dust cover.

CONCLUSION

The success our department has enjoyed with the AIM 500 compels me to recommend it highly. The ease of operation, many exceptional features, and record of dependability are all good reasons to purchase additional units. If you have further questions about the AIM 500, please contact me at extension 3646.

Model 3-1 *continued*

ADDITIONAL FEATURES OF MAGCAD

This report has presented two main advantages of the MagCad Drawing System: ease of correction and multiple use of drawings. However, there are two other features that make this system a wise purchase: the selective print feature and the cost.

Selective Printing

When printing a MagCad drawing, you can "turn off" specific objects that are in the drawing with a series of keystrokes. The excluded items will not appear in the printout of the drawing. That is, the printed drawing will reflect exactly what you have temporarily left on the screen, after the deletions. Yet the drawing that remains in the memory of the machine is complete and ready to be reconstructed for another printout.

The selective print feature is especially useful on jobs where different groups have different needs. For example, in a drawing of a construction project intended only for the builder, one drawing may contain only land contours and the building structures. If the same drawing is going to the paving company, we may need to include only land contours and parking lots. In each case, we will have used the selective print feature to tailor the drawing to the specific needs of each reader.

This feature improves our service to the client. In the past, we either had to complete several different drawings or we had to clutter one drawing with details sufficient for the needs of all clients.

Cost of MagCad

When we started this inquiry, we set a project cost limit of $12,000. The MagCad system stays well within this budget, even considering the five stations that we need to purchase.

The main cost savings occurs because we have to buy only one copy of the MagCad program. For additional workstations, we need pay only a $300 licensing fee per station. The complete costs quoted by the MagCad representative are listed below:

1. MagCad Version 5	$5,000
2. Licences for five additional stations	1,500
3. Plotter	2,000
4. Installation	1,000
TOTAL	$9,500

With the $2,500 difference between the budgeted amount and the projected cost of the system, we could purchase additional workstations or other peripheral equipment. The next section suggests some add-ons we might want to purchase later, once we see how the MagCad can improve our responsiveness to client needs.

Model 3-2 ABC format in document section

Conversion to a partial solar heating and cooling system would upgrade the hospital building considerably. In fact, the use of modern solar equipment could decrease your utility bills by up to 50%, using the formula explained in Appendix B. As you may know, state-of-the-art solar systems are much more efficient than earlier models. In addition, equipment now being installed around the country is much more pleasing to the eye than was the equipment of 10 years ago. The overall effect will be to enhance the appearance of the building, as well as to save on utility costs.

We also believe that changes in landscaping would be a useful improvement to the hospital's physical plant. Specifically, planting shade trees in front of the windows on the eastern side of the complex would block sun and wind. The result would be a decrease in utility costs and enhancement of the appearance of the building. Of course, shade trees will have to grow for about five years before they begin to affect utility bills. Once they have reached adequate height, however, they will be a permanent change with low maintenance. In addition, your employees, visitors, and patients alike will notice the way that trees cut down on glare from the building walls and add "green space" to the hospital grounds.

Model 3-3 ABC format in paragraph

CHAPTER 4

Page Design and Web Design

The first five chapters of the book cover basics you need to know before moving to the applications in later chapters. The first chapter described the technical writing process, with emphasis on writing for your reader; the second introduced M&K, this book's example company; the third dealt with organizing information. This chapter covers page design, another basic building block in technical writing, as well as some of the principles of Web design. Chapter 5 discusses effective graphics. Here is an operating definition of page design:

> **Page design:** a term that refers to formatting options used to create clear, readable, and visually interesting documents. Some of these options relate to judicious use of white space, headings, lists, and varied fonts. The term *page design* became an integral part of technical writing with the advent of word processing and desktop publishing (DTP). *DTP* refers to sophisticated hardware and software systems that individuals can use to write, edit, design, and print both text and graphics.

This first half of the chapter presents guidelines and examples for page design. As you read the material, remember that you can use this chapter during all three stages of the writing process: planning, drafting, and editing.

GUIDELINES FOR PAGE DESIGN

As one expert says, often you will write for readers who are "in a hurry, frustrated, and bored, and who would prefer to get the information needed from text *in any other way but reading*" [authors' emphasis].[1] Most readers dislike solid text. Your challenge is to respond to this prejudice by making pages interesting to the eye.

Good organization, as pointed out in the last chapter, can fight readers' indifference by offering the information when and where they want it. But to keep readers interested, you must use effective page design on each page in your document. Each page needs the right combination of visual elements to match the needs of readers and the purpose of the document.

Many firms know the benefits of such "visual imaging" and develop company style sheets for frequently used documents, including letters, memos, various types of reports, and proposals. The style sheets are then assembled into a style manual and distributed for general use or loaded into the company's text editing software for easy access.

Using style sheets saves time and reinforces the firm's corporate image. Their use makes it possible for members of writing teams to work independently while

---

[1] K.A. Schriver, "Document Design from 1980 to 1989: Challenges That Remain," *Technical Communication* 36(1989): 319.

adhering to corporate formatting guidelines. Using style sheets also ensures that readers see a clear relationship among ideas because headings and subheadings are used consistently.

If the company you work for does not use a style manual, you will want to use the following elements of page design to develop your own style sheet: white space, headings, lists, in-text emphasis, fonts, and colour.

White Space

The term *white space* simply means the open places on the page with no text or graphics—literally, the parts of the page that are white. Experts have learned that readers are attracted to text because of the white space that surrounds it, as with a newspaper ad that includes a few lines of copy in the middle of a white page. Readers connect white space with important information.

In technical writing you should use white space in a way that (1) attracts attention, (2) guides the eye to important information on the page, (3) relieves the boredom of reading text, and (4) helps readers organize information. Following are some opportunities for using white space effectively:

1. **Margins:** Most readers appreciate generous use of white space around the edges of text. Marginal space tends to frame your document, so that the text doesn't appear to push the boundaries of the page. Good practice is to use 2.5- to 3.5-cm margins, with additional space on the bottom margin. When the document is bound on the left, as in Figure 4-1, increase the space in the left margin to make up for space lost during the binding process.

2. **Columns:** Long lines can prevent you from keeping your readers' attention. Eyes get weary of overly long lines, so some writers add double columns to their design options. This "book look," as shown in Figure 4-2, uses white space between columns to break up text and thus reduce line length.

3. **Line space:** When choosing single, double, or $1\frac{1}{2}$-line spacing, consider the document's length and degree of formality. Letters, memos, short reports, and

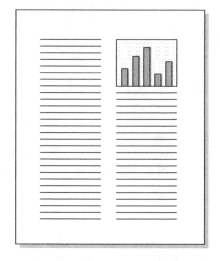

Figure 4-1 Use of white space: margins   **Figure 4-2** Use of white space: columns

other documents that are read in one sitting are usually single spaced, with one line space between paragraphs. Longer documents, especially if they are formal, are usually $1\frac{1}{2}$-line spaced or double spaced, and usually, although not always, without extra spacing between paragraphs (see Figure 4-3).

4. **Right-justified versus ragged edge:** To justify or not to justify lines is often the question. In right-justified copy—as on this textbook page—all lines are the same length. In ragged-edge copy, lines are variable in length. Some readers prefer ragged-edge copy because it adds variation to the page, making reading less predictable for the eye. Yet many readers like the professional appearance of right-justified lines, especially in formal documents. Both views have merit.

   As a rule, (1) use ragged edge on densely packed, single-spaced documents and (2) use either ragged or justified margins on $1\frac{1}{2}$-spaced and double-spaced documents, depending on reader preference or company style (see Figure 4-3). However, only use justified margins if your word-processing software maintains uniform spacing between letters within words. It is distracting to read justified text with inconsistent spacing.

5. **Paragraph length:** New paragraphs give readers a chance to regroup as one topic ends and another begins. These shifts also have a visual impact. The amount of white space produced by paragraph lengths can shape reader expectations. For example, two long paragraphs suggest a heavier reading burden than do three or four paragraphs of differing lengths. Most readers skip long

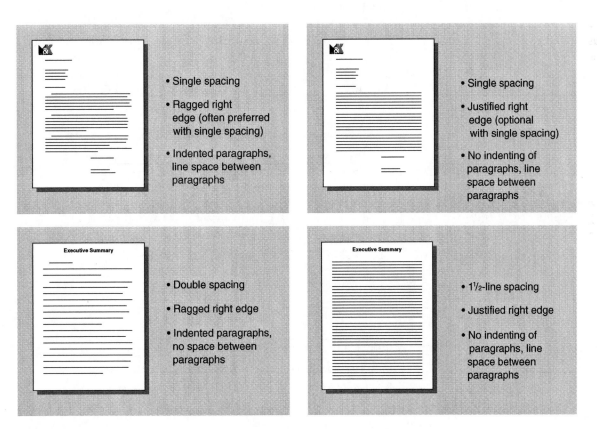

Figure 4-3 Use of white space: lines

paragraphs, so vary paragraph lengths and avoid putting more than 10 lines in any one paragraph (see Figure 4-4).

6. **Paragraph indenting:** The argument goes on about indenting or not indenting the first lines of paragraphs. Most readers prefer indented paragraphs because the extra white space creates visual variety. Reading text is hard work for the eyes. You should take advantage of any opportunity to snag the reader's attention (see Figure 4-3).

7. **In-text graphics:** Any illustration within the text needs special attention. Chapter 5 provides a complete discussion of graphics; here we discuss their placement for visual appeal. Following are some pointers:

   - Make sure there is ample white space between any in-text graphic and the text. If the figure is too large to permit adequate margins, reduce its size.
   - When you have the choice, place in-text graphics near the top of the page. That position gives them the most attention.
   - When a graphic doesn't fit well on a page with text, place it on its own page where there will be adequate space. Normally, a graphic appears on the page following the first reference to it.
   - Pay special attention to page balance when graphics will be included on multi-column pages, two-page spreads, or both.
   - Draw rough sketches of the layout for the entire document so that you can use white space consistently and persuasively from start to finish.

8. **Heading space and lines:** White space helps the reader connect related information immediately. Always have slightly more space above a heading than below it. That extra space visually connects the heading with the material that it leads to. In a double-spaced document, for example, you would add a third line of space between the heading and the text that came before it. In addition, some writers add a horizontal line across the page above headings to emphasize the visual break. The next section will cover other aspects of headings.

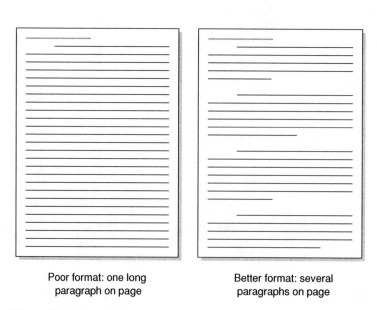

Poor format: one long
paragraph on page

Better format: several
paragraphs on page

Figure 4-4 Use of white space: paragraphs

In summary, well-placed white space can increase your text's persuasive power. As with any design element, however, white space can be overused and abused. Make sure there is a reason for every decision you make regarding white space on your pages.

Headings

Headings are brief labels used to introduce each new section or subsection of text. Headings serve as (1) a signpost for the reader who wants to know the content, (2) a "grabber" to entice the reader to read the document, and (3) a visual oasis of white space where the reader gets relief from text.

As a general rule, every page of any document over one page should have at least one heading. Readers need these markers to find their way through your writing. Models throughout this text show how headings can be used in informal and formal documents. Of course, heading formats differ greatly from company to company and even from writer to writer. With all the typographical possibilities of word processing, there is incredible variety in typeface, type size, and the use of bold, italics, underlining, and capitals. Following are some general guidelines:

1. **Use your outline to create headings and subheadings.** A well-organized outline lists major and minor topics. With little or no change in wording, these topic headings can be converted into headings and subheadings within the document. As with outlines, you need to follow basic principles of organization:

   - First, if you have one subheading, you must have at least one more at that same level—anything that is divided has at least two parts.
   - Second, the number of subheadings should be one indication of a section's relative length or importance. Be consistent in your approach to headings throughout the document.

2. **Use substantive wording.** Headings give readers an overview of what content will follow. Headings entice readers; they can determine whether readers—especially those who are hurried and impatient—will read or skip over the text. Strive to use concrete rather than abstract nouns, even if that means making headings a bit longer. Note the improvements in the following revised headings:

   Original: "Background"
   Revised: "How the Simmons Road Project Got Started" or "Background on Simmons Road Project"

   Original: "Discussion"
   Revised: "Procedure for Measuring Toxicity" or "How to Measure Toxicity"

   Original: "Costs"
   Revised: "Production Costs of the FastCopy 800" or "Producing the FastCopy 800: How Much?"

3. **Maintain parallel form in wording.** Headings of equal value and degree should have the same grammatical form, as shown in the following:

   A) *Headings with Parallel Form*
   Scope of Services
   Schedule for Fieldwork
   Conditions of Contract

B) *Headings That Lack Parallel Form*
Scope of Services
How Will Fieldwork Be Scheduled?
Establish Contract Conditions

You don't have to be a grammar expert to see that the three headings in *B* are in different forms. The first is a noun phrase, the second is a question, and the third is an action phrase beginning with a verb. Because such inconsistencies distract the reader, you should make all headings in a section uniform in structure.

4. **Establish clear hierarchy in headings.** Whatever typographical techniques you choose for headings, your readers must be able to distinguish one heading level from another. Visual features should be increasingly more striking as you move up the levels. Figure 4-5 shows several heading options that reflect such distinctions. Following are specific guidelines for using such typographical distinctions:

- *Use larger type size for higher-level headings.* As your audience reads your document, you want them to grasp quickly the relative importance of heading levels. Type size fixes this relative importance in their minds so that they can easily find their way through your material both the first time and upon rereading it. The examples in Figure 4-5 contain two to three different type sizes. The incremental upgrading of type size helps readers determine the relative importance of the information.
- *Use heading position to show ranking.* In formal documents, your high-level headings can be centred. The next two or three levels of headings are at or off the left margin, as shown in Figure 4-5. Be sure these lower-level headings also use other typographical techniques, such as size, to help the reader distinguish levels.
- *Use typographical techniques to accomplish your purpose.* Besides using type size and position, you can distinguish heading levels with features such as the following:

  Uppercase and lowercase
  Bold type
  Italics
  Changes in font

  Writers must be careful, however, not to create "busy" pages of print. Use only those features that will look good on the page and that will provide an easy-to-grasp hierarchy of levels for the reader.
- *Consider using decimal headings for long documents.* Decimal headings include a hierarchy of numbers for every heading and subheading listed in the table of contents. Many an argument has been waged over their use. People who like them say that they help readers find their way through documents and refer to subsections in later discussions. People who dislike them say that they are cumbersome and give the appearance of "bureaucratic" writing.

  Unless decimal headings are expected by your reader, use them only with formal documents that are fairly long. Include at least three heading levels. The normal progression of numbering in decimal headings for a three-level document is as follows:

```
1.0  xxxxxxxxxxxxxx
     1.1  xxxxxxxxxxx
          1.1.1  xxxxxxxxxx
          1.1.2  xxxxxxxxxx
     1.2  xxxxxxxxxxx
          1.2.1  xxxxxxxxxx
          1.2.2  xxxxxxxxxx
2.0  xxxxxxxxxxxxxx
     2.1  xxxxxxxxxxx
          2.1.1  xxxxxxxxxx
          2.1.2  xxxxxxxxxx
     2.2 xxxxxxxxxxx
3.0  xxxxxxxxxxxxxx
```

Listings

Technical writing benefits from the use of lists. Readers welcome your efforts to cluster items into lists for easy reading. In fact, almost any group of three or more related points can be made into a bulleted or numbered listing. Following are some points to consider as you apply this important feature of page design:

1. **Typical uses:** Lists emphasize important points and provide a welcome change in format. Because they attract more attention than surrounding text, they are usually reserved for the following uses:

   Examples
   Reasons for a decision
   Conclusions
   Recommendations
   Steps in a process
   Cautions or warnings about a product
   Limitations or restrictions on conclusions

2. **Number of items:** The best lists are those that subscribe to the rule of short-term memory (i.e., people can retain no more than five to nine items in their short-term memory). A listing of more than nine items may confuse rather than clarify an issue. Consider placing 10 or more items in two or three groupings, or grouped lists, as you would in an outline. This format helps the reader grasp the information.

3. **Use of bullets and numbers:** The most common visual clues for listings are numbers and bullets (enlarged dots or squares like those used in the following listing). Here are a few pointers for choosing one or the other:

   - *Bullets:* Best in lists of five or fewer items, unless the order in which they appear is important.
   - *Numbers:* Best in lists of more than five items or when needed to indicate an ordering of steps, procedures, or ranked alternatives. Remember that your readers sometimes will infer sequence or ranking in a numbered list.

4. **Format on page:** Every listing should be easy to read and pleasing to the eye. The following specific guidelines cover practices preferred by most readers:

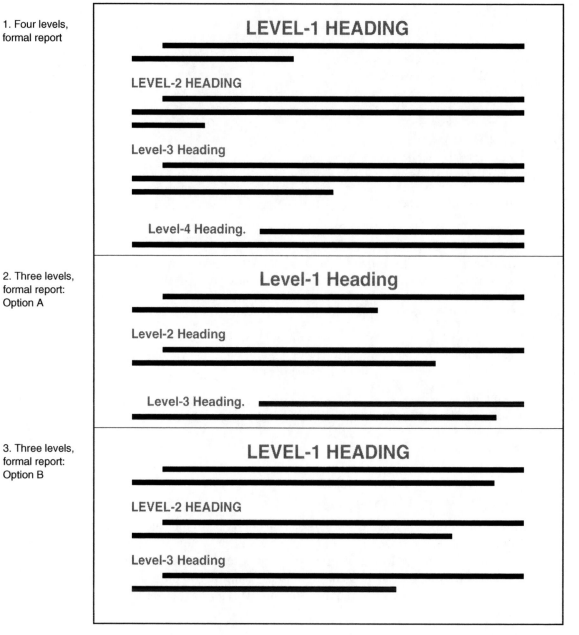

1. Four levels, formal report

2. Three levels, formal report: Option A

3. Three levels, formal report: Option B

continues

Figure 4-5 Some heading options

- *Indent the listing.* Although there is no standard list format, readers prefer lists that are indented farther than the standard left margin. Five spaces is usually adequate.
- *Hang your numbers and bullets.* Visual appeal is enhanced by placing numbers or bullets to the left of the margin used for the list, as with the items in this list.
- *Use line spaces for easier reading.* When one or more listed items contain over a line of text, an extra line space between listed items can enhance readability.

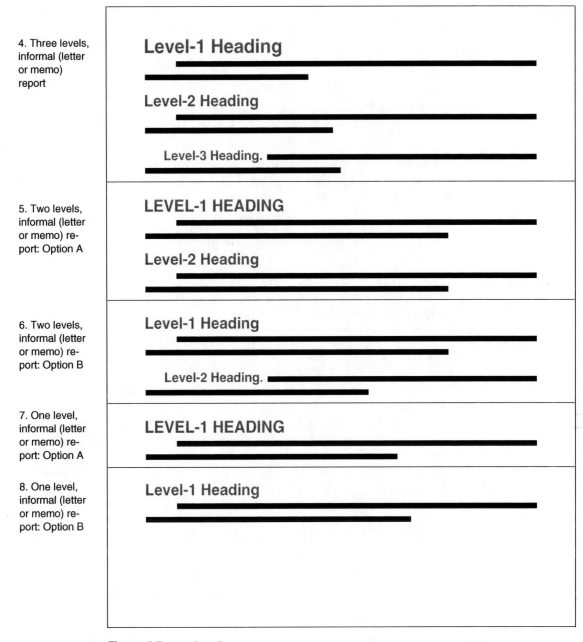

4. Three levels, informal (letter or memo) report

5. Two levels, informal (letter or memo) report: Option A

6. Two levels, informal (letter or memo) report: Option B

7. One level, informal (letter or memo) report: Option A

8. One level, informal (letter or memo) report: Option B

Figure 4-5 *continued*

- *Keep items as short as possible.* Depending on purpose and substance, lists can consist of words, phrases, or sentences. Whichever format you choose, pare down the wording as much as possible to retain the impact of the list format.

5. **Parallelism and lead-ins:** Make the listing easy to read by keeping all points parallel and by including a smooth transition from the lead-in to the listing itself. (The term *lead-in* refers to the sentence or fragment preceding the listing.) *Parallel* means that each point in the list is in the same grammatical form,

whether a complete sentence, a verb phrase, or a noun phrase. If you change form in the middle of a listing, you are probably impeding the information.

Example:

To complete this project, we plan to do the following:

- Survey the site
- Take samples from the three boring locations
- Test selected samples in our lab
- Report on the results of the study

The listed items are in verb form (note the introductory words survey, take, test, and report). An alternative would be to put them in noun form, with a slightly different lead-in.

Example:

To complete the project, we will perform the following activities:

- Surveying the site
- Taking samples from the three boring locations
- Testing selected samples in our lab
- Reporting on the results of the study

6. **Punctuation and capitalization:** Although there are acceptable variations on the punctuation of lists, preferred usage includes a colon before a listing and capitalization of the first letter of the first word of each item. Some people punctuate the end of each item, others don't. Refer to the Handbook under "Punctuation: Lists" for alternative ways to punctuate lists.

7. **Overuse:** With listings it is possible to have too much of a good thing. Too many lists on one page can result in a distracting, fragmented effect. One rule of thumb is to use no more than one or two lists per page. When you have too many lists on the same page, you are forcing the reader to decide which one deserves attention first.

In-text Emphasis

Sometimes you want to emphasize an important word or phrase within a sentence. Computers give you the following options: underlining, boldface, italics, and caps. The least effective are FULL CAPS and <u>underlining</u>. You should avoid using them because they make text difficult to read and are distracting to the eye. The most effective highlighting techniques are *italics* and **boldface**: they add emphasis without distracting the reader.

Whatever typographical techniques you select, use them sparingly. Using too many can result in a busy page that leaves the reader confused about what to read. Excessive in-text emphasis also detracts from the impact of headings and subheadings, which should be receiving significant attention.

FONTS AND COLOUR

Besides page format, you have something else in your word-processing bag of tricks: changes in the size and type of font you use in the text itself, and colour use.

Size of Type

Traditionally, type size has been measured in *points* (72 points to an inch). When you go to your font-selection menu on your computer screen, the sizes may be listed as such: 9, 10, 12, 14, 18, and 24. Other features of your software will allow you to expand type even further, for special uses.

Despite these many options, most technical writing is printed off the desktop in 10- or 12-point type. When you are choosing type size, however, be aware that the actual size of letters varies among font types. Some 12-point type appears larger than other 12-point type. Differences stem from the fact that your selection of a font affects (1) the thickness of the letters, (2) the size of lowercase letters, and (3) the length and style of the parts of letters that extend above and below the line. The examples in Figure 4-6 show the differences between three common fonts.

Before selecting your type size, run samples on your printer so that you are certain of how your copy will appear in final form.

Figure 4-6 Common fonts

Helvetica
9 point
10 point
12 point
14 point
18 point
24 point

New Century Schoolbook
9 point
10 point
12 point
14 point
18 point
24 point

Times Roman
9 point
10 point
12 point
14 point
18 point
24 point

Font Types

Font types vary hugely. Most word-processing systems give you more choices than you will ever use. Generally, these types are classified into two groups:

- Serif fonts—the characters have "feet" or "tails" at the ends of the letterlines.
- Sans serif fonts—the characters do not have "feet" or "tails" (see Figure 4-7).

If you are able to choose your font, the obvious advice is to use the one that you know your readers prefer. A phone call or a look at documents generated by your reader may help you. If you have no reader-specific guidelines, follow these three general rules:

1. **Use serif fonts for regular text in your documents.** The tails on letters make letters and entire words more visually interesting to the reader's eye. In this sense, they serve the same purpose as ragged-edge copy (that is, helping your reader move smoothly through the document).
2. **Consider using another typeface—sans serif—for headings.** Headings benefit from a clean look that emphasizes the white space around letters. Sans serif type helps attract attention to these elements of organization within your text.
3. **Avoid too many font variations in the same document.** There is a line between interesting font variations and busy and distracting text. Don't cross it. Your rule of thumb might be to use no more than two fonts per document—one for text and another for headings and subheadings.

Because font selection is an important tool for developing graphics as well as page format, fonts are covered in more detail in Chapter 5.

Figure 4-7   Font types

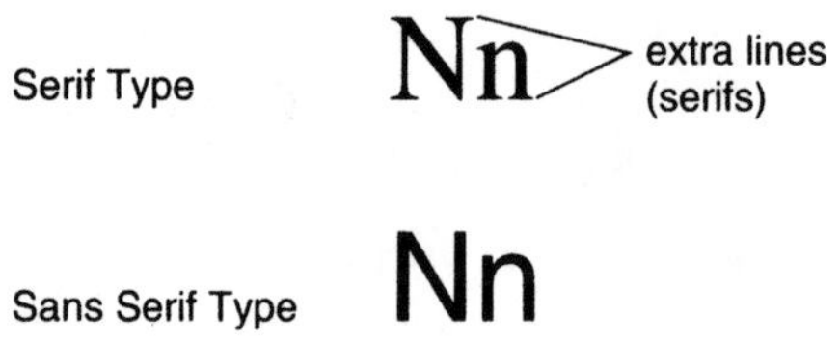

Serif Type   Nn ▷ extra lines (serifs)

Sans Serif Type   Nn

Colour

Colour, like fonts, is a graphic design tool that should reflect your document's tone, mood, and image. When used effectively, colour focuses your reader's attention on important details. When used indiscriminately, however—inserted into a document just to show that colour can be used—it can be distracting.

You'll want to limit your use of colour in routine documents because (1) when you use professional printers, printing in colour can be expensive, and (2) when you use desktop printers, printing colour documents can be prohibitively slow. Colour use is discussed in detail in Chapter 5.

GUIDELINES FOR WEB DESIGN

Web design involves developing graphic content, designing page layouts, and designing the *interface* (that is, what the user sees on the screen) into a whole site.

In fact, designing a Web site comprises most of the site's actual production work. Your work will involve arranging, formatting, and perhaps even redesigning some of your content to fit the site design. You will need to design site maps, navigation tools (such as hyperlinks, toolbar menus, and search fields), buttons, headers, backgrounds, and other design elements. As well as an effective interface design, you will create individual page layouts for the site.

This second half of the chapter will discuss Web design conventions and principles, development of graphic identity and content, different file formats and graphics, and guidelines for designing effective interface layouts. See "Web Pages and Writing for the Web" on the text enrichment site for further information on developing Web content and structures.

Design Conventions and Principles

Effective Web design involves much more than good aesthetics and instincts. Whether designing a graphic logo or an advertising banner or laying out what the user will see on the screen (the interface), use the following established Web design conventions and principles to guide your design work:

- Place a *hyperlink* (words, phrases, or images that, when clicked, link to another page of related content) on the site's header or logo that leads the user to the home page.
- Place the site's main navigation tools in the left margin.
- Use descriptive titles and captions for each graphic and on every page to help users understand how information is arranged.
- Provide contextual clues, such as colours, icons, or graphics, that represent themes or categories that quickly suggest which pages go together as a collection.
- Maintain a graphic identity, or look, using consistent colours and visual elements.
- Provide more than one way of searching and browsing your site. (For example, if you provide a *graphic* toolbar menu then you should also provide a duplicate set of *text* links for users who may have trouble loading or using the graphics.)
- Provide alternate versions of graphic content, such as scanned images saved as JPG files as well as formats that can be viewed with free viewers or software plug-ins (see more information following).
- Use no more than three fonts for text inside your site.
- Use colours that contrast well.

While the preceding list may prove useful in your design work, there really is no definitive list of design rules that applies to all Web sites. Your design team will determine if there is a good reason to follow a particular convention, depending on your project's scope, purpose, and context. To begin your design work, make a list of possible design conventions. Then look at how particular conventions are used in Web sites that have a similar purpose and function. Add to your list any conventions that seem to apply to your site, ultimately arriving at a list that will guide your design on a specific project.

Design principles are also based on theories of design. While not prescriptive, they provide you with *broad* guidance in graphic design and page layout. The following design principles can be used to guide your Web design work:

- *Consistency in the use of elements in repetitive and similar ways creates a unified look.* Demonstrate this consistency and maintain a graphic identity by repeatedly using specific logos, icons, and colours.

- *Contrast in the use of visual elements, such as colours, lines, or shaded regions, draws the eye to those elements and creates visual emphasis.* Place white text on a black background, for example, to create good visual contrast—the text stands out and is easier to read.
- *Grouping elements together through the use of space, colour, or other graphic elements shows a relationship between those elements.* For example, place all elements of a search feature, such as the text boxes, buttons, and instructions, in a shaded region to create conceptual grouping. This tells users which elements belong to the feature.

Figure 4-8 demonstrates good use of these three design principles. The page demonstrates consistency by using consistent fonts, sizes, colours, headers, and logos. The page also shows good contrast, using colours that make text easy to read and that emphasize headers and hyperlinks on a variety of background colours. And finally, the page demonstrates the design principle of grouping by using shaded headers, boxes, and white space to group related content.

Finding a Theme and Developing Graphic Content

Once you have a set of design conventions and design principles, you can start designing your graphic content. First, you should establish a graphic identity or

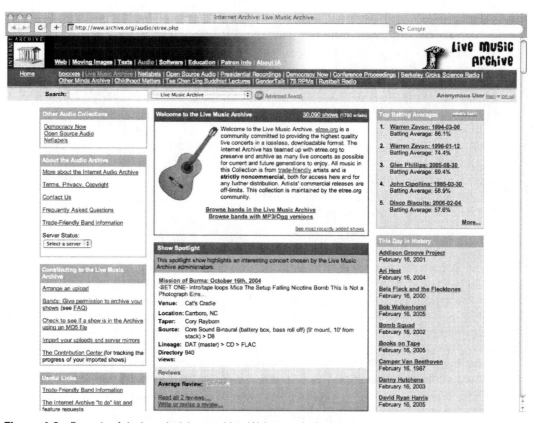

Figure 4-8   Example of design principles used in a Web page design
Source: *Internet Archive: Live Music Archive,* www.archive.org/audio/etree.php.

design theme for your site. The site's graphic identity conveys the site's unique brand and is defined by your choice of colours, fonts, lines, boxes, shapes, graphics, animation, and other visual information. Rather than choosing at random, select a specific theme or metaphor. You should consider the tone and impression you want the site to convey—taking into account who your users will be, what the site's purpose will be, and what the content will be. Then, use the defined theme to help you develop graphics for your site's design.

Many development teams use a variety of methods in developing graphic content for Web sites. If you already have existing graphic content that you want to use in your site, you may need to convert or improve it for a Web environment. Graphic content for your Web site can come from a variety of sources. For example, if you have printed material, such as sketches or photos, you can scan them and convert them to graphic file formats. Also, you can create your own graphics or hire a graphic design professional to create them using graphic design software.

If you don't have the time or resources to develop your own content, you can search the Web's vast number of sites for graphic libraries—some are free, and some charge a fee. You might be able to get some good recommendations from colleagues or friends. Choose the methods that best fit your budget, time, and project scope.

File Formats and Graphics

For static, or nonanimated, images the three most common types of file formats used in Web sites are the Graphic Interchange Format (.GIF), the Joint Photographic Experts Group format (.JPG), and the Portable Network Graphic format (.PNG). Each type has relatively good *file compression capabilities*, which means that they typically have smaller file sizes compared to other formats. And smaller file sizes mean shorter download times on the Web.

When deciding which format to use, you should consider the following information about each format's available features:

- *Colour depth* affects an image's quality and file size. True colour images display up to 16.7 million colours and produce images of photographic quality. However, not all graphics require this amount of colour depth.
- *Transparency* allows a single colour in a graphic to be set to be transparent, allowing graphics to blend well against different backgrounds.
- Some types of *animations* don't require special software plug-ins or programs for readers to view them.
- *Interlacing* allows users to see pieces of the graphic on the screen as they load. *Noninterlaced* graphics remain unseen until the entire image is downloaded.

Figure 4-9 summarizes the capabilities of the three main graphics file formats.

In addition, you can find graphic design software and programs that offer 3-D modelling, drafting files, and video clips. Most require specific software programs or plug-ins in order to view the graphic. If your site uses these types of files, make sure you instruct users on how to properly download and view them. Provide file formats that will not require readers to purchase additional software or spend a lot of time downloading appropriate viewers. Be sure to consider who your audience is when making the choice. In designing a site for a general audience, for example, consider using file formats that can be viewed with free viewers or software plug-ins, or provide users with alternate versions. Sometimes simple scanned images, saved as .JPG files, allow users to view nonanimated versions of parts of your animated content. If

File Format	Graphic Interchange Format (.GIF)	Joint Photographic Experts Group (.JPG)	Portable Network Graphic (.PNG)
Colour Depth	• 256 colours	• 16.7 million colours	• 16.7 million colours
Transparency	• transparency	• no transparency	• transparency
Animation	• animation	• no animation	• no animation
Interlacing	• interlaced	• noninterlaced	• interlaced

Figure 4-9   Graphic file formats

members of your team lack the expertise to address some of these issues, it might be best to hire a graphic design consultant to help you solve some of them.

Interface Layouts

Once you have developed the graphic content, the next task is to begin laying out the *interface*—what the user sees on the screen. The interface serves as the user's control panel for browsing, searching, and interacting with the site. The typical Web interface includes the following five elements:

- **Header:** Includes the logo and a title banner that identifies the site's title and/or company name
- **Navigation:** Includes hyperlinks, site maps, toolbar menus, and search features, which are the main navigation tools for the user to search and browse the site
- **Content window:** Displays, on the screen, most *content chunks* (a stand-alone unit of text and/or graphics that can be accessed by clicking on a hyperlink) and graphic content and appears in consistent locations throughout the site
- **Graphic identity:** Includes visual information (logo, icons, graphics, colours, or other visual elements) found throughout the site to give the site a unique brand
- **Contextual clues:** Includes information that helps users understand the nature or organization of information on pages or in the site

Before you begin designing the interface, make a list of the graphics, content chunks, and objects that will be used in each of the basic screen elements.

The Algonquin College site, shown in Figure 4-10, uses these five interface elements. The header displays the college name and pictures of the college as well as important links. The site's main navigation is placed under the header and in the left margin. The content window is in the centre of the page and features links and information by program topic. Elements used in the site's graphic identity include a photo of the college itself as well as photos of students, and photo icons that provide links to other sites. The page also uses contextual clues such as headers, boldface text, menus, toolbars, and arrow tabs to help users understand how the site's contents are organized.

Designing the interface also includes arranging content chunks, navigation tools, and graphics, as well as the site's interactive features, such as buttons, links, and forms. Most sites use the same layout for all the pages in the site. Some sites, however, may need to use two or more layouts, depending on the function and purpose of the site's other pages or sections. For example, a *splash page*, or an introduction page with a short animated movie, might have a simpler layout for that page and a separate one for the rest of the site. A site that sells music CDs, moreover, might use one layout for the home page, a second layout for all pages with product information, and a third layout for the shopping cart or purchasing page. You should decide if there are certain pages or sections of your site that require different interface layouts, and make a list of the characteristics each layout should have. Some typical types of interface layouts are single-frame, two-frame, three-frame, and custom-frame. Figure 4-11 shows a sample of each of these layouts, but there are many other ways of arranging the two-, three-, and custom-frame layouts. One advantage of multiple-frame layouts is that you can anchor headers, navigation, and content in consistent locations on the screen even as users move around in your site. But custom layouts usually are more complex and can be difficult to navigate or understand. Generally, the more complex the layout, the more you need to add *contextual clues* to help users understand the site's arrangement of information.

In drafting your site's layout, identify where to place the header, navigation tools, content window, graphic elements, and contextual clues. You might sketch a couple of different layouts to see which seems to best fit your site's needs. Sometimes, the true test of an interface layout is to take your paper sketches and set them up in your software program to see how they look on the screen. Remember

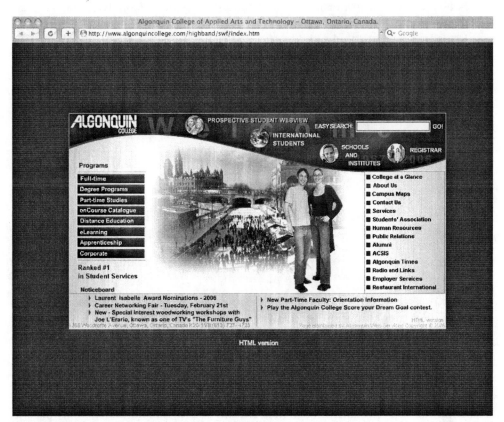

Figure 4-10 Interface elements used in a Web page
Copyright Algonquin College of Applied Arts and Technology, Ottawa, Ontario.

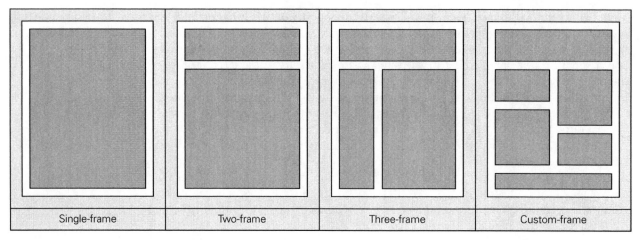

| Single-frame | Two-frame | Three-frame | Custom-frame |

Figure 4-11 Interface layout types

to apply the three design principles: consistency, contrast, and grouping. Following are some guidelines based on these principles:

- Use site maps, indexes, *breadcrumb links* (that show the trail of links a user has followed in the site), and consistent graphics to help users identify the site's structure and major content areas.
- Follow the design principle of *contrast* to signal which elements readers should focus on: navigation tools, search interfaces, and Help.
- Use animation or *mouseovers* (images that change their appearance or animate when the mouse pointer is placed over them) in navigation toolbars to indicate clickable items.
- Visually emphasize elements that are most important, to focus readers' attention— for example, group navigation links into toolbars—and place them in consistent locations. This will also focus readers' attention on the major content areas or links.
- Highlight information pathways for readers by using descriptive headings, site maps, and indexes.
- Provide *contextual clues* throughout the site, but more frequently at higher levels (that is, on those pages that are closer to the home page), to help users understand the site's structure and organization.
- Use familiar shapes, icons, and other visuals to suggest concepts to users.
- Pair unusual graphics with text descriptions, to help users understand the graphics.
- Group related content using shapes or space so that readers can understand their relationship to or function in the whole.

Your main goal should be to select a layout that organizes your screen elements consistently throughout the site. Consistency will make it easier for users to understand your site's organization, layout, and functions. Select backgrounds, colours, and other elements that create good contrast on the screen to make your content clear and readable. Use white space, lines, or shaded regions to group or set apart individual elements. Once you have come up with an effective layout, you can begin to add content, navigation tools, graphics, and other elements onto individual pages. Then you can link those pages together to create the finished product, or whole site.

Employability Skills

A. Page design
The Conference Board of Canada's *Employability Skills 2000+* has determined that your ability to use written material is an element in a successful career. Relevant communication and information management skills include the following:

- Read and understand information presented in a variety of forms (e.g., words, graphs, charts, diagrams).
- Locate, gather, and organize information using appropriate technology and information systems.*

Take the information package you developed for potential applicants in the Employability Skills box in Chapter 3 and arrange it so that the critical information can be readily noticed on the page. Explain why you have decided to arrange the information as you have.

B. Web design
The Conference Board of Canada's *Employability Skills 2000+* has found that the use of technology and the application of skills from other fields is a necessary element in all working situations. Relevant communication skills include the following:

- Share information using a range of information and communications technologies (e.g., voice, email, computers).
- Use relevant scientific, technological, and mathematical knowledge and skills to explain or clarify ideas.*

Create a Web site for your class. The purpose of the site is to market the people and their skills to potential employers. Use the initial pages to provide links to highlight the skills that the members of the group have in common. In addition, provide links that will lead to information about each of the individuals in the class. In the Employability Skills box in Chapter 15, you will be asked to add to those links.

* *Employability Skills 2000+* Brochure 2000 E/F (Ottawa: The Conference Board of Canada, 2000).

CHAPTER SUMMARY

This chapter shows you how to apply principles of page design to your assignments in this class and to your on-the-job writing. The term *page design* refers to the array of formatting options you can use to improve your document's visual effect.

Effective page design requires that you use specific elements such as white space, headings, listings, and in-text emphasis. White space draws attention to adjacent items. Headings quickly lead the reader to important points and subpoints. Listings emphasize related groups of points. And conservative use of in-text emphasis, such as italics and boldface, can draw attention to items within sentences and paragraphs.

Another strategy for page design is to change the size and type of fonts in your documents. Like other strategies, this one must be used with care so that your document does not become too busy. Page design remains a technique for highlighting content, not a substitute for careful organization and editing.

Web design involves developing a graphic identity, optimizing graphic content for the Web, and creating effective interface designs and layouts.

ASSIGNMENTS

1. **Group evaluation of page design.** Working in small groups, analyze the effectiveness of the page design of the document in Model 4-1 on pages 90–91. Your instructor will indicate whether you should prepare a written or an oral report of your findings. Give specific support for your praise or criticism. (Assignment 4 uses this same memorandum for a writing exercise.)

2. **Individual evaluation of page design.**

   Option A: Visit your library and locate an example of technical writing, such as a government document or a company's annual report. Use the guidelines in this chapter to analyze the document's page design. Your instructor will indicate whether your report should be oral or written.

   Option B: Use the guidelines in this chapter to evaluate the page design of one of the project sheets in Chapter 2 of this textbook. What works well? What could be improved? Be specific in your comments.

3. **Individual practice in page design.** As a manager at M&K, you have just finished a major report to a client. It gives recommendations for transporting a variety of hazardous materials by sea, land, and air. The body of your report contains a section that defines the term *stowage plan* and describes its use. Given your mixed technical and nontechnical audience, this basic information is much needed. What follows is the text of that section. Revise the passage by applying any of this chapter's principles of page design that seem appropriate, such as adding headings, graphics, lists, and white space. If you wish, you also can make changes in organization and style. *Optional:* If your class has access to email, transmit your version to another student to receive his or her response.

In the chemical shipping industry, a stowage plan is a kind of blueprint for a vessel. It lists all stowage tanks and provides information about tank volume, tank coating, stowed product, weight of product, loading port, and discharging port. A stowage plan is made out for each vessel on each voyage and records all chemicals loaded. The following information concerns cargo considerations (chemical properties and tank features) and some specific uses of the stowage plan in industry.

The three main cargo considerations in planning stowage are temperature, compatibility, and safety. Chemicals have physical properties that distinguish them from one another. To maintain the natural state of chemicals and to prevent alteration of their physical properties, a controlled environment becomes necessary. Some chemicals, for example, require firm temperature controls to maintain their physical characteristics and degree of viscosity (thickness) and to prevent contamination of the chemicals by any moisture in the tanks. In addition, some chemicals, like acids, react violently with each other and should not be stowed in adjoining, or even neighbouring, tanks. In shipping, this relationship is known as chemical compatibility.

The controlled environment and compatibility of chemicals have resulted in safety regulations for the handling and transporting of these chemicals. These regulations originate with the federal government, which bases them on research done by the private manufacturers. Location and size of tanks also determine the placement of cargo. A ship's tanks are arranged with all smaller tanks around the periphery of the tank grouping and all larger tanks in the centre. These tanks, made of heavy steel and coated with zinc or epoxy, are highly resistant to most chemicals, thereby reducing the chance of cargo contamination. Each tank has a maximum cargo capacity, and the amounts of each chemical are matched with the tanks. Often chemicals to be discharged at the same port are staggered in the stowage plan layout so that after they are discharged the ship maintains its equilibrium.

The stowage plan is finalized after considering the cargo and tank characteristics. In its final form, the plan is used as a reference document with all information relevant to the loading/discharging voyage recorded. If an accident occurs involving a ship, or when questions arise involving discharging operations, this document serves as a visual reference and brings about quick decisions.

4. **Group practice in page design.** Working in small groups, prepare a redesigned version of the memorandum in Model 4-1. If your class is being held in a computer lab, present your group's version onscreen. If you are not using a lab, present your version on an overhead transparency.

5. **Group practice in page design: using computer communication.** This assignment is feasible only if you and your classmates have access to software that will allow you to post messages to team members, edit onscreen, and send edited copy back and forth. Your task is to add appropriate page design features to either (a) the "stowage plan" excerpt in assignment 3 or (b) any other piece of straight text your instructor permits you to use. Choose a team leader who will collect and collate the individual edits. Choose another group member to type or scan the excerpt into the computer and then send the passage to other group members. Then each person should add the features desired and mail the edited document to the team leader, who will collate the revisions and mail the new version to team members for a final edit. Throughout this process, participants may conduct email conversations about the draft; they will resolve differences, if possible, before sending drafts to the leader. The group may need one or two short meetings in person, but most business should be conducted via the computer. The goal is to arrive at one final version for your group.

6. **Individual evaluation of entertainment Web site.** Select and familiarize yourself with an entertainment Web site. Identify the elements used in the site's design that give it its graphic identity or brand. Look for titles, logos, colours, graphics, and other visuals that are used consistently throughout the site. In a few sentences, describe the overall design theme or graphic identity. What general impression do these elements convey? Are there elements that don't fit the design theme?

MEMORANDUM

DATE: August 19, 2006
TO: Randall Demorest, Dean
FROM: Kenneth Payne, Professor and Coordinator *KP*
SUBJECT: Tech. Wr. Advisory Board

What? Lunch meetings between Advisory Board members and me
Why? To get more Board support for the Tech. Wr. degree program
Who? Each individual member at a separate luncheon
When? Fall 2006
How? Allocation of $360 to pay for the lunches

Rationale

When we seek support for the college, we have to (1) make people feel that they will get something in return and (2) make them feel comfortable about us and our organization. As businesses have demonstrated, one way we can accomplish these goals is by taking potential donors to lunch.

As you and I have discussed, the Technical Writer program needs to strengthen ties to its Advisory Board. We must ask Board participants to provide tangible support for the program *and* give them meaningful involvement in the work we are doing.

Method

The immediate need is to involve members of the Advisory Board in the coming year's program. I want to do this in two ways:

1. Plan carefully for a fall Board meeting
2. Discuss with each of them individually what we want to accomplish this year

Cost

To do the second item mentioned, I request an allocation of $360 so that I can take each member to lunch for an extended one-on-one discussion. I plan to discuss the needs of our program and each member's capabilities to support it.

continues

Model 4-1 Page design in memorandum

Payne to Demorest, 2

Specifics

Each member of the Board will be asked individually to consider the following ways to contribute:

1. Continuing support for the internship program
2. Participation in the research project we began a year ago
3. Cooperative work experiences for Tech. Wr. faculty, possibly during the summer of 2007
4. Financial support for the following items:
   • The college's membership as a sponsoring organization in the Society for Technical Communication
   • Contributions——financial or otherwise——to library holdings in technical writing
   • Usability testing laboratory
   • A workshop series bringing to the campus some outstanding technical communicators (for example, Edward Tufte, expert in graphics; JoAnn Hackos, expert in quality management; and William Horton, expert in online documentation)

Benefits

What are Board members going to get from this?

Long range: A better Tech. Wr. program, which will produce better technical writers for them to hire

Immediately: Meaningful involvement in the program

Specifically: Training opportunities for their personnel through the workshops mentioned

My tentative plan for those workshops is to provide a one-day seminar for our students and a second seminar for employees of Advisory Board members. (We will allow them a number of participants based on how much they contribute to the workshops.)

Response Needed

Please let me know as soon as possible if money is available for the lunches. I hope to begin scheduling meetings within a week.

Model 4-1 *continued*

CHAPTER 5

Graphics

Technology has radically changed the world of graphics. Now, almost anyone with a computer and the right software can quickly produce illustrations that used to take hours to construct. As a result, today there are sophisticated graphics in every medium—newspapers, magazines, television, and, of course, technical communication.

Readers now expect graphics to accompany text, and you as a technical professional must respond to this expectation. Well-designed and well-placed graphics will keep you competitive. Your graphics do not, however, have to be fancy. Nor is it true that adding graphics will necessarily improve a document. Readers are impressed by visuals only when they are well done and appropriate.

Fortunately, you do not have to be an expert to understand and use the fundamentals of graphics. However, the availability of high-tech graphics has made it even more important that technical professionals understand the basics of graphics before applying sophisticated techniques. To emphasize these basics, this chapter (1) defines some common graphics terms; (2) explains the main reasons to use special fonts, colour, and graphics; (3) describes how to use fonts; (4) describes how to use colour; (5) presents basic graphics guidelines; (6) lists specific guidelines for eight common graphics; and (7) shows you how to avoid misuse of graphics. Although the chapter does include some production tips, the main emphasis is on *why* and *when* to use graphics.

TERMS IN GRAPHICS

Graphics terminology is not uniform, which can lead to some confusion. For the purposes of this chapter, however, some common definitions are adopted and listed here:

- **Graphics:** This generic term refers to any nontextual portion of documents or oral presentations. It can be used in two ways: (1) to designate the field (for example: "*Graphics* is an area in which he shows great interest"), or (2) to name individual graphical items (for example: "She placed three *graphics* in her report").
- **Illustrations, visual aids:** Used synonymously with *graphics*, these terms also can refer to all nontextual parts of a document. The term *visual aids,* however, often is limited to the context of oral presentations.
- **Tables and figures:** These terms name the two subsets of graphics. *Tables* are illustrations that place numbers or words in columns or in rows, or both. *Figures* include all graphics other than tables. Examples include charts (pie, bar, line, flow, and organization), engineering drawings, maps, and photographs.
- **Charts/graphs:** A subset of "figures," these synonymous terms refer to a type of graphic that displays data in visual form—as with bars, pie shapes, or lines on graphs. *Chart* is the term used most often in this text.
- **Technical drawing:** Another subset of "figures," a technical drawing is a representation of a physical object. Such illustrations can be drawn from many perspectives and can include *exploded views* (closeups of a particular part of the main drawing).

Of course, you may see other graphics terms. For example, some technical companies use the word *plates* for figures. Be sure to know the terms your readers understand and the types of graphics they use.

REASONS FOR USING SPECIAL FONTS, COLOUR, AND GRAPHICS

Although the technology for producing graphics is constantly changing, the rationale for using them remains the same. This section covers some reasons why readers might choose special fonts, colour, and graphics to accompany text.

Reason 1: Special Fonts, Colour, and Graphics Simplify Ideas

Your readers usually know less about the subject than you. Font styles, colour, and graphics can help them cut through technical details and grasp basic ideas. For example, if a **Danger** symbol, styled as shown with the boldface Impact font, is given a bright orange background, the message is much more powerful than a buried warning that looks just like the text around it. Also, a simple illustration of a laboratory instrument, such as a Bunsen burner, can make the description of a lab procedure much easier to understand. In a more complex example, Figure 5-1 uses a group of four different charts to convey the one main point—that M&K's new Equipment Development group lags behind the company's other profit centres. A quick look at the charts tells the story of the group's difficulties much better than would several hundred words of text. Of course, the text itself must still focus the reader's attention on the relevant information.

Reason 2: Special Fonts, Colour, and Graphics Reinforce Ideas

When you need to emphasize a point, you can use a graphic element, such as a special font or colour, or you can create a graphic. For example, if you need readers to instantly recognize section or chapter breaks, you might use a distinctive font or colour to capture readers' attention. Also, you might draw a map to show where computer terminals will be located within a building or use a pie chart to show how a budget will be spent. You might even include a drawing that indicates how to operate a VCR. Each of these solutions would reinforce points made in the accompanying text.

Reason 3: Special Fonts, Colour, and Graphics Create Interest

Tools such as font styles, colour, and graphics are "grabbers"—they engage readers' interest. If your customers have three reports on their desks and must quickly decide which one to read first, they probably will pick up the one with a distinctive look—one that complements the text. It may be something as simple as (1) a map outline of the province, region, or city where you will be doing a project, (2) a picture of the product or service you are providing, or (3) a symbol of the purpose of your writing project.

Figure 5-2 shows how an outside consultant used a well-known Leonardo da Vinci drawing to attract attention to his M&K proposal. The drawing helps to (1) add a classical touch to the cover, (2) focus on the human side of employee testing, and (3) associate the innovation of Infinite Vision, Inc., with the creativity of da Vinci.

Problems in M&K's ED Group

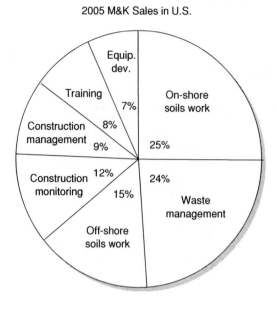

2005 M&K Sales in U.S.

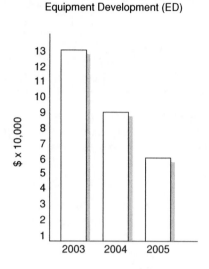

2003–2005 Profits for
Equipment Development (ED)

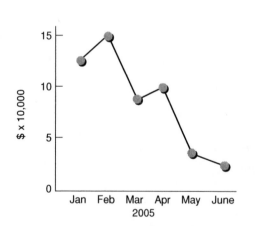

$ Value of ED Contracts

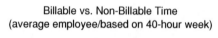
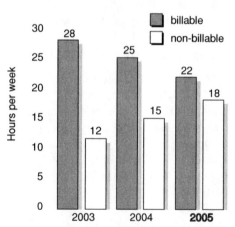

Billable vs. Non-Billable Time
(average employee/based on 40-hour week)

Figure 5-1 Graphics used to simplify ideas

Also, by using the client's font style and colour preference, the writer allows the reader to "take ownership" of the proposal before ever reading the contents.

Reason 4: Special Fonts, Colour, and Graphics Are Universal

Some people wrongly associate the growing importance of graphics with today's reliance on television and other popular media—as if graphics pander to less-intellectual instincts. While media such as television and the Web obviously rely on visual effects, graphics have been our universal language since cave drawings.

Although those who sell or advertise products and services have long known the power of images, writers of technical documents have only recently started to merge the force of graphics with their text.

USING FONTS

Chapter 4 gave you an overview of two basic points about fonts to consider when designing documents: *font types* and *sizes of type*. The following section provides more

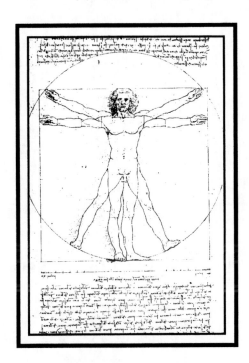

Improving Productivity at M&K, Inc.
An Innovative Approach to Employee Testing

Prepared for Jacques Martin
President, Martin & Koffman

by
Jamal Ahmad
Infinite Vision, Inc.

February 22, 2006

Figure 5-2   Graphics used to create interest

details to help you meet the creative challenge of designing documents, such as manuals, proposals, annual reports, and promotional materials.

Font Types

You already may have identified and grouped fonts into two categories—*sans serif* ("without feet or tails") and *serif* ("with feet or tails")—as you have explored the selection of fonts available to you on your desktop publishing software. Perhaps you have also noticed that many other font types exist, such as the following:

- *Brush Script* and *Freestyle Script*—appear to be handwritten
- *Zaph Chancery* and *Medici Script*—seem to have an austere, more formal appearance
- Bauer Bodoni—reflects a high-fashion silhouette
- Comic sans—looks uneven, even awkward, as though it was printed by a child

Your choice of fonts may determine whether or not your documents get read.

General Guidelines

How do you know which fonts to choose? Although there are no hard-and-fast rules to follow, keep the following five guidelines in mind to make the task easier:

Font Style Guidelines

Consider:

1. The reader's or company's preferences
2. The need for clarity
3. The space available
4. The document's purpose
5. The tone you want to convey

Font Style Guideline 1: Consider the Reader's or Company's Preferences

Give your choice in font style the same consideration you give your message. If your reader has clear preferences, by all means adhere to them. If, on the other hand, your audience is receptive to new ideas and images, you can be creative in selecting fonts.

Font Style Guideline 2: Consider the Need for Clarity

All technical writers recognize the need for their messages to be clear. As you select a font, ask yourself questions such as the following:

- Am I using this font for captions or for long passages of text?
- Does the material I've written contain technical terms or formulae, or was it written for a general audience?
- Will the font style enhance or detract from the material's readability?

A font style's readability partly depends on whether it uses sans serif or serif characters. Sans serif font styles ("without feet or tails") and serif font styles ("with feet or tails") are shown in 18 pt. type in Figure 5-3 in the word *Readability*.

SANS SERIF FONT STYLES	
Arial	Readability
Avant Garde	Readability
Basic Sans SF	Readability
Christina	Readability
Futura Bold	**Readability**
Impact	**Readability**

Serif Font Styles	
Caslon Bold	**Readability**
New Baskerville Bold	**Readability**
Bauer Bodoni Bold	**Readability**
Galliard Bold	**Readability**
Medici Script	*Readability*

Figure 5-3   Font styles

Sans serif font styles are more effective when used for headers, numeric data, and transparencies for the following reasons: characters appear cleaner, and more white space exists between the letters. Serif font styles are more appropriate for straight text. The feet (or "tails") of serif font styles seem to lead the readers' eyes across the text in a natural flow, making it easier to scan the page. The result is better readability.

Font Style Guideline 3: Consider the Space Available

Although all font styles are measured vertically, using a scale of 72 points to an inch, they vary horizontally. If you are writing a long formal proposal, the space available might not be important. Adding or deleting one page might not matter. However, if you are writing the text for a software package, you might need to select a font style that is clear but that will fit into a small field.

Refer to Figure 5-3. What kinds of differences do you see? Wider letters? Thicker strokes? More or less white space between the characters (*kerning*)? More or less white space between rows of typed material (*leading*)? Each of these criteria varies from one font style to another.

In some cases, you may decide to use the same font style that the original material uses. You can make minor adjustments in line length by reducing the kerning between the characters to fit all your information on one page or to prevent the carryover of one word to the next page.

In other situations, you may want to adjust the leading. In this way, the lines are closed up by one "point" of space, and one more line can fit on the page. Unless your organization uses a mandatory style sheet, these choices will be up to you.

Font Style Guideline 4: Consider the Document's Purpose

Before making font style decisions, evaluate how different font styles may reinforce your document's purpose. Ask yourself the following questions:

- Will the document be referred to frequently?
- Does the document present financial or statistical data that must be easily read and comprehended?
- Must it be eye-catching enough to make the audience eager to read it?
- Is it a routine document that needs only to be read once, handled, and filed?

Considering the above questions will help you choose a font style that serves the purpose of your entire document.

Font Style Guideline 5: Consider the Tone You Want to Convey

Finally, give careful thought to which font style will reinforce the tone of your message. For example, assume you have worked diligently to develop an annual report reflecting serious growth problems for the company and for the company's industry. The document is formal in tone; however, it is also a no-nonsense business document. A font type such as *Zapf Chancery* is formal; however, it does not present the serious tone required for this annual report. In this instance, you may want to use **Arial** or *Avant Garde* because of their crisp, sans serif image.

In another example, you have been asked to invite management and hourly employees to a retirement party given for a mid-level manager. The tone, you correctly assess, will be informal, warm, and hospitable. As you scroll down the list of font styles, you find several that seem appropriate—Tekton, Eurostyle, and **Triplex**—and you wonder which, if any, will convey the right image. The first one looks interesting and casual, but it appears too small. The second one looks too impersonal. The third appears casual, large, and powerful—like someone is shouting, *"Come on in!"*

In addition to the diversity of font styles, desktop publishing packages today offer you an opportunity to reconfigure your text into arcs, waves, slopes, and even circles. You can outline, shade, print vertically, and do much more whenever it is appropriate. That is the key: your font styles must be *appropriate* for the tone you are trying to convey.

USING COLOUR

Just as people expect colour in photographs, movies, advertisements, and TV, colour has emerged as a necessity in technical communications. This tool adds excitement to and stimulates interest in your documents. Most writers have software that lets them simply "click" on the colours they think are appropriate for a document and, when the job is completed, send the document to a colour printer. However, their colour choices—and even the decision to use colour—may be inappropriate for a number of reasons.

Because colour is so costly and requires a longer time to print, you need to know more about its effective use. In this segment we will discuss what you must consider before you use colour, including ways you can use it effectively.

The Cost and Time of Using Colour

The cost of using colour in technical communications is much like the cost of buying a luxury automobile. You receive many benefits, but you must be ready to pay for them. Before you spend your time and energy on colour, you'll want to ask some important questions:

- **Has a budget been established for the job? If so, what does it include?** Whether we like it or not, budgets control our creative efforts. You won't want to invest massive amounts of time in thinking through your colour strategy if you know up front that colour is too costly. The seemingly high cost, though, may be justified by an anticipated return on investment.

  Developing colour documents is usually a less significant cost factor than printing the materials. Most printer software gives you the option to print four-colour documents. However, you will want to design your colour graphics with clear, crisp images that retain their impact *even if they cannot be printed in colour.*

- **What is the distribution?** You'll want to ask yourself these questions about distribution: Will the document be sent to potential customers or key executives in your organization? How many other people will receive copies? Must all recipients have colour copies?

  The number of colour copies you are able to print may be directly related to the hierarchy of receivers—that is, your budget may allow you to print colour copies only for those receivers deemed most "important." If only five or six copies are needed and the pages are few, you may be able to print the documents on your desktop printer. If more copies are needed, you may need to use a printer to mass-produce your documents. Four-colour printing costs per document increase dramatically as volumes increase because (1) the printer must make a separate "master" for each page and ink colour used (*Yellow, Magenta, Cyan,* and *Black*) and (2) the printer then "runs" each colour for each page separately.

- **Does the company have printing/reproduction facilities?** Large companies frequently plan for high-volume reproduction of reports, advertising, training, and documentation. If they have the capability, you may receive more rapid turnaround times and benefit from lower costs.

- **Are other options available?** If you have a tight budget and still want to use colour to stimulate interest in your document, you may want to consider (1) using coloured paper to distinguish one section from another, (2) printing one or two copies in colour for your most important readers and printing the balance in black and white, and (3) using one colour with black to add some interest (perhaps the colour most readily identified with your company's image).

Developing a Colour Style Sheet

Once you decide to use colour in your documents, you'll see a difference in how people react to your messages. If your company doesn't already have a colour style sheet—which provides guidelines for the use of colour—develop your own so you can use colour consistently from one project to another. Avoid overusing colour. Too many colours, like too much data, will distort your message, confuse your audience, cost more, and take more time to produce. To develop a style sheet, ask yourself the following four questions:

1. **How can I use colour to help my audience read and retain the document's message?** You can define the levels of importance in a document by using a different colour for different headings, and lighter or darker tones of a colour to distinguish between subheadings or between major and minor concepts within a heading.

2. **How can I use colour to attract attention to important data?** Use *one colour* to highlight significant points or to provide a specific function. For example, if you consistently use colour to frame tables or graphics, you create a visual cue that prompts your reader to look at the graphics. Or, you may want to use one colour to *consistently* emphasize keywords, phrases, or specific actions. In so doing, you build *continuity* in your document and enhance readability.

3. **Will my audience be able to see the differences in colour?** About 10% of the male population has some degree of red/green colour blindness. Therefore, be careful about using red and green together in your documents.

4. **Will the document be universally distributed in colour, or will one or more sections be printed in black and white?** If your document will be reproduced—either all, or in part—in black and white, you need to place greater emphasis on textural differences as well as use distinctive shading and tinting. Most importantly, do not use blue images; unless shaded considerably, they will not reproduce on a photocopier. You must do everything you can to sharpen the images you want your audience to read.

After you answer questions about the general use of colour, you can begin the process of selecting and combining colours to enhance your message and your graphics.

Colour Terms

Most of us are familiar with the spectrum of colours seen when light passes through a prism or when a rainbow appears in the sky. In most instances, your desktop publishing software displays a full colour array that resembles a colour wheel. However, you may not be familiar with some common colour-related terms, such as *hues, primary, secondary, tertiary,* and *complementary.* Let us look at them briefly.

- *Hues:* **Hues** are the intense "true" colours we see on a colour wheel, which displays the relationships and intensities of colours.
- *Primary colours:* Red, blue, and yellow are considered **primary** colours. We have learned ways to combine primary colours and make other colours, through light, pigments, or inks, that also appear on the colour wheel.
- *Secondary colours:* As children we often learn that when we mix equal parts of red and blue pigments, the result is purple. Blue and yellow become green, and yellow and red become orange. Because purple, green, and orange are mixed from the primary colours, they are often referred to as **secondary** colours.
- *Tertiary colours:* **Tertiary** colours are colours mixed by a combination of a primary colour and a secondary colour. They are also considered hues because of their intensity.

- *Complementary colours:* **Complementary** colours are those that appear *immediately opposite* one another on the colour wheel. For example, red and green are opposite each other—as are blue and orange and yellow and violet. Because complementary colours are opposites, they are frequently used together to give the best contrast.

Guidelines for Using Colour

This section includes four guidelines to help you select colours for your documents.

Colour Selection Guideline 1: Use Colours Your Audience Will Associate with Your Topic in a Positive Way

Take time to research your readers' reactions to colours. In particular, if your document has an international audience, make certain you know which colours are considered appropriate or inappropriate in specific cultures.

Colour Selection Guideline 2: Use Colours That Enhance Your Company's Logo

By using colours that complement and reinforce your company's logo, you are more likely to get immediate acceptance of your ideas.

Colour Selection Guideline 3: Use Dark or Textured Backgrounds Infrequently

For years, advertisers thought the most productive newspaper ads were those with solid black backgrounds and large, white letters. When writers learned more about the use of white space, the myth of "reverse" messages (that is, the belief that black backgrounds with white lettering were more effective) was shattered. Although dark or textured backgrounds can be effective, like other design tools they may be overdone. Use them when you want to focus your reader's attention on a graphic by using darker tones as a frame.

If your documents will be printed in black, white, and grey, try using texture for only one or two elements of your graphic to avoid a cluttered, busy appearance. If you decide to use shading to mask—but not obliterate—important data, don't use shading any darker than a 10%–25% screen.

Finally, if you really want your message to be surrounded by a dark colour, remember you'll also need to use a larger, bolder font style and a lighter, brighter hue, or the information you want your reader to notice will fade into the background.

Colour Selection Guideline 4: Learn How Any Colour Will Be Affected by the Medium It Will Be Printed on and Make Adjustments Accordingly

Textures and colours of paper stock can drastically alter your document's appearance. It is best to test the colours *before* you use them in a final draft. Ask your peers, your boss, and your public relations department for their opinions and suggestions. A little planning can help you improve the look of your document.

USING GRAPHICS

This section covers some fundamentals before exploring specific types of illustrations. What basic guidelines should you follow with all illustrations? What specific guidelines should you follow for pie charts, bar charts, line charts, schedule charts, flow charts, organization charts, technical drawings, and tables?

General Guidelines

A few basic guidelines apply to all graphics. Keep them in mind as you move from one type of illustration to another.

Graphics Guideline 1: Refer to All Graphics in the Text

With a few exceptions—such as cover illustrations to grab attention—graphics should be accompanied by clear references within your text. Specifically, you should follow these rules:

- Include the graphic number in Arabic, not Roman, numerals when you are using more than one graphic.
- Include the title, and sometimes the page number, if either is needed for clarity or emphasis.
- Incorporate the reference smoothly into text wording.

Following are two ways to phrase and position a graphics reference. In Example 1, there is the additional emphasis of the graphics title; in Example 2, the title is left out. Also, note that you can draw more attention to the graphic by placing the reference at the start of the sentence in a separate clause. Alternatively, you can place the reference within a parenthetical expression at the end or middle of the passage. Do not place the parenthetical expression in the middle of a sentence. Choose the option that best suits your purposes.

- **Example 1:** "In the past five years, 56 businesses in the province have started in-house recycling programs. The result has been a dramatic decrease in the amount of property the province has acquired for new waste sites, as shown in Figure 5 ('Landfill Purchases, 2000–2005')."
- **Example 2:** "As shown in Figure 5, the province has acquired much less land for landfills during the last five years. This dramatic reduction results from the fact that 56 businesses have started in-house recycling programs."

Graphics Guideline 2: Think about Where to Put Graphics

In most cases, locate a graphic close to the text in which it is mentioned. Graphics are most powerful when they immediately reinforce text in this way. Variations of this option, as well as several other possibilities, are presented here:

- **Same page as text reference:** A simple visual, such as an informal table, should go on the same page as the text reference if you think it is too small for a separate page.
- **Page opposite text reference:** A complex graphic, such as a long table, that accompanies a specific page of text can go on the page opposite the text—that is, on the opposite page of a two-page spread. Usually this option is exercised only in documents that are printed on both sides of the paper throughout.

- **Page following first text reference:** Most text graphics appear on the page after the first reference. If the graphic is referred to throughout the text, it can be repeated at later points. (*Note:* Readers prefer to have graphics positioned exactly where they need them, instead of having to refer to another part of the document.)
- **Attachments or appendices:** Graphics can go at the end of the document in two cases: first, if the text contains so many references to the graphic that placement in a central location, such as an appendix, would make it more accessible; and second, if the graphic contains less important supporting material that would only interrupt the text.

Graphics Guideline 3: Position Graphics Vertically When Possible

Readers prefer graphics they can view without having to turn the document sideways. However, if the table or figure cannot fit vertically on a standard letter-sized page, either use a foldout or place the graphic horizontally on the page. In the latter case, position the illustration so that the top is on the left margin.

Graphics Guideline 4: Avoid Clutter

Let simplicity be your guide. Readers go to graphics for relief from, or reinforcement of, the text. They do not want to be bombarded by visual clutter. Omit information that is not relevant to your purpose, while still making the illustration clear and self-contained. Also, use enough white space that the readers' eyes are drawn to the graphic. The final section of this chapter discusses graphics clutter in more detail.

Graphics Guideline 5: Provide Titles, Notes, Keys, and Source Data

Graphics should be as self-contained and self-explanatory as possible. Moreover, they must note any borrowed information. Follow these basic rules for format and acknowledgment of sources:

- **Title:** Follow the graphic number with a short, precise title—either on the line below the number or on the same line after a colon or dash (for example, "Figure 3: Salary Scales").
  Tables: The number and title go at the top. (As noted in Table Guideline 1 on page 121, one exception is informal tables. They have no table number or title.)
  Figures: The number and title normally go below the illustration. Centre titles or place them flush with the left margin.
- **Notes for explanation:** When introductory information for the graphic is needed, place a note directly underneath the title or at the bottom of the graphic.
- **Keys or legends for simplicity:** If a graphic needs many labels, consider using a legend or key, which lists the labels and corresponding symbols on the graphic. For example, a pie chart might have the letters *A, B, C, D,* and *E* printed on the pie pieces, while a legend at the top, bottom, or side of the figure would list what the letters represent.
- **Source information at the bottom:** You have a moral, and sometimes legal, obligation to cite the person, organization, or publication that you borrowed information from for the figure. Either (1) precede the description with the word "Source" and a colon, or (2) if you borrowed just part of a graphic, introduce the citation with "Adapted from."

Besides citing the source, it is usually necessary to request permission to use copyrighted or proprietary information, depending on your use and the amount you are borrowing. (A prominent exception is most information provided by the federal government. Most government publications are not copyrighted.) Consult a reference librarian for details about seeking permission.

SPECIFIC GUIDELINES FOR EIGHT GRAPHICS

Illustrations come in many forms; almost any nontextual part of your document can be placed under the umbrella term *graphic*. Among the many types, the following eight are often used in technical writing: (1) pie charts, (2) bar charts, (3) line charts, (4) schedule charts, (5) flow charts, (6) organization charts, (7) technical drawings, and (8) tables. This section of the chapter highlights their different purposes and gives guidelines for their use.

Guidelines for Pie Charts

Pie charts, which are familiar to most readers, show relationships between the parts and the whole, when just approximate information is needed. Their simple circles with clear labels can provide comforting simplicity within even the most complicated report. However, their simplicity keeps them from being useful when you must reveal detailed information. Following are specific guidelines for constructing pie charts:

Pie Chart Guideline 1: Use No More Than 10 Divisions

To make pie charts work well, limit the number of pie pieces to no more than 10. In fact, the fewer the better. This approach lets the reader grasp major relationships without having to wade through the clutter of tiny divisions that are difficult to read. In Figure 5-4, for example, the client can see that the project staff will come from two M&K offices, with an equal number from one of M&K's American offices, and that a large contingent of contract workers will be used.

Pie Chart Guideline 2: Move Clockwise from 12:00, from Largest to Smallest Wedge

Readers prefer pie charts oriented like a clock, with the first wedge starting at 12:00. As a convenient organizing principle, move from the largest to the smallest wedge.

Make exceptions to this design only for good reason. In Figure 5-4, for example, the last wedge represents a greater percentage than the previous wedge. This is so that the slices of the chart for Canadian staff will be side by side.

Pie Chart Guideline 3: Use Pie Charts Especially for Percentages and Money

Pie charts catch the reader's eye best when they represent items that are divisible by 100 (e.g., percentages and dollars). Figure 5-4 shows percentages; Figure 5-5 shows money. The coinlike shape of the chart makes money breakdowns particularly appropriate.

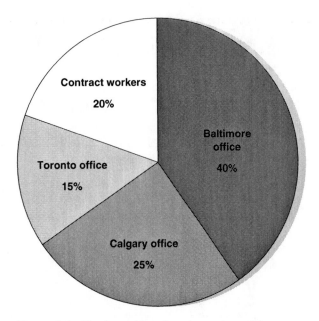

Figure 5-4 Pie chart with as few pieces as possible

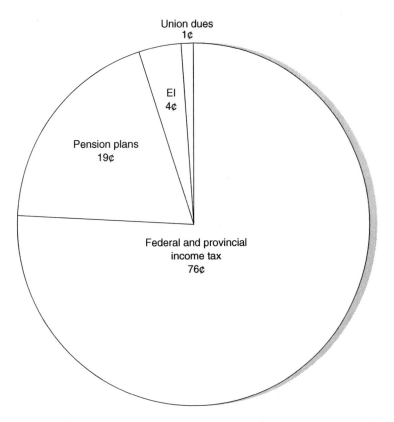

Figure 5-5 Pie chart showing money breakdown for average deductions from an M&K paycheque

Pie Chart Guideline 4: Be Creative, but Stay Simple

Figure 5-6 shows that you can emphasize one piece of the pie by:

A Shading a wedge
B Removing a wedge from the main pie
C Placing related pie charts in a three-dimensional drawing

Today there are graphics software packages that can create these and other variations for you, so experiment a bit. Of course, always make sure to keep your charts from becoming too detailed. Pie charts should stay simple.

Pie Chart Guideline 5: Draw and Label Carefully

The most common pie chart errors are (1) wedge sizes that do not correspond correctly to percentages or money amounts and (2) pie sizes that are too small to accommodate the information placed in them. Some suggestions for avoiding these mistakes follow.

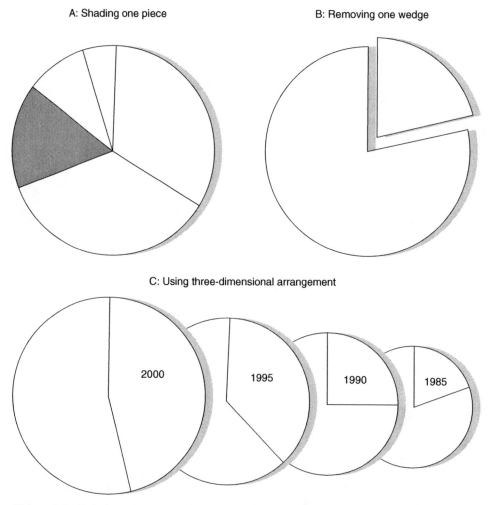

Figure 5-6   Techniques for emphasis in pie charts
Adapted from William S. Pfeiffer, *Proposal Writing* (Columbus, OH: Merrill, 1989), p. 145.

- **Pie size:** Make sure the chart occupies enough of the page. On a standard letter-sized sheet with only one pie chart, your circle should be from 8 to 15 cm in diameter—large enough not to be dwarfed by labels and small enough to leave sufficient white space in the margins.
- **Labels:** Place the wedge labels either inside the pie or outside, depending on the number of wedges, the number of wedge labels, and the length of the labels. Choose the option that produces the cleanest-looking chart.
- **Conversion of percentages:** If you are drawing the pie chart by hand, not using a computer program, use a protractor or similar device. One percent of the pie equals 3.6 degrees (3.6 x 100% = 360 degrees in a circle). With that formula as your guide, you can convert percentages or cents to degrees.

Finally, remember that a pie chart does not reveal fine distinctions very well; it is best used for showing larger differences.

Guidelines for Bar Charts

Like pie charts, bar charts are easily recognized, for they appear every day in newspapers and magazines. Unlike pie charts, however, bar charts can accommodate a good deal of technical detail. Comparisons are provided by means of two or more bars running either horizontally or vertically on the page. Follow these five guidelines to create effective bar charts:

Bar Chart Guideline 1: Use a Limited Number of Bars

Though bar charts can show more information than pie charts, both types of illustrations have their limits. Bar charts begin to break down when there are so many bars that information is not easily grasped. The maximum bar number can vary according to chart size, of course. Figure 5-7 shows three multibar charts. The impact of the charts is enhanced by the limited number of bars.

Bar Chart Guideline 2: Show Comparisons Clearly

Bar lengths should be varied enough to show comparisons quickly and clearly. Avoid using bars that are too close in length, for then readers must study the chart before understanding it. Such a chart lacks immediate visual impact.

Also, avoid the opposite tendency, which is to use bar charts to show data that are very different in magnitude. To relate such differences, some writers resort to the dubious technique of inserting "break lines" (two parallel lines) on an axis to reflect breaks in scale (see Figure 5-8). The break lines show that the axis has been abbreviated. Although this approach at least reminds readers of the breaks, it is still deceptive. For example, note that Figure 5-8 provides no visual demonstration of the relationship between 50 and 2,800. The reader must think about these differences before making sense out of the chart. In other words, using break lines runs counter to a main goal of graphics, which is to create an immediate and accurate visual impact.

Bar Chart Guideline 3: Keep Bar Widths Equal and Adjust Space between Bars Carefully

While bar length varies, bar width must remain constant. As for distance between the bars, following are three options (along with examples in Figure 5-9):

- **Option A: Use no space** when there are close comparisons or many bars, so that differences are easier to grasp.

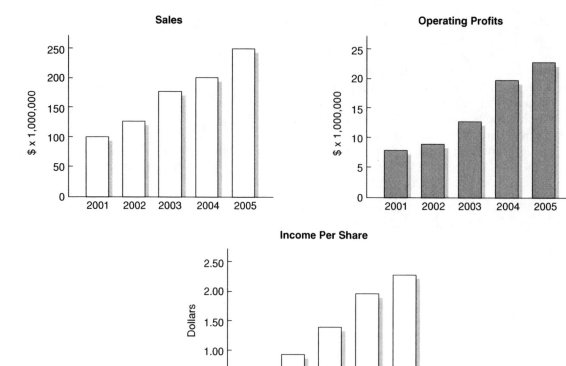

Figure 5-7   Bar charts

- **Option B: Use equal space, but less than bar width** when bar height differences are great enough to be seen in spite of the distance between bars.
- **Option C: Use variable space** when gaps between some bars are needed to reflect gaps in the data.

Bar Chart Guideline 4: Carefully Arrange the Order of Bars

The arrangement of bars is what reveals meaning to readers. Here are two common approaches:

- **Sequential:** Used when the progress of the bars shows a trend—for example, M&K's increasing number of environmental projects in the last five years
- **Ascending or descending order:** Used when you want to make a point by the rising or falling of the bars—for example, the 2002 profits of M&K's branch offices, from lowest to highest

Bar Chart Guideline 5: Be Creative

Figure 5-10 shows two bar chart variations that help display multiple trends. The *segmented bars* in Option A produce four types of information: the total sales (*A + B + C*) and the individual sales for *A*, *B*, and *C*. The *grouped bars* in Option B show the individual sales trends for *D*, *F*, and *G*, along with a comparison of all three by year. Note that the amounts are written on/above the bars to highlight comparisons.

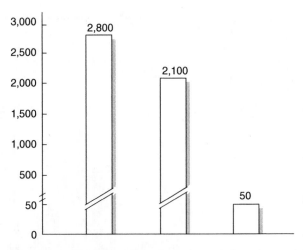

Figure 5-8   Break lines on bar charts—a technique that can lead to misunderstanding
Adapted from William S. Pfeiffer, *Proposal Writing* (Columbus, OH: Merrill, 1989), p. 147.

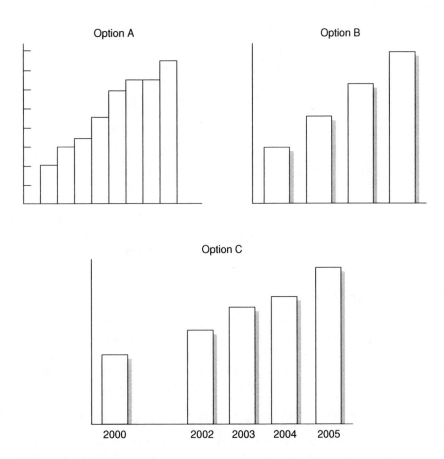

Figure 5-9   Bar chart variations
Adapted from William S. Pfeiffer, *Proposal Writing* (Columbus, OH: Merrill, 1989), p. 148.

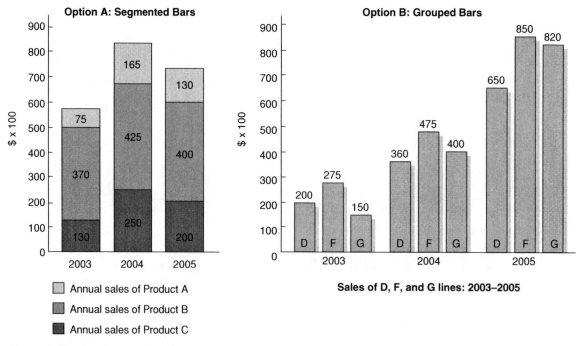

Figure 5-10   Bar chart variations for multiple trends
Adapted from William S. Pfeiffer, *Proposal Writing* (Columbus, OH: Merrill, 1989), p. 150.

Although these and other bar chart variations may be useful, remember to retain the bar chart's basic simplicity.

Guidelines for Line Charts

Line charts are a common graphic. Almost every newspaper contains a few charts covering topics such as stock trends, car prices, or weather. More than other graphics, line charts telegraph complex trends immediately.

They work by using vertical and horizontal axes to reflect quantities of two different variables. The vertical (or *y*) axis usually plots the *dependent variable*; the horizontal (or *x*) axis usually plots the *independent variable*. (The dependent variable is affected by changes in the independent variable.) Lines then connect points that have been plotted on the chart. When drawing line charts, follow these five main guidelines:

Line Chart Guideline 1: Use Line Charts for Trends

Readers are affected by the direction and angle of the chart's line(s). Take advantage of this persuasive potential. In Figure 5-11, for example, the writer wants to show the feasibility of adopting a new medical plan for M&K. Including a line chart in the study gives immediate emphasis to the most important issue—the effect the new plan would have on stabilizing the firm's medical costs.

Line Chart Guideline 2: Locate Line Charts with Care

Given their strong impact, line charts can be especially useful as attention-grabbers. Consider placing them (1) on cover pages, to engage the reader's interest in the document, (2) at the beginning of sections that describe trends, and (3) in conclusions, to reinforce a major point of your document.

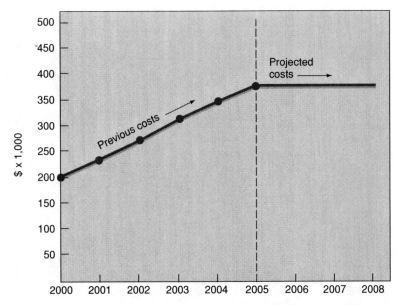

Figure 5-11 Line chart used to show effect of proposed medical plan on M&K health costs
Adapted from William S. Pfeiffer, *Proposal Writing* (Columbus, OH: Merrill, 1989), p. 151.

Line Chart Guideline 3: Strive for Accuracy and Clarity

Like bar charts, line charts can be misused or just poorly constructed. Be sure that the line or lines on the graph truly reflect the data you have drawn from. Also, select a scale that does not mislead readers with visual gimmicks. Following are some specific suggestions to keep your line charts accurate and clear:

- Start all scales from zero to eliminate confusion (see Bar Chart Guideline 2 on page 107).
- Select a vertical-to-horizontal ratio for axis lengths that is pleasing to the eye (typically the *y*-axis is about three-quarters the length of the *x*-axis).
- Make chart lines as thick as or thicker than the axis lines.
- Use shading under the line when it will make the chart more readable.

Line Chart Guideline 4: Do Not Place Numbers on the Chart Itself

Line charts derive their main effect from the simplicity of lines that show trends. Avoid cluttering the chart with a lot of numbers that only detract from the visual impact.

Line Chart Guideline 5: Use Multiple Lines with Care

Like bar charts, line charts can show multiple trends: simply add another line or two. If you place too many lines on one chart, however, you run the risk of confusing the reader with too much data. Use no more than four or five lines on a single chart (see Figure 5-12).

Guidelines for Schedule Charts

Many documents, especially proposals and feasibility studies, include a special kind of chart that shows readers when certain activities will be accomplished. This kind

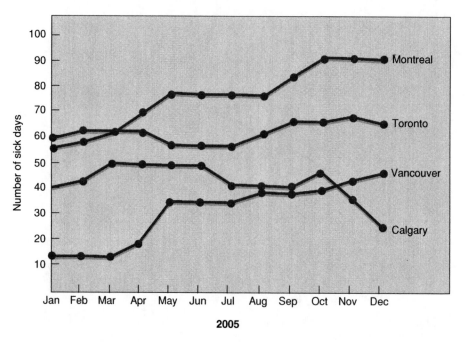

Figure 5-12   Line chart using multiple lines to show number of sick days taken at M&K's offices: 2005
Adapted from William S. Pfeiffer, *Proposal Writing* (Columbus, OH: Merrill, 1989), p. 152.

of chart usually highlights tasks and times already mentioned in the text. Often called a milestone or Gantt chart (after Henry Laurence Gantt, 1861–1919), it usually includes the following parts (see Figure 5-13):

- **Vertical axis,** which lists the various parts of the project, in sequential order
- **Horizontal axis,** which registers the appropriate time units
- **Horizontal bar lines** (Gantt) or separate markers (milestone), which show the starting and ending times for each task

Follow these basic guidelines for constructing effective schedule charts in your proposals, feasibility studies, or other documents:

Schedule Chart Guideline 1: Include Only Main Activities

Keep readers focused on no more than 10 to 15 main activities. If more detail is needed, construct a series of schedule charts linked to the main "overview" chart.

Schedule Chart Guideline 2: List Activities in Sequence, Starting at the Top of the Chart

As shown in Figure 5-13, the convention is to list activities from the top to the bottom of the vertical axis. Thus the reader's eye moves from the top left to the bottom right of the page—the most natural flow for most readers.

Schedule Chart Guideline 3: Run Labels in the Same Direction

If readers have to turn the chart sideways to read labels, they may lose interest.

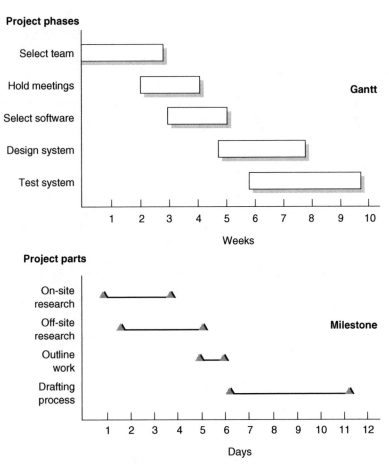

Figure 5-13 Gantt and milestone schedule charts
Adapted from William S. Pfeiffer, *Proposal Writing* (Columbus, OH: Merrill, 1989), p. 153.

Schedule Chart Guideline 4: Create New Formats When Needed

Figure 5-13 shows only two common types of schedule charts; you should devise your own hybrid form when it suits your purposes. Your goal is to find the simplest format for telling your reader when a product will be delivered, a service completed, or something similar. Figure 5-14 includes one such variation.

Schedule Chart Guideline 5: Be Realistic about the Schedule

Schedule charts can come back to haunt you if you do not include feasible deadlines. As you set dates for activities, be realistic about the likely time in which something can be accomplished. Your managers and clients will understand delays caused by weather, equipment breakdowns, and other unforeseen events. However, they will be less charitable about schedule errors that result from sloppy planning.

Guidelines for Flow Charts

Flow charts tell a story about a process, usually by stringing together a series of boxes and other shapes that represent separate activities (see Figure 5-15). Because

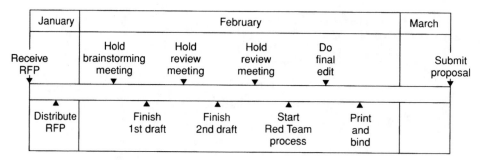

Figure 5-14 Schedule chart variation

they have a reputation for being hard to read, you need to take extra care in designing them. The following five guidelines will help:

Flow Chart Guideline 1: Present Only Overviews

Readers usually want flow charts to give them only a capsule version of the process, not all the details. Reserve your particulars for the text or the appendices, where readers expect them.

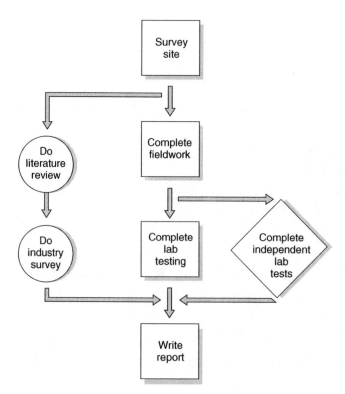

Figure 5-15 Flow chart for a project
Adapted from William S. Pfeiffer, *Proposal Writing* (Columbus, OH: Merrill, 1989), p. 155.

Flow Chart Guideline 2: Limit the Number of Shapes

Flow charts rely on rectangles and other shapes to relate a process—in effect, to tell a story. Different shapes represent different types of activities. This variety helps in describing a complex process but can also produce confusion. For the sake of clarity and simplicity, limit the number of different shapes in your flow charts. Figure 5-16 shows a flow chart that is complex but still readable. Note that the writer has modified geometric shapes to match what they represent (for example, the computer monitor, which represents database inputs).

Flow Chart Guideline 3: Provide a Legend When Necessary

Simple flow charts often need no legend. The few shapes on the chart may already be labelled by their specific steps. When charts get more complex, however, include a legend that identifies the meaning of each shape used.

Flow Chart Guideline 4: Run the Sequence from Top to Bottom or from Left to Right

Long flow charts like the one in Figure 5-16 may cover the page with several columns or rows. Yet they should always show some degree of uniformity by assuming either a basically vertical or horizontal direction.

Flow Chart Guideline 5: Label All Shapes Clearly

Besides a legend that gives the meanings of different shapes, the chart usually includes a label for each individual shape or step. Follow one of the following approaches:

- Place the label inside the shape.
- Place the label immediately outside the shape.
- Put a number in each shape and place a legend for all numbers in another location (preferably on the same page).

Guidelines for Organization Charts

Organization charts reveal the structure of a company or other organization—the people, positions, or work units. The challenge in producing this graphic is to make sure the arrangement of information accurately reflects the organization.

Organization Chart Guideline 1: Use the Linear "Boxes" Approach to Emphasize High-Level Positions

This traditional format uses rectangles connected by lines to represent some or all of the positions in an organization (see Figure 5-17). Because high-level positions usually appear at the top of the chart, where most readers focus their attention, this design tends to emphasize upper management.

Organization Chart Guideline 2: Connect Boxes with Solid or Dotted Lines

Solid lines show direct reporting relationships; dotted lines show indirect or staff relationships (see Figure 5-17).

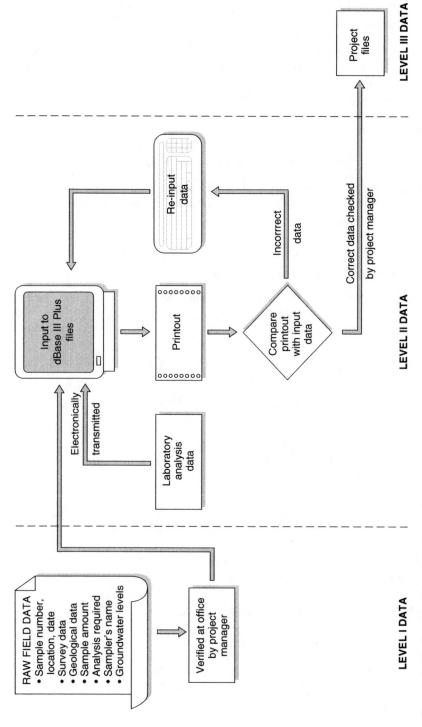

Figure 5-16 Flow chart for a complex project

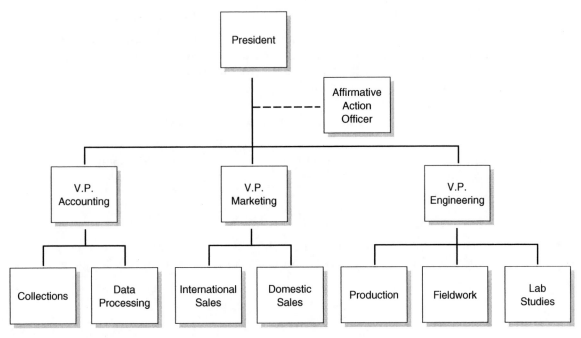

Figure 5-17   Basic organization chart
Adapted from William S. Pfeiffer, *Proposal Writing* (Columbus, OH: Merrill, 1989), p. 157.

Organization Chart Guideline 3: Use a Circular Design to Emphasize Mid- and Low-Level Positions

This arrangement of concentric circles gives more visibility to workers outside upper management. These are often the technical workers most deeply involved in the details of a project. For example, Figure 5-18 draws attention to the project engineers perched on the chart's outer ring.

Figure 5-18   Concentric organization chart
Source: William S. Pfeiffer, *Proposal Writing* (Columbus, OH: Merrill, 1989), p. 158.

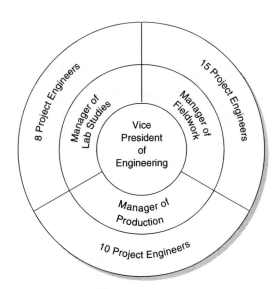

Organization Chart Guideline 4: Use Varied Shapes Carefully

Like flow charts, organization charts can use different shapes to indicate different levels or types of jobs. However, beware of introducing more complexity than you need. Use more than one shape only if you are convinced this approach is needed to convey meaning to the reader.

Organization Chart Guideline 5: Be Creative

When standard forms will not work, create new ones. For example, Figure 5-19 uses an organization chart as the vehicle for showing the lines of responsibility in a specific project.

Guidelines for Technical Drawings

Technical drawings are important tools for companies that produce or use technical products. These drawings can accompany documents such as instructions, reports,

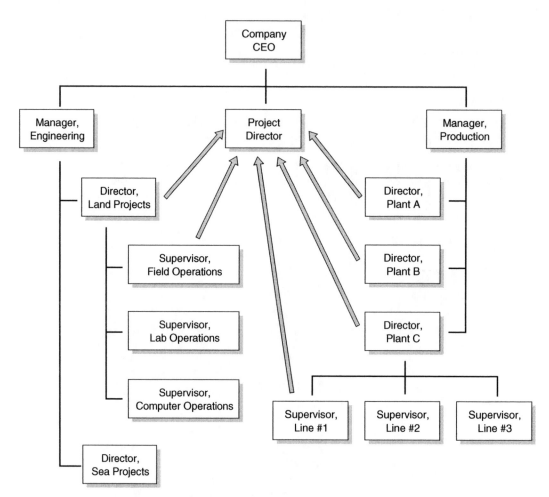

Figure 5-19   Organization chart focusing on project (indicates individuals most involved with upcoming project)
Source: William S. Pfeiffer, *Proposal Writing* (Columbus, OH: Merrill, 1989), p. 159.

sales orders, and proposals. They are preferred over photographs when specific views are more important than photographic detail. Whereas all drawings used to be produced mainly by hand, now they are usually created by *CAD* (computer-assisted design) systems. Follow these guidelines for producing technical drawings that complement your text:

Drawing Guideline 1: Choose the Right Amount of Detail

Keep drawings as simple as possible. Use only the level of detail that serves your document's purpose and satisfies your reader's needs. For example, Figure 5-20 will be used in an M&K brochure on maintaining home heating systems. Its intention is to focus on one part of the thermostat—the lever and attached roller. Completed on a CAD system, this drawing also presents an *exploded view* (a closeup of a particular part of the main drawing) so that the location of the arm can be easily seen.

Drawing Guideline 2: Label Parts Well

A common complaint about drawings is that parts included in the illustration are not carefully or clearly labelled. Place labels on every part you want your reader to see. (Conversely, you can choose not to label those parts that are irrelevant to your purpose.)

When you label parts, use a typeface large enough for easy reading. Also, arrange labels so that (1) they are as easy as possible for your reader to locate and (2) they do not detract from the importance of the drawing itself. The simple labelling in Figure 5-20 fulfills these objectives.

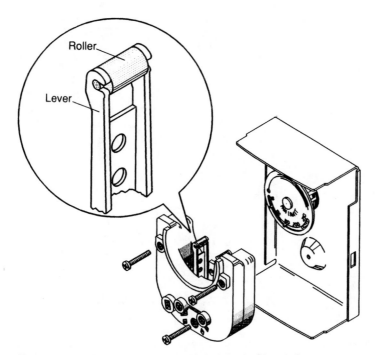

Figure 5-20 Technical drawing (exploded view) of home thermostat

Drawing Guideline 3: Choose the Most Appropriate View

As already noted, illustrations—unlike photographs—permit you to choose the level of detail needed. In addition, drawings offer you a number of options for perspective or view:

- **Exterior view** (shows surface features with either a two- or three-dimensional appearance—see Figure 5-21)
- **Cross-section view** (shows a "slice" of the object so that interiors can be viewed)
- **Exploded view** (shows relationship of parts to each other by "exploding" the mechanism—see Figure 5-20)

Drawing Guideline 4: Use Legends When There Are Many Parts

In complex drawings, avoid cluttering the illustration with many labels. Figure 5-21, for example, places all labels in one easy-to-find spot, rather than leaving them on the drawing.

Assume that Figure 5-21 is part of an M&K report to the U.S. National Park System. A group of specialists just completed a restoration project at a Civil War

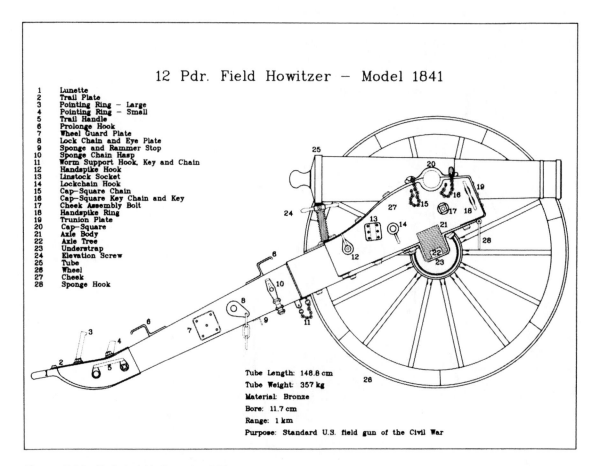

Figure 5-21 Technical drawing using CAD system

battlefield. Among many other tasks, the company (1) stopped erosion that had been destroying several hilly sites, (2) moved five howitzer cannon to permanent sites on a mountain ridge, where they were located during the war, and (3) built walking paths that would allow some public access to the battle locations without damaging the terrain. Given the importance of the cannon to the project, an M&K CAD draftsperson completed a technical illustration. The complete drawing, with labels, appears in the text of the report. A reduced-size version appears on the cover of the report.

Guidelines for Tables

Tables present readers with raw data, usually in the form of numbers but sometimes in the form of words. Tables are classified as either formal or informal:

- **Informal tables:** limited data in the form of either rows or columns
- **Formal tables:** data in a grid, always with both horizontal rows and vertical columns

The following five guidelines will help you design and position tables within the text of your documents:

Table Guideline 1: Use Informal Tables as Extensions of Text

Informal tables are usually merged with the text on a page, rather than isolated on a separate page or attachment. As such, an informal table usually has (1) no table number or title, (2) no listing in the list of illustrations in a formal report or proposal, and (3) few if any headings for rows or columns.

Example:
Our project in northern Alberta will involve engineers, technicians, and salespeople from three offices, in these numbers:

Calgary office	14
Vancouver office	12
Toronto office	6
	32

Table Guideline 2: Use Formal Tables for Complex Data Separated from Text

Formal tables may appear on the page of text that includes the table reference, on the page following the first text reference, or in an attachment or appendix. In any case, you should do the following:

- Extract important data from the table and highlight them in the text.
- Make every formal table as clear and visually appealing as possible.

Table Guideline 3: Use Plenty of White Space

Used around and within tables, white space guides the eye through a table much better than do black lines. Leave 2 cm more white space than you would normally leave around text.

Table Guideline 4: Follow Usual Conventions for Dividing and Explaining Data

Figure 5-22 shows a typical formal table. It satisfies the overriding goal of being clear and self-contained. To achieve that objective in your tables, follow these guidelines:

1. **Titles and numberings:** Give a title to each formal table, and place title and number above the table. Number each table if the document contains two or more tables.
2. **Headings:** Create short, clear headings for all columns and rows.
3. **Abbreviations:** Include in the headings any necessary abbreviations or symbols, such as kg or %. Spell out abbreviations and define terms in a key or footnote if any reader may need such assistance.
4. **Numbers:** Round off numbers when possible, for ease of reading. Also, align multidigit numbers on the right edge, or at the decimal when shown.
5. **Notes:** Place any necessary explanatory headnotes either between the title and the table (if the notes are short) or at the bottom of the table.
6. **Footnotes:** Place any necessary footnotes below the table.
7. **Sources:** Place any necessary source references below the footnotes.
8. **Caps:** Use uppercase and lowercase letters, rather than full caps.

Table Guideline 5: Pay Special Attention to Cost Data

Most readers prefer to have complicated financial information placed in tabular form. Given the importance of such data, edit cost tables with great care. Devote extra attention to these two issues:

- Placement of decimals in costs
- Correct totals of figures

Documents such as proposals can be considered contracts in some courts of law, so there is no room for error in relating costs.

TABLE 6: M&K Employee Retirement Fund			
Investment Type	Book Value	Market Value	% of Total Market Value
Temporary securities	$ 434,084	$ 434,084	18.6%
Bonds	679,081	842,056	36.0
Common stocks	508,146	1,039,350	44.5
Mortgages	18,063	18,063	.9
Real estate	1,939	1,939	nil
Totals	$1,641,313	$2,335,492	100.0%

Note: This table contrasts the book value versus the market value of the M&K Employee Retirement Fund, as of December 31, 2005.

Figure 5-22 Example of formal table

MISUSE OF GRAPHICS

Technology has revolutionized the world of graphics by placing sophisticated tools in the hands of many writers. Yet this largely positive event has its dark side. You will see many graphics that—in spite of their slickness—distort data and misinform the reader. The previous sections of this chapter established principles and guidelines to help writers avoid such distortion and misinformation. This last section shows what can happen to graphics when sound design principles are not applied.

Description of the Problem

The popular media offer a good glimpse into the problem of faulty graphics. One observer has used newspaper reports about the October 19, 1987, stock market plunge as one indication of the problem. Writing in *Aldus Magazine*, Daryl Moen noted that 60% of U.S. newspapers included charts and other graphics about the market drop the day after it occurred.[1] Moen's study revealed that one out of eight had data errors, and one out of three distorted the facts with visual effects. That startling statistic suggests that faulty illustrations are a genuine problem.

Edward R. Tufte analyzes graphics errors in more detail in his excellent work *The Visual Display of Quantitative Information*. In setting forth his main principles, Tufte notes that "graphical excellence is the well designed presentation of interesting data—a matter of *substance*, of *statistics*, and of *design*." He further contends that graphics must "give to the viewer the greatest number of ideas in the shortest time with the least ink in the smallest space)."[2]

One of Tufte's main criticisms is that charts are often disproportional to the actual differences in the data represented. The next subsection shows some specific ways in which this error has worked its way into contemporary graphics.

Examples of Distorted Graphics

There are probably as many ways to distort graphics as there are graphical types. This section gets at the problem of misrepresentation by showing several examples and describing the errors involved. None of the examples commits major errors, yet each one fails to represent the data accurately.

Example 1: Faulty Comparisons on Modified Bar Chart

Figure 5-23 accompanied a newspaper article about changes in mailing costs and service. The problem here is that the chart's decoration—the mailboxes—inhibits rather than promotes clear communication. Although the writer intends to use mailbox symbolism in lieu of precise bars, the height of the mailboxes does not correspond to the actual increase in second-class postage rates.

---

[1] Daryl Moen, "Misinformation Graphics," *Aldus Magazine*, January/February 1990, p. 64.

[2] Edward R. Tufte, *The Visual Display of Quantitative Information* (Cheshire, CT: Graphics Press, 1983), p. 51.

A revised graph should include either (1) mailboxes that correctly approximate the actual differences in second-class rates or (2) a traditional bar chart without the mailboxes.

Example 2: "Chartjunk" That Confuses the Reader

Figure 5-24 concludes a report from a municipal government. Whereas the dollar backdrop is meant to reinforce the topic—that is, how tax funds are used—in fact, it impedes communication. Readers cannot quickly see comparisons. Instead, they must read all of the labels surrounding the illustration, mentally rearranging the items into some order.

At the very least, the expenditures should have been placed in sequence, from least to greatest percentage or vice versa. Even with this order, however, one could argue that the dollar coin is a piece of "chartjunk" that fails to display the data effectively.

Example 3: Confusing Pie Charts

The pie chart in Figure 5-25 (1) omits percentages that should be attached to each of the budgetary expenditures; (2) fails to move in a largest-to-smallest, clockwise sequence; (3) includes too many divisions, many of which are about the same size and thus difficult to distinguish; and (4) introduces a third dimension that adds no value to the graphic.

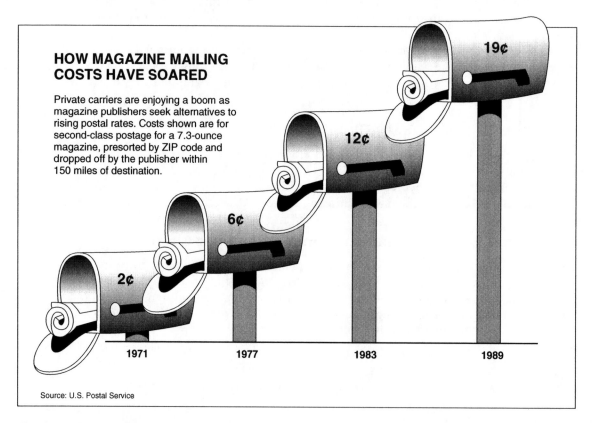

Figure 5-23 Faulty comparisons on modified bar chart
Source: US Postal Service. Adapted from *Atlanta Constitution*, November 30, 1989, p. H-1. Used by permission.

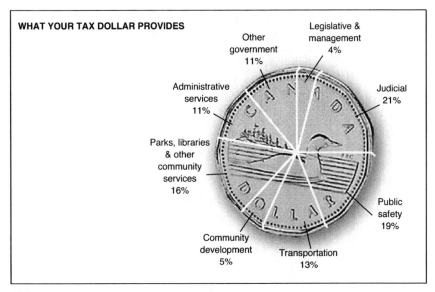

Figure 5-24 "Chartjunk" that confuses the reader

Figure 5-26 attempts the visual strategy of alternating shades, but it only succeeds in overloading the chart with too many small percentage divisions in uncertain order. A grouped bar chart would have better served the purpose, with Atlantic Canada, Central Canada, Prairies, West Coast, and Other providing the groupings.

Figure 5-27 negates the value of the pie chart by assuming an oblong shape, rather than a circle. This distortion can make it difficult for the reader to distinguish among sections that are similar in size, such as sections 1 and 2 in this figure. The pie chart should be a perfect circle, should have percentages on each part that added together equal 100%, and should move in large-to-small sequence from the 12:00 position.

Employability Skills

The Conference Board of Canada's *Employability Skills 2000+* points out that the ability to present information in graphic form is an integral part of the skill set that employees bring to their place of work. Relevant communication skills include the following:

- Read and understand information presented in a variety of forms (e.g., words, graphs, charts, diagrams).
- Assess situations and identify problems.*

In graphic form, display all of the expenses that you will have in the next month. Prepare two graphics. The first is to show what proportion of your total expenditure each expense represents. The second is to show the relative importance of each expenditure. Using this information, identify the least critical expenses in order to determine what you should do without if the money you had available to you was 20% less than what was required.

* *Employability Skills 2000+* Brochure 2000 E/F (Ottawa: The Conference Board of Canada, 2000).

	FUND NAME	DESCRIPTION	FY '89 BUDGET
A	General Fund	Basic government activities	$112,895,822
B	Transit Fund	Implementation of bus system	10,812,522
C	Fire District Fund	Operation of Fire Department	21,253,523
D	Bond Funds	General obligation bond issue proceeds	11,073,371
E	Road Sales Tax Fund	1% special purpose sales tax for road improvements	116,869,904
F	Water & Pollution Control Fund	Daily water system operation	60,572,506
G	Debt Service Fund	Principal & interest payments for general obligation bonds	8,240,313
H	Water RE&I Fund	Maintenance of existing facilities	27,365,744
I	Solid Waste RE&I Fund	Maintenance of existing facilities	1,111,237
J	Solid Waste Disposal Facilities	Landfill operations	6,003,367
K	Water Construction Fund	Construction of new facilities	110,884,507
L	Other Uses*		18,384,364
		SUB-TOTAL	$505,467,180
		LESS INTERFUND ACTIVITY	− 23,393,042
		TOTAL EXPENDITURES	**$482,074,138**

*Other Uses includes: Community Service Block Grants, Law Library, Claims Fund, Capital Projects, Senior Services, Community Development Block Grant, Grant Fund

In addition to the General Fund, the county budgets a number of other specialized funds. These include the Fire District Fund, Transit Fund, Road Sales Tax Fund, and enterprise funds such as Water and Pollution Control, and Solid Waste Disposal Facilities.

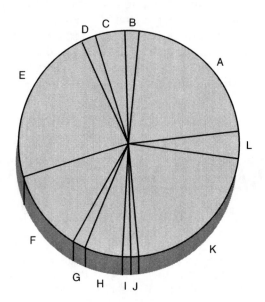

Figure 5-25 Confusing pie chart
Adapted from Cobb County 1988–89 Annual Report (Cobb County, GA), p. 14. Used by permission.

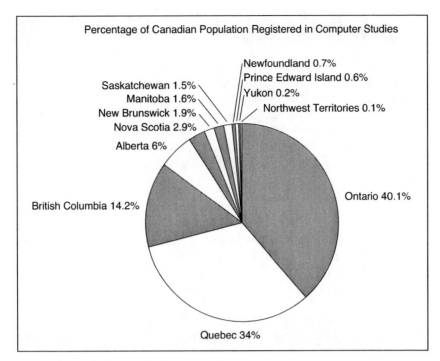

Figure 5-26 Confusing pie chart

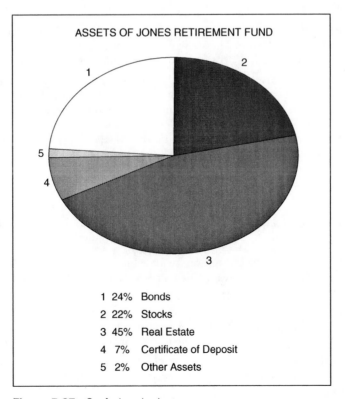

Figure 5-27 Confusing pie chart

CHAPTER SUMMARY

More than ever before, readers of technical documents expect good graphics to accompany text. Graphics (also called *illustrations* or *visual aids*) can be in the form of (1) tables (rows and/or columns of data) or (2) figures (a catch-all term for all nontable illustrations). Both types are used to simplify ideas, reinforce points made in the text, generate interest, and create a universal appeal.

Eight common graphics used in technical writing are pie charts, bar charts, line charts, schedule charts, flow charts, organization charts, technical drawings, and tables. As detailed in this chapter, you should follow specific guidelines in constructing each type. The following basic guidelines apply to all graphics:

1. Refer to all graphics in the text.
2. Think about where to put graphics.
3. Position graphics vertically when possible.
4. Avoid clutter.
5. Provide titles, notes, keys, and source data.

ASSIGNMENTS

Your instructor may want you to practise graphics in the context of some of the writing assignments in this textbook, especially in Chapters 10, 11, and 12. Following are a few additional exercises.

1. **Pie, bar, and line charts.** Figure 5-28 shows tennis racquet production from 1973 to 1998 while also breaking down the production into wood, aluminum, graphite, and other frames. Use the data provided to complete the following:

   - A pie chart that shows four groupings of racquet frames for 1990
   - A bar chart that shows the production of aluminum frames in five-year increments
   - A line graph that shows the increase in graphite frame production between 1975 and 1990
   - A multiple-line graph showing the changes in the market shares of the different kinds of frames between 1985 and 1995

2. **Schedule charts.** Using any options discussed in this chapter, draw a schedule chart that reflects your work on one of the following:

   - A project at work
   - A laboratory course at school
   - A lengthy project in a course such as this one

3. **Flow charts.** Select a process with which you are familiar because of work, school, home, or other interests. Then draw a flow chart that outlines the main activities involved in this process.

4. **Organization chart.** Select an organization that you are familiar with, or one that you can find information about. Then construct a linear flow chart that would help an outsider understand the management structure of all or part of the organization.

5. **Technical drawing.** Drawing freehand or using computer-assisted design, produce a simple technical drawing of an object that you are familiar with through work, school, or home use.

6. **Misuse of graphics.** Find three deficient graphics in newspapers, magazines, reports, or other technical documents. Submit copies of the graphics along with a written critique

TENNIS RACQUET MANUFACTURE BY COMPOSITION

Year	Units Made (million)	Percent of Production			
		Wood	Aluminum	Graphite	Other
1973	32	89	11	0	0
1974	33	87	12	1	0
1975	33	85	14	1	0
1976	34	62	32	6	0
1977	32	58	31	11	0
1978	33	54	22	24	0
1979	31	42	21	26	3
1980	30	31	22	42	5
1981	31	22	24	47	7
1982	30	20	22	50	8
1983	29	20	29	39	12
1984	30	19	22	45	14
1985	27	18	21	48	13
1986	26	16	29	41	14
1987	27	12	26	47	15
1988	24	12	24	52	12
1989	25	8	22	54	16
1990	24	5	20	61	14
1991	23	2	19	66	13
1992	21	2	18	68	12
1993	21	1	14	74	11
1994	21	0	15	71	14
1995	19	0	14	74	12
1996	19	0	13	76	11
1997	18	0	12	78	10
1998	17	0	11	78	11

Figure 5-28   Reference for assignment 1

that (1) describes in detail the deficiencies of the graphics and (2) offers suggestions for improving them.

7. **Misuse of graphics.** Analyze the graphics in Figures 5-29, 5-30, and 5-31. Describe any deficiencies and offer suggestions for improvement.

Figure 5-29

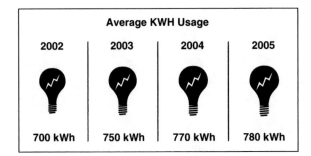

Figure 5-30

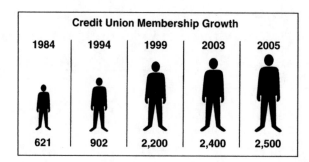

Figure 5-31

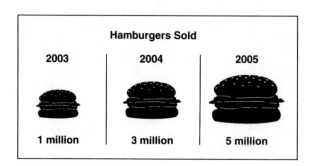

CHAPTER 6

Patterns of Organization

Chapters 1–5 gave you some background on technical writing and graphics and on Martin & Koffman, the example company used throughout this book. Building on that foundation, the next chapters focus on specific types of technical writing. This chapter and the next cover seven common patterns for organizing information: argument, definition, description, classification/division, comparison/contrast, process description, and instruction. Then Chapters 8–12 discuss these formats for the following documents: email and memos, letters, informal reports, formal reports, and proposals and feasibility studies.

If you have already taken a basic composition course, you will see similarities between patterns studied in that course and those described in this chapter. Indeed, technical writing uses the same building blocks as all other good writing. What follows are separate sections on five of these main patterns: argument, definition, description, classification/division, and comparison/contrast. They are roughly arranged by the frequency with which they are used in technical writing, starting with the most common pattern. Each section contains the following three parts:

1. Introduction about the pattern
2. Short case studies from M&K
3. Writing guidelines

Then the assignments challenge you to use the chapter's five patterns in the context of some short letter or memo reports.

ARGUMENT

Good argument forms the basis for all technical writing. Some people have the mistaken impression that only recommendation reports and proposals argue their case to the reader, and that all other writing should be objective rather than argumentative. The fact is, every time you commit words to paper you are arguing your point. This text uses the following broad-based definition of argument:

> **Argument:** the strategies you use in presenting evidence to support your point and to support your professional credibility, while still keeping the reader's goodwill.

Thus, even the most uncontroversial document, like a trip report, involves argument in the sense defined here. That is, a trip report would present information to support the fact that you accomplished certain objectives on a business trip. The report also would show the reader, usually your boss, that you worked hard to accomplish your objectives. In fact, you hope that every document you write becomes a written argument for your own conscientiousness as a professional.

The strongest form of argument—called *persuasion*—tries to convince your reader to adopt a certain point of view or pursue a certain line of action (see Chapter 12, "Proposals and Feasibility Studies," which discusses persuasive writing). In other words, persuasion seeks obvious changes in opinions or actions, whereas argument only presents evidence or logic to support a point of view. To help you use argument correctly, the next section provides you with some short case studies, guidelines for applying argument, and an annotated example.

Short Cases from M&K: Argument

Under the definition just given, many in-house and external documents could be considered argument. Following are three M&K examples:

Argument Case 1: Fire Control in Northern Ontario

As a fire-control expert in M&K's Toronto office, you have just completed a project for the province of Ontario. You spent two weeks in Northern Ontario examining the likelihood of major fires this season. Last season, major fires and westerly winds destroyed several small communities and forced the evacuation of others. Your investigation suggests that fires are likely and, in fact, necessary this season. Naturally caused and contained fires help keep down underbrush and thus reduce the chance for much bigger fires. Limited fires will not cause significant damage to wildlife or big trees, whereas major fires will. Now you must write a report to provincial authorities arguing that naturally occurring fires in Northern Ontario are desirable, despite the general feeling that all fires should be prevented.

Argument Case 2: Back Pain in the Calgary Office

The engineers, programmers, scientists, and other office workers in M&K's Calgary branch spend a lot of time in their chairs. Although all the office furniture is new and expensive, you and your branch colleagues have experienced regular back pain since the new chairs arrived. Unfortunately, the furniture was ordered through the corporate office, so your complaint cannot be handled in a routine, informal way in your own office. As the branch manager, you have mentioned the problem to your boss, the vice president for domestic operations. Predictably, he has asked you to "put it in writing." Although this memo report must explain the problem, you do not want to come across as a complainer. Instead, you must thoroughly and objectively document the problems associated with the arrival of the new chairs.

Argument Case 3: Quality Control in the Labs

As M&K's Baltimore manager, you have the sensitive job of making sure that the quality of the products and services remains high. During a recent road trip to every office, you noticed problems at the company's labs. In particular, testing procedures were not being followed exactly, equipment was sometimes not properly cleaned, and samples from the field were not always clearly labelled. Now you must write a memo report to all lab supervisors noting these lapses.

All three cases involve argument as defined in this chapter. That is, you must collect evidence to support your point, while still maintaining your readers' goodwill.

Guidelines for Writing Argument

Argumentative writing has a long tradition, from the rhetoric of ancient times to the political debate of today. This section describes five guidelines about argument that apply to your on-the-job writing.

Argument Guideline 1: Use Evidence Correctly

Whether writing a proposal to a customer or a memo to your boss, you often move from specific evidence toward a general conclusion supported by the evidence. Called *inductive reasoning,* this approach to argument requires that you follow some accepted guidelines. Following are three, along with brief examples:

- **Use points the reader can grasp.** For example, as the fire-control expert in Case 1, you would need to educate readers about how limited fires can benefit forest ecosystems. Your report must include evidence that could be understood by a mixed audience of park technicians and bureaucrats.
- **Use points that are a representative sample.** For example, as the quality-control expert in Case 3, you would want to have collected evidence from all labs mentioned in the memorandum before sending the memo calling for corrective action. As the writer in Case 2, you would want to have collected information from enough colleagues to support your point about the office furniture.
- **Have enough points to justify your conclusion.** Again from Case 3, you would want to have made many observations, not just two or three, to justify the memo's conclusions about poor lab procedures.

Argument Guideline 2: Choose the Most Convincing Order for Points

Chapter 3 points out that readers pay most attention to a report's beginning and ending, not the middle. Thus, you should include your stronger points at the beginning and ending of an argument sequence, with the weaker points in the middle. It follows that the strongest point usually appears in one of the following two locations:

- **Last**—in arguments that are fairly short
- **First**—in arguments that are fairly long

Readers finish short passages in one sitting. You can expect them to stay attentive as you lead up to your strongest point. For long passages, however, the audience may take several sittings to read through your argument. For this reason, place the most important evidence at the beginning of longer arguments, where readers will see it before they get distracted.

For Case 2, then, assume you plan to write a fairly short memo about the new office chairs, as a follow-up to your phone call to your manager at the corporate office. Your main points are that (1) employees have had medical problems leading to frequent sick leave, (2) productivity has suffered among those who are at work, (3) a local expert on health in the workplace has confirmed design flaws in the chairs, and (4) you have contacted a representative of the chair company, who has agreed to trade your chairs for a better model, for a net cost to M&K of only $2,000.

You decide that your fourth point is the strongest because it suggests a feasible solution. The next strongest is the first point because it deals with employee health. Given the brevity of your memo, therefore, you decide to place the medical point first, and the suggested solution last. In between will occur the point about reduced productivity and the expert's views. This arrangement holds the best chance for gaining your reader's support.

Argument Guideline 3: Be Logical

Some arguments rest on a logical structure called a *syllogism*. When it occurs formally (which is rare), a syllogism may look something like this:

Major premise:	All chairs with straight backs are unacceptable for prolonged office work.
Minor premise:	The chairs at the Calgary office have straight backs.
Conclusion:	The chairs at the Calgary office are unacceptable for prolonged office work.

In fact, syllogisms are usually implied, and appear in a less-structured fashion than in the sample shown here. For example, recall that your M&K chair report would include a testimonial from an outside expert in office furniture design. That person could have confirmed the major premise, leading to your statement of the minor premise and the conclusion. Indeed, this example shows that a syllogism is effective—that is, logical—only if the premises (1) can be verified as true and (2) will be accepted by the reader.

Argument Guideline 4: Use Only Appropriate Authorities

In the technical world, experts often supply evidence that will win the day in reports, proposals, and other documents. Using Case 2 again, your argument would rely on opinions by the expert in workplace health. This testimonial, however, would work only if you could verify that (1) there is a legitimate body of research on the health effects of chair design and (2) the expert you have chosen has credentials that readers will accept.

You will encounter a similar rule in Chapter 14, which covers proper documentation in research writing. Research papers also require that you cite sources that will be accepted as valid in the field about which you are writing.

Argument Guideline 5: Avoid Argumentative Fallacies

Guidelines 1–4 mention a few ways you can err in arguing your point. Listed next are some other fallacies that can damage your argument. Accompanying each fallacy is an example from Case 2:

- **Ad hominem** (Latin: "To the man"): arguing against a person rather than discussing the issue. (Example: suggesting that the chairs should be replaced because the purchasing agent, who ordered the chairs, is surly and incompetent.)
- **Circular reasoning:** failing to give any reason for why something is or is not true, other than stating that it is. (Example: proposing that the straight-backed chairs should be replaced simply because they are straight-backed chairs.)
- **Either/or fallacy:** stating that only two alternatives exist—yours and another one that is much worse—when in fact there are other options. (Example: claiming that if the office does not purchase new chairs next week, 15 employees will quit.)
- **False analogy:** suggesting that one thing should be true because of its similarity to something else, when in fact the two items are not enough alike to justify the analogy. (Example: suggesting that the chairs in the Calgary office should be replaced because the Montreal office has much more expensive chairs.)
- **Hasty generalization:** forming a generalization without adequate supporting evidence. (Example: proposing that all Jones office furniture will be unacceptable, simply because the current chairs carry the Jones trademark.)
- **Non sequitur** (Latin: "It does not follow"): making a statement that does not follow logically from what came before it. (Example: claiming that if the office chairs are not replaced soon, productivity will decrease so much that the future of the office will be in jeopardy—even though there is no evidence that the chairs would have this sort of dramatic effect on business.)

- **Post hoc ergo propter hoc** (Latin: "After this, therefore because of this"): claiming a cause–effect relationship between two events simply because one occurred before the other. (Example: associating the departure of an excellent secretary with the purchase of the poorly designed chairs a week earlier—even though no evidence supports the connection.)

Example of Argument

At the end of this chapter there is a complete memo report resulting from Argument Case 2 (see Model 6-1, pages 159–60). As the branch manager in M&K's Calgary office, you are writing to your supervisor in the Toronto corporate office. From your brief phone conversation, you expect that she supports the recommendation in your memo. Yet you know that she will show the memo to a few other corporate colleagues, including the procurement officer who ordered the chairs. Thus, you cannot assume support. You must present good arguments, in a tactful manner.

DEFINITION

During your career, you will use technical terms known only to those in your profession. As a civil engineer, for example, you would know that a *triaxial compression test* helps determine the strength of soil samples. As a computer professional, you would know the meaning of RAM (random access memory), ROM (read only memory), and LAN (local area network). When writing to readers unfamiliar with these fields, however, you would need to define technical terms.

Good definitions can support findings, conclusions, and recommendations throughout your document. They also keep readers interested. Conversely, the most organized, well-written report will fall on deaf ears if it includes terms that readers do not grasp. "Define your terms!" is the frustrated exclamation of many a reader. For your reader's sake, then, you need to be asking questions like the following about definitions:

- How often do you use them?
- Where should they be placed?
- What format should they take?
- How much information is enough, and how much is too much?

To answer these questions, the following sections give guidelines for definitions and supply an annotated example. First are some typical contexts for definitions within M&K.

Short Cases from M&K: Definition

These cases may help you visualize the use of definitions in your own on-the-job writing.

Definition Case 1: New Power Plant

As an M&K technician helping to build a power plant, you often use the term *turbine* in speech and writing. Obviously your co-workers and clients understand the term. Now, however, you are using it in a plant brochure to be sent to consumers.

For this general audience, you decide to define *turbine* as follows: "a machine that receives energy from a moving fluid and then uses this energy to make a shaft rotate." You accompany the definition with an illustration so that the unfamiliar audience can visualize how the turbine works.

Definition Case 2: Health Bulletin to Employees

As a health and benefits specialist in M&K's corporate office, you have watched the company's health insurance costs increase dramatically over the past five years. Much of this cost has not been passed on to the employee, resulting in a drain on profits. You have convinced management to support a major campaign to encourage healthy habits by employees. The campaign might include the following free benefits: in-house quit-smoking seminars, stress-reduction sessions, and annual physicals.

Your first project, however, is a health memorandum to all employees. In it you must (1) explain the nature of the cholesterol problem and (2) invite employees to free cholesterol-screening tests sponsored by the company. Your memo must provide clear definitions for terms such as "good" cholesterol and "bad" cholesterol.

Definition Case 3: Forestry Report

As a forestry and agriculture expert with M&K's Vancouver office, you have coordinated a major study for the province of British Columbia. Your job has been to recommend ways that a major forested region can be used for timber with little or no damage to the region's ecological balance.

Although the report will go first to technical experts in British Columbia's Ministry of Natural Resources, other potential nontechnical readers must be able to understand the report, including politicians, bureaucrats, and citizen groups. Thus, you have decided to include a glossary that defines terms such as the following:

- **Silviculture**—cultivation of forests to supply a renewable crop of timber
- **Shelterwood cutting**—removal of only mature trees in several cuttings over a few decades
- **Seed-tree cutting**—removal in one cutting of all but a few trees, which are left to regenerate the forest
- **Clear-cutting**—removal of all trees in an area in one cutting[1]

These three cases all require well-placed definitions for their readers. When in doubt, insert definitions! Readers can always skip over ones they do not need.

Guidelines for Writing Definitions

Once you know definitions are needed, you must decide on their format and location. Again, consider your readers. How much information do they need? Where is this information best placed within the document? To answer these and other questions, here are five working guidelines for writing effective definitions.

Definition Guideline 1: Keep It Simple

Occasionally the sole purpose of a report is to define a term. Most times, however, a definition just clarifies a term in a document with a larger purpose. Your defini-

---

[1]Adapted from G. Tyler Miller, *Environmental Science: An Introduction*, 2nd Edition, ©1988 by Wadsworth, Inc. Reprinted by permission of the publisher.

tions should be as simple and unobtrusive as possible. Always present the simplest possible definition, with only that level of detail needed by the reader.

For example, in writing to a client on your land survey of her farm, you might briefly define a *transit* as "the instrument used by land surveyors to measure horizontal and vertical angles." The report's main purpose is to present property lines and total area, not to give a lesson in surveying, so this sentence definition is adequate. Choose from the following three main formats (listed from least to most complex) in deciding the form and length of definitions:

- **Informal definition:** a word or brief phrase, often in parentheses, that gives only a synonym or other minimal information about the term
- **Formal definition:** a full sentence that distinguishes the term from other similar terms and that includes three parts: the term itself, the class to which the term belongs, and distinguishing features of the term
- **Expanded definition:** a lengthy explanation that begins with a formal definition and is developed into several paragraphs or more

Guidelines 2–4 show you when to use these three options and where to put them in your document.

Definition Guideline 2: Use Informal Definitions for Simple Terms Most Readers Understand

Informal definitions appear right after the terms being defined, often as one-word synonyms in parentheses. They give just enough information to keep the reader moving quickly. As such, they are best used with simple terms that can be adequately defined without much detail.

Here is a situation in which an informal definition would apply. M&K has been hired to examine a possible shopping-mall site. The buyers, a group of physicians, want a list of previous owners and an opinion about the site's suitability. As legal assistant at M&K, you must assemble a list of owners in your part of the group-written report. You want your report to agree with court records, so you decide to include real-estate jargon such as *grantor* and *grantee*. For your nontechnical readers, you include parenthetical definitions, such as the following:

> All **grantors** (persons from whom the property was obtained) and **grantees** (persons who purchased the property) are listed on the following chart, by year of ownership.

This same M&K report has a section describing *creosote pollution* found at the site. The chemist writing the contamination section also uses an informal definition for the readers' benefit:

> At the southwest corner of the mall site, we found 16 barrels of **creosote** (a coal tar derivative) buried under about 1m of sand.

The readers do not need a fancy chemical explanation of creosote. They only need enough information to keep them from getting lost in the terminology. Informal definitions adequately fulfill this requirement.

Definition Guideline 3: Use Formal Definitions for More Complex Terms

A formal definition appears in the form of a sentence that lists (1) the **term** to be defined, (2) the **class** to which it belongs, and (3) the **features** that distinguish the term from others in the same class. Use it when your reader needs more background than an informal definition provides. Formal definitions define a term in two stages:

- First, formal definitions place the term into a *class* (group) of similar items.
- Second, they list *features* (characteristics) of the term that separate it from all others in that same class.

In the list of sample definitions that follows, note that some terms are tangible (like *pumper*), while others are intangible (like *arrest*). Yet all can be defined by first choosing a class and then selecting features that distinguish the term from others in the same class.

Term	*Class*	*Features*
An *arrest* is	restraint of persons	that deprives them of freedom of movement and binds them to the will and control of the arresting officer.
A *financial statement* is	a historical report about a business	and is prepared by an accountant to provide information useful in making economic decisions, particularly for owners and creditors.
A *triaxial compression test* is	a soils lab test	that determines the amount of force needed to cause a shear failure in a soil sample.
A *pumper* is	a fire-fighting apparatus	used to provide adequate pressure to propel streams of water toward a fire.

Checklist for Formal Definitions

1. Your definition of a term should include all of the things the term can refer to.
   - If you defined a watch as a "time-keeping device that is worn on the wrist," your definition would be inadequate because it would not include items such as pocket watches.

2. Your definition of a term should exclude all things the term does not refer to.
   - It would be incorrect to define an automobile as a "four-wheel passenger vehicle powered by an engine" because that definition would also refer to buses and vans.

3. Your formal definition must be a *single, complete* sentence.
   - The function of a formal definition is to meet the first two items on this checklist. When you feel that further explanation is required, write an expanded definition (see Definition Guideline 4, below).

4. Your definition must not contain terms that could possibly be confusing to a reader.
   - The definition of *triaxial compression test*, for example, assumes readers will understand the term *shear failure*. If they do not, the term should not be used.

5. You must restrict the class so that you will not have to list too many distinguishing features.

- Instead of saying that a calculator belongs to the class "device," you could simplify the task of defining calculator by saying that it belongs to the class of "hand-held electronic devices."

6. You may never use the phrase *is when*.

7. You must not use the term being defined as part of the definition.
   - Defining a file separator as "a device that separates files" would not increase a reader's understanding.

Definition Guideline 4: Use Expanded Definitions for Supporting Information

Sometimes a parenthetical phrase or formal sentence definition is not enough. If readers need more information, use an expanded definition with the following three-part structure:

- **An overview at the beginning.** Begin with a formal sentence definition and include a description of the ways you will expand the definition.
- **Supporting information in the middle.** Use headings and lists as helpful format devices for the reader.
- **Brief closing remarks at the end.** Remind the reader of the definition's relevance to the whole document.

Following are seven ways to expand a definition, along with brief examples:

1. **Background and/or history of term.** Expand the definition of *triaxial compression test* by giving a dictionary definition of *triaxial* and a brief history of the origin of the test.
2. **Applications.** Expand the definition of *financial statement* to include a description of the use of such a statement by a company about to purchase controlling interest in another.
3. **List of parts.** Expand the definition of *pumper* by listing the parts of the device, such as the compressor, the hose compartment, and the water tank.
4. **Graphics.** Expand the description of the triaxial compression test with an illustration showing the laboratory test apparatus.
5. **Comparison/contrast.** Expand the definition of a term such as *management by objectives* (a technique for motivating and assessing the performance of employees) by pointing out similarities and differences between it and other management techniques.
6. **Basic principle.** Expand the definition of *ohm* (a unit of electrical resistance equal to that of a conductor in which a current of one ampere is produced by a potential of one volt across its terminals) by explaining the principle of Ohm's Law (that for any circuit the electric current is directly proportional to the voltage and inversely proportional to the resistance).
7. **Illustration.** Expand the definition of *CAD/CAM* (computer-aided design/computer-aided manufacturing—computerized techniques to automate the design and manufacture of products) by giving examples of how CAD/CAM is changing methods of manufacturing many items, from blue jeans to airplanes.

Obviously, long definitions might seem unwieldy within the text of a report, or even within a footnote. For this reason, they often appear in appendices, as noted in the next guideline. Readers who want additional information can seek them out; other readers will not be distracted by digressions in the text.

Definition Guideline 5: Choose the Right Location for Your Definition

Short definitions are likely to be in the main text; long ones are often relegated to footnotes or appendices. However, length is not the main consideration. Think first about the importance of the definition to your reader. If you know that decision makers reading your report will need the definition, then place it in the text—even if it is fairly lengthy. If the definition only provides supplementary information, then it can go elsewhere. You have the following five choices for locating a definition:

1. **In the same sentence as the term:** as with an informal, parenthetical definition
2. **In a separate sentence:** as with a formal sentence definition occurring right after a term is mentioned
3. **In a footnote:** as with a formal or expanded definition listed at the bottom of the page on which the term is first mentioned
4. **In a glossary at the beginning or end of the document:** along with all other terms needing definition in that document (an informal definition often appears in the text even if a glossary exists)
5. **In an appendix at the end of the document:** as with an expanded definition that would otherwise clutter the text of the document.

Example of Expanded Definition

Expanded definitions are especially useful in reports from technical experts to nontechnical readers. M&K's report writers, for example, often must explain environmental, structural, or geological problems to concerned citizens or nontechnical decision makers. Figure 6-1 gives a definition that might appear in a report to a county government about the placement of a landfill.

DESCRIPTION

Technical descriptions, like expanded definitions, require that you pay special attention to *details*. In fact, you can consider a description to be a special type of definition that focuses on parts, functions, or other features. It emphasizes *physical* details. Descriptions can appear in any part of a document, from the introduction to the appendix. As a rule, however, detailed descriptions tend to be placed in the technical sections.

Short Cases from M&K: Description

Descriptions often appear as supporting information in the document body or in appendices. Here are three situations from M&K in which a detailed description would add to the effectiveness of the complete document.

Description Case 1: Asbestos Site

M&K's Montreal office was hired to examine asbestos contamination in a large high school built in 1949. As a member of the investigating team, you found asbestos

Starts with formal sentence definition— including term, class, and features.

Indicates way definition will be developed (description of acute and chronic types).

Gives examples of first type.

Gives examples of second type.

> A **toxic substance** is a chemical that is harmful to people or other living organisms. The effects from exposure to a toxic substance may be acute or chronic. Acute effects are those that appear shortly after exposure, usually due to a large concentration or dose over a short time. Examples are skin burns or rashes, eye irritation, chest pains, kidney damage, headache, convulsions, and death.
>
> Effects that are delayed and usually long-lasting are called "chronic" effects. They may not appear for months or years after exposure and usually last for years. Examples are cancer, lung and heart disease, birth defects, genetic defects, and nerve and behavioural disorders. Chronic effects often occur as a result of prolonged exposure to fairly low concentrations or doses of a toxin. However, they may occur as the delayed effects of short-term exposure to high doses.

Figure 6-1 Definitions in a report

Source: Excerpted from G. Tyler Miller, *Living in the Environment: An Introduction to Environmental Science*, 6th edition © 1990 by Wadsworth, Inc. Reprinted by permission of the publisher.

throughout the basement in old pipe coverings. Your final report to the school board provides conclusions about the level of contamination and recommendations for removal. An appendix gives a detailed technical description of the entire basement, including a map with a layout of the plumbing system.

Description Case 2: Possible Harbours

M&K's San Francisco office has been hired to recommend possible locations for a new swimming and surfing park in northern California. Written to a county commission (five laypersons who will make the decision), your report gives three possible locations and your reasons for selecting them. Then it refers to appendices that give brief physical descriptions of the sites.

Specifically, your appendices to the report describe (1) surface features, (2) current structures, (3) types of soils gathered from the surface, (4) water quality, and (5) aesthetic features, such as quality of the ocean views. Language is nontechnical, considering the lay background of the commissioners.

Description Case 3: Sonar Testing Equipment

Rebecca Stern, a potential client, calls you in your capacity as a geologist at M&K's Vancouver office. She wants information about the kind of sonar equipment M&K uses to map geological features on the sea floor.

This client has a strong technical background, so you write a letter with a detailed technical description of the M&K system. The body of the letter describes the locations and functions of (1) the seismic source (a device, towed behind a boat, that sends the sound waves) and (2) the receiver (a unit, also towed behind the boat, that receives the signals).

Guidelines for Writing Descriptions

Now that you know how descriptions fit into entire documents, here are some simple guidelines for writing accurate, detailed descriptions. Follow them carefully as you prepare assignments in this class and on the job.

Description Guideline 1: Remember Your Readers' Needs

The level of detail in a technical description depends on the purpose a description serves. Give readers precisely what they need—but no more. In the harbour description in Case 2, for example, the commissioners do not want a detailed description of soil samples taken from borings. That level of detail will be reserved for a few sites selected later for further study. Instead, they want only surface descriptions. Always know just how much detail will get the job done.

Description Guideline 2: Be Accurate and Objective

More than anything else, readers expect accuracy in descriptions. Pay close attention to details. (As noted previously, the degree of detail in a description depends on the document's purpose.) In the basement description in Case 1, for example, you would want to describe every possible location of asbestos in the school basement. Accuracy here is crucial because the description will become the basis for a cost proposal to remove the material.

While objectivity is also important, it is more difficult to pin down. Some writers assume that an objective description leaves out all opinion. This is not the case. Instead, an objective description may well include opinions that have the following features:

- They are based on your professional background.
- They can be justified by the time the report is submitted. (For example, if you know that poured concrete will cure *before* the report is delivered to the client, in the description you can state the date by which you predict the concrete will cure.)
- They can be supported by details from the site or object being described.

For example, your description of the basement pipes mentioned in Case 1 might include a statement like this: "Because there is asbestos wrapping on the exposed pipes above the boiler, my experience suggests that asbestos wrapping probably also exists around the pipes above the ceiling—in areas that we were not able to view." This opinion does not reduce your description's objectivity—rather, it is a logical conclusion based on your experience.

Description Guideline 3: Choose an Overall Organization Plan

Like other patterns discussed in this chapter, technical descriptions usually make up only parts of documents. Nevertheless, such descriptions must have an organization plan that permits them to be read as self-contained, stand-alone sections. Indeed, a description may be excerpted later for separate use.

The organization of a technical description will always move from the general to the specific. This follows the sequence of questions that you might ask if you were not familiar with an object (see Figure 6-2).

Following are three ways to organize the list of components:

1. **Description of the parts:** For many physical objects, like the basement floor and coastal scene in the previous cases, you will simply organize the description by moving from part to part.
2. **Description of the functions:** Often the most appropriate overall plan relies on how things work, not on how they look. In the sonar example, the reader was more interested in the way the sender and receiver worked together to provide a map of the sea floor. This function-oriented description would include only a brief description of the parts.

	The Questions	The Responses
1.	What is it?	Provide the reader with a formal sentence definition (introductory section).
2.	What is it for?	If the formal definition has not done so and if it is necessary, explain the purpose of the item (introductory section).
3.	What does it look like?	Give the reader an idea of the item's appearance (introductory section). An analogy is often useful here.
4.	What are the most important things?	List the major components of the items to be described (introductory section).
5.	What exactly is the item composed of?	Describe in detail the elements that make up each of the components you have listed (body). Remember to follow the order established in the list of major components.
6.	Why is this important?	Provide a brief conclusion to remind the reader of

Figure 6-2   Organization of a technical description

3. **Description of the sequence:** If your description involves events, as in a police officer's description of an accident investigation, you can organize ideas around the major actions that occurred, in their correct sequence. As with any list, it is best to place a series of many activities into just a few groups. Four groups of five events each is much easier for readers to comprehend than a single list of 20 events.

Description Guideline 4: Use "Helpers" Like Graphics and Analogies

The words of a technical description need to come alive. Because your readers may be unfamiliar with the item, you must search for ways to connect with their experience and with their senses. Two effective tools are graphics and analogies.

Graphics respond to the desire of most readers to see pictures along with words. As readers move through your part-by-part or functional breakdown of a mechanism, they can refer to your graphic aid for assistance. The illustration helps you too, of course, in that you need not be as detailed in describing locations and dimensions of parts when you know the reader has easy access to a visual. Note how the diagrams in Models 6-2 and 6-3 on pages 161–65 give meaning to the technical details in the verbal descriptions.

Analogies, like illustrations, give readers a convenient handle for understanding your description. Put simply, an analogy allows you to describe something unknown or uncommon in terms of something that is known or more common. A brief analogy can sometimes save you hundreds of words of technical description. The following paragraph description contains three analogies (in italics):

> M&K is equipped to help clean up oil spills with its patented product, SeaClean. This highly absorbent chemical is spread over the entire spill by means of a helicopter,

which makes passes over the spill *much as a lawn mower would cover the complete sur-face area of a lawn*. When the chemical contacts the oil, it acts *like sawdust coming in contact with oil on a garage floor*. That is, the oil is immediately absorbed into the chem-ical and physically transformed into a product that is easily collected. Then our nearby ship can collect the product, using a machine that operates *much like a vac-uum cleaner*. This machine sucks the SeaClean (now full of oil) off the water's surface and into a sealed container in the ship's hold.

Description Guideline 5: Give Your Description the "Visualizing Test"

After completing a description, test its effectiveness by reading it to someone unfa-miliar with the material—someone with about the same level of knowledge as your intended reader. If this person can draw a rough sketch of the object or events while listening to your description, then you have done a good job. If not, ask your listener for suggestions to improve the description. If you are too close to the subject yourself, sometimes an outside point of view will help refine your technical description.

Examples of Description

This section introduces two descriptions from M&K. The descriptions themselves are at the end of the chapter, in Models 6-2 and 6-3. The first example includes a description of physical parts and a brief operating procedure. (For a thorough discussion of process descriptions and instructions, see Chapter 7.) The second includes only a description of physical parts. Both show the importance of graphics in technical descriptions.

Description 1: Blueprint Machine

Donna Kovacs, human resources coordinator at M&K's Toronto office, has been asked to assemble an orientation guide for new secretaries, office assistants, and other members of the office staff. The manual will contain descriptions and locations of the most common pieces of equipment in the office, sometimes with brief instruc-tions for their use.

One section of her manual includes a series of short equipment descriptions organized by general purpose of the equipment. Model 6-2 at the end of this chap-ter includes a description of the office blueprint machine, which gets used by a wide variety of employees. Because the blueprint machine has an operating procedure that is not self-evident, the description includes a brief procedure that shows the manner in which the machine should be used.

Description 2: Bunsen Burner

Fahdi Ahmad, the director of procurement at M&K's office in Saudi Arabia, is changing his buying procedures. He has decided to purchase some basic lab supplies from companies in nearby developing nations, rather than from firms in industrial-ized countries. For one thing, he thinks this move may save some money. For another, he believes it will help the company get more projects from these nations, because M&K will become known as a firm that pumps back some of its profits into the local economies.

As a first step in this process, Fahdi is providing potential suppliers with descrip-tions of some basic lab equipment used at M&K, such as pH meters, laboratory scales, glass beakers, and burners. Model 6-3 at the end of this chapter presents a moderately detailed description of one such piece of equipment—a Bunsen burner. Fahdi selects a burner model that is being successfully used at many M&K offices in Canada. The Model 6-3 description can serve as a starting point for suppliers. However, M&K and the suppliers realize that burners will have slightly different features, depending on the manufacturer.

CLASSIFICATION/DIVISION

In technical writing, you often perform the following related tasks: (1) grouping lists of items into categories, a process called *classification*, or (2) separating an individual item into its parts, a process called *division*. In practice, the patterns usually work together. So that you can see classification and division in action, this section starts with some case studies from M&K, followed by some basic classification guidelines with an example, and then some basic division guidelines with an example.

Short Cases from M&K: Classification/Division

The first case shows how you might use both classification and division in the same context. The other cases show only one pattern at work.

Classification/Division Case 1: Civil-engineering Projects

A major client needs some detailed information before deciding between M&K and a competitor for a big project. Specifically, the firm wants a detailed description of the civil-engineering projects completed by M&K's Caracas office over the past 10 years.

- First, you *divide* the office's civil-engineering capabilities into five groupings, based on type of project: (1) city planning, (2) construction, (3) transportation, (4) sanitation, and (5) hydraulics. (In each case, you describe the type of work done. For example, hydraulics projects concern the use of water.)
- Second, you collect descriptions of the 214 projects completed.
- Third, you *classify* the 214 projects into the five groupings mentioned. Thus, the combined process of division and classification gives you a way to organize details for the client.

Classification/Division Case 2: Birds Near a Freighter Terminal

The federal government wants to expand a freighter terminal off the British Columbia coast. Plans went along fine until last year, when a major environmental group raised questions about the effect the expansion would have on bird nesting areas.

The concerned organization, BirdWatch, hired M&K to determine the environmental impact of increased base traffic on the bird populations of a nearby national seashore. As project director, you determine that 61 species of birds on the island could be affected by the expansion. For the purposes of your report, you classify the 61 species by physical features into the following groupings: (1) loons; (2) grebes; (3) gulls and terns; (4) cranes, rails, and coots; and (5) ducks, geese, and swans. These classifications, often used in ornithological work, will help readers understand the significance of your environmental impact statement.

Classification/Division Case 3: Employee Grievances

Jacques Martin, M&K's president, wants to change the procedure by which employees can register grievances. He prefers that a committee be appointed to hear all grievances. Before he makes his final decision, however, he wants you to submit a summary of the types of grievances filed since the company was founded. Your painstaking research uncovers 116 separate grievances for which there is paperwork. For easier reading, your report to Jacques classifies the 116 incidents into four main categories, by type: (1) firing or discharge from the firm; (2) the use of seniority in layoffs, promotions, or transfers; (3) yearly performance evaluations; and (4) overtime pay and the issue of required overtime at some offices.

Guidelines for Classification

Classification helps you (and your reader) make sense out of diverse but related items. The process of outlining a writing assignment requires classifying. Outlining (as described in Chapter 1) forces you to apply both classification and division to organize information into manageable "chunks." The following guidelines provide a three-step procedure for classifying any group of related items:

Classification Guideline 1: Find a Common Basis

Classification requires that you establish your groupings on one main basis. This basis can relate to size, function, purpose, or any other factor that serves to produce logical groupings. For example, following are the bases for groupings established in the three cases cited:

Case 1 basis: the *type of work* being done in the civil-engineering field at M&K (such as sanitation or city planning)

Case 2 basis: the *physical features* of the marsh or ocean birds found at the site (note that the classifications in this case are not original but rather are ones commonly used in ornithology)

Case 3 basis: the *purpose for the grievance* (that is, the grievances can be grouped under four main reasons why the employees made formal complaints to the company)

Classification Guideline 2: Limit the Number of Groups

In Chapter 4, you learned that readers prefer groupings of under nine items—in fact, the fewer the better. This principle of organization, as well as the appropriateness of the basis, should guide your use of classification. Strive to select a basis that will result in a limited number of groupings.

In Case 1, another basis for classifying the 214 civil-engineering projects would be by the country the project was located in, rather than by type of work. Assume that after applying this project-site basis, you end up with 18 different classifications (that is, countries) for the 214 projects. Given this unwieldy number of groupings, you should either (1) avoid using this basis or (2) reduce the number of classifications by grouping countries together, perhaps by continent. In other words, the number of classifications affects the degree to which this pattern of organization succeeds with the reader.

Classification Guideline 3: Carefully Classify Each Item

The final step is to place each item in its appropriate classification. If you have chosen classifications carefully, this step is no problem. For example, assume that you work at M&K's Toronto office in the payroll department. You are asked to create a list of financial institutions where employees will be able to receive their cheques by direct deposit. Since the list is quite long, you decide to classify them by charter. The resulting groups are as follows:

1. Canadian customer banks
2. Credit unions
3. Foreign banks with branches in Canada

With three such classifications that do not overlap, you can assign each of the financial institutions to one of the three classifications.

Example of Classification

Now apply the three-part classification strategy to a detailed problem at M&K. You are on a committee to write an outline summary of safety practices for use in M&K's offices. Since more and more work done in Canada involves hazardous materials, you want to place special emphasis on techniques to protect workers from toxic chemicals, polluted air, asbestos fibres, and so forth. This outline will be used as an attachment to sales letters and proposals sent to potential clients, such as the federal government and various provincial governments. Good organization is crucial in enabling the reader to locate information quickly. At its first meeting, your committee comes up with this list of topics to be included in the outline:

1. Headgear provided by company
2. Complete physicals done yearly
3. Partial physicals done at six-month intervals
4. Blood monitoring throughout work at hazardous sites
5. State-of-the-art face masks and oxygen equipment
6. Twenty-hour safety program during employment orientation
7. Certified safety official on-site during hazardous projects
8. Pre-employment drug testing
9. Random drug testing of all workers in dangerous jobs
10. State-of-the-art hand and body protection equipment
11. Biweekly training sessions on safety-related topics
12. Pre-employment complete physical
13. Monthly in-house newsletter with safety column
14. Incentive awards for employees with safety suggestions
15. Company membership in national safety organizations

Next, the committee (1) selects an appropriate basis (the *time* at which these safety precautions should take place), (2) establishes three main groupings, (3) classifies each of the 15 items into one of the groups, and (4) assembles the following outline for use in M&K sales literature. (Numbers in parentheses below refer to the topics just listed.)

I. Procedures before employment
    A. Twenty-hour safety program during employee orientation (6)
    B. Pre-employment drug testing (8)
    C. Pre-employment complete physical (12)

II. Procedures during a project
    A. Headgear provided by company (1)
    B. Blood monitoring throughout work at hazardous sites (4)
    C. State-of-the-art face masks and oxygen equipment (5)
    D. Certified safety official on-site during hazardous projects (7)
    E. State-of-the-art hand and body protection equipment (10)

III. Procedures that take place periodically during employment at M&K
    A. Complete physicals done yearly (2)
    B. Partial physicals done at six-month intervals (3)
    C. Random drug testing of all workers in dangerous jobs (9)
    D. Biweekly training sessions on safety-related topics (11)
    E. Monthly in-house newsletter with safety column (13)
    F. Incentive awards for employees with safety suggestions (14)
    G. Company membership in national safety organizations (15)

Guidelines for Division

Division begins with an entire item that must be *broken down* or *partitioned* into its parts, whereas classification begins with a series of items that must be *grouped* into related categories. Division is especially useful when you need to explain a complicated piece of equipment to an audience that is unfamiliar with it. Follow three guidelines for applying this pattern:

Division Guideline 1: Choose the Right Basis for Dividing

Like classification, division means you must find a logical reason for establishing groups or parts. Assume, for example, that you are planning to teach an M&K training seminar in project management. In dividing this four-day training seminar into appropriate segments, it seems clear to you that each day should cover one of these crucial parts of managing projects: meeting budgets, scheduling staff, completing written reports, and seeking follow-up work from the client. In this case, the principle of division seems easy to use.

Yet other cases present you with choices. If, for example, you were planning a training seminar on report writing, you could divide it in the following three ways, among others: (1) by *purpose of the report* (for example, progress, trip, recommendation), (2) by *parts of the writing process* (for example, brainstorming, outlining, drafting, revising), or (3) by *report format* (for example, letter report, informal report, formal report). Here you would have to choose the basis most appropriate for your purpose and audience.

Division Guideline 2: Subdivide Parts When Necessary

As with classification, the division pattern of organization can suffer from the "laundry list" syndrome. Specifically, any particular level of groupings should have from three to seven partitions—the number that most readers find they can absorb. When you go over that number, consider reorganizing information or subdividing it.

Assume you want to partition a short manual on writing formal proposals. Your first effort to divide the topic results in nine segments: cover page, letter of transmittal, table of contents, executive summary, introduction, discussion, conclusions, recommendations, appendices. You would prefer fewer groupings, so you then establish three main divisions: front matter, discussion, and back matter, with breakdowns of each. In other words, your effort to partition was guided by every reader's preference for a limited number of groupings.

Division Guideline 3: Describe Each Part with Care

This last step may seem obvious. Make sure to give equal treatment to each part of the item or process you have partitioned. Readers expect this sort of parallelism, just as they prefer the limited number of parts mentioned in Guideline 2.

Example of Division

You are an M&K manager helping to prepare a client's report. The main task is to describe major types of offshore oil rigs. You decide to partition the subject on the basis of *environmental application,* which gives you five main types. In the following list, notice that each of the five is described in a parallel fashion: the rig's purpose, type of structure, and design with respect to wave strength.

Five Main Types of Offshore Oil Rigs

1. **Platform rig:** Generally for drilling at water depths of less than 300 m. Permanent structure supported by steel and concrete legs driven into ocean floor. Designed to withstand waves of about 15 m.
2. **Submersible rig:** Generally for drilling at water depths of less than 30 m. Temporary structure supported by large tanks that, when filled, go to the ocean floor and thus form the foundation for the columns extending to the deck structure above. Designed to withstand waves of about 9 m.
3. **Semisubmersible rig:** Generally for drilling in extreme water depths of 300 m or more. Temporary structure with large, water-filled pontoons that keep it suspended just below the water surface, with anchors or cables extending to the ocean bottom. Designed to withstand extreme wave heights of 27 m or more.
4. **Drillship:** Generally for drilling at water depths between 30 and 300 m. Drilling operations take place through opening in the middle of the ship. Designed to operate in relatively low wave heights of less than 9 m.
5. **Jack-up rig:** Generally for drilling at water depths between 7.5 and 150 m. Temporary structure with platformlike legs that can be jacked up and down to rest on the ocean surface, much like the jacking system used to elevate a car when changing a tire. Designed to withstand hurricane-force winds that produce waves of over 15 m.

COMPARISON/CONTRAST

Many writing projects obligate you to show similarities or differences between ideas or objects. (For our purposes, the word **comparison** emphasizes similarities, whereas the word **contrast** emphasizes differences.) In the real world of career writing, this technique applies especially to situations where readers are making buying decisions. To help you write effective comparisons, this section presents several cases, puts forth some simple guidelines, and introduces an annotated example that you will find at the end of the chapter.

Short Cases from M&K: Comparison/Contrast

One of the most common patterns, comparison/contrast is used in many in-house and external reports. Examples of each are noted here.

Comparison/Contrast Case 1: Jamaica Hotels

As an architect for M&K, you have had the good fortune to travel to Jamaica three times on business in the past year. Each time, you stayed at a different hotel in Montego Bay. Now your boss, Byron Scarsdale, is going there for an extended business trip. Before making his travel arrangements, he asks you for a memorandum that compares and contrasts the main features of the three hotels. Presumably, he will use the information to decide where he will stay.

Comparison/Contrast Case 2: Security Systems

One of your jobs as M&K's corporate purchasing agent is to advise managers. Angela Koffman, the Montreal branch manager, has asked you to send her a summary of similarities and differences among five high-quality infrared detectors. She wants to install several in a new computer lab, to detect movement of any after-hours intruders and then send a signal to local police.

Comparison/Contrast Case 3: Poisons

Your job in M&K's toxicology laboratory brings you into contact with dozens of poisons. One client has asked you to compare and contrast the relative dangers of five poisonous chemicals found in the well water at the site where the client firm wants to build a warehouse. Your report will be used in making the decision whether to build.

Guidelines for Comparison/Contrast

The three cases just cited show you real contexts in which you will use the comparison/contrast pattern of organization. Now here are guidelines for writing effective comparisons and contrasts.

Comparison/Contrast Guideline 1: Remember Your Purpose

When using comparison/contrast in on-the-job writing, your purpose usually falls into one of the following two categories:

1. **Objective:** Essentially an unbiased presentation of features wherein you have no real complaint
2. **Persuasive:** An approach wherein you compare features in such a way as to recommend a preference

You must constantly remember your main purpose. You will either provide raw data that someone else will use to make decisions or you will urge someone toward your preference. In either case, the comparison must show fairness in dealing with all alternatives. Only in this way can you establish credibility in the eyes of the reader.

Comparison/Contrast Guideline 2: Establish Clear Criteria and Use Them Consistently

In any technical comparison, you must set clear standards of comparison and then apply them uniformly. Otherwise, your reader will not understand the evaluation or accept your recommendation (if there is one).

For example, assume you are an M&K field supervisor who must recommend the purchase of a bulldozer for construction sites. You have been asked to recommend just one of these models: Cannon-D, Foley-G, or Koso-L. After background reading and field tests, you decide on three main criteria for your comparison: (1) pushing capacity, (2) purchase details, and (3) dependability. These three factors, in your view, are most relevant to M&K's needs. Having made this decision about criteria, you then must discuss all three criteria with regard to each of the three bulldozers. Only in this way can readers get the data needed for an informed decision.

Comparison/Contrast Guideline 3: Choose the "Whole-by-Whole" Approach for Short Comparisons/Contrasts

This strategy requires that you discuss one item in full, then another item in full, and so on. Using the bulldozer example, you might first discuss all features of the Cannon, then all features of the Foley, and finally all features of the Koso. This strategy works best if individual descriptions are quite short so readers can remember points made about the Cannon bulldozer as they proceed to read sections on the Foley and then the Koso machines.

Keep the following two points in mind if you select the whole-by-whole approach:

- Discuss subpoints in the same order—that is, if you start the Cannon description with information about dependability, begin the Foley and Koso discussions in the same way.
- If you are making a recommendation, move from least important to most important, or vice versa, depending on which approach will be most effective with your reader. Busy readers usually prefer that you start with the recommended item, followed by the others in descending order of importance.

Comparison/Contrast Guideline 4: Choose the "Part-by-Part" Approach for Long Comparisons/Contrasts

Longer comparisons/contrasts require readers to remember much information. Thus, readers usually prefer that you organize the comparison around major criteria, not around the whole items. Using the bulldozer example, your text would follow this outline:

  I. Pushing Capacity
    A. Cannon
    B. Foley
    C. Koso

    II. Purchase Details
      A. Cannon
      B. Foley
      C. Koso

    III. Dependability
      A. Cannon
      B. Foley
      C. Koso

Note that the bulldozers are discussed in the same order within each major section. As with the whole-by-whole approach, the order of the items can go either from most important to least important or vice versa—depending on which strategy you believe would be most effective with your audience.

Comparison/Contrast Guideline 5: Use Illustrations

Comparisons/contrasts of all kinds benefit from accompanying graphics. In particular, tables are an effective way to present comparative data. For example, your report on the bulldozers might present some pushing-capacity data you found in company brochures.

Example of Comparison/Contrast

Using the bulldozer example, Model 6-4 on pages 166–67 presents a sample of the part-by-part pattern. Remember that such a comparison would be only part of a final report—in this case, one that recommends the Cannon-D. The complete report would include an introductory summary at the beginning and a list of conclusions and recommendations at the end (see Chapter 10). This example could be written in either a whole-by-whole or part-by-part manner. The latter is used here to emphasize the importance of the three criteria for comparison.

Employability Skills

The Conference Board of Canada's *Employability Skills 2000+* points out that you will need to be able to think, decide, and act in a working environment. Relevant problem-solving skills include the following:

- Assess situations and identify problems.
- Seek different points of view and evaluate them based on facts.
- Recognize the human, interpersonal, technical, scientific, and mathematical dimensions of a problem.
- Identify the root cause of a problem.
- Be creative and innovative in exploring possible solutions.

- Evaluate solutions to make recommendations or decisions.*

List three of the career possibilities that are open to you. Attempt to determine what characteristics will enable someone to be successful in each of those careers. Match these characteristics in each to your strengths and weaknesses and make a determination of which career you are best suited for even if that may not be the career you aspire to.

* *Employability Skills 2000+* Brochure 2000 E/F (Ottawa: The Conference Board of Canada, 2000).

CHAPTER SUMMARY

This chapter examined five common patterns of organization used in reports, proposals, and correspondence. By studying these patterns, you will be better prepared to write the documents covered later in this book.

Argument is used when the writer needs to support points with evidence. (Persuasion, the strongest form of argument, occurs when the writer seeks to change the reader's opinions or actions.) To write effective arguments, follow these guidelines:

1. Use evidence correctly.
2. Choose the most convincing order for points.
3. Be logical.
4. Use only appropriate authorities.
5. Avoid argumentative fallacies.

Definitions occur in technical writing in one of three forms: informal (in parentheses), formal (in sentence form with term, class, and features), and expanded (in a paragraph or more). The following main guidelines apply:

1. Keep it simple.
2. Use informal definitions for simple terms most readers understand.
3. Use formal definitions for more complex terms.
4. Use expanded definitions for supporting information.
5. Choose the right location for your definition.

Description, like definition, depends on detail and accuracy for its effect. Careful descriptions usually include a lengthy itemizing of the parts of a mechanism or the functions of a term. Follow these basic guidelines for producing effective descriptions:

1. Remember your readers' needs.
2. Be accurate and objective.
3. Choose an overall organization plan.
4. Use "helpers" like graphics and analogies.
5. Give your description the "visualizing test."

Classification/division patterns help you organize groups of related items (classification) and break down an item into its parts (division). The guidelines for classification are as follows:

1. Find a common basis (for grouping diverse items).
2. Limit the number of groups.
3. Carefully classify each item.

Similarly, the guidelines for division are as follows:

1. Choose the right basis for dividing.
2. Subdivide parts when necessary.
3. Describe each part with care.

Comparison/contrast provides you with an organized way to highlight similarities and differences in related items, whether you are simply presenting data or are attempting to argue a point. These main writing rules apply:

1. Remember your purpose.
2. Establish clear criteria and use them consistently.
3. Choose the "whole-by-whole" approach for short comparisons/contrasts.
4. Choose the "part-by-part" approach for long comparisons/contrasts.
5. Use illustrations.

ASSIGNMENTS

Part 1: Short Assignments

The following short assignments can be completed either orally or in writing. Unless a group project is specifically indicated, an assignment can be either a group or an individual effort. Your instructor will give you specific directions.

1. **All patterns of organization: recognition exercise.** For this group assignment, your instructor will provide each group with a different packet of "junk mail" (catalogues, sales letters, promotions, etc.) and perhaps other documents such as memos or product information sheets. Your group will search for and evaluate examples of various patterns of organization in the documents. Then it will report its findings to the whole class.

2. **Argument.** Analyze the argumentative effectiveness, or lack thereof, in the following passage:

After a good deal of thought, I have decided not to accept the committee's recommendation to allow employees up to two weeks of unpaid vacation leave (in addition to whatever paid vacation leave the employee receives). My reasons are as follows:
   a. The proposal obviously would cause the company to lose many customers, for we definitely would not have the staff to cover our daily operations in the office and in the field.
   b. Just as the policy of flex-time hours has caused some companies to fail to respond adequately to phone calls early in the morning, the leave plan would keep the office uncovered during days when an excessive number of employees were taking leave.
   c. The salary of employees using unpaid vacation leave would decrease, and they would be less able to pay their bills. In effect, then, the leave time policy would hurt their families.
   d. Unpaid vacation leave has been supported by some members of the provincial legislature, and we all know how little that organization knows about how to operate business. In fact, I heard the other day that our local MLA, who supports the idea of unpaid vacation leave, bounced 17 cheques during the last several years. That will tell you something about his knowledge of business activities.
   e. One of our competitors, Jonquil Engineering, adopted an unpaid vacation leave policy two years ago, and I have just learned that the firm's stock dropped 10% recently.
   f. Unpaid leave has been supported by the Canadians for Family, an organization whose president is Arlin Thomas. And we all know about his antics in the media. In the last few years, he has supported any cause that has come his way.

---

3. **Argument: M&K project.** For this assignment, use points from Project #5 (in the project sheets in Chapter 2) to complete one of the options below. Each option will also require that you create additional information that could relate to M&K's technical writing seminar in Canada.

Option A: *Creating an Effective Argument.* Assume you were one of the individuals attending the seminar. Create an argument you would present to your boss to justify offering another seminar for some members of your department.

Option B: *Creating Argumentative Fallacies.* Assume you attended the seminar and are presenting an evaluation of it to your supervisor. Create an example of each of the argumentative fallacies included in this chapter. Your seven answers can be in support of the seminar, against it, or both.

4. **Definition.** Using the guidelines in this chapter, discuss the relative effectiveness of the following short definitions. Speculate on the likely audience the definitions are addressing.[2]

---

a. *Watershed*—the geographic area from which surface water drains into a particular lake or point along a stream.

b. *Acid mine drainage*—runoff having high concentrations of metals and sulphate and high levels of acidity resulting from the oxidation of sulphide minerals that have been exposed to air and water by mining activities.

c. *Steady-state model*—a model in which the variables under investigation are assumed to reach equilibrium and are independent of time.

d. *Acidic lake or stream*—a lake or stream in which the acid-neutralizing capacity is less than or equal to zero.

e. *Biomass*—the total quantity of organic matter in units of weight or mass.

f. *Detritus*—dead and decaying organic matter originating from plants and animals.

g. *Hydrology*—the science that deals with the waters of the earth—their occurrence, circulation, and distribution; their chemical and physical properties; and their relationship to living things.

h. *Plankton*—plant or animal species that spend part or all of their lives carried passively by water currents.

i. *Mineral weathering*—dissolution of rocks and minerals by chemical and physical processes.

---

5. **Definition: M&K project.** This assignment can be completed as an individual or a group project. Select one of the projects in Chapter 2. Using the outline of information on the project as a starting point, do the following:

- Conduct some research on the technical field reflected in the project.
- Select some terms related to the field.
- Write either short formal definitions or expanded definitions of the terms.

    In assigning this project, your instructor will indicate (a) how many terms you should select and (b) whether you should write formal or expanded definitions.

6. **Description.** Write a description of a piece of equipment or furniture located in your classroom or brought to class by your instructor—for example, a classroom chair, an overhead projector, a screen, a three-hole punch, a mechanical pencil, or a computer floppy disk. Write the description for a reader totally unfamiliar with the item.

7. **Description: M&K project.** For this project put yourself in the position of someone who worked on the Ottawa library project (Project #2 in Chapter 2). Write a description of a piece of equipment that either (a) could have been used in the construction of the library or (b) could be housed in any modern library, such as the new one in Ottawa. This assignment will require a visit to a library or a construction company. Some libraries will have special resources in the fields of construction and/or medical care.

---

[2] Excerpted from R.S. Turner, R.B. Cook, H. Van Miegroet, D.W. Johnson, J.W. Elwood, O.P. Bricker, S.E. Lindberg, and G.M. Hornberger, "Watershed and Lake Processes Affecting Surface Water Acid–Base Chemistry," NAPAP Report 10 (September 1990), in *Acidic Deposition: State of Science and Technology*, National Acid Precipitation Assessment Program, 722 Jackson Place, NW, Washington, DC.

8. **Classification/division.** Divide into groups of eight or ten as selected by your instructor. Then, as a group, take an inventory of the career plans of each member of your group. Finally, using career plans as your basis, classify the group participants into a limited number of groupings. Be sure to adjust the size and focus of categories so that you have at least two students in each grouping. Present the group results to the entire class.

9. **Classification/division: M&K projects.** For this assignment you will use the "main technical tasks" listed with the five projects in the project sheets in Chapter 2. Perform a classification exercise by finding a common basis, selecting an appropriate number of groups, and placing each of the technical tasks into one of the groups.

10. **Comparison/contrast.** Divide into groups of three to five students, as determined by your instructor. Select two members who will give the other group members information about their (a) academic careers, (b) extracurricular activities, and (c) work experience. Using the information gathered during this exercise, develop an outline of either a whole-by-whole or part-by-part comparison/contrast.

11. **Comparison/contrast: M&K projects.** Select two or three of the projects from the project sheets in Chapter 2. Perform a part-by-part comparison/contrast of the two or three projects. Use some or all of the information on the projects. If necessary, create some of your own information to supply adequate detail for your response.

Part 2: Longer Assignments

These assignments test your ability to use the patterns of organization covered in this chapter. To lend realism, they are placed in the context of short reports within M&K. Follow the guidelines for each assignment:

- Write each exercise in the form of a *memo report* (if it is directed within M&K Inc.) or a *letter report* (if it is directed to an outside reader).
- Follow organization and design guidelines given in Chapters 3 and 4, especially with regard to the ABC format (**A**bstract/**B**ody/**C**onclusion) and the use of headings. Chapter 10 gives thorough format guidelines for informal reports, but such detail is not necessary to complete the assignments here.
- For each assignment, fill out a copy of the Planning Form that appears in Chapter 1. Invent any audience analysis information not included in the following so that you have a "real" person to whom you are writing.

12. **Argument for new wastewater specialist.** You are a wastewater specialist and manager of a four-person crew with M&K's Toronto office. Recently you have become concerned about the amount of overtime worked by you and your group. Here are your main concerns, from most to least important. First, you are worried that excessive overtime might lead to errors by exhausted workers. The four employees on your crew often work at dangerous sites with poisonous chemicals and polluted water. Mistakes could lead to worker exposure to chemicals or errors in recording data or collecting samples. Second, three of your four fieldworkers have complained about their 50- to 55-hour workweeks and the excessive time spent out of town on projects. Although they like the overtime pay, they would prefer to average just an extra five hours a week. You are concerned that they may quit to work at a competing firm. Third, you are convinced that there is enough work to support a fifth field employee, and still have three or four hours of overtime per employee per week. (Of course, you realize that there is always the risk that a future work slowdown would mean laying off an additional worker.)

Given these concerns, you want to write a short report to the branch manager, José Miranda, describing the problems. You also want to suggest that M&K hire another fieldworker, or at least give the matter some study. Present this information to Miranda, using the argumentative strategies described in this chapter.

13. **Technical definitions in your field.** Select a technical area in which you have taken course work or in which you have technical experience. Now assume that you are employed as an outside consulting expert, acting as a resource in your particular area for an M&K manager not familiar with your specialty. For example, a food science expert might provide information related to the dietary needs of oil workers working on an off-shore rig for three months; a business or management expert might report on a new management technique; an electronics expert might explain the operation of some new piece of equipment that M&K is considering buying; a computer programmer might explain some new piece of hardware that could provide supporting services to M&K; and a legal expert might define *sexism in the workplace* for the benefit of M&K's human resources professionals.

    For the purpose of this report, develop a context in which you would have to define terms for an uninformed reader. Incorporate *one expanded definition* and *at least one sentence definition* into your report.

14. **Description of equipment in your field.** Select a common piece of laboratory, office, or field equipment that you are familiar with. Now assume that you must write a short report to your M&K supervisor, who wants this report to contain a thorough physical description of the equipment. Later he or she plans to incorporate your description into a training manual for those who need to know how to use, and perform minor repairs on, the equipment. For the body of your description, choose either a part-by-part physical description or a thorough description of functions.

15. **Description of position in your field.** Interview a friend or colleague about the specific job that person holds. Make certain it is a job that you yourself have not had. On the basis of data collected in the interview, write a thorough description of the person's position—including major responsibilities, reporting relationships, educational preparation, experience required, and so on.

    Now place this description in the context of a letter report to the manager of human resources at M&K. Assume she has hired you, a technical consultant to M&K, to submit a letter report that contains the description. She is preparing to advertise such an opening at M&K but needs your report to write the job description and the advertisement. Because she has little first-hand knowledge of the position about which you are writing, you should avoid technical jargon.

16. **Classification/division in technical courses.** For this assignment, you will need a catalogue from your college or university or that of another school. First, select a number of courses that have not yet been classified except perhaps by academic department. Using course descriptions in the catalogue or any other information you can find, *classify* the courses using an appropriate basis (for example, the course level, topic, purpose in the department, or prerequisites). Also *partition* one of the courses, using information gathered from a course syllabus or an interview with someone familiar with the course.

    The context for this exercise is a memo report written by you, a technical training specialist at M&K's Toronto office. Assume that the courses are taught at George Brown, a nearby college. A group of M&K's Toronto employees have expressed interest in further education in the area you have investigated. Your classification of the courses and your in-depth partition of one particular course will help these employees decide whether to consider enrolling.

17. **Comparison/contrast for the purchasing agent.** For this memo report, select a category in the list following or another category approved by your instructor. Then choose three specific types or brand-name products that fit within the category and for which you can find data. Write either a whole-by-whole or a part-by-part comparison/contrast. Place this comparison/contrast pattern within the context of a short report from you, as an M&K employee, to the company purchasing agent. You may or may not include a preference for one item or the other. However, understand that the purpose of your report is to give the reader the information needed to order one of the items in your comparison/contrast.

Categories

1. Briefcases
2. Calculators
3. Compact discs
4. Credit cards
5. Electric pencil sharpeners
6. Electric sanders or saws
7. Lawn mowers
8. Mortgages
9. Personal computers
10. Photocopiers
11. Pickup trucks
12. Professional journals in a technical field
13. Refrigerators
14. Software programs
15. Retirement plans
16. Surveying methods
17. Telephone systems or companies
18. Types of savings accounts
19. Vacuum cleaners
20. DVD players

MEMORANDUM

DATE: February 25, 2006
TO: Kerry F. Camp, Vice President of Domestic Operations
FROM: Your Name, Calgary Branch Manager
SUBJECT: Problems with Office Chairs

    I enjoyed talking to you yesterday and look forward to seeing you at the Environmental Science Convention. In the meantime, I am writing to ask your help with the chair problem I mentioned in our conversation. This memo will give you some background on our difficulties with the chairs. Also, I have presented a solution for you to consider.

SPECIFIC PROBLEMS WITH OFFICE CHAIRS
    About six months ago, we received new office furniture ordered by the corporate office. In many ways, it has been a considerable improvement over the 20-year-old furniture it replaced. The desks, cabinets, and credenzas have been especially well received. Besides being quite practical, they give a much more professional appearance to our office.
    As I mentioned in our conversation, the chairs (Model 223) that accompany the new desks have not worked out as well as the other furniture. Here are the two main problems.

Increased Employee Illness
    Starting about a month after the chairs arrived, I received complaints from 10 employees about back pains they claimed were related to the new chairs. Taking a wait-and-see approach, I asked managers to have chairs adjusted and to give the furniture more break-in time. In the second month, however, I heard from a dozen additional employees about the chairs and noticed a 25 percent increase in sick days. Upon further inquiry, I learned that most managers attributed the increased sick time to back problems related to the office chairs.

Decreased Productivity
    The increased sick leave presented a serious enough concern. Adding to the problem, however, was roughly a 10 percent decrease in productivity last month among employees who were not sick. I measured this decrease by three criteria:

- Number of pages produced by the word-processing staff
- Number of billable hours logged by the professional staff
- Number of client calls made by the marketing staff

In my seven years managing this office, I have never witnessed so large a drop with no clear cause.

Approaches problem tactfully.

Mentions points of agreement— before moving toward argumentative issues.

Presents evidence clearly— including statistic.

Cites reliable authority.

States supporting statistic.

Gives basis for statistical information.

continues

Model 6-1 Memo report—example using argument

Memo to: Kerry F. Camp   Page 2
February 25, 2006

CONFIRMATION OF PROBLEM

Cites authority
and gives her
credentials.

Mentions this
expert's opinion
last, because it
is the strongest
evidence in this
short report.

Gives *specific*
points to support
expert's views.

Sets up clear
contrast
between two
chair types,
to support chair
exchange.

Describes alter-
native clearly—
giving necessary
details about
cost, etc.

Ends with re-
quest for action.

Closes with tone
that encourages
agreement on
mutual problem.

Concerned about the health problems and lower productivity, I sought a recognized consultant in the area of workplace health and office design. Dr. Stacy Y. Stephens, professor of
ergonomics at East Calgary College, was referred to me when I called the local office of the
Occupational Safety and Health Administration.

Dr. Stephens visited our office on January 17. She spent two days (1) interviewing and
observing users of the new chairs, (2) examining the chairs in detail, and (3) meeting with
me to offer her conclusions. At her suggestion, I called the supplier, Jones Office Furniture,
to ask about the availability of other Jones chairs with different features. According to
Dr. Stephens, the Jones Model 623 is much better suited to normal office use. Specifically,
the Model 623 has these advantages:

- Excellent lower-lumbar support, compared with the inadequate support in the
  straight-backed Model 223
- Twelve inches of vertical adjustment, as opposed to the six inches available in
  Model 223
- Ball casters for easier rolling, as opposed to the Model 223 casters that move with
  difficulty on our office carpeting
- Adjustable back spring that provides limited movement backward, as opposed to
  the rigid Model 223

Considering Dr. Stephens's suggestions, I decided to seek more information from Jones
Office Furniture Company.

PROPOSED SOLUTION

Last week, I met twice with Mr. Dan McCartney, the Calgary sales representative for
Jones Office Furniture. In response to our problem, he has offered this proposal. Jones will
trade our 45 Model 223 chairs for 45 new Model 623s, for only an extra $2,000 from us.
Under this arrangement, he would be (1) crediting us for the full purchase of our four-month-
old Model 223s and (2) discounting the new chairs about $3,000. I believe Jones is making
this offer because it truly wants to retain our goodwill—and our future business.

CONCLUSION

As noted, this problem affects our employees' well-being and our office productivity.
Would you please present my proposed solution to Bridget Garner, vice president of business
and marketing, so that she can approve the $2,000 funding? We could have the new chairs
within a week after approval.

Thanks for your help, Kerry. With relatively small investment, we should be able to
solve our medical and productivity problems.

Model 6-1 *continued*

TECHNICAL DESCRIPTION: BLUEPRINT MACHINE

A blueprint machine is a piece of office equipment used to make photographic reproductions of architectural plans, technical drawings, and other types of figures. The blueprint shows as white lines on blue paper. This description covers the physical parts of the machine and a brief operation procedure.

PHYSICAL DESCRIPTION

The blueprint machine is contained in a metal cabinet measuring 100 cm wide, 25 cm tall, and 50 cm deep. Typically, the machine is placed on a cabinet containing blueprint supplies. The most obvious features of the machine are the controls and the paper path.

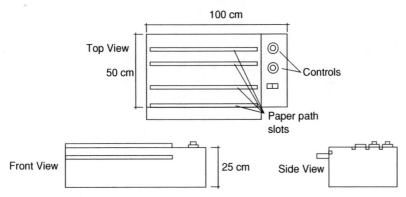

Blueprint Machine

Controls: The controls for the machine are located on the top right-hand side of the case, as shown in the illustration below.

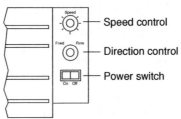

There are two knobs and one power switch. The topmost knob controls the speed of the paper feed. The lower knob changes the direction of the paper. The power switch turns the machine on and off.

Starts with a sentence definition and brief overview of two sections that follow.

Begins section with dimensions of machine, before noting two main parts.

Uses three perspectives in illustration, for clarity.

Describes three controls in same order that they are viewed—top to bottom.

continues

Model 6-2 Detailed description: blueprint machine

Integrates procedure with illustration.

Paper Path: The top of the machine has four horizontal slots. These slots are the openings to the paper path, as shown in the illustration below.

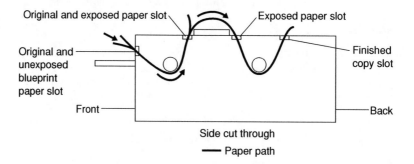

The first slot, beginning at the front of the machine, is the feed slot for the original and the unexposed blueprint paper. The second slot is the discharge for the original and the exposed print paper. The third slot is the feed for developing the exposed blueprint paper. The fourth slot is the discharge for the finished blueprint copy.

OPERATION OF THE BLUEPRINT MACHINE
Operating the blueprint machine involves setting the controls and making copies.

Setting the Controls:
1. Turn on the machine.
2. Set the paper path to forward.
3. Set the speed for the type of paper used.

Includes brief instructions that help expand upon description of mechanism.

Making Copies:
1. Place the original, face side up, on top of the blueprint paper, yellow side up.
2. Feed the two pieces of paper into the original feed slot.
3. Separate the original from the copy as they emerge from the discharge slot.
4. Feed the exposed blueprint paper into the developer slot.
5. Collect the copy as it emerges from the discharge slot.
6. Turn power off when desired copies have been made.

CONCLUSION
Blueprint machines are found in all M&K offices and are used frequently. If a wide variety of employees understands how these machines function, our office will continue to run smoothly.

Model 6-2 *continued*

TECHNICAL DESCRIPTION: BUNSEN BURNER

M&K uses Bunsen burners in all its laboratories. Following some background information, this technical description provides details about three main parts of a typical burner:

- Base
- Gas valve
- Pipe

The conclusion lists some standards for the burner's performance.

Background

The Bunsen burner is a basic piece of laboratory equipment used to produce a continuous flame at relatively low temperatures. Originally designed by Robert W. Bunsen in the late 1800s, the "Bunsen burner" has become a generic term for basic lab burners made by many firms.

Most burners look and perform alike, though burners from different companies do include slightly different features. What follows is a description of the Model 03–962 Bunsen-style burner manufactured by the Fisher Scientific Company. It runs on natural gas.

Base

The heavy die-cast base of the Fisher burner is very stable. It is made from nonferrous metal and has a nickel finish. Here are its main features and dimensions:

- Hexagonal-shaped foundation that is 7 cm in diameter and 5 cm high

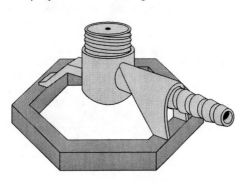

Notes burner's main parts and sections that follow.

Gives formal sentence definition and general information for nontechnical readers.

Uses bullets for technical detail.

continues

Model 6-3   Technical description: Bunsen burner

- A 1.9 cm diameter threaded cylinder at the top of the base
- A 1.25 cm diameter hexagonal brass nut at the top of the cylinder, with a small hole in the centre from which gas is emitted into the pipe

A valve is threaded vertically up into the bottom centre of the base of the burner. It allows the user to adjust the volume of gas that flows from the gas inlet up through the base cylinder.

Gas Valve

Jutting out from the side of the cylinder, parallel to the surface on which the base of the burner rests, is a tapered gas inlet 6.35 cm long. The inlet has serrated edges that hold the gas tube securely to the burner.

The valve looks like a car axle with only one wheel attached. The 5.1 cm stem, or "axle," rests on a round 1.9 cm diameter base, or "wheel." Actually, this base is about the diameter and thickness of a 5-cent piece. It has serrated edges so that it can be twisted with ease. The 0.32 cm diameter stem is threaded and screws vertically into the base of the burner. When twisted clockwise, it closes and decreases gas flow. When twisted counterclockwise, it opens and increases gas flow.

Pipe

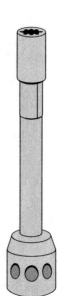

An 11.5 cm long pipe extends straight up from the top of the base of the burner. Except for its flared ends, the pipe is 1.25 cm in diameter. The combining of gas and air at the bottom of the pipe produces a flame that emerges at the top.

The pipe threads onto the cylinder at the top of the burner base. The bottom of the pipe flares out to form an end piece with eight 0.48 cm holes drilled around its circumference. The holes let in air that mixes with gas entering from the base. When the pipe is turned clockwise, the amount of air entering the holes is reduced and the temperature of the flame is lowered. When the pipe is turned counterclockwise, the amount of air entering the holes is increased and the temperature of the flame is raised.

The flared top end of the pipe looks much like a socket piece for a socket wrench. Called a "flame retainer" by the manufacturer, it helps keep the flame from going out. Viewed vertically from above the burner, the top of the retainer is shaped like a wagon wheel with short spokes. The "spokes" are actually eight ports that open to the pipe hole but close off before they reach the circumference of the pipe. Spaced evenly on the circumference, these ports help control the flame.

Uses analogies such as wheel, axle, and nickel coin.

Describes movement to help reader understand purpose of part.

Includes common visual terms like *flared*.

Reveals purpose of parts through description.

Employs two more analogies to help less technical readers.

continues

Model 6-3   *continued*

Performance Specifications

The Fisher version of the Bunsen burner offers the following performance standards:

- Produces flame that is adjustable from 1.9 to 30.1 cm
- Has heat output of over 1465 W (5000 BTU/hr.)
- Consumes 80 cu. M/hr. of natural gas
- Meets CSA, U.S., NIST, USTM, and ASTM standards

Uses bullets for technical detail.

Model 6-3 *continued*

Leads off by noting three dozers and main criteria.

Starts each section with Cannon (the preferred machine).

Follows descending order of importance (Cannon, then Foley, then Koso).

Lists three subpoints to be discussed in section.

Again, follows C-F-K order.

Uses separate paragraph for each main subpoint.

Mentions sources of information—to increase credibility.

PART-BY-PART PATTERN COMPARISON OF BULLDOZERS

This is a comparison of the Cannon-D, Foley-G, and Koso-L bulldozers. The major criteria considered are pushing capacity, purchase details, and dependability.

Pushing Capacity

Both the Cannon-D and Foley-G have an excellent pushing capacity that is more than adequate for our U.S. construction projects. The Cannon has a pushing capacity of 1,300 tons per hour (TPH) over 500 ft. (1179.3 tonnes per hour over 0.15 km), whereas the Foley has a pushing capacity of 1,100 TPH over 500 ft. (997.9 tonnes per hour over 0.15 km). Both figures are mentioned in brochures from their respective companies. Furthermore, they are confirmed by recent tests reported in the trade journal *Bulldozer Unlimited.*

The Koso-L, however, lags behind its two competitors, being able to push only 1,000 TPH over 500 ft. (907.2 tonnes over 0.15 km). Furthermore, this figure was found only in the company's sales brochures, with no verification available in the trade journals I researched.

Purchase Details

The main elements of the purchase—price, warranty, and cost of extended warranty—vary considerably among the three machines. The basic purchase prices are as follows:

1. $250,000 for the Cannon-D
2. $300,000 for the Foley-G
3. $310,000 for the Koso-L

Concerning warranties, Cannon provides a complete parts-and-service warranty for 90 days, with an additional parts warranty on the drivetrain for another 12 months. Foley offers the same initial parts-and-service warranty, but it has a longer parts warranty on the drivetrain—18 months. Koso has a complete parts-and-service warranty for six months, with no additional parts warranty on the drivetrain.

Beyond these warranties that come with the machines, all three companies offer the same option of an additional two-year warranty that covers parts in the drivetrain. This additional warranty must be acquired at time of purchase and costs $4,000 for the Cannon, $4,000 for the Foley, and $7,000 for the Koso.

Dependability

Bulldozer downtime can cost the firm a good deal of money, either in project delays or in the added expense of renting another bulldozer, so dependability is an important criterion in comparing the three models. Although the trade journals I consulted contained no model-by-model comparison of dependability of the three bulldozers, I did find occasional references to features that affect reliability. In

continues

Model 6-4 Part-by-part comparison/contrast: three bulldozers

addition, I sought out anecdotal evidence from nearby construction firms that have used the machines. Here is what I discovered.

Cannon-D. This machine is an established commercial bulldozer with a good reputation for reliability in the field. The "D" model is the latest version of a machine that began with the "A" model in 1954, so the company has had years to refine its technology. Interestingly, several years ago Cannon decided not to add sealed tracks to its list of features, even though this sealed approach is one of the newest track innovations in the industry. Even so, the Cannon-D generally will operate for 10,000 hours without major maintenance in the tracks. It remains to be seen if the decision about sealed tracks was the correct one.

> Uses subheadings because of large amount of information to relate.

Foley-G. While the Foley also has a good reputation for reliability in the field, the firm began making bulldozers only in 1970—16 years after Cannon started. Foley has the general reputation of being quicker than Cannon to introduce new technology into its bulldozer line. For example, two years ago it started using sealed tracks that lubricate themselves automatically. The track assembly should not need major maintenance for 15,000 hours, a 5000-hour improvement over Cannon. Of course, the newness of this advance suggests that there hasn't yet been enough time to judge the long-term effectiveness of sealed tracks.

> Introduces Foley's main feature (technical innovation).
>
> But reinforces Cannon preference by noting that sealed tracks are not fully tested.

Koso-L. This machine is definitely the "new guy on the block." Unlike the American-made Cannon and Foley, the Koso is produced in Korea by a company that got into business rather recently—1986. The Koso-L uses fairly traditional technology, not having incorporated sealed tracks into its design, for example. Despite the recent entry into the market, Koso has already built a strong reputation for reliability on projects in other countries. However, there are not yet enough data about performance on construction projects in the United States.

> Keeps option open for buying Koso *later*—but makes it clear that more data are needed.

Model 6-4 *continued*

CHAPTER 7

Process Descriptions and Instructions

Like other M&K offices, M&K's office in Vancouver is using an electronic calendar for its personnel. The calendar allows people to organize their own time, determine the availability of others, and schedule meetings using the software to determine if there are scheduling conflicts. The idea seems to have pleased everyone. People do feel that they can use their time more effectively. As office services manager, you met the M&K technician responsible for installing the software. Your boss, Leonard Szymanski, expected a memo from you summarizing the installation process (see Model 7-1 on page 184).

You also wrote a memo to all employees, giving them instructions about how to view their calendar (see Model 7-2, on page 185).

This brief M&K case study demonstrates two types of technical writing you will often face: process descriptions and instructions. Both are important patterns, but instructions will play the greater part in your career. As noted in one essay, "The field of technical writing has expanded greatly in the last ten years, and the new work is in writing *instructions* . . . Many graduates of technical programs now find themselves writing *instructions* more often than they write descriptions and reports"[1] [italics added]. For this reason, instructions receive the most emphasis in this chapter.

Instructions and process descriptions share an important common bond: both must accurately describe a series of steps leading to a specific result. Yet they differ in purpose, audience, and format. This chapter will (1) explore these similarities and differences, with specific reference to M&K applications, (2) give specific guidelines for developing both types, and (3) provide models to use in your own writing.

PROCESS DESCRIPTIONS VERSUS INSTRUCTIONS

In the example just given, the memo to your boss (Model 7-1) explained the process by which the technician installed the calendar software. The other memo (Model 7-2) gave directions to employees on how to view their calendar. In other words, you write a process description to help readers *understand* what has been, is being, or will be done, whereas you write instructions to show readers how to *perform* the process themselves.

Process descriptions are appropriate when the reader needs to be informed about the action but does not need to perform it. If you suspect a reader may in fact be a *user*—i.e., someone who uses your document to perform the process—always write instructions. Figure 7-1 provides a list of the contrasting features of process descriptions and instructions. The two subsections that follow give examples of these features in an M&K context.

---

[1] Reprinted by permission of the Modern Language Association of America from Janice C. Redish and David A. Schell, "Writing and Testing Usability Instructions," in *Technical Writing: Theory and Practice,* ed. Bertie E. Fearing and W. Keats Sparrow (New York: Modern Language Association of America, 1989), p. 63.

Process Descriptions at M&K

Process descriptions provide information for interested readers who do not need instructional details. At times, describing a process may be the sole purpose of your document, as in Model 7-1. More often, however, you use process description only as a pattern of organization within a document with a larger purpose. The following examples (1) show the supporting purpose of process descriptions and (2) reinforce the difference between process descriptions and instructions:

- **Accounting:** As an accountant at M&K's head office, you have just finished auditing the firm's books. Now you must write a report to M&K's vice president of operations on the state of the firm's finances. Along with your findings, the vice president wants an overview of the procedure you followed to arrive at your conclusions.
- **Maintenance:** As a maintenance supervisor at M&K's Calgary branch, you travelled to a construction site to repair a machine that tests the strength of concrete. The procedure requires billing the client for additional charges. Along with your bill, you send an attachment that summarizes the procedure you followed.
- **Laboratory work:** As lab supervisor at M&K's Montreal office, you spent all day Saturday in the lab assembling a new gas chromatograph needed to analyze gases. To justify the overtime hours, you write a memo to your manager describing the assembly process.
- **Marketing:** As M&K's marketing manager, you have devised a new procedure for tracking contacts with prospective clients (from first sales call to getting the job). You must write a memo to M&K's vice presidents for operations, briefly describing the process. Their approval is needed before the new marketing technique can be introduced at all company offices.

Process Descriptions

Purpose:	Explain a sequence of steps in such a way that the reader *understands* a process.
Format:	Use paragraph descriptions, listed steps, or some combination of the two.
Style:	Use "objective" point of view ("2. The operator started the engine . . ."), as opposed to "command" point of view ("2. Start the engine . . .").
Emphasis:	Highlight the result ("5. In order to operate with maximum efficiency, the operator runs the engine at 5,000 rpm"), rather than the action ("5. Run the engine at 5,000 rpm in order to . . .").

Instructions

Purpose:	Describe a sequence of steps in such a way that the reader can *perform* the sequence of steps.
Format:	Employ numbered or bulleted lists, organized into subgroups of easily understandable units of information.
Style:	Use "command" point of view ("3. Plug the phone jack into the recorder unit"), as opposed to "objective" point of view ("3. The phone jack was plugged into the recorder unit").
Emphasis:	Highlight the action ("4. Slide the weight forward until the leading edge hits the 27 kg mark"), rather than the result ("4. The tension is determined by setting the weight's

---

Figure 7-1 Process descriptions versus instructions

In each case, you are writing for a reader who wants to know what has happened or will happen, but who does not need to perform the process.

Instructions at M&K

Think of instructions this way: they must provide users with a road map to do the procedure, not just understand it. That is, someone must complete a task on the basis of words and pictures you provide. Clearly, instructions present you, the writer, with a much greater challenge and risk. The reader must be able to replicate the procedure without error and, most important, with full knowledge of any dangers. The situations that follow reflect this challenge. Note that they parallel the case studies presented for process descriptions.

- **Accounting:** As M&K's lead accountant, you have always been responsible for auditing the firm's books. Because you developed the procedure yourself over many years, there is no comprehensive set of instructions for completing the process. Now you want to record the steps so that other company accountants can perform them.
- **Maintenance:** As a maintenance supervisor at M&K's branch in Calgary, you must repair a piece of equipment for testing concrete. You have never disassembled this particular machine, and there are no manufacturer's instructions available. Therefore, the job takes you three full days. To help other employees perform this task in the future, you write a set of detailed instructions for making the repair.
- **Laboratory work:** As lab supervisor for M&K's Montreal office, you have assembled one of the two new gas chromatographs just purchased by the company. You are supposed to send the other unit to the Tokyo branch, where it will be put together by Japanese technicians. Unfortunately, the manufacturer's instructions are poorly written, so you plan to rewrite them for the English-speaking technicians at the Tokyo office.
- **Marketing:** As M&K's marketing manager, you have suggested a new approach for tracking sales leads. Having had your proposal approved by the corporate staff, you now need to explain the marketing procedure to technical professionals at all 15 offices. Your written instructions must be understandable for technical experts in many fields, who have little if any marketing experience.

In each case, your instructions must describe steps so thoroughly that the reader will be able to replicate the process, without having to speak in person with the writer of the instructions. The next two sections give rules for preparing both process descriptions and sets of instructions.

PROCESS DESCRIPTIONS

You have already learned that process descriptions are aimed at persons who need to understand the process, not perform it. Process descriptions often have the following purposes:

- Describing an experiment
- Explaining how a machine works
- Recording steps in developing a new product
- Describing what happened during a field test

Guidelines for Process Descriptions

Follow these guidelines for creating first-rate process descriptions:

Process Guideline 1: Know Your Purpose and Audience

Your intended purpose and expected audience influence every detail of your description. Here are some preliminary questions you should be able to answer before writing:

- Are you supposed to give just an overview, or are details needed?
- Do readers understand the technical subject, or are they laypersons?
- Do readers have mixed technical backgrounds?
- Does the process description supply supporting information (perhaps in an appendix), or is it the main part of the document?

Process descriptions are most challenging to write when they are directed to a mixed audience. In this case, write for the lowest common denominator—that is, for your least technical readers. It is better to write below the level of your most technical readers than to write above the level of your nontechnical readers.

For example, the process description in Model 7-3 on page 186 is directed to a mixed audience of city officials—some technical staff and some nontechnical political officials. It is contained in an appendix to a long M&K report that recommends immediate cleanup of a toxic-waste dump. Note that the writer either uses nontechnical language or defines any technical terms used.

Process Guideline 2: Follow the ABC Format

In Chapter 3 you learned about the ABC format (**A**bstract/**B**ody/**C**onclusion), which applies to all documents. The abstract gives a summary, the body supplies details, and the conclusion provides a wrap-up or leads to the next step in the communication process. Whether a process description forms all or part of a document, it usually subscribes to the following version of the three-part ABC format:

- The *Abstract* component answers the five *W*'s, while *how* is answered in the body:

  What? Provide a formal sentence definition so that your reader understands which process is to be explained.

  Why? Explain why you are providing your reader with an explanation of the process.

  When? If the process can be performed only at certain times—planting tulips, for example—tell the reader.

  Who? If only certain individuals are able or qualified to perform the process, mention the necessary abilities or qualifications.

  Where? If the process can only be performed at certain locations or under certain environmental conditions, mention them.

  The Abstract concludes with (1) a list of the major steps involved, and (2) a list of the equipment required.

  Note that Model 7-3 includes a separate heading for equipment. In that model, the purpose statement places the description in the context of the entire document. Then the main steps of the process are given to provide readers with a framework for interpreting the details that follow. Note also that the list of equipment or materials provides a central reference point as readers work through all the steps.

- The *Body* component of the process description moves logically through the steps of the process. By definition, all process descriptions follow a chronological, or step-by-step, pattern of organization. These steps can be conveyed in two ways:

   1. **Paragraphs:** This approach weaves steps of the process into the fabric of typical paragraphs, with appropriate transitions between sentences. Use paragraphs when your readers would prefer a smooth explanation of the entire process, rather than emphasis on individual steps.

   2. **List of steps:** This approach includes a list of steps, usually with numbers or bullets. Much like instructions, a listing emphasizes the individual parts of the process. Readers prefer it when they will need to refer to specific steps later on.

   Both paragraph format and list format have a place in process descriptions. In fact, most descriptions can be written in either. See Figure 7-2 for examples of both—in this case to describe laying a concrete patio. As a public-service gesture, M&K has written a pamphlet that briefly describes simple home improvements. It is intended for owners of small homes who complete renovations with little or no help from contractors. If home owners are interested in one of the projects, they can write for detailed instructions to an address listed in the pamphlet.

   Building a concrete patio is one project covered; the process description has a subsection about constructing the wooden form into which concrete is poured.

- The *Conclusion* component of a process description keeps the process from ending abruptly with the last step. Here you should help the reader assemble a coherent whole. When the process description is part of a larger document, you can show how the process fits into a larger context (see Model 7-3).

Steps of process are embedded in paragraph.

A. PARAGRAPH OPTION

The homeowner should select rough-grade 2 x 4s for building the wooden form for the patio. The form is just a box, with an open top and with the ground for the bottom, into which concrete will be poured. First the four sides are nailed together, and then the form is levelled with a standard carpenter's level. Finally, 2 x 4 stakes are driven into the ground about every metre on the outside of the form, to keep it in place during the pouring of the concrete.

After brief lead-in, steps of process are placed in list format.

B. LIST OPTION

Building a wooden form for a home concrete patio can be accomplished with some rough-grade 2 x 4s. This form is just a box with an open top and the ground for the bottom. Building involves three basic steps:

1. Nailing 2 x 4s into the intended shape of the patio
2. Levelling the box-shaped form with a standard carpenter's level
3. Nailing stakes (made from 2 x 4 lumber) every 60 to 80 cm at the outside edge of the form, to keep it in place during the pouring of the concrete

Figure 7-2 Two options for process description: (A) paragraph option, (B) list option

Process Guideline 3: Use an Objective Point of View

Process descriptions explain a process rather than direct how to do it. Thus they are written from an objective point of view—not from the personal "you" or "command" point of view that is common to instructions. Note the difference in the following examples:

Process: The technician pours the concrete into the two-by-four frame.

or

The concrete is poured into the two-by-four frame.

Instructions: Pour the concrete into the two-by-four frame.

The process excerpts *explain* the step, whereas the instructions excerpt *gives a command* for completing the instructions.

Process Guideline 4: Choose the Right Amount of Detail

Only a thorough audience analysis will tell you how much detail to include. Model 7-3, for example, could have contained much more technical detail about the substeps for testing air quality at the site. The writer, however, decided that the city officials would not need more scientific and technical detail.

In supplying specifics, be sure to subdivide information for easy reading. In paragraph format, headings and subheadings can be used to make the process easier to grasp. In list format, an outline arrangement of points and subpoints may be appropriate. When such detail is necessary, remember the general rule of thumb: *place related steps into groups of three to seven points*. Readers find it easier to remember several groupings with subpoints, as opposed to one long list. Following are two rough outlines for a process description. The second is preferred, in that it groups the many steps into three easily grasped categories.

Employment Interview Process–I

1. Interviewer reviews job description
2. Interviewer analyzes candidate's application
3. Candidate and interviewer engage in "small talk"
4. Interviewer asks open-ended questions related to candidate's résumé and completed application form
5. Interviewer expands topic to include matters of personal interest and the candidate's long-term career plans
6. Interviewer provides candidate with information about the position (salary, benefits, location, etc.)
7. Candidate is encouraged to ask questions about the position
8. Interviewer asks candidate about her or his general interest, at this point, in the position
9. Interviewer informs candidate about next step in hiring process

Employment Interview Process–II

- **Pre-interview Phase**

    1. Interviewer reviews job description
    2. Interviewer analyzes candidate's application

- **Interview**

    3. Candidate and interviewer engage in "small talk"
    4. Interviewer asks open-ended questions related to candidate's résumé and completed application form
    5. Interviewer expands topic to include matters of personal interest and the candidate's long-term career plans
    6. Interviewer provides candidate with information about the position (salary, benefits, location, etc.)
    7. Candidate is encouraged to ask questions about the position

- **Closure**

    8. Interviewer asks candidate about his or her general interest, at this point, in the position
    9. Interviewer informs candidate about next step in hiring process

Process Guideline 5: Use Flow Charts for Complex Processes

Some process descriptions contain steps that are occurring at the same time. In this case you may want to supplement a paragraph or list description with a flow chart. Such charts use boxes, circles, and other geometric shapes to show progression and relationships among various steps.

Model 7-4 on page 187, for example, shows a flow chart and an accompanying process description at M&K. Both denote services that M&K's Calgary branch provides for oil companies in the Gulf of St. Lawrence. The chart helps demonstrate that the geophysical study (mapping by sonar equipment) and the engineering study (securing and testing of sea floor samples) take place at the same time. Such simultaneous steps are difficult to show in a list of sequential steps.

INSTRUCTIONS

The rules change considerably when you move from process descriptions to instructions. Although both patterns are organized by time, the similarities stop there. Instructions walk readers through the process so that they can do it, not just understand it. It is one thing to explain the process by which a word-processing program works; it is quite another to write a set of instructions for using that word-processing program. This section explores the challenge of writing instructions by giving you some basic writing and design guidelines.

Guidelines for Instructions

These guidelines for instructions also apply to complete operating *manuals*, a document type that many technical professionals will help write during their careers. Those manuals include the instructions themselves, as well as related information such as (1) features, (2) physical parts, and (3) troubleshooting tips. In other words, manuals are complete documents, whereas instructions can be part of a larger piece.

Instructions Guideline 1: Select the Correct Technical Level

This guideline is just another way of saying you need to know exactly who will be reading your instructions. Are your readers technicians, engineers, managers, general users, or some combination of these groups? Once you answer this question, select language that every reader can understand. If, for example, the instructions will include technical terms or names of objects that may not be understood, use the techniques of definition and description discussed in Chapter 6.

Instructions Guideline 2: Provide Introductory Information

Like process descriptions, instructions follow the ABC format (**A**bstract/**B**ody/**C**onclusion) described in Chapter 3. The introductory (or abstract) information should include (1) a purpose statement, (2) a summary of the main steps, and (3) a list or an illustration giving the equipment or materials needed (or a reference to an attachment with this information). These three items set the scene for the procedure itself.

Besides these three "musts," you should consider whether some additional items might help set the scene for your user:

- Pointers that will help with installation
- Definitions of terms
- Theory of how something works
- Notes, cautions, warnings, or dangers that apply to all steps

Instructions Guideline 3: Use Numbered Lists in the Body

A simple format is crucial to the body of the instructions—that is, to the steps themselves. Most users constantly go back and forth between these steps and the project that the steps apply to. Thus, you should avoid paragraph format and instead use a simple numbering system. Model 7-5 on pages 188–89 shows before and after examples. The original version is written in paragraphs that are difficult to follow; the revised version includes nine separate, numbered steps.

Instructions Guideline 4: Group Steps under Task Headings

Readers prefer that you group together related steps under headings, rather than present an uninterrupted "laundry list" of steps.

Groupings provide two main benefits. First, they divide fragmented information into manageable chunks that readers find easier to read. Second, they give readers a sense of accomplishment as they complete each task, on the way to finishing the whole activity.

Instructions Guideline 5: Place One Action in a Step

A common error is to bury several actions in a single step. This approach can confuse and irritate readers. Instead, break up complex steps into discrete units, as shown:

- **Original:**
  - **Step 3:** Fill in your name and address on the coupon, send it to the manufacturer within two weeks, return to the retail merchant when your letter of approval arrives from the manufacturer, and pick up your free toaster oven.
- **Revision:**
  - **Step 3:** Fill in your name and address on the coupon.
  - **Step 4:** Send the coupon to the manufacturer within two weeks.
  - **Step 5:** Show your retail merchant the letter of approval after it arrives from the manufacturer.
  - **Step 6:** Pick up your free toaster oven.

The only exception to this rule occurs when two or more actions are to be performed at the same time.

Instructions Guideline 6: Lead off Each Action Step with a Verb

Instructions should include the command form of a verb at the start of each step. This style best conveys a sense of action to your readers. Model 7-5 consistently uses command verbs for all steps throughout the procedures.

Instructions Guideline 7: Remove Extra Information from the Step

Sometimes you may want to follow the command sentence with an explanatory sentence or two. In this case, distinguish such helpful information from actions by labelling the information with, for example, *Note* or *Result* (for example, see Model 7-2 on page 185).

Instructions Guideline 8: Use Bullets or Letters for Emphasis

Sometimes you may need to highlight information, especially within a particular step. Avoid using numbers for this purpose, since you are already using them to signify steps. Bullets work best if there are just a few items; letters are best if there are many, especially if they are in a sequence. The revised version in Model 7-5 shows the appropriate use of letters.

In particular, consider using bullets at any point at which users have an option as to how they will respond. The following example uses bullets in this way; it also eliminates the problem of having too many actions embedded in one step.

Part of Procedure for Firing Clay in a Kiln

(Note: A pyrometric "cone" is a piece of test clay used in a kiln, an oven for baking pottery. The melting of the small cone helps the operator determine that the clay piece has completed the firing process.)

- **Original:**
  - **Step 6:** Check the cone frequently as the kiln reaches its maximum temperature of 1010°C. If the cone retains its shape, continue firing the clay and checking the cone frequently. When the cone begins to bend, turn off the kiln. Then let the kiln cool overnight before opening it and removing the pottery.

- **Revision:**
  - **Step 6:** Check the cone frequently as the kiln reaches its maximum temperature of 1010°C.
  - **Step 7:** Has the cone started to bend?
    - If *no,* continue firing the piece of pottery and checking the cone frequently to see if it has bent.
    - If *yes,* turn off the kiln.
  - **Step 8:** Let the kiln cool overnight after turning it off.
  - **Step 9:** Open the kiln and remove the pottery.

Instructions Guideline 9: Emphasize Cautions, Warnings, and Dangers

Instructions often require drawing attention to risks in using products and equipment. Your most important obligation is to highlight such information. Generally, the following three terms are used as red flags to the reader. The level of risk increases as you move from 1 to 3:

1. **Caution:** possibility of damage to equipment or materials
2. **Warning:** possibility of injury to people
3. **Danger:** probability of injury or death to people

If you are not certain that your readers will understand these distinctions, define the terms *caution, warning,* and *danger* in a prominent place before you begin your instructions.

As for placement of the actual cautions, warnings, or danger messages, following are your options:

- **Option 1:** *In a separate section right before the instructions begin.* This approach is appropriate only when you have a list of general warnings that apply to much of the procedure or when one special warning should be heeded throughout the instructions—for example, "DANGER: Keep main breaker on Off during entire installation procedure." Figure 7-3 shows such a warning at the start of instructions to install a security keypad.
- **Option 2:** *In the text of the instructions.* This approach is required if the caution, warning, or danger message applies to the step that immediately follows it. Thus, users are warned about a problem before they read the step that it applies to. For an example, see the following:

    CAUTION: Use 220-grade sandpaper, to avoid scratching the surface of furniture.

In other words, give information about potential risks before the operator has the chance to make the mistake. Also, the caution, warning, or danger message can be made visually prominent by the following techniques:

- Underlining: <u>Warning</u>
- Bold: **Warning**
- Full Caps: WARNING
- Italics: *Warning*
- Oversized Print: Warning
- Boxing: Warning
- Combined Methods: *<u>Warning</u>*
                   <u>WARNING</u>
                   WARNING

Instructions Guideline 10: Keep a Simple Style

Perhaps more than any other type of technical writing, instructions must be easy to read. Readers expect a no-nonsense approach to writing that gives them required information without fanfare. Following are some techniques:

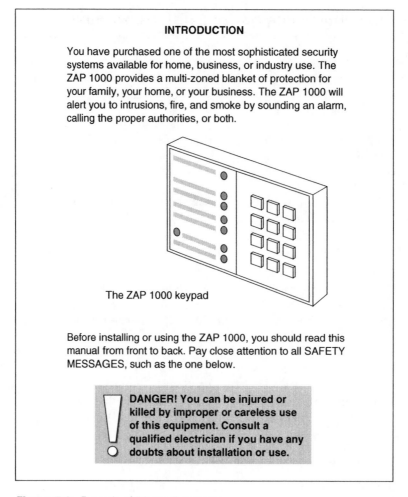

Figure 7-3   Example of "danger" message

- Keep sentences short, with an average length of under 10 words.
- Use informal definitions (parenthetical, like this one) to define any terms not understood by all readers.
- Never use a long word when a short one will do.
- Be specific and avoid words with multiple interpretations (*frequently, seldom, occasionally*, etc.).

Instructions Guideline 11: Use Graphics

Illustrations are essential for instructions that involve equipment. Place an illustration next to every major step when (1) the instructions or equipment are quite complicated or (2) the audience may contain poor readers or people who are in a hurry. Such word-picture associations create a page design that is easy to follow.

In other cases, just one or two diagrams may suffice for the entire set of instructions.

Another useful graphic in instructions is the table. Sometimes within a step you need to show correspondence between related data. For example, the instructions that follow would benefit from a table.

- **Original:**

  Step 3: Use pyrometric cones to determine when a kiln has reached the proper temperature to fire pottery. Common cone ratings are as follows: a Cone 018 corresponds to 650°C; a Cone 07 corresponds to 990°C; a Cone 06 corresponds to 1015°C; and a Cone 04 corresponds to 1060°C.

- **Revision:**

  Step 3: Use pyrometric cones to determine when a kiln has reached the proper temperature for firing pottery. *Note:* Common cone ratings are as follows:

Cone 018	650°C
Cone 07	990°C
Cone 06	1015°C
Cone 04	1060°C

Instructions Guideline 12: Test Your Instructions

Professional writers often test their instructions on potential users before completing the final draft. The most sophisticated technique for such testing involves a "usability laboratory." Here test subjects are asked to use the instructions or manual to perform the process, often while voicing their observations and frustrations (if any). The writers or lab personnel unobtrusively observe the process from behind a one-way mirror. Later they may review audiotaped or videotaped observations of the test subjects or they may interview these persons. This complex process helps writers to anticipate and then eliminate problems that users will confront when they follow written instructions.

Of course, you probably will not have access to a usability laboratory to test your instructions. However, you can adapt the following user-based approach to testing assignments in this class and projects in your career. Specifically, follow these four steps:

1. Team up with another class member (or a colleague on the job). This person should be unfamiliar with the process and should approximate the technical level of your intended audience.
2. Give this person a draft of your instructions and provide any equipment or materials necessary to complete the process. Of course, for the purposes of a class assignment, this approach would work only for a simple process with little equipment or few materials.
3. Observe your colleague following the instructions you have provided. You should record both your observations and any responses this person makes while moving through the steps.
4. Revise your instructions to solve problems your user encountered during the test.

Employability Skills

The Conference Board of Canada's *Employability Skills 2000+* states that your ability to communicate clearly and effectively is critical to your success. Relevant communication skills include the following:

- Read and understand information presented in a variety of forms (e.g., words, graphs, charts, diagrams).
- Write and speak so others pay attention and understand.
- Use relevant scientific, technological, and mathematical knowledge and skills to explain or clarify ideas.*

With fitted *Lego* or *Duplo* blocks, build a simple structure. Write a set of instructions that will enable another person to build the identical structure. Provide one of your fellow students with the unassembled blocks and the set of instructions and allow him or her to follow the instructions. Make certain that you are not in the other person's line of sight and make certain that you make no noise. If the other person is successful in duplicating what you have asked, your instructions have been adequate.

* *Employability Skills 2000+* Brochure 2000 E/F (Ottawa: The Conference Board of Canada, 2000).

CHAPTER SUMMARY

Both process descriptions and instructions share the same organization principle: time. That is, both relate a step-by-step description of events. Process descriptions address an audience that wants to be informed but does not need to perform the process itself. Instructions are geared specifically for persons who need to complete the procedure.

In writing good process descriptions, follow these basic guidelines:

1. Know your purpose and audience.
2. Follow the ABC format.
3. Use an objective point of view.
4. Choose the right amount of detail.
5. Use flow charts for complex processes.

For instructions, follow these 12 rules:

1. Select the correct technical level.
2. Provide introductory information.
3. Use numbered lists in the body.
4. Group steps under task headings.
5. Place one action in a step.
6. Lead off each action step with a verb.
7. Remove extra information from the step.
8. Use bullets or letters for emphasis.
9. Emphasize cautions, warnings, and dangers.
10. Keep a simple style.
11. Use graphics.
12. Test your instructions.

A S S I G N M E N T S

Part 1: Short Assignments

Assignments 1 to 5 can be completed either as individual exercises or as group projects, depending on the instructions you are given in class.

1. **Writing a process description—school-related.** Your college or university has decided to evaluate the process by which students are advised about and registered for classes. As part of this evaluation, the registrar has asked a select group of students—you among them—to describe the actual process each of you went through individually during the last advising/registration cycle. These case studies collected from individual students, the customers, will be transmitted directly to an institution-wide committee studying registration and advising problems.

   Your job is to give a detailed account of the process. Remain as objective as possible, without giving opinions. If you had problems during the process, the facts you relate will speak for themselves. Simply describe the process you personally experienced. Then let the committee members judge for themselves whether the steps you describe should or should not be part of the process.

2. **Writing a process description—M&K context.** Choose one of the projects from Chapter 2. For this assignment use (a) points listed in the "Main Technical Tasks" section of the project you have chosen; or (b) related information you wish to supply from your own experience, reading, or imagination; or (c) both. Your assignment is to write a process description dealing with one or more of the bulleted points.

3. **Writing instructions—M&K context.** Choose one of the projects from Chapter 2. For this assignment, conduct some research on either (a) one task or several related tasks in the "Main Technical Tasks" section or (b) a task that conceivably could be related to the project but is not specifically listed. Then write a set of numbered instructions for the task(s). Following are some sample tasks, with project references:

   - Project #1: Estimating the age of a geologic sample
   - Project #2: Examining buildings at adjacent locations
   - Project #3: Taking inventory of existing hardware and software
   - Project #4: Evaluating the ergonometric features of a control panel
   - Project #5: Evaluating the effectiveness of a technical report

   If you prefer to write about less specific tasks, select a general topic related to a project. For example, following are four general topics derived from specific ones above: conducting a lab test, running an effective meeting, evaluating the ergonometric features of any product, and evaluating the effectiveness of any document.

4. **Writing instructions—M&K context.** As an employee at M&K's corporate office, you have just received the job of writing a set of instructions for completing performance appraisal reviews (PARs). The instructions will be included in a memo that goes to all supervisors at all branches of the firm, along with related forms. To help you get started on the instructions, you have been given a narrative description of the process (see the following). Your task is to convert this narrative into a simple set of instructions to go into the memorandum to supervisors.

PARs are conducted annually for each employee, during the anniversary month in which the employee was originally hired. Several days before the month in which the PARs are to be conducted, the corporate office will send each supervisor a list of employees in that supervisor's group who should receive PARs. The main part of the PAR process is an interview between the supervisor and the employee receiving the PAR. Before this interview takes place, however, the supervisor should give the employee a copy of the M&K

PAR Discussion Guide, which offers suggestions for the topics and tone of a PAR inter-view. The supervisor completes a PAR Report Form after each interview and then sends copies to the Canadian operations vice president, to head office, and to the employee, with the original staying in the personnel files of the supervisor's branch. If for any rea-son a PAR interview and report form are not completed in the required month, the super-visor must send a memo of explanation to the Human Resources department, with a copy to the supervisor's branch manager.

5. **Writing instructions—school-related.** In either outline or final written form, provide a set of instructions for completing assignments in this class. Consider your audience to be another student who has been ill and missed much of the term. You have agreed to provide her with an overview that will help her to plan and then write any papers she has missed.

Your instructions may include (1) highlights of the writing process from Chapter 1 and (2) other assignment guidelines provided by your instructor in the syllabus or in class. Remember to present a generic procedure for all assignments in the class, not spe-cific instructions for a particular assignment.

Part 2: Longer Assignments

These assignments test your ability to write and evaluate the two patterns covered in this chapter—process descriptions and instructions. Specifically, follow these guidelines:

- Write each exercise in the form of a letter report or memo report, as specified.
- Follow organization and design guidelines given in Chapters 3 and 4, especially con-cerning the ABC format (**A**bstract/**B**ody/**C**onclusion) and the use of headings. Chapter 10 gives rules for informal reports, but such detail is not necessary to com-plete the assignments here.
- Fill out a Planning Form (found in Chapter 1) for each assignment.

6. **Evaluating a process description.** Using a textbook in a technical subject area, find a description of a process. For example, a physics text might describe the process of waves developing and then breaking at a beach, an anatomy text might describe the process of blood circulating, and a criminal justice text might describe the process of a criminal investigation.

Keeping in mind the author's purpose and audience, evaluate the effectiveness of the process description as presented in the textbook. Submit your evaluation—in the form of a memo report—to your instructor in this writing course, along with a copy of the textbook description.

For the purposes of this assignment, assume that the publisher of the text you have chosen has asked your writing instructor to review the book as an example of good or bad technical writing. Thus, your instructor would incorporate comments from your memo report into his or her comprehensive evaluation.

7. **Writing a process description—school-related.** Conduct a brief research project in your campus library. Specifically, use company directories, annual reports, or other library sources to find information about a company or other organization that could hire students from your course.

In a memo report to your instructor, (1) describe the process you followed in con-ducting the search and (2) provide an outline or paragraph summary of the information you found concerning the company or organization. Assume that your report will become part of a volume your faculty is assembling for juniors and seniors who are beginning to look for work. These students will benefit both from information about the specific orga-nization you chose and from a description of the process that you followed in getting the information—since they may want to conduct research on other companies.

8. **Evaluating a set of instructions.** Find a set of operating or assembly instructions for a VCR, microwave oven, CD player, computer, timing light, or other electronic device. Evaluate all or part of the document according to the criteria for instructions in this chapter.

Write a memo report on your findings and send it, along with a copy of the instructions, to Natalie Bern. As a technical writer at the company that produced the electronic device, Natalie wrote the set of instructions. In your position as Natalie's supervisor, you are responsible for evaluating her work. Use your memo report either to compliment her on the instructions or to suggest modifications.

9. **User test of instructions.** Find a relatively simple set of instructions. Then ask another person to follow the instructions from beginning to end. Observe the person's activity, keeping notes on any problems she or he encounters.

   Use your notes to summarize the instructions' effectiveness. Present your summary as a memo report to Natalie Bern, using the same situational context as described in assignment 8. That is, as Natalie's boss, you are to give her your evaluation of her efforts to produce the set of instructions.

10. **Writing simple instructions.** Choose a simple office procedure of 20 or fewer steps (for example, changing a printer cartridge, filling a mechanical pencil, adding dry ink to a copy machine, or adding paper to a laser printer). Then write a simple set of instructions for this process, in the form of a memo report. Your readers are assistants at the many offices of a large national firm. Consider them new employees who have no background or experience in office work and no education beyond high school. You are responsible for their training.

11. **Writing complex instructions, with graphics—group project.** Complete this assignment as a group project (see the guidelines for group writing in Chapter 1). Choose a process connected with school life or courses—for example, completing a lab experiment, doing a field test, designing a model, writing a research paper, getting a parking sticker, paying fees, or registering for classes.

   Using memo report format, write a set of instructions for students who have never performed this task. Follow all the guidelines in this chapter. Include at least one illustration (along with warnings or cautions, if appropriate). If possible, conduct a user test before completing the final draft.

12. **Writing instructions—M&K context.** M&K does a good deal of environmental work in Canada and the U.S.—cleaning up toxic-waste sites, building energy-efficient structures, removing asbestos from old buildings, and investigating construction sites to determine the most environmentally sound approach to design and construction. For business reasons—and also because of its sense of civic duty—the company encourages citizens to get directly involved in environmental action.

   As public relations manager for M&K, you have just received an interesting assignment. You are to prepare a set of instructions that will go out to citizen and school groups. In the form of a memo report, this document should give readers specific directions for recycling one or more types of waste. Your instructions should be directed toward a broad audience, of course. Moreover, the instructions should give the kinds of details that allow someone to act without having to get more information.

   To get information for this report, you might consider (1) calling individuals in the waste-management department of your local government, (2) reading relevant articles from recent periodicals, or (3) checking an environmental science textbook at your college.

13. **Writing instructions—group project with M&K context.** M&K's move into international work has generated interest among the corporate staff in gaining ISO 9000 certification. (The International Organization for Standardization [ISO], which is based in Geneva, Switzerland, helps organizations around the world develop standards in quality.) Your group will conduct some research on this topic of growing interest. Write a set of instructions for a company that wishes to gain such certification. You may either (a) provide a generalized overview for completing the entire process or (b) focus on one limited, specific part of the process, such as the process for gaining certification for a particular product or service.

MEMORANDUM

DATE: May 29, 2006
TO: Leonard Szymanski
FROM: Your Name
SUBJECT: New Electronic Calendar

States purpose clearly.

    Yesterday I met with Jane Ansel, the installation manager at BHG Electronics, about our new electronic calendar. Ms. Ansel explained the process by which the system will be installed. As you requested, this memo summarizes what I learned about that process.

    The technicians will be at our offices on June 18 to complete these five tasks:

Describes five main tasks, using parallel grammatical form.

1. Installing the software on the server
2. Creating the client accounts for each of those who will have access to the system
3. Installing software on the desktops belonging to each of the clients
4. Providing each client with a username and temporary password
5. Providing tutorials to those who have trouble learning the new system

Confirms the follow-up activities they have already discussed.

    As you and I have agreed, next week I will send a memo to all office employees who will have access to the calendar. That memo will mention the installation date and summarize the procedures for viewing appointments. Shortly thereafter, I will send another memo instructing them about entering appointments.

Gives reader opportunity to respond.

    Let me know, Leonard, if you have further suggestions about how I can help make our transition to the electronic calendar as smooth as possible.

Model 7-1 M&K process description: electronic calendar

MEMORANDUM

DATE: June 5, 2006
TO: All Employees
FROM: Your Name
SUBJECT: Basic Instructions for Viewing Your Calendar

Last month, you attended a brief seminar on the features of the new electronic calendar. We have just learned that the system will be installed on June 18. This memo provides some basic instructions for viewing your appointments on this system. Soon you will receive another set of instructions for entering your appointments.

NOTE: In these instructions, the messages or prompts on your terminal screen appear in *italics*. Any key you push or response you type is shown in **bold** print.

1. Double click on the calendar or icon on your desktop.
    NOTE: The technician will have placed one there when installing the software.

2. Type in your username when the system requests it.
    Example: *username:* **EvanKinney**

3. Enter the temporary password provided to you.
    NOTE: Your temporary password will be the same as your username.
    Example: *password:* **EvanKinney**
    RESULT: After the system has verified your password, it will prompt you to

4. Enter your new password.
    NOTE: We recommend a password that does not describe a personal preference or characteristic since those are prone to hacking.

5. Confirm your choice by entering the password again.

6. Click on the button marked *AGENDA*.
    NOTE: The day's appointments entered for or by you will appear on the screen.

As noted earlier, the system will be installed on June 18. Feel free to call me if you have any questions about the installation or the instructions for viewing your calendar.

Marginal notes:
Gives clear purpose.

Indicates what instructions *do* and *do not* cover.

Provides information to help reader understand instructions that follow.

Limits each step to *one* action.

Separates action from results.

Restates important date and tells reader how to get more information.

Model 7-2 M&K instructions: electronic calendar

ABC format begins with abstract—with purpose statement and summary of appendix in this paragraph.

Abstract ends with list of equipment used in process that follows.

Body section of this process uses paragraph format and is aimed at non-technical audience.

Listing is used to highlight locations for sampling.

Conclusion part of ABC format puts this process in larger context.

APPENDIX A: ON-SITE MONITORING

The purpose of monitoring the air is to determine the level of protective equipment needed for each day's work. This appendix gives an overview of the process for monitoring on-site air quality each day. Besides describing the main parts of the process, it notes other relevant information to be recorded and the manner in which data will be logged.

EQUIPMENT

This process requires the following equipment:

- Organic vapour analyzers (OVA)
- Combustible-gas instruments
- Personal sampling devices

PROCESS

The project manager at the site is responsible for supervising the technician who performs the air-quality tests. At the start of every day, a technician uses an OVA to check the quality of air at selected locations around the site. Throughout the workday (at times specified by the project manager), the technician monitors the air with combustible-gas instruments and personal sampling devices. This monitoring takes place at these locations:

1. Around the perimeter of the site
2. Downwind of the site (to determine the extent of migration of vapours and gases)
3. Generally throughout the site
4. At active work locations within the site

Then at the end of every workday, the technician uses the OVA to monitor the site for organic vapours and gases.

CONCLUSION

Besides the air-quality data, the following information is collected by the technician at each sampling time: percent relative humidity, wind direction and speed, temperature, and atmospheric pressure. The project manager keeps records of air quality and weather conditions in dated entries in a bound log.

Model 7-3 Process description

COMBINED SITE INVESTIGATION

In helping to select the site for an offshore oil platform, M&K recommends a combined site investigation. This approach achieves the best results by integrating sophisticated geophysical work with traditional engineering activities.

As the accompanying flow chart shows, a combined site investigation consists of these main steps:

1. Planning the program, with M&K scientists and engineers and the client's representatives
2. Reviewing existing data
3. Completing a high-resolution geophysical survey of the site, followed by a preliminary analysis of the data
4. Collecting, testing, and analyzing soil samples
5. Combining geophysical and engineering information into one final report for the client

The report from this combined study will show how geological conditions at the site may affect the planned offshore oil platform.

Steps 1 and 2 are shown in top centre portion of flow chart.

Steps 3 and 4 are shown in left and right portions of flow chart, respectively.

Step 5 is shown in bottom centre portion of flow chart.

Flow chart shows relationship among steps occurring at the same time.

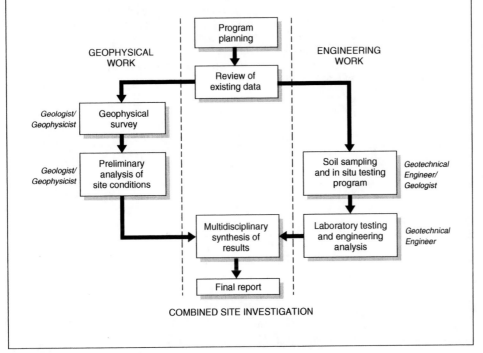

COMBINED SITE INVESTIGATION

Model 7-4 An M&K process description with a flow chart (both are included in an appendix to a report to a client)

MAKING TRAVEL ARRANGEMENTS
(Original Version)

Paragraph format makes it difficult for reader to locate individual steps.

When you're making travel arrangements, ask the person taking the trip to give you most of the details needed—dates, destinations, flight numbers, flight times, hotel requirements, rental car requirements, purpose of trip, and account number. Before proceeding, the first thing I do is confirm the flight information in the Official Airline Guide (OAG). You'll find the OAG on top of the credenza beside my computer. The next step is to call Turner Travel (555-0998). Although I've had great luck with all the people there, ask for Bonnie or Charlie—these two are most familiar with our firm. Turner Travel will handle reservations for flights, hotels, and rental cars. Remind them that we always use Avis midsize cars.

After you have confirmed the reservations information, fill out the travel form. Here's where you need to know the purpose of the trip and the traveller's account number. Blank forms are in the top drawer of my file cabinet in the folder labelled Travel Forms—Blank. Once the form is complete, file the original in my Travel Forms—Completed folder, also in the top drawer of the file cabinet. Give the copy to the person taking the trip.

When you get the ticket in the mail from Turner Travel, check the flight information against the completed travel form. If everything checks out, give the ticket to the traveller. If there are errors, call Turner.

Also, when making any reservations for visitors to our office, call either the Warner Inn (555-7888) or the Hasker Hotel (555-9000). We have company accounts there, and they will bill us directly.

continues

Model 7-5   Instructions for making travel arrangements

MAKING TRAVEL ARRANGEMENTS
(Revised Version)

Arranging Travel for Employees

To make travel arrangements for employees, follow these instructions:

Step	Action
1.	Obtain the following information from the traveller:

    a. Dates
    b. Destinations
    c. Flight numbers
    d. Flight times
    e. Hotel requirements
    f. Rental car requirements
    g. Purpose of trip
    h. Account number

2.   Confirm flight information in the Official Airline Guide (OAG).
    Note: The OAG is on the credenza beside my computer.

3.   Call Turner Travel (555-0998) to make reservations.
    Note: Ask for Bonnie or Charlie.
    Note: For car rental, use Avis midsize cars.

4.   Complete the travel form.
    Note: Blank forms are in the folder labelled Travel
    Forms—Blank, in the top drawer of my file cabinet.

5.   Make one copy of the completed travel form.

6.   Place the original form in the folder labelled Travel
    Forms—Completed, in the top drawer of my file cabinet.

7.   Send the copy to the person taking the trip.

8.   Check the ticket and the completed travel form after the ticket
    arrives from Turner Travel.

9.   Do the ticket and the completed travel form agree?

    a. If *yes*, give the ticket to the traveller.
    b. If *no*, call Turner Travel.

Arranging Hotel Reservations for Visitors

    To make reservations for visitors, call the Warner Inn (555-7888) or the Hasker Hotel (555-9000). We have company accounts there, and they will bill us.

Action steps all begin with "command" form of verb.

Letters are used to show long list of subpoints, for easy reference.

Notes are used to provide reader with *extra* information, separate from action of steps.

Though closely related, Steps 5–7 are best separated—for convenient reference by reader.

As noted in Guideline 9, two subpoints can show reader the *options* that exist.

Model 7-5 *continued*

CHAPTER 8

Email and Memos

Stella Malenga, M&K's fire science expert, has just returned from a seminar that emphasized new techniques for preventing injuries from job-site fires. Within 24 hours of her return, she has already done three things:

1. Written her manager a memo summarizing the seminar
2. Sent an email to an M&K client suggesting the use of fire-retardant gloves she learned about at the seminar
3. Sent the conference director an email thanking her for putting together the seminar

Like Stella, you will undoubtedly write many email memos in your career. In fact, you probably will write more of them than any other type of document.

Memos and email are short documents written to accomplish a limited purpose. Memos are directed within your organization, and email can be directed to either an external or internal audience. (Longer, more complicated memos—called *memo reports*—are covered in Chapter 10.) Following are some working definitions:

> **Memorandum:** a document written from a member of an organization to one or more members within the same organization. Abbreviated to *memo*, the document usually covers just one main point, and no more than a few. Readers prefer one-page memos.
>
> **Email:** a document written usually in an informal style either to members of one's own organization or to an external audience. Characterized by the speed with which it is written and delivered, an email can include more formal attachments that the audience can read and possibly print.

As with other forms of technical communication, your ability to write good memos, letters, and email depends on a clear sense of purpose, a thorough understanding of reader needs, and close attention to correct formats.

This chapter provides you with the strategies that will allow you to achieve the purpose for each of the emails and memos you will produce by presenting sections that cover (1) general rules for the creation of effective email and memos and (2) specific formats for email and memos.

EMAIL

Electronic communication (email) has become the preferred means of communication for many people in their professional lives and, often, in their personal lives as well. Some of us receive 100 or more messages a day. Any medium so widely used deserves special attention in a chapter on informal options of technical communication. The purpose of this overview is to describe the appropriate use and style of email, provide an ABC format, list some basic guidelines for using email, and give several examples.

Appropriate Use and Style of Email

Email is an appropriate reflection of the speed at which we conduct business today. Indeed, email mirrors the pace of popular culture as well. Following are some of the obvious advantages that using email provides:

- It gets quickly to the intended receiver.
- Its arrival can be easily confirmed.
- Your reader can reply to your message quickly.
- It is inexpensive to use—once you have invested in the hardware and software.
- It permits inexpensive transmission of multiple copies and attachments.

In addition to its ease of transmission, email allows you to create mailing lists. One address label can be an "umbrella" for multiple recipients, saving you much time.

Of course, remember the flip side of this ease of use: email is *not* private. Every time you send an email, remember that it may end up being read by "the world." Either by mistake or design, many supposedly private emails often are received by unintended readers.

Email communication is often considered less formal and, therefore, less demanding in its format and structure than print-based messages, such as memos and letters. However, because email use has become so widespread, you should consider constructing your email communication as carefully as you would a memo or a letter. Another reason to exercise great care is that email, like conventional documents, can be used in legal proceedings and other formal contexts.

Chapter 1, which mentions email in the context of group writing, shows how electronic mail helps you collaborate with others during the writing process— especially the planning stage. Interestingly, the email medium has produced a casual writing style similar to that of handwritten notes. Email even has its own set of abbreviations and shortcut languages (such as "cu" for "see you") which ranges so widely and changes so often that no list of abbreviations is included here. Following is an email message from one M&K employee to another. Josh Bergen and Natalie Long are working together on a report wherein they must offer suggestions for designing an operator's control panel at a large dam. Josh has just learned about another control panel that M&K designed and installed for a Russian nuclear power plant. (See Project #4 at the end of Chapter 2.) Josh wrote this email message to draw Natalie's attention to the related M&K project:

DATE: September 15, 2006
TO: Natalie Long
FROM: Josh Bergen
SUBJECT: Zanger Dam Project
Natalie—
I've got an idea that might save us A LOT of time on the Zanger Dam project. Check out the company project sheet on the Russian nuclear plant job done last year.
Operators of hi-tech dams and nuke plants seem to face the same hassles:
- Confusing displays
- Need to respond fast
- Distractions
When either a dam or nuke operator makes a mistake, there's often big trouble. I think we'd save time—and our client's money—if we could go right to some of the technical experts used in the nuke job, at least as a starting place. Maybe we'd even make our deadline on this project. That would be a change, considering the schedule delays this month on other jobs.
What do you think about this idea? Let me know today, if possible.

This message displays some of the most common stylistic features of electronic mail, using standard spelling and conversational, informal diction.

ABC Format for Email

Knowing that email *should* have a format puts you ahead of many writers, who consider email a licence to ramble. Yes, email is casual and quick, but that does not mean it should be without structure. In fact, when composing an email keep in mind the following rule:

> Don't send it *too* quickly!

By taking an extra minute to give your message structure—and to check its style and tone, as will be noted later—you'll have the best chance of sending an email that will be well received. Use the ABC format when composing your email:

ABC Email

Abstract

- Casual, friendly greeting if justified by relationship
- Short, clear statement of purpose for writing
- List of main topics to be covered

Body

- Supporting information for points mentioned in abstract
- Short paragraphs that start with main ideas
- Headings and lists
- Abbreviations and jargon only when understood by all readers

Conclusion

- Summary of main point
- Recommendations for what comes next

Remember—your reader is inundated with emails during the day. Furthermore, reading email on a computer screen can be harder on the eyes than reading print memos. So give each email a structure that will make it easy for your reader to find important information.

Guidelines for Email

Besides the appropriate style and ABC format, there are some additional guidelines that apply to email. Again, you are trying to strike the appropriate balance between speed of delivery, on the one hand, and clarity and quality of the communication to your reader, on the other.

Email Guideline 1: Begin with Standard Memo Format

The message should contain an indication of the date, to, from, and subject information that a print-based memo would have. (See Memo Guideline 3 on page 198.) The exact wording and order will depend on the particular email system in your organization.

Email Guideline 2: Focus on One Main Subject in a Message

State your subject in the Subject line as briefly, clearly, and specifically as possible. Then in the body of the message, begin with a succinct description of your subject.

Email Guideline 3: Use a Positive Conversational Style

As mentioned earlier, a casual style is usually appropriate. Adopt a style that resembles how you would talk to the recipient on the phone. Sentence fragments and slang are acceptable, as long as they contribute to your objectives and are in good taste. Most important, avoid displaying a negative, angry tone. Don't push the Send button unless the email will lead to a *constructive* exchange.

Note that a formal business style might be more appropriate in certain situations. In such cases, avoid slang, casual grammar, abbreviations, and shortcuts.

Email Guideline 4: Put Your Message into Context

Tell your readers what the subject is and what prompts you to write your message. If, for example, you are replying to a message, be sure to either include the previous message or summarize it. Most email software packages, when you push the Reply button, include a copy of the message you are replying to.

Email Guideline 5: Choose the Most Appropriate Method for Replying to a Message

Short email messages may only require that you include a brief response at the beginning or end of the email you are responding to. For complex, multitopic messages, however, you may wish to split your reply by commenting on each point individually (see Figure 8-1).

Email Guideline 6: Format Your Message Carefully

Because email messages frequently replace more formal print-based documents, you should organize and format them so that readers can easily locate the information you want to communicate. Following are some guidelines:

- Use headings, possibly in upper case or boldface, to identify important *chunks* of information.
- Use bulleted lists to display a series of information.
- Use sufficient white space to separate important pieces of information.
- Use separators (such as a row of dashes or asterisks, or a solid line) to separate one piece of information from another.

Figure 8-2 illustrates an email message with headings, separators, and sufficient white space.

Email Guideline 7: Chunk Information for Easy Reading

Break the information into coherent *chunks* dealing with one specific topic, and include all essential details. For example, depending on the nature of the information, include specific topics, time, date, location, and necessary prerequisites and details (see Figure 8-2).

```
*****************************************************************************
X-Sender:       mckinley@mail2.M&K.com
Date:           Tues., 8 Nov. 2006 09:25:30-0800
To:             pcarmich@advantage.com
From:           Mike McKinley <mckinley@M&K.com>
Subject:        Our Recent Visit
Mime-Version:   1.0
```

Dear Paul,

YOU WROTE:

>I hope that you had a good flight back home. I certainly enjoyed meeting you and look forward to the possibility of working with you this coming spring on the project that your firm, M&K, may do for us.

REPLY:

The trip back was fine, but tiring. I enjoyed meeting you also and visiting with your staff. I particularly enjoyed meeting Harold Black, for he will be very valuable in developing the plans for the possible water purification plant.

YOU WROTE:

>If Advantage, Inc., does decide to build the water purification plant, we would be very interested in having M&K's Mary Stevens as the project manager.

REPLY:

That certainly will be a possibility; Mary is one of our best managers.

YOU WROTE:

>After you left, I called the city administration here in Murrayville. M&K does not need a business licence for your work here, but, of course, you will need the necessary construction permits.

REPLY:

Thanks for taking care of this matter—I had not thought of that. We will supply the details to you for applying for the construction permits if you accept our proposal.

```
*****************************************************************************
```

Figure 8-1   An email message that separates different topics for reply

```
*************************************************************************
X-Sender:      mckinley@mail2.M&K.com
Date:          Tues., 10 Oct. 2006 09:25:30-0800
To:            Branch employees
From:          Paul Carmichael <pcarmich@advantage.com>
Subject:       October update
Mime-Version:  1.0
```

This is the October Electronic Update for Advantage, Inc. If you do not wish to receive this electronic update, send a message to

      pcarmich@advantage.com

      With the message in the subject line: Unsubscribe.

```
                         *********************
                            UPCOMING EVENTS
                         *********************
```

Project managers' meeting

October 21—project managers' meeting (notice the change of location): Hereford building, room 209.

```
**************************
```

November department meetings

All departments will have their planning and reporting meetings on November 18 at noon, with a joint lunch in the main dining room and breakout sessions at 12:30. Meetings should conclude at 2 p.m.

```
**************************
```

December department meetings

NOTE CHANGE OF DATE: The December department meetings will be held on December 9 (second Wednesday), NOT December 16 (third Wednesday).

```
*************************************************************************
```

Figure 8-2 Long email message with use of appropriate headings, separators, and white space

Email Guideline 8: When Writing to Groups, Give Readers a Method to Abstain from Receiving Future Notices

Email can easily become invasive and troublesome for recipients. You will gain favour—or at least not lose favour—if you are considerate and allow recipients to decide what email they wish to receive. There will be a number of people with whom you communicate often, and they will appreciate it if you discuss with them what messages you will send.

Email Guideline 9: When Writing to Groups, Suppress Recipients' Email Addresses

It is inappropriate to reveal the email addresses of group members to other group members unless they have agreed to let their addresses be shown. Use the bcc (blind copy) line to suppress group members' addresses so other members cannot see them.

Email Guideline 10: When Composing an Important Message, Consider Composing It on Your Word Processor

Important email messages should be not only clear in format but also correct in mechanics. Since some email software may not have a spelling checker, compose important messages on your word processor and use your spelling checker to check accuracy. Then either cut and paste the text into an email message or send it as an attachment to your email.

See Model 8-1 on page 205 for another email example.

MEMOS

By applying the guidelines in this section, you can master the craft of writing good memos. You need to plan, draft, and revise each memo as if your job depended on it—for it may.

Appropriate Format for Memos

With minor variations, all memos look much the same. Model 8-2 on page 206 shows one basic format. Following are some guidelines:

- **Date/To/From/Subject lines:** The obligatory Date/To/From/Subject information hangs at the top left margin, in whatever order your organization requires. These four lines allow you to dispense with lengthy introductory passages seen in more formal documents.
- **Subject line:** Give the subject line special attention, for it telegraphs meaning to the audience immediately. In fact, readers use it to decide when, or if, they will read the complete memo. Be brief, but also engage interest. For example, the Subject line of the Model 8-3 memo on page 207 could have been *Editing*. Yet such brevity would have sacrificed reader interest. The actual Subject line, *New Employee to Help with Technical Editing*, conveys more information and shows readers that the contents of the memo will make their lives easier.
- **From line:** Note that the sender signs his or her initials after or above the typed name in the From line.
- **Facsimile reference:** Readers often need to know—for convenience and for the record—when memos have been sent by fax. Type *Fax Transmission* or

Facsimile before the Date/To/From/Subject lines for a memo. This line also can be used for other similar notations such as *Confidential* or *Personal* or *Registered*.

- **Reference initials:** If someone other than the writer types the memo, place the typist's initials below the last paragraph (example: jt). Some organizations prefer that the writer's initials also be included, followed by those of the typist (example: GTY/jt).
- **Enclosure notation:** If attachments or enclosures accompany the memo, type the singular or plural form of *Enclosure* or *Attachment* one or two lines below the reference initials. Some writers also list the item itself (example: Enclosure: Code of Ethics).
- **Copy notation:** If the writer sends the memo to anyone other than the recipient, type *Copy* or *Copies* one or two lines below *From*, followed by the name(s) of the person or persons receiving copies (example: Copy: Jennifer Singh). Some organizations prefer the initials *c* (for *copy*), *cc* (for *carbon copy*, even though carbons hardly exist anymore), or *pc* (for *photocopy*). If you are sending a copy but do not want the original memo to include a reference to that copy, write *bc* (for *blind copy*) and the person's name on the copy only—not on the original (example: bc: Angela Koffman). **Note:** send blind copies only when you are certain it is appropriate and ethical to do so.
- **Postscripts:** Items marked *PS* or *P.S.* rarely appear in memos. They are considered to be symbols of poor planning, so use them with caution. The only exception occurs when you want to add a personal note to an otherwise more formal memo. If used, they appear as the last item on the document (below the copy notation) and can be typed or written in longhand.
- **Multiple-page headings:** Pages following the first page often have a heading that includes the name of the person or company receiving the memo, the date, and the page number. Some organizations may prefer an abbreviated form such as *Lacavalier to Bingham, 2*, without the date.

Guidelines For Memos

Refer to Model 8-3 for an example that demonstrates the guidelines that follow. Later examples in this chapter show additional memos.

Memo Guideline 1: Know Your Purpose

Before beginning your draft, write down your purpose in one clear sentence. This approach forces you to sift through details to find a main reason for writing the memo. This "purpose sentence" often becomes the first sentence in the document. Following are some samples:

- **Purpose sentence:** "Please review the list of items in the suggested standard software bundle for M&K employees and return any comments by reply email."
- **Purpose sentence:** "This memo will explain M&K's new policy for selecting rental cars on business trips."

Some purpose statements are implied; others are stated. In Model 8-3 the writer, Ralph Simmons, clearly states his purpose in the second sentence.

Memo Guideline 2: Know Your Readers

Whom are you trying to inform or influence? The answer to this question affects the vocabulary you choose, the arguments you make, and the tone you adopt. Pay particular attention when more than one person will read a memo. If these readers are from different technical backgrounds or different levels within an organization, the challenge increases. A complex audience compels you to either (1) reduce the level of technicality so that all readers can understand the memo or (2) write different parts of the document for different readers.

Model 8-3, directed to an in-house technical audience, contains fairly general information about the new technical editor. This information would apply to, and be understood by, all readers.

Memo Guideline 3: Follow Correct Format

Most organizations adopt memo formats that must be used uniformly by all employees (again, see Models 8-2 and 8-3).

Memo Guideline 4: Follow the ABC Format for All Memos

Abide by this one main rule in every memo-writing situation:

> **Be clear, brief, and tactful.**

Because many activities are competing for their time, readers expect information to be related as quickly and clearly as possible. Yet be sure not to sacrifice tact and sensitivity as you strive to achieve conciseness. The following ABC format for memos will help you accomplish both goals.

ABC Format: Memo

Abstract

- Clear statement of memo's purpose
- Outline of memo's main parts

Body

- Supporting points, with strong points at the beginning and/or end
- Frequent short paragraphs or listed items
- Absolute clarity about how memo relates to reader
- Tactful presentation of any negative news
- Reference to attachments, when further detail is required

Conclusion

- Clear statement of what step should occur next
- Another effort to retain goodwill and cooperation of readers.

Memo Guideline 5: Use the 3Cs Strategy for Persuasive Messages

The ABC format provides a way to organize memos. Another pattern of organization is the "3Cs strategy"—especially when your memo has a persuasive objective. This strategy has three main goals:

- **Capture** interest with a good opener, which tells readers what the memo can do for them.
- **Convince** readers with supporting points, which confirm the opening point.
- **Control** the closing, with a statement that puts you in the position of following up on the memo *and* solidifies your relationship with the readers.

Although Model 8-3 is not overtly persuasive, it has an underlying persuasive purpose. Note how it uses the 3Cs strategy.

Memo Guideline 6: Stress the "You" Attitude

Using the reader's name in the body helps convey interest. But your efforts to see things from the reader's perspective must go deeper than a name reference. For example, you should perform the following tasks:

- **Anticipate questions** your reader might raise and then answer those questions. You can even follow an actual question ("And how will our new testing lab help your firm?") with an answer ("Now M&K's labs can process samples in 24 hours").
- **Replace the pronouns *I, me,* and *we* with *you*.** Of course, you have to use first-person pronouns at certain points, but many pronouns should be second person. The technique is quite simple. You can change almost any sentence from writer-focused prose ("We feel that this new service will . . .") to reader-focused prose ("You'll find that this new service will . . .").

Model 8-3 shows this "you" attitude by stressing that the new editor will make the reader's job easier.

Memo Guideline 7: Use Attachments for Details

Keep text brief by placing details in attachments, which readers can examine later, rather than bogging down the middle of the memo. In this way, the supporting facts are available for future reference, without distracting readers from the main message. The memo in Model 8-3, for example, includes a list of possible job tasks for the new M&K editor. The listing would only clutter the body of the memo, especially since its purpose is to stimulate discussion at the next meeting.

Memo Guideline 8: Be Diplomatic

Without a tactful tone, all your planning and drafting will be wasted. Choose words that will persuade and cajole, not demand. Be especially careful of memos written to subordinates. If you sound too authoritarian, your message may be ignored—even if it is clear that what you are suggesting will help the readers. Generally speaking, negative (or "bad news") memos often use the passive voice, whereas positive (or "good news") memos often use the active voice.

The editing memo in Model 8-3 would be poorly received if it used stuffy, condescending wording such as "Be advised that starting next month, you are to make use of proofreading services provided in-house by . . ."

Memo Guideline 9: Edit Carefully

Because memos are short, editing errors will be obvious to readers. Take special care to avoid the following errors:

Mechanics

- Misspelled words of any kind, but especially the reader's name
- Wrong job title (call the reader's office to double-check, if necessary)
- Old address (again, call the reader's office to check)

Grammar

- Incorrect subject–verb and pronoun agreement
- Misused commas

Style

- Stuffy phrases, such as "as per your request" and "enclosed herewith"
- Long sentences with more than one main and one dependent clause
- Presumptuous phrases, such as "Thanking you in advance for . . ."
- Negative tone suggested by phrases such as "We cannot," "I won't," and "Please don't hesitate to . . ."

Use the editing stage to rewrite any passage that could be phrased in a more positive tone. You must always keep the reader's goodwill, no matter what the message.

Memo Guideline 10: Respond Quickly

A memo that comes too late will fail in its purpose, no matter how well written. Send memos in plenty of time for your reader to make the appropriate adjustments in schedule, behaviour, and so forth. This rule applies, for example, to memos written in response to the following situations:

- You want to document the points agreed to in a meeting or discussion.
- Someone requests information or clarification.
- A deadline will not be met.
- You announce a change in company policy.
- You set the time for a company meeting.

Types of Memos

Printed memos can contain any of four types of messages—positive, negative, neutral, and sales. Following are some situations within an organization that would require these different kinds of memos.

Positive

- Announcing high bonuses for the fiscal year
- Commending an employee for performance on a project
- Informing employees about improved fringe benefits

Negative

- Reporting decreased quarterly revenues for the year
- Requesting closer attention to filling out time sheets
- Asking for volunteers to work on a holiday

Neutral

- Announcing a meeting
- Summarizing the results of a meeting with a client
- Explaining a new laboratory procedure

Sales

- Requesting funding for a training seminar
- Recommending another staff member for the proposals unit
- Suggesting changes in the performance evaluation system

The following M&K case study illustrates the principles for writing successful memos.

M&K Case Study for Memos

At M&K, memos are written to and from employees at all levels. The following describes one context for writing memos. The lead secretary at M&K's Toronto office has chaired an office committee to encourage more efficient use of the centralized word-processing centre. The committee was formed when the branch manager realized that many technical staff had not been trained to use the centre. This lack of training led to sloppy habits and loss of productivity. Rather than issue a "dictum" from his office, the branch manager established a small committee to review the problem and offer guidelines to the office staff. The memorandum in Model 8-4 at the end of this chapter resulted from the committee's meetings.

Employability Skills

The Conference Board of Canada's *Employability Skills 2000+* states that the ability to communicate in writing is one of the most important skills that you can bring to your place of work. As well, the ability to contribute effectively to the efforts of a team is critical to your success in the workplace. Relevant communication and teamwork skills include the following:

- Read and understand information presented in a variety of forms (e.g., words, graphs, charts, diagrams).
- Write and speak so others pay attention and understand.
- Share information using a range of information and communications technologies (e.g., voice, email, computers).
- Understand and work within the dynamics of a group.
- Accept and provide feedback in a constructive and considerate manner.

- Contribute to a team by sharing information and expertise.*

As a group, prepare an email to be sent to people working in your intended field. The email will be a request for information concerning the nature of the written materials they receive and produce. You can find information about developing questionnaires in Chapter 14. Collect information about the number and kinds of messages received as well as about the number and kinds of messages written.

Report the information to your classmates in a written and graphic message. See Chapter 5 for information on graphics. Choose the form that you feel will most effectively convey your findings.

* *Employability Skills 2000+* Brochure 2000 E/F (Ottawa: The Conference Board of Canada, 2000).

CHAPTER SUMMARY

Emails and memoranda keep the machinery of business, industry, and government moving. In both types of correspondence, abide by the following rules:

1. Know your purpose.
2. Know your readers.
3. Follow correct format.
4. Follow the ABC format.
5. Use the 3Cs strategy for persuasive messages.
6. Stress the "you" attitude.
7. Use attachments for details.
8. Be diplomatic.
9. Edit carefully.
10. Respond quickly.

Memos and emails should strive for brevity, clarity, and tact. Use email when speed and a degree of familiarity are desired. Your relationship with both superiors and subordinates depends in part on how well you write both emails and memoranda.

ASSIGNMENTS

Follow these general guidelines for all the assignments:

- Write brief responses (preferably one page or less).
- Invent addresses when necessary.
- Invent any extra information you may need, but do not change the information presented here.

1. **Email—positive news.** As president of M&K, you have just learned from your accounting firm that last year's profits were even higher than previously expected. Apparently, several large construction jobs had not been counted in the first reporting of profits. You and your managers had already announced individual raises before you learned this good news. Write an email stating that every employee will get a $500 across-the-board bonus, in addition to whatever individual raises have been announced for next year.

2. **Memo—positive news.** Kevin Kehoe, an employee at the Toronto office, is being considered for promotion to Manager of Technical Services. He has asked you to write a memo to the Toronto branch manager on his behalf. Although you now work as a marketing expert at the corporate office, several years ago you worked directly for Kevin on the City of Ottawa project (see Project #2 in the project sheets in Chapter 2). Kevin has asked that your memo deal exclusively with his work on that program. Kevin was manager of the project; you believe that it was largely through his technical expertise, boundless energy, and organizational skills that the project was so successful. Write a memo that conveys this information to the branch manager who is considering Kevin for the promotion. Because the branch manager is new, he is not familiar with the project on which you and Kevin worked. Thus your memo may need to mention some details from Project #2.

3. **Email—negative news.** You are project manager of the construction management group. The current policy in your office states that employees must pass a pre-employment drug

screening before being hired. After that, there are no tests unless you or one of your job supervisors has reason to suspect that an employee is under the influence of drugs on the job.

Lately a number of clients have strongly suggested that you should have a *random* drug-screening policy for all employees in the construction management group. They argue that the on-the-job risk to life and property is great enough to justify this periodic testing. You have consulted with branch managers, who like the idea. You have also talked with the company's attorney, who assures you that such random testing should be legal, given the character of the group's work. After considerable thought, you decide to implement the policy in three weeks. Write an email to all employees of your group and relate this news.

4. **Memo—negative news.** A year ago you introduced a pilot program to M&K's Vancouver office, where you are branch manager. The program gave up to half the office employees the choice to work four 10-hour days each week, as opposed to five 8-hour days. You wanted to offer this flexibility to workers who, for whatever reason, desired longer weekends. As branch manager, you made it clear at the time that you would evaluate the program at the end of the one-year pilot.

Having completed your review, you've decided that employees need to return to the old schedule. Your main reason is that having the office short of staff on Friday (when the four-day employees are gone) has proved awkward for relations with current and prospective clients. On many occasions, clients have called to find that their company contact is not working that day. In addition, the secretarial and word-processing staff that does work on Friday cannot keep up with the end-of-week workload. Whereas you originally thought a split schedule in the office would work, now you know it causes more confusion than it's worth. People in the office are constantly forgetting who is working what schedule, though the schedule is published. So, your memo to office employees must inform them of your decision to discontinue the pilot program and to return to a five-day workweek for the whole office. The change will take place in one month.

5. **Memo—neutral message.** As mailroom supervisor at M&K's Vancouver office, you have a number of changes to announce to employees of the corporate office. Write a memo that clearly relates the following information. Deliveries and pickups of mail, which currently are at 8:30 a.m. and 3:00 p.m., will change to 9:00 a.m. and 3:30 p.m., starting in two weeks. Also, there will be an additional pickup at noon on Monday, Wednesday, and Friday. The mailroom will start picking up mail to go out by Federal Express or any other one-day carrier, rather than the sender having to wait for the carrier's representative to come to the sender's office. The sender must call the mailroom to request the pickup; and the carrier must be told by the sender to go to the mailroom to pick up the package. The memo should also remind employees that the mail does not go out on federal holidays, even though the mailroom continues to pick up mail from the offices on those days.

6. **Email—persuasive message.** For this assignment, choose either (1) a good reference book or textbook in your field of study or (2) an excellent periodical in your field. The book or periodical should be one that could be useful to someone working in a profession, preferably one that you may want to enter yourself.

Now assume that you are an employee of an organization that would benefit by having this book or periodical in its staff library or customer waiting room. Write a one-page email to your supervisor recommending the purchase. You might want to consider criteria such as the following:

- Relevance of information in the source to the job
- Level of material with respect to potential readers
- Cost of book or periodical as compared with its value
- Amount of probable use
- Important features of the book or periodical (such as bibliographies or special sections)

7. **Email—neutral message.** Assume you work in the public relations area at M&K's corporate office in Toronto. Recently your office began designing and producing company project sheets, each of which uses one page to describe a specific project completed by M&K and provides an accompanying graphic. The five projects described at the end of Chapter 2 of this textbook are examples of such project sheets. Write an email to all 15 branch managers and to M&K managers. Give them the information that follows. Beginning next month, project sheets will be written for every M&K job that grosses $10,000 or more. Your office will have each sheet finished within 30 days of project completion and will then send each office the sheets for projects that were coordinated by that office. Then, as time permits, the public relations office will go back to significant previous projects, like the ones in the project sheets, to do additional project sheets on previous work.

8. **Memo—persuasive message.** Assume you work at an M&K office and have no undergraduate degree. You are not yet sure what degree program you want to enter, but you have decided to take one night course each term. Your M&K office has agreed to pay 100% of your education expenses on two conditions. First, before taking each course, you must write a memo of request to your supervisor, justifying the value of the class to your specific job or to your future work with the company. Clearly, your boss wants to know that the course has specific application or that it will form the foundation for later courses. Second, you must receive a C grade or better in every class for which you want reimbursement.

   Write the persuasive memo just described. For the purposes of this assignment, choose one course that you actually have taken or are now taking. However, in your simulated role for the assignment, write as if you have not yet taken the course.

9. **Email—collaborative project #1.** This assignment applies only if your campus offers students the use of email. Complete one of the preceding memo assignments as a group-writing project with two or three members of your class. Set up a plan of work that (1) involves the group in several face-to-face meetings and (2) requires each member of the group to send and receive at least one assignment-related email message to and from every other member of the group.

10. **Email—international communication.** Email messages can be sent around the world as easily as they can be sent to the next office. If you end up working for a company with international offices or clients, you probably will use email to conduct business.

    Investigate the email conventions of one or more countries outside your own. Search for any ways the format, content, or style of international email may differ from email in your country. Gather information by collecting hard copies of email messages sent from other countries, interviewing people who use international email, and/or consulting the library for information on international business communication. Write a memo to your instructor in which you (1) note differences you found and (2) explain why these differences exist. If possible, focus on any differences in culture that may affect email transactions.

11. **Email—collaborative project #2.** Pair up with one or two members of your class. Assume your team has been asked to write a M&K project sheet to add to the project sheets in Chapter 2. Although you do not need to include a photo, hand in a description of the photograph you would recommend for the sheet you are writing.

    After your group has one or two face-to-face meetings to agree on a topic and research agenda, conduct all further team communication by email. One member will be responsible for emailing a draft of the project sheet to the others. Then other members will make all comments and suggestions by email. Once the email communication is complete, print and submit the project sheet along with hard copy of all email correspondence within the group.

TO: Lab, Marketing, and Administrative Staff in U.S. Offices
FROM: Janice Simmons, Benefits Manager
SUBJECT: Training Funds for Fiscal Year 2006
DATE: January 2, 2006

Happy New Year to all of you! I hope you had a good break. I'm writing to announce some guidelines for approved training for the next 12 months—including an increased reimbursement. Please read on to see how these changes affect all lab, marketing, and administrative staff.

1. LAB STAFF
    Maximum Reimbursement: $3,000 (up from $2,000)
    Approval Process: Discuss with your manager 21 days before trip
    Trip Purpose: To improve lab procedures

2. MARKETING STAFF
    Maximum Reimbursement: $4,000 (up from $3,500)
    Approval Process: Discuss with your manager 21 days before trip
    Trip Purpose: To learn new sales techniques

3. ADMINISTRATIVE STAFF
    Maximum Reimbursement: $4,500 (up from $4,000)
    Approval Process: Discuss with your manager 21 days before trip
    Trip Purpose: To improve productivity of office procedures

In the past most employees have failed to make use of their maximum training allotment. I encourage all of you to seek training opportunities that fit the guidelines listed above. **Please note the required 21-day lead time in the approval process.**

Just send me an email if you have any questions about the procedure.

Janice

Begins with casual, friendly tone.

Includes clear purpose statement and three topics to be covered.

Supplies details about topics mentioned in first paragraph.

Uses list and parallel structure for easy reading.

Uses short paragraphs.

Concludes with reminder about an important part of the procedure.

Encourages readers to contact her if there are questions.

Model 8-1 Simple email message

Facsimile reference
One or more blank lines
Date of memo
Reader's name (and position, if appropriate)
Writer's name (and position, if appropriate)
Subject of memo
One or more blank lines
Paragraph: Single spaced (optional–first line indented)
One blank line
Paragraph: Single spaced (optional–first line indented)
One blank line
Paragraph: Single spaced (optional–first line indented)
One blank line
Typist's initials (optional–writer's initals before typist's initials)
One blank line
Enclosure notation
One blank line
Copy notation

Model 8-2   Memo style

MEMORANDUM

DATE: December 4, 2006
TO: Technical Staff
FROM: Ralph Simmons, Technical Manager RS
SUBJECT: New Employee to Help with Technical Editing

Last week we hired an editor to help you produce top-quality reports, proposals, and other documents. This memorandum gives you some background on this change, highlights the credentials of our new editor, and explains what the change will mean to you.

BACKGROUND

At September's staff meeting, many technical staff members noted the excessive time spent editing and proofreading. For example, some of you said that this final stage of writing takes from 15%–30% of the billable time on an average report. Most important, editing often ends up being done by project managers—the employees with the highest billable time.

Despite these editing efforts, many errors still show up in documents that go out the door. Last month I asked a committee of the Society of Technical Writers to review documents produced at Martin & Koffman. Their evaluation report reveals serious problems with our editing process. Given the importance of our documentation—it is the product delivered to our clients—I decided to seek a solution.

SOLUTION: IN-HOUSE EDITOR

To come to grips with this editing problem, the office just hired Ron Polus, an experienced technical editor. He'll start work January 3. For the last six years, Ron has worked as an editor at Jones Technical Services, a Toronto firm that does work similar to ours. Before that he completed a master's degree in technical writing at Sage University in Buffalo.

At next week's staff meeting, we'll discuss the best way to use Ron's skills to help us out. For now, he will be getting to know our work by reviewing recent reports and proposals. Also, the attached list of possible activities can serve as a springboard for our discussion.

CONCLUSION

By working together with Ron, we'll be able to improve the editorial quality of our documents, free up more of your time for technical tasks, and save the client and ourselves some money.

I look forward to meeting with you next week to discuss the best use of Ron's services.

Enclosure
Copy: Ron Polus

continues

Model 8-3 M&K sample memo

Uses informative subject line.

Gives purpose of memo and highlights contents.

Uses side headings for easy reading.

Shows that the change arose from *their* concerns.

Adds evidence from outside observer.

Gives important information about Ron in *first* sentence.

Establishes his credibility.

Refers to attachment.

Focuses on *benefit* of change to reader. Restates next action to occur.

POSSIBLE ACTIVITIES FOR IN-HOUSE EDITOR

1. Reviewing reports at all levels of production

2. Helping to coordinate the writing of proposals

3. Preparing a format manual for the word-processing operators and secretaries

4. Preparing a report/proposal guide for the technical staff

5. Teaching luncheon sessions on editing

6. Teaching writing seminars for the technical staff

7. Working with the graphics department to improve the page design of our documents

8. Helping to write and edit public-relations copy for the company

9. Visiting other offices to help produce consistency in the editing of documents throughout the company

Model 8-3 *continued*

MEMORANDUM

DATE: August 1, 2006
TO: Technical Staff
FROM: Gini Perez, Chair, Word-Processing Committee *GP*
SUBJECT: Word-Processing Suggestions

The Word-Processing Committee has met for six weeks to consider changes in M&K's Word-Processing Centre. This memo highlights the recommendations that have been approved by management.

Please note these changes in your daily use of the company's Word-Processing Centre.

1. **Document status:** Documents will be designated either "rush" or "regular" status, depending on what you request. If at all possible, rush documents will be returned within four hours. Regular documents will be returned within one working day.
2. **Draft stages:** Both users and operators should make every effort to produce no more than three hard-copy drafts of any document. Typically, these would include:

   - **First typed draft** (typed from writer's handwritten or cut-and-paste copy)
   - **Second typed draft** (produced after user has made editing corrections on first-draft copy)
   - **Final typed draft** (produced after user makes final editing changes, after the proofreader makes a pass through the document, and after the operator incorporates final changes into the copy)

3. **New proofreader:** A company proofreader has been hired to improve the quality of our documents. This individual will have an office in the Word-Processing Centre and will review all documents produced by the word-processing operators.

These changes will all take effect August 15. Your efforts to implement them will help improve the efficiency of the centre, the quality of your documents, and the productivity of the company.

Feel free to call me at ext. 567 if you have any questions.

Copy: Jacques Martin

Gives brief purpose statement and overview of contents.

Provides lead-in to list.

Uses numbered list of three main changes reader needs to note.

Emphasizes need for limiting number of hard copies—uses list within list.

Makes it clear when change will take place.

Model 8-4 Memorandum: changes in procedures

CHAPTER 9

Letters

During your career, you will need to write letters when matters of importance—to you or the organization you work for—must be addressed.

Burt Hopkins, a computer systems technician working for M&K in Calgary, says that three letters he has written in his working career have determined his future:

1. The letter he wrote to Martin & Koffman offering his services as a contractor
2. The letter he wrote that secured M&K its largest client in Western Canada
3. The letter he wrote to accept M&K's offer of a management position with the company

Because letters are received by people who are not members of your organization and who often do not know you, they create the reader's first impression of you. For that reason they must be faultless in tone, language, and format.

> **Letter:** a document that conveys information to a member of an organization from someone outside that organization. Also called *correspondence*, letters usually cover one major point and go on one page. This chapter classifies letters into four groups, according to type of message: (1) positive, (2) negative, (3) neutral, and (4) sales.

This chapter covers (1) general rules for letters and (2) specific formats for positive letters, negative letters, neutral letters, and sales letters. Job letters and résumés are discussed in a separate chapter on the job search (Chapter 15).

GENERAL RULES FOR LETTERS

Letters convey your message to readers *outside* your organization. By applying the guidelines in this chapter, you can master the craft of writing successful letters. You need to plan, draft, and revise each letter as if your job depended on it—for it may.

Refer to Model 9-1 on page 224 for an example that demonstrates the guidelines that follow. Later examples in this chapter show specific types of letters.

Letter Guidelines

Letter Guideline 1: Know Your Purpose

Make certain that you have defined your letter's purpose by writing it out as a single sentence. Do not confuse your topic with the purpose and do not confuse your purpose with the letter's purpose. For example:

Topic sentence:	This letter is about the new productivity bonus.
Your purpose:	This letter is to encourage people to make my department more productive.
Purpose of the letter:	This letter is to inform you that you will be rewarded if you are productive.

Obviously, your purpose will be implied when someone reads your letter, but you will receive a more positive response if you are careful to state only the purpose of the letter.

The writer's own purpose is implied in the second paragraph of Model 9-1. That paragraph shows that the writer wishes both to respond to requests for M&K brochures and, just as important, to seek the professor's help in soliciting good graduates for M&K's Calgary office. In a sense, one purpose leads into the other.

Letter Guideline 2: Know Your Readers

Assume that more than one person will read your letter. Letters are normally retained as the record of a communication between people or organizations. It is therefore important that you maintain a more formal tone. Even though the first reader may know you well, you cannot assume that every reader is an acquaintance of yours. Make sure that a general audience can understand the message even if the letter must include technical data.

Model 9-1 is directed to a professor with whom the writer wants to develop a reciprocal relationship—that is, George Lux gives free guest lectures in civil-engineering classes and hopes that the professor will help him inform potential job applicants about M&K.

Letter Guideline 3: Follow Correct Format

Most organizations adopt letter formats that all employees must use consistently. If such formats already exist, use them. If not, use a recognized format and follow it precisely. Following are the basic guidelines:

There are three main letter formats—block, modified block, and simplified. Models 9-2, 9-3, and 9-4 on pages 225–27 show the basic page design of each format; letter examples throughout this chapter use the three formats. As noted, you should follow your own organization's preferred format.

Some of the more important format conventions are listed here. See the models at the end of the chapter for details about spacing.

- *Facsimile reference:* Readers often need to know—for convenience and for the record—when letters have been sent by fax. Type FAX TRANSMISSION or FACSIMILE between the date and inside address for a letter. This line also can be used for other similar notations such as CONFIDENTIAL or PERSONAL or REGISTERED.
- *Reference initials:* If the document has been typed by someone other than the writer, place the typist's initials two lines below the signature block (example: jt). Some organizations prefer that the writer's initials also be included, followed by those of the typist (example: GTY/jt).
- *Enclosure notation:* If attachments or enclosures accompany the letter, type the singular or plural form of *Enclosure* or *Attachment* one or two lines below the reference initials. Some writers also list the item itself (example: Enclosure: Code of Ethics).
- *Copy notation:* If the letter has been sent to anyone other than the recipient, type *Copy* or *Copies* one or two lines below the enclosure notation, followed by the name(s) of the person or persons receiving copies (example: Copy: Jennifer Singh). Some organizations prefer the initials c (for *copy*), cc (for *carbon copy*, even though carbons hardly exist anymore), or pc (for *photocopy*). If you are sending a copy but do not want the original letter to include a reference to that copy,

write *bc* (for *blind copy*) and the person's name only on the copy—not on the original (example: bc: Angela Koffman). Note: only send blind copies when you are certain it is appropriate and ethical to do so.

- *Postscripts:* Items marked *PS* or *P.S.* can appear occasionally in letters. They are sometimes used to add a more personal touch but are considered by many readers to be signs of poor planning, so use them with caution. If used, they appear as the last item on the document (below the copy notation) and can be typed or written in longhand.
- *Multiple-page headings:* Pages following the first page often have a heading that includes the name of the person or company receiving the letter; the date; and the page number. Some organizations may prefer an abbreviated form such as *Lacavalier to Bingham, 2,* without the date.

Letter Guideline 4: Follow the ABC Format for All Letters

Letters subscribe to the same three-part ABC (**A**bstract/**B**ody/**C**onclusion) format used throughout this book. This approach responds to each reader's need to know "What does this document have to do with me?" According to the ABC format, your letter comprises the following three main sections:

- **Abstract:** The abstract states the purpose and usually gives a summary of main points to follow. It includes one or two short paragraphs.
- **Body:** The body contains supporting details and thus makes up the largest part of a letter. You can help your readers by using techniques such as the following:

  Deductive patterns for paragraphs: In this general-to-specific plan, your first sentence should state the point that will help the reader understand the rest of the paragraph. This pattern avoids burying important points in the middle or end of the paragraph, where they might be missed. Fast readers tend to focus on paragraph beginnings and expect to find crucial information there.

  Personal names: If they know you, readers like to see their names in the body of the letter. Your effort here shows concern for the reader's perspective, gives the letter a personal touch, and helps strengthen your personal relationship with the reader. (See the last paragraph in Model 9-1.) Of course, the same technique in direct mail can sometimes backfire, since it is an obvious ploy to create an artificially personal relationship.

  Lists that break up the text: Listed points are a good strategy for highlighting details. Readers are especially attracted to groupings of three items, which create a certain rhythm, attract attention, and encourage recall. Use bullets, numbers, dashes, or other typographical techniques to signal the listed items. For example, the bulleted list in Model 9-1 draws attention to three important points about M&K that the writer wants to emphasize.

  Strongest points first or last: If your letter presents support for something or makes an argument, include the most important points at the beginning and/or at the end—not in the middle.

  Headings to divide information: Even one-page letters sometimes benefit from the emphasis that headings can achieve.

- **Conclusion:** Readers remember first what they read last. The final paragraph of your letter should leave the reader with an important piece of information—for example, (1) a summary of the main idea or (2) a clear statement of what will happen next. For example, the Model 9-1 letter makes an offer that will help to continue the reader's association with the university.

Letter Guideline 5: Use the 3Cs Strategy for Persuasive Messages

The ABC format provides a way to organize all letters. Another pattern of organization for you to use is the "3Cs strategy"—especially when your letter has a persuasive objective. This strategy has three main goals:

- **Capture** interest with a good opener, which tells the reader what the letter can do for him or her.
- **Convince** the reader with supporting points, all of which confirm the opening point that this document will make life easier.
- **Control** the closing, with a statement that puts you in the position of following up on the letter and solidifies your relationship with the reader.

Although Model 9-1 is not overtly persuasive, it has an underlying persuasive purpose. Note how it uses the 3Cs strategy.

Letter Guideline 6: Stress the "You" Attitude

As noted earlier, using the reader's name in the body helps convey interest. But your efforts to see things from the reader's perspective must go deeper than a name reference. For example, you should perform the following tasks:

- **Anticipate questions** your reader might raise and then answer these questions. You can even follow an actual question ("And how will our new testing lab help your firm?") with an answer ("Now M&K's labs can process samples in 24 hours").
- **Replace the pronouns *I*, *me*, and *we* with *you*.** Of course, you have to use first-person pronouns at certain points in a letter, but many pronouns should be second-person. The technique is quite simple. You can change almost any sentence from writer-focused prose ("We feel that this new service will . . .") to reader-focused prose ("You'll find that this new service will . . .").

Model 9-1 shows this "you" attitude by stressing what M&K and the writer himself can do for the professor and his students.

Letter Guideline 7: Use Attachments for Details

Keep text brief by placing details in attachments, which readers can examine later, rather than bogging down the middle of the letter. In this way, the supporting facts are available for future reference, without distracting readers from the main message.

Letter Guideline 8: Be Diplomatic

Without a tactful tone, all your planning and drafting will be wasted. Choose words that will persuade and cajole, not demand. Generally speaking, negative (or "bad news") letters often use the passive voice, whereas positive (or "good news") letters often use the active voice.

For example, the letter in Model 9-1 would fail in its purpose if it sounded too pushy and one-sided about M&K's interest in hiring graduates.

Letter Guideline 9: Edit Carefully

Because letters represent your organization to another, any errors you make can create a negative impression of both you and your organization. In addition, the presence of errors suggests that you do not care enough about your readers to proof-read. Take special care to avoid the following errors:

Mechanics

- Misspelled words of any kind, but especially the reader's name
- Wrong job title (call the reader's office to double-check, if necessary)
- Old address (again, call the reader's office to check)

Grammar

- Lack of subject–verb and pronoun agreement
- Misused commas

Style

- Stuffy phrases such as "as per your request" and "enclosed herewith"
- Long sentences with more than one main and one dependent clause
- Presumptuous phrases such as "Thanking you in advance for . . ."
- Negative tone suggested by phrases such as "We cannot," "I won't," and "Please don't hesitate to . . ."

The last point is crucial and gets more attention later in this chapter. Use the editing stage to rewrite any passage that could be phrased in a more positive tone. You must always keep the reader's goodwill, no matter what the message.

Letter Guideline 10: Respond Quickly

A letter that comes too late will fail in its purpose, no matter how well written. Mail letters within 48 hours of your contact with, or request from, the reader. This rule applies, for example, to letters written in response to the following situations:

- You want to write a follow-up letter after meeting or talking with a client.
- A customer requests information about a product or service.
- You discover that there will be a delay in your supply of a product or service to a customer.

The first sentence in the Model 9-1 letter, for example, shows that George Lux writes the day after his guest lecture. This responsiveness will help secure the professor's goodwill.

SPECIFIC GUIDELINES FOR LETTERS

Letters relay information quickly and keep business flowing. This section gives you specific guidelines for the following types of letters:

- Letters with a positive message
- Letters with a negative message
- Letters with a neutral message
- Letters with a sales message

To be sure, many documents are hybrid forms that combine these patterns. As a technical sales expert for M&K, for example, you may be writing to answer a customer question about a new piece of equipment just purchased from M&K's equipment development group. Your main task is to solve a problem caused by a confusing passage in the owner's manual. At the same time, however, your concern for the customer's satisfaction can pave the way for purchase of a second machine later in the year. Thus, the letter has both a positive message and a sales message. This example also points to a common thread that weaves all four letter types together: the need to maintain the reader's goodwill toward you and your organization.

The following sections present a pattern for each type of correspondence, based on the ABC (**A**bstract/**B**ody/**C**onclusion) format used throughout this text, and one or more brief case studies in which the pattern might be used at M&K.

Positive Letters

Everyone likes to give good news; fortunately, you will often be in the position of providing it when you write. Following are some sample situations:

- Replying to a question about products or services
- Acknowledging that an order has been received
- Recommending a colleague for a promotion or job
- Responding favourably to a routine request
- Responding favourably to a complaint or an adjustment
- Hiring an employee

The trick is to recognize the good-news potential of many situations. Below is an all-purpose format for positive letters, followed by a case study from M&K.

ABC format for positive letters. All positive letters follow one overriding rule. You must always:

> ## State good news immediately!

Any delay gives readers the chance to wonder whether the news will be good or bad, thus causing momentary confusion. Here is a complete outline for positive letters that corresponds to the ABC format:

ABC Format: Positive Letter

Abstract
- Bridge between this letter and last communication with person
- Clear statement of good news you have to report

Body
- Supporting data for main point mentioned in abstract
- Clarification of any questions reader may have
- Qualification, if any, of the good news

Conclusion
- Statement of eagerness to continue relationship, complete project, etc.
- Clear statement, if appropriate, of what step should come next

---

M&K case study for a positive letter. As a project manager at M&K's Calgary office, Nancy Wurcinski has agreed to complete a foundation investigation for a large church in Regina. There are cracks in the basement floor slab and doors that do not close, so her crew will need a day to analyze the problem (observing the site, measuring walls, digging soil borings, taking samples, and so on). She has taken this small job on the condition that she can schedule it around several larger and more profitable projects in the same area during mid-August.

Yesterday Nancy received a letter from the minister (speaking for the church committee) requesting that M&K change the date. He has been asked by the regional headquarters to host a three-day conference at the church during the same time that M&K originally scheduled the project. After checking her project schedule, Nancy determines that she can reschedule the church job. Model 9-5 on page 228 shows her response to the minister.

Negative Letters

It would be nice if all your letters could be as positive as those just described. Unfortunately, the real world does not work like that. You will have many opportunities to display both tact and clarity in relating negative information. Here are a few examples:

- Explaining delays in projects or delivery of services
- Declining invitations or requests
- Registering complaints about products or services
- Refusing to make adjustments based on complaints
- Denying credit
- Giving bad news about employment or performance
- Explaining changes from original orders

The following provides a format for writing sensitive letters with negative information, followed by one application at M&K.

ABC format for negative letters. One main rule applies to all negative letters:

> Buffer the bad news, but still be clear.

Despite the bad news, you want to keep the reader's goodwill. Before you zero in on the main message, spend some time at the beginning building your relationship with the reader by introducing less controversial information. Following is an overall pattern to apply in each negative letter:

ABC Format: Negative Letter

Abstract
- Bridge between your letter and previous communication
- General statement of purpose or appreciation, in an effort to find common bond or area of agreement

Body
- Strong emphasis on what *can* be done, when possible
- Buffered yet clear statement of what cannot be done, with clear statement of reasons for negative news
- Facts that support your views

Conclusion
- Closing remarks that express interest in continued association
- Statement, if appropriate, of what will happen next

M&K case study for a negative letter. Reread the letter situation described in the section on positive letters. Now assume that instead of being able to comply with the minister's request, the writer is unable to complete the work on another date without changing the fee. This change would be necessary because Nancy would have to send a new crew to Regina, rather than using a crew already working on a nearby project.

Nancy knows the church is on a tight budget, but she also knows that M&K would not be in business too long by working for free. Most important, since the church is asking for a change in the original agreement, she believes it is fair to request a change in the fee. Model 9-6 on page 229 is the letter she sends. Note her effort to buffer the negative news.

Neutral Letters

Some letters express neither positive nor negative news. They are simply the routine correspondence written every day to keep businesses and other organizations operating. Some sample situations follow:

- Requesting information about a product or service
- Inviting the reader to an event
- Responding to an invitation or routine request
- Placing orders
- Providing a transmittal letter for fax transmissions
- Sending solicited or unsolicited items through the mail

Use the following outline in writing your neutral letters. Also, refer to the M&K examples that follow the outline.

ABC format for neutral letters. Because the reader usually has no personal stake in the news, neutral letters require less emphasis on tone and tact than other types. Yet they still require careful planning. In particular, always abide by this main rule:

> Be absolutely clear about your inquiry or response.

Neutral letters operate a bit like good-news letters. You need to make your point early, without giving the reader time to wonder about your message. Neutral letters vary greatly in specific organization patterns. The "umbrella plan" suggested here emphasizes the main criterion, which is clarity.

ABC Format: Neutral Letter

Abstract
- Bridge or transition between letter and previous communication, if any
- Precise purpose of letter (request, invitation, response to invitation)

Body
- Details that support the purpose statement, for example—
Description of item(s) requested
Requirements related to the invitation
Description of item(s) being sent

Conclusion
- Statement of appreciation
- Description of actions that should occur next

M&K case studies for neutral letters. Here are four situations that would require a neutral letter; items 2 and 4 provide the context for the examples in Model 9-7 on page 230 and Model 9-8 on page 231:

1. Zach Bowers, a lab assistant, writes to a laboratory supply company for information about a new unbreakable beaker to use in testing.
2. Faron Abdullah, president of the student union at Dawson College, asks representatives of M&K's Montreal office to attend a career fair.
3. Donna Martinich, a geologist, responds to the request of a past client for a copy of a report done three years ago.
4. Farah Linkletter, a supply assistant with M&K's Calgary office, orders three new transits, making sure to emphasize that one is not to include a field case.

Sales Letters

Upon hearing the term *sales letter,* some people have visions of direct-mail requests for magazine subscriptions, vacation land, or diet plans. In this text, however, *sales letters* mean something quite different and, in fact, refer to all of your correspondence with a customer, from the first contact letter through the last thank-you note. The following list gives you some idea of the possibilities for sales letters:

- Starting a relationship ("I'll be calling you . . .")
- Following a phone call ("Good talking to you . . . Can we meet to discuss your needs regarding . . .")
- Following a meeting ("You mentioned that you could use more information . . . so here's a brochure on . . .")
- Following completion of a sale or project ("We enjoyed working with you on . . .")
- Seeking repeat business ("I'd like to know how the new machinery has been working . . .")

Notice that sales letters almost always work together with personal contacts, such as meetings and phone calls. Your goal is to build a continuing relationship with the customer. Consult the following outline when writing sales letters in any context; the M&K example shows the outline in action.

ABC format for sales letters. The one main rule that governs all sales letters is as follows:

> **Help readers solve their problems.**

Customers are interested in your product or service only insofar as it can assist them. You must engage the readers' interest by showing that you understand their needs and can help fulfill them. Here is a plan for writing a successful sales letter. Note reference to the 3Cs (**C**apture/**C**onvince/**C**ontrol) strategy mentioned earlier in the chapter.

ABC Format: Sales Letter

Abstract

(choose one or two to capture attention)

- Cite a surprising fact.
- Announce a new product or service that a client needs.
- Ask a question.
- Show understanding of a client's problem.
- Show potential for solving a client's problem.
- Present a testimonial.
- Make a challenging claim.
- Summarize results of a meeting.
- Answer a question reader previously asked.

Body

(choose one or two to convince the reader)

- Stress one main problem reader has concern about.
- Stress one main selling point of your solution.
- Emphasize what is unique about your solution.
- Focus on value and quality, rather than price.
- Put details in enclosures.
- Briefly explain the value of any enclosures.

Conclusion

(keep control of the next step in sales process)

- Leave the reader with one crucial point to remember.
- Offer to call (first choice) or ask reader to call (last choice).

M&K case study for a sales letter. M&K provides customers with professional services and equipment, so sales letters have an important place in the firm. Barbara Canzi is one employee who writes them almost every day. As a first-year employee with a degree in industrial hygiene, Barbara works in the newly formed asbestos-abatement group. Basically, she helps clients find out if there is any asbestos that needs to be removed from structures, recommends a plan for removal, and has another division of M&K do the work.

Here is one series of sales contacts that involved several letters. First, Barbara sent "cold call" sales letters to 100 schools and small businesses in the Quebec area, suggesting they might want to have their structures checked for unsafe levels of asbestos. The letter contained a reply card. After calling and then meeting with a number of the respondents, she sent individualized follow-up letters answering questions that came up in discussions and providing additional information. After another series of phone calls and meetings with some of the potential customers, she negotiated contracts with five of the businesses and completed the projects. Then, within a few months of completion, she sent a letter proposing additional M&K services and began the cycle again. Model 9-9 on page 232 provides a sample sales letter that Barbara used at the beginning of the cycle.

Employability Skills

The Conference Board of Canada's *Employability Skills 2000+* states that one of the most important indicators of success is the ability to manage one's self. Relevant personal management skills include the following (see the complete *Employability Skills 2000+* in Figure 1-11 on page 27 in Chapter 1 for specific details within each of these categories):

- Demonstrate positive attitudes and behaviours.
- Be responsible.
- Be adaptable.
- Learn continuously.
- Work safely*

Write a letter to the mayor of your local municipality asking him or her to recognize one of the leaders in your community because of demonstrated personal characteristics that have served to enrich your community.

* *Employability Skills 2000+* Brochure 2000 E/F (Ottawa: The Conference Board of Canada, 2000).

CHAPTER SUMMARY

Letters help to keep the machinery of business, industry, and government moving. Letters usually go to readers outside your organization. When writing letters, you should abide by the following rules:

1. Know your purpose.
2. Know your readers.
3. Follow correct format.
4. Follow the ABC format for all letters.
5. Use the 3Cs strategy for persuasive messages.
6. Stress the "you" attitude.
7. Use attachments for details.
8. Be diplomatic.
9. Edit carefully.
10. Respond quickly.

In addition to following these basics, you need to follow specific strategies for the four basic business letters. In letters with a positive message, the good news always goes first. In letters with a negative message, work on maintaining goodwill by placing a "buffer" before the bad news. Neutral letters, such as requests for information, should be absolutely clear in their message. Sales letters should show an interest in solving the readers' problems more than an eagerness to sell a product or service.

ASSIGNMENTS

Follow these general guidelines for all the assignments:

- Write brief responses (preferably one page or less).
- Print or design a letterhead when necessary.
- Use whichever letter format your instructor requires.
- Invent addresses when necessary.
- Invent any extra information you may need, but do not change the information presented here.

1. **Positive letter—job offer.** Assume that you are the personnel director for M&K's Vancouver office. Yesterday, you and your hiring committee decided to offer a job to Ali Talifa, one of 10 recent graduates you interviewed for an entry-level position as a lab technician. Write Ali an offer letter and indicate a starting date (in two weeks), a specific salary, and the need for him to sign and return an acceptance letter immediately. In the interview, you outlined the company's benefit plan, but you are enclosing with your letter a detailed description of fringe benefits (such as long-term disability insurance, retirement plan, and vacation policy). Although Ali is your first choice for this position, you will offer the job to another top candidate if Ali is unable to start in two weeks at the salary you stated in the letter.

2. **Positive letter—recommendation.**
   Option A: Select one of the model résumés in Chapter 15. Assume you have known the writer in your capacity as professor, supervisor, or colleague. Now write a letter of recommendation that highlights what you see as the person's strong points. Keep in mind the job objective on the résumé. Have a specific job and reader in mind for this exercise.
   Option B: Pair up with a class colleague and share information about your respective academic backgrounds, work experiences, and career goals. Now write a letter that recommends your counterpart for either (a) a scholarship based on grades, need, and/or some other criterion; (b) a specific job; (c) an internship in an organization related to the person's career interest; or (d) an academic award. Give yourself a simulated role that would give you first-hand knowledge of the person's background.
   Option C: Assume that a professor in a class you have already completed—and a class that you found valuable—has asked you to write a letter of recommendation for the professor's promotion package at the university. You are assuming that this individual, in assembling the promotion materials, is permitted to include reference letters from a variety of sources, such as fellow professors and former students. Your letter should address only what you know about the professor's abilities from your first-hand experience.

3. **Positive letter—favourable response to complaint.** The following letter was written in response to a complaint from the office manager at M&K's Calgary office. She wrote to the manufacturer that the lunchroom toaster oven broke down just three days after the warranty expired. Although she did not ask for a specific monetary adjustment, she did make clear her extreme dissatisfaction with the product. The manufacturer responded with the following letter. Be prepared to discuss what is right and what is wrong with the letter. Also, rewrite it using this chapter's guidelines.

This letter is in response to your August 3 complaint about the Justrite toaster oven you purchased six months ago for your lunchroom at Martin & Koffman. We understand that the "light-dark" adjustment switch for the toaster device broke shortly after the warranty expired.

Did you know that last year our toaster oven was rated "best in its class" and "most reliable" by *Consumers Count* magazine? Indeed, we have received so few complaints about the product that a recent survey of selected purchasers revealed that 98.5% of first-time purchasers of our toaster ovens are pleased that they chose our products and would buy another.

Please double-check your toaster oven to make sure that the switch is broken—it may just be temporarily stuck. We rarely have had customers make this specific complaint about our product. But if the switch is in need of repair, return the entire appliance to us, and we will have it repaired free of charge or have a new replacement sent to you. We stand behind our product, since the warranty period only recently expired.

It is our sincere hope that you continue to be a satisfied customer of Justrite appliances.

---

4. **Negative letter—explanation of project delay.** You work for M&K's Vancouver office. As project manager for the construction of a small strip-shopping centre, you have

had delays about halfway through the project because of bad weather. Even worse, the forecast is for another week of heavy rain. Yesterday, just when you thought nothing else could go wrong, you discovered that your concrete supplier, Atlas Concrete, has a truck drivers' strike in progress. Because you still need half the concrete for the project, you have started searching for another supplier.

Your client, an investor/developer named Tanya Lee located in Victoria, probably will be upset by any delays in construction, whether or not they are within your control. Write her a letter in which you explain weather and concrete problems. Try to ease her concern, especially because you will want additional jobs from her in the future.

5. **Negative letter—declining a request.** Assume that you work at the M&K office that provided seminars in technical writing to federal government employees (see Project #5 in Chapter 2). Word of your good work has spread to the deputy minister. He has asked you, as manager of the training project, to deliver a 20-minute speech on the importance of technical writing to a group of civil service managers. Unfortunately, you have already agreed to be at a project site in another province on that day, and you cannot reschedule the site visit. Write to the deputy minister—who is both a former and, you hope, future client—and decline the request. Though you know he expressly wanted *you* to speak, offer to send a substitute from your office.

6. **Negative letter—change in project scope and schedule.** As branch manager at the Calgary office, you oversee many of the office's large accounts. One important account is a company that owns and operates a dozen radio and television stations throughout the Prairies. On one recent project, M&K engineers and technicians did the foundation investigation for, and supervised construction of, a new transmitting tower for a television station in Saskatoon. First, your staff members completed a foundation investigation, at which time they examined the soils and rock below grade at the site. On the basis of what they learned, M&K ordered the tower and the guy wires that connect it to the ground. Once the construction crew actually began excavating for the foundation, however, they found mud that could not support the tower's foundation. While unfortunate, sometimes actual soil conditions cannot be predicted by the preliminary study. Because of this discovery of mud, the tower must be shifted to another location on the site. As a result, the precut guy wires will be the wrong length for the new site, requiring M&K to order wire extenders. The extenders will arrive in two weeks, delaying the tower placement by that much time. All other parts of the project are on schedule, so far.

Your client, Ms. Sharon West of Prairie Media Systems in Edmonton, doesn't understand much about soils and foundation work. But she does understand what construction delays mean to the profit margin of her firm's new television station as it attempts to compete with other stations in Saskatoon. You need to console this important client, while informing her of this recent finding.

7. **Neutral letter—response to request for information.** As reservations clerk for the Schooner Inn, you just received a letter from Jerald Pelletier, an administrative secretary making arrangements for a meeting of M&K managers. The group is considering holding its quarterly meeting in Halifax in six months. Pelletier has asked you to send some brief information on hotel rates, conference facilities (meeting rooms), and availability. Send him some room rates for double and single rooms, and let him know that you have four conference rooms to rent out at $50 each per day. Also, tell him that at this time the hotel rooms and conference rooms are available for the three days he mentioned.

8. **Neutral letter—request for information.** For this assignment choose one of the projects in the project sheets in Chapter 2. Assume you are a potential client of M&K and have happened onto this project, which is similar to one your organization may need completed in the near future. Although you are not yet at the stage where you want to receive proposals, you would like additional information about firms that might be interested in your project. Using this context and information in the project description, write to the marketing manager of M&K for more information. Be specific about what you want to receive.

9. **Sales letter—to M&K.** Select a product or service that you are familiar with because of home, work, or school experience. Now assume that you are responsible for marketing this product or service to Ms. Janis Black, purchasing agent for M&K. In a phone conversation earlier today, she showed some initial interest in purchasing the product or service for her firm. In fact, you have managed to set up a meeting for two weeks from today, after she returns from a business trip. Now you need to write a follow-up letter in which you summarize the phone conversation, confirm the meeting date and time, and offer some additional information about your product or service that will keep her interest.

   In selecting your product or service, you might want to review the information about M&K contained in Chapter 2. Following are some sample products and services that Janis must routinely evaluate for use by the firm:

   * Cleaning supplies, such as lavatory soap and paper towels
   * Laboratory equipment, such as glass beakers and lab coats
   * Office materials, such as notepads and pencils
   * Office equipment, such as fax machines and pencil sharpeners
   * Leased products, such as automobiles for managers and salespeople

10. **Sales letter—from M&K.** For this assignment, choose one of the project sheets in Chapter 2. Although you will be using the sheets as a source of information in writing your letter, you will not be sending the sheets as an attachment.

   Option A: Assume that you are an M&K employee writing to a new client. This client has shown initial interest in the service or product described in the project sheet you're using for this assignment. You've had one phone conversation with the potential client. Now you hope your letter will lay the foundation for a personal meeting. Write a sales letter that briefly describes (1) the service or product on the project sheet and/or (2) your success on the specific project.

   Option B: Assume you are an M&K employee writing to the same client for whom you completed the project described on the sheet. You have heard there may be similar work available with this client, so you are seeking repeat business. Write your follow-up letter, referring to the success on the project and seeking information about possible future work.

200 Fourth Avenue NW
Calgary AB T2N 0N3
(403) 555-7524

August 2, 2006

Professor Willard R. Burton, Ph.D.
Department of Civil Engineering
Southern Alberta Institute of Technology
1301 16th Avenue NW
Calgary AB T2M 0L4

Dear Professor Burton:

Subject?

Bridge needed

Thanks very much for your hospitality during my visit to your class yesterday. I appreciated the interest your students showed in my presentation on stress fractures in highway bridges. Their questions were very perceptive.

You may recall that several students requested further information on Martin & Koffman, so I have enclosed a dozen brochures for any students who may be interested. As you know, job openings for civil-engineering graduates have increased markedly in the past five years. Some of the best opportunities lie in these three areas of the discipline:

• Evaluation of environmental problems
• Renovation of the nation's infrastructure
• Management of construction projects

These areas are three of M&K's main interests. As a result, we are always searching for top-notch graduates from solid departments like yours.

Again, I enjoyed my visit back to SAIT last Friday, Professor Burton. Please call when you want additional guest lectures by me or other members of the M&K staff.

Sincerely,

George F. Lux

George F. Lux, P.Eng

Enclosures

Side annotations:

Expresses appreciation *and* provides lead-in to body.

Responds to question that arose at class presentation.

Uses bulleted list to emphasize information of value to professor's students.

Adds unobtrusive reference to M&K's needs.

Closes with offer to visit class again.

Includes reference to enclosures.

Model 9-1   M&K sample letter

Letterhead of your organization

Two or more blank lines (adjust space to centre letter on page)

Date of letter

Two or more blank lines (adjust space to centre letter on page)

Name, title, company name, and address of reader

One blank line

Greeting

One blank line

Paragraph: single-spaced (indenting optional)

One blank line

Paragraph: single-spaced (indenting optional)

One blank line

Paragraph: single-spaced (indenting optional)

One blank line

Complimentary close

Three blank lines (for signature)

Typed name and title

One blank line

Typist's initials (optional: Writer's initials before typist's initials)

Computer file # (if applicable)

One blank line (optional)

Enclosure notation

One blank line (optional)

Copy notation

Model 9-2 Block style for letters

Letterhead of your organization

Two or more blank lines (adjust space to centre letter on page)

Date of letter

Two or more blank lines (adjust space to centre letter on page)

Name, title, company name, and address of reader

One blank line

Greeting

One blank line

Paragraph: single-spaced, with first line indented 5 spaces

One blank line

Paragraph: single-spaced, with first line indented 5 spaces

One blank line

Paragraph: single-spaced, with first line indented 5 spaces

One blank line

Complimentary close

Three blank lines (for signature)

Typed name and title

One blank line

Typist's initials (optional: Writer's initials before typist's initials)

Computer file # (if applicable)

One blank line (optional)

Enclosure notation

One blank line (optional)

Copy notation

Model 9-3 Modified block style (with indented paragraphs) for letters

Letterhead of your organization

Two or more blank lines (adjust space to centre letter on page)

Date of letter

Two or more blank lines (adjust space to centre letter on page)

Name, title, company name, and address of reader

Three blank lines

Short subject line

Three blank lines

Paragraph: single-spaced, no indenting

One blank line

Paragraph: single-spaced, no indenting

One blank line

Paragraph: single-spaced, no indenting

Five blank lines (for signature)

Typed name and title

One blank line (optional)

Typist's initials (optional: Writer's initials before typist's initials)

Computer file # (if applicable)

One blank line (optional)

Enclosure notation

One blank line (optional)

Copy notation

Model 9-4   Simplified style for letters

200 Fourth Avenue NW
Calgary AB T2N 0N3
(403) 555-7524

July 23, 2006

The Reverend Mr. John C. Davidson
Maxwell Street Church
43 Maxwell Street
Regina SK S3Y 4P1

Dear Reverend Davidson:

Thanks for your letter asking to reschedule the church project from mid-August to another, more convenient time. Yes, we'll be able to do the project on one of two possible dates in September, as explained below.

As you know, M&K originally planned to fit your foundation investigation between two other projects planned for the Regina area. In making every effort to lessen church costs, we would be saving money by having a crew already on site in your area—rather than having to charge you mobilization costs to and from Regina.

As it happens, we have just agreed to perform another large project in the Regina area beginning on September 18. We would be glad to schedule your project either before or after that job. Specifically, we could be at the church site for our one-day field investigation on either September 17 or September 25, whichever date you prefer.

Please call me by September 2 to let me know your scheduling preference for the project. In the meantime, have a productive and enjoyable conference at the church next month.

Sincerely,

Nancy Wurcinski

Nancy Wurcinski, P.Eng
Project Manager

NW/mh
File #34678

Marginal notes:

Mentions letter that prompted this response. Gives good news *immediately.*

Reminds reader of rationale for original schedule—*cost savings.*

Offers two options—both save the church money.

Shows M&K's flexibility.

Makes clear what should happen next.

Model 9-5   Positive letter in block style

200 Fourth Avenue NW
Calgary AB T2N 0N3
(403) 555-7524

July 23, 2006

The Reverend Mr. John C. Davidson
Maxwell Street Church
43 Maxwell Street
Regina SK S3Y 4P1

Dear Reverend Davidson:

Thanks for your letter asking to reschedule the foundation project at your church from mid-August to late August, because of the regional conference. I am sure you are proud that Maxwell was chosen as the conference site.

One reason for our original schedule, as you may recall, was to save the travel costs for a project crew going back and forth between Calgary and Regina. Because M&K has several other jobs in the area, we had planned not to charge you for travel.

We can reschedule the project, as you request, to a more convenient date in late August, but the change will increase project costs from $1,500 to $2,400 to cover travel. At this point, we just don't have any other projects scheduled in your area in late August that would help defray the additional expenses. Given our low profit margin on such jobs, that additional $900 would make the difference between our firm making or losing money on the foundation investigation at your church.

I'll call you next week, Reverend Davidson, to select a new date that would be most suitable. M&K welcomes its association with the Maxwell Street Church and looks forward to a successful project in late August.

Sincerely,

Nancy Wurcinski

Nancy Wurcinski, P.Eng
Project Manager

NW/mh
File #34678

Provides "bridge" and compliments Davidson on conference.

Reminds him about original agreement—in tactful manner.

Phrases negative message as *positively* as possible, giving rationale for necessary change.

Makes it clear what will happen next. Ends on *positive* note.

Model 9-6 Negative letter in modified block style (with indented paragraphs)

Dawson
College

January 4, 2007

Ms. Angela Koffman, Manager
Martin & Koffman
2219 Rue Decarie
Montreal PQ H4T 1P9

Dear Ms. Koffman:

States purpose clearly.

Martin & Koffman has hired eight graduates of Dawson College since 1991. To help continue that tradition, we would like to invite you to the collegeís first Career Fair, to be held February 21, 2007, from 8 a.m. until noon.

Describes Career Fair and its importance.

Sponsored by the Student Government Association, the Career Fair gives students the opportunity to get to know more about a number of potential employers. We give special attention to organizations, like M&K, that have already had success in hiring Dawson College graduates. Indeed, we have already had a number of inquiries about whether your firm will be represented at the fair.

Shows value of event to M&K.

Gives clear instructions for participating.

Participating in the Career Fair is simple. We will provide you with a booth where one or two M&K representatives can talk with students that come by to ask about your firm's career opportunities. Feel free to bring along whatever brochures or other written information would help our students learn more about M&K's products and services.

States appreciation and indicates what will happen next.

I will call you next week, Ms. Koffman, to give more details about the fair and offer a specific booth location. We at Dawson College look forward to building on our already strong association with M&K.

Sincerely,

Faron G. Abdulla

Faron G. Abdullah, President
Student Government Association

Copy: Gene Abrams, Placement Director

14 Chemin Parizeau
Montreal PQ
H1R 9B0
(514) 555-0272

Model 9-7 Neutral letter (invitation) in block style

200 Fourth Ave NW
Calgary AB T2N 0W3
(403) 555-7524

April 2, 2007

Faraday Supply Company
34 Main St.
Lethbridge AB T2N 4P4

ORDER FOR FIELD TRANSITS

Yesterday I called Ms. Gayle Nichols to ask what transits you had in current inventory.
Having considered what you have in stock, I wish to order those listed below.

Please send us these items:

    1. One Jordan #456 Transit, with special field case
    2. One Smith-Beasley #101FR, with special field case
    3. One Riggins #6NMG, without special field case

Note that we *do* want the special field cases with the Jordan and Smith-Beasley units, but do
not want the case with the Riggins unit.

Please send the units and the bill to my attention. As always, we appreciate doing business
with Faraday.

Farah Linkletter

Farah Linkletter
Supply Assistant

gh

Provides bridge
to previous con-
tact.

States purpose
clearly.

Gives *exact*
information
needed by
reader.

Emphasizes
important details
about the order.

States exactly
what should
happen next.

Model 9-8 Neutral letter (placing order) in simplified style

Martin & Koffman

328 Ravine Road
Toronto ON M2P 8J6
416-555-8438

Simplified style eliminates salutation and closing.

August 21, 2006

Mr. James Swartz, Safety Director
Jessup County School System
1111 Chemin Rouge
Pointe Claire PQ H1R 7Q7

Uses subject line to gain attention.

Refers to previous successful work.

Leads in naturally to letter's subject (asbestos abatement).

Comforts reader by showing how problem can be discovered and solved.

Reinforces relationship between writer's and reader's organizations.

Refers briefly to enclosures; stays in control by mentioning follow-up phone call.

NEW ASBESTOS-ABATEMENT SERVICE NOW AVAILABLE

We enjoyed working with you last year, James, to update your entire fire alarm system. Given the current concern in the country about another safety issue, asbestos, we wanted you to know that our staff now does abatement work.

As you know, many of the province's school systems were constructed during years when asbestos was used as a primary insulator. No one knew then, of course, that the material can cause illness and even premature death for those who work in buildings where asbestos was used in construction. Now we know that just a small portion of asbestos produces a major health hazard.

Fortunately, there's a way to tell whether you have a problem: the asbestos survey. This procedure, done by our certified asbestos-abatement professionals, results in a report that tells whether or not your buildings are affected. And if we find asbestos, we can remove it for you.

Jessup showed real foresight in modernizing its alarm system last year, James. Your desire for a thorough job on that project was matched, as you know, by the approach we take to our business. Now we'd like to help give you the peace of mind that will come from knowing that either (1) there is no asbestos problem in your 35 structures or (2) you have removed the material.

The enclosed brochure outlines our asbestos services. I'll call you in a few days to see whether M&K can help you out.

Barbara Canzi

Barbara H. Canzi
Certified Industrial Hygienist

BHC/sg

Model 9-9 Sales letter in simplified style

CHAPTER 10

Informal Reports

Alain Murphy, a salesperson for M&K's Montreal office, has a full day ahead. Besides having to make some sales calls in the morning, he must complete two short reports back in the office. The first is a short progress report to Bytown Bearings, a company that recently hired M&K to train its technical staff in effective sales techniques. According to the contract, Alain must send a progress report to Bytown every three weeks during the project; as project manager, Alain has overseen the efforts of three M&K trainers for the past three weeks. Alain's second report is internal. His boss wants a short report recommending ways that M&K can pursue more training projects such as the Bytown job.

Like Alain Murphy, you will spend much of your career writing informal reports. Though short and easy to read like letters and memos, informal reports have more substance, are longer, and thus require more organization skills than correspondence. A working definition follows:

> **Informal report:** this document contains about two to five pages of text, not including

attachments. It has more substance than a simple letter or memo but less than a formal report. It can be directed to readers either outside or inside your organization. If outside, it may be called a *letter report*. If inside, it may be called a *memo report*. In either case, its purpose can be informative (to clarify or explain), or persuasive (to convince), or both.

This chapter has three sections. The first shows you when to use informal reports in your career by describing some M&K cases. The second provides 10 main writing guidelines that apply to both letter and memo reports. The third focuses on specific suggestions for writing five common types of informal reports.

At the end of the chapter are examples, with marginal annotations. They are specific, real-life applications of the chapter's writing guidelines. As such, the models will help you complete chapter assignments and do actual reports on the job. During your career, you will write many types of informal reports other than those presented here. If you grasp this chapter's principles, however, you can adapt to other formats.

WHEN TO USE INFORMAL REPORTS

As noted in the definition just given, informal reports are clearly distinguishable from both formal reports and routine letters and memos. Early in your career, however, you may have trouble deciding exactly where to draw the line. To help you do this, the two sections that follow briefly describe situations in which informal reports would be appropriate.

Letter Reports at M&K

Written to people outside your organization, letter reports use the format of a business letter because of their brevity. Yet they include more detail than a simple business letter. Here are some sample projects at M&K that would require letter reports:

- **Training recommendation:** M&K's corporate training staff recommends changes in the training program of a large construction company. Courses that are recommended include technical writing, interpersonal communication, and quality management.
- **Sea floor study:** M&K's staff writes a preliminary report on the stability of the sea floor where an oil rig may be located off the coast of Africa. This preliminary study includes only a survey of information on file about the site. The final report, involving fieldwork, will be longer and more formal.
- **Marketing report:** A marketing specialist at the corporate office completes a study on "New Markets Beyond 2006." The report has been solicited by a professional marketing association that M&K belongs to.
- **Asbestos project:** M&K's staff reports to a suburban school board about possible asbestos contamination of an old elementary school. After two days on-site, the crew of two technicians determined that the structure had no asbestos in its walls, plumbing, floors, or storerooms.
- **Environmental study:** M&K's Vancouver staff reports to the local Pollution Probe chapter on the possible environmental effects of a tourist complex that has been proposed for a coastal area where eagles often nest. The project involved one site visit, interviews with a biologist, and some brief library research.
- **Equipment design project:** M&K's equipment-development staff reports to a manufacturer on tentative designs for a computer-controlled device to cut plastic drainage pipe. The project involved several days' drafting work.

As these examples show, letter reports are the best format for projects with a limited scope. Also, this informal format is a good sales strategy when dealing with customers greatly concerned about the cost of your work. When reading letter reports, they realize—consciously or subconsciously—that these documents cost them less money than formal reports. Your use of letter reports for small jobs shows a sensitivity to their budget and may help gain their repeat work. See Model 10-1 on pages 253–54 for a letter report based on a small project at M&K.

Memo Reports at M&K

Memo reports are the informal reports that go back and forth among M&K's own employees. Though in memorandum format, they include more technical detail and are longer than routine memos. The following situations at M&K show the varied contexts of memo reports:

- **Need for testing equipment:** Joan Watson, a lab technician in the Toronto office, evaluates a new piece of chemical testing equipment for her department manager, Wes Powell. Powell discusses the report with his manager.
- **Personnel problem:** Werner Hoffman, a field engineer in the Calgary office, writes to his project manager, Kim Lubinski, about disciplinary problems with a field hand. Hoffman discusses the report with his manager and with the personnel manager.
- **Need for computer workstations:** Susan Gindle, an equipment development technician in Vancouver, writes a report to the equipment development manager, Li Po. Gindle recommends the company purchase five computer workstations from Simulon, Inc., as opposed to similar stations from Sonet, Inc. Po will discuss the report with the company's vice president for research and with the finance officer.

- **Progress in hiring minorities:** Aziz Rashid, personnel manager, reports to Lynn Redmond, vice president of human resources, on the company's initial efforts to hire more minorities. Redmond will discuss Rashid's progress report with the company president and with all office managers.
- **Report on training session:** Pamela Belanger, a field engineer in Montreal, reports to her manager, Angela Koffman, on a one-week course she took in Omaha on new techniques for removing asbestos from buildings. Koffman circulates the report through her office, then sends copies to the manager of every company office and to corporate headquarters in Toronto, because asbestos projects are becoming common throughout the firm.

These five reports will require enough detail to justify writing memo reports rather than simple memos. As for audience, each report will go directly to, or at least be discussed with, readers at high levels within the company. Clearly, good memo reports can help advance your career. Model 10-2 on pages 255–56 provides an annotated example of a memo report about proposed computer software at M&K.

GENERAL GUIDELINES

The following 10 guidelines focus mainly on report format.

For Informal Reports

Informal Report Guideline 1: Plan Well Before You Write

Like other chapters in this book, this section emphasizes the importance of the planning process. Complete the Planning Form found in Chapter 1 for each assignment in this chapter, as well as for informal reports you write in your career. Before you begin writing a draft, use the Planning Form to record specific information about the following points:

- The document's purpose
- The variety of readers who will receive the document
- The needs and expectations of readers, particularly decision makers
- An outline of the main points to be covered in the body

Informal Report Guideline 2: Use Letter or Memo Format

Model 10-1 shows that a letter report follows about the same format as a typical business letter (see Chapter 9). For example, both are produced on letterhead and both often include the reader's name, the date, and the page number on all pages after the first. Yet the format of letter reports differs from that of letters in the following respects:

- The greeting is sometimes left out or replaced by an Attention line, especially when your letter report will go to many readers in an organization.
- A report title often comes immediately after the inside address. It identifies the specific project covered in the report. You may have to use several lines because the project title should be described fully, in the same words that the reader would use.
- Spacing between lines might be single, one-and-one-half, or double, depending on the reader's preference.

Model 10-2 shows the typical format for a memo report. Like most memos, it includes "date/to/from/subject" information at the top and has the reader's name, date, and page number on every page after the first. Also, both memos and memo reports have a Subject line that should engage interest, give readers their first quick look at your topic, and be both specific and concise—for example, "Fracture Problems with Moulds 43-D and 42-G" is preferable to "Problems with Moulds."

There are, however, some format differences between memos and memo reports. Memo reports are longer and tend to contain more headings than routine memos. Also, spacing between lines varies from company to company, though one-and-one-half or double spacing is most common.

Informal Report Guideline 3: Make the Text Visually Appealing

Your letter or memo report must compete with other documents for each reader's attention. Here are three visual devices that help get attention, maintain interest, and highlight important information:

- Bulleted points, for short lists like this one
- Numbered points, for lists that are longer or that include a list of ordered steps
- Frequent use of headings and subheadings

Headings are particularly useful in memo and letter reports. As Models 10-1 and 10-2 show, they give readers much-needed visual breaks. Since informal reports have no table of contents, headings also help readers locate information quickly. (Chapters 4 and 5 give more detail on headings and other features of page design.)

Informal Report Guideline 4: Use the ABC Format for Organization

Headings and lists attract attention, but these alone will not keep readers interested. You also need to organize information effectively. Most technical documents, including informal reports, follow what this book calls the ABC format. As mentioned, this approach to organization includes three parts: (1) **A**bstract, (2) **B**ody, and (3) **C**onclusion.

- **Abstract:** Start with a capsule version of the information most needed by decision makers.
- **Body:** Give details in the body of the report, where technical readers are most likely to linger a while to examine supporting evidence.
- **Conclusion:** Reserve the end of the report for a description or list of findings, conclusions, or recommendations.

Abstract, body, and *conclusion* are only generic terms. They indicate the *types* of information included at the beginning, middle, and end of your reports—not necessarily the exact headings you will use. The next three guidelines give details on the ABC format as applied to memo and letter reports.

Informal Report Guideline 5: Call the Abstract an "Introductory Summary"

Abstracts should give readers a summary, the big picture. This text suggests that in informal reports, you label this overview as "Introductory Summary"—a term that gives the reader a good idea of what the section contains. (You do have the option of leaving off a heading label. In this case, above the first body heading of the report, your first few paragraphs would contain the introductory summary information.)

In letter reports, the introductory summary comes immediately after the title. In memo reports, it comes after the Subject line. Note that informal reports do not require long, drawn-out beginnings; just one or two paragraphs in this first section will give readers three essential pieces of information:

1. **Purpose** of the report—why are you writing it?
2. **Scope** statement—what range of information does the report contain?
3. **Summary** of essentials—what main information does the reader most want or need to know?

Informal Report Guideline 6: Put Important Details in the Body

The body section provides details needed to expand on the outline presented in the introductory summary. If your report goes to a diverse audience, managers often read the quick overview in the introductory summary and then skip to conclusions and recommendations. Technical readers, on the other hand, may look first to the body section(s), where they expect to find supporting details presented in a logical fashion. In other words, here is your chance to make your case and to explain points thoroughly.

Yet the discussion section is no place to ramble. Details must be organized so well and put forth so logically that the reader feels compelled to read on. And remember, background information—raw data—should not be part of the body. Deal with the results in the body and put background information in the appendices. Here are three main suggestions for organization:

- **Use headings generously.** Each time you change a major or minor point, consider whether a heading change would help the reader. Informal reports should include at least one heading per page.
- **Precede subheadings with a lead-in passage.** Here you mention the subsections to follow, before you launch into the first subheading. (e.g., "This section covers three phases of the field study: clearing the site, collecting samples, and classifying samples.") This passage does for the entire section exactly what the introductory summary does for the entire report—it sets the scene for what is to come by providing a road map.
- **Move from general to specific in paragraphs.** Start each paragraph with a topic sentence that includes your main point. Then give supporting details. This approach always keeps your most important information at the beginnings of paragraphs, where readers tend to focus first while reading.

Another important consideration in organizing the report discussion is the way you handle facts as opposed to opinions.

Informal Report Guideline 7: Separate Fact from Opinion

Some informal reports contain strong points of view. Others contain only subtle statements of opinion, if any. In either case, you must avoid any confusion about what constitutes fact or opinion. The safest approach in the report discussion is to move logically from findings to your conclusions and, finally, to your recommendations. Since these terms are often confused, here are some working definitions:

- **Findings:** Facts you uncover (e.g., you observed severe cracks in the foundations of two adjacent homes in a subdivision).
- **Conclusions:** Ideas or beliefs you develop based on your findings (e.g., you conclude that foundation cracks occurred because the two homes were built on soft fill, where original soil had been replaced by construction scraps). Opinion is clearly a part of conclusions.
- **Recommendations:** Suggestions or action items based on your conclusions (e.g., you recommend that the foundation slab be supported by adding concrete posts below it). Recommendations are almost exclusively made up of opinions.

Informal Report Guideline 8: Focus Attention in Your Conclusion

Letter and memo reports end with a section labelled either *Conclusion, Closing, Conclusions,* or *Conclusions and Recommendations.* Choose the wording that best fits the content of your report. In all cases, this section gives details about your major findings, your conclusions, and, if called for, your recommendations. People often remember best what they read last, so think about what you place at the end of a report.

The precise amount of detail in your conclusion depends on which of the following two options you choose for your particular report:

Option 1:   If your major conclusions or recommendations have already been stated in the discussion, then you only need to restate them briefly to reinforce their importance (see Model 10-2).

Option 2:   If the discussion leads up to, but has not covered, these conclusions or recommendations, then you may want to give more detail in this final section (see Model 10-1).

As in Models 10-1 and 10-2, lists often are mixed with paragraphs in the conclusion. Use lists if you believe they will help readers remember your main points.

Informal Report Guideline 9: Use Attachments for Details

The trend today is to avoid lengthy text in informal reports. Yet technical detail is often needed for support. One solution to this dilemma is to replace as much report text as possible with clearly labelled attachments, which could include the following items:

- **Tables and figures:** Illustrations in informal reports usually appear in attachments unless they are crucial to the text. Memo and letter reports are so short, however, that attached illustrations are easily accessible.
- **Costs:** It is best to list costs on a separate sheet. First, you do not want to bury important financial information within paragraphs. Second, readers often need to circulate cost information, and a separate cost attachment is easy to photocopy and send.

Informal Report Guideline 10: Edit Carefully

Many readers judge you on how well you edit a report. A few spelling errors or some careless punctuation makes you look unprofessional. Your career and your firm's future can depend on your ability to write final drafts carefully. Chapter 16 and the Handbook at the end of this book give detailed information about editing. For now, remember the following basic guidelines:

- Keep most sentences short and simple.
- Proofread several times for mechanical errors, such as misspellings (particularly personal names).
- Triple-check all cost figures for accuracy.
- Make sure all attachments are included, are mentioned in the text, and are accurate.
- Check the format and wording of all headings and subheadings.
- Ask colleagues to check over the report.

These 10 guidelines help memo and letter reports accomplish their objectives. Remember, both your supervisors and your clients will judge you as much on communication skills as they do on technical ability. Consider each report a part of your résumé.

SPECIFIC GUIDELINES FOR FIVE INFORMAL REPORTS

Report types vary from company to company. The ones described here are only a sampling of what you will be asked to write on the job; they were chosen because they are common, because they can be written as either memo reports or letter reports, and because they incorporate the writing patterns described in Chapters 6 and 7. If you master these five informal reports, you can probably handle other types that come your way.

The next sections include an ABC format for each report discussed, brief case studies from M&K, and report models based on the cases. Remember to consult Chapters 6 and 7 if you need to review general patterns of organization used in informal and formal reports.

For Problem Analyses

Every organization faces both routine and complex problems. The routine ones often get handled without much paperwork; they are discussed and then solved. But other problems often need to be described in reports, particularly if they involve many people, are difficult to solve, or have been brewing for a long time. Use the following working definition of a report that analyzes a problem:

> **Problem analysis:** this informal report presents readers with a detailed description of problems in areas such as personnel, equipment, products, services, and so forth. Its main goal is to provide *objective* information so that the readers can choose the next step. Any opinions must be well supported by facts.

Problem analyses, which can be either internal or external documents, should follow the pattern of organization described here.

ABC format for problem analyses. Like other informal reports, problem analyses fit the simple ABC (**A**bstract/**B**ody/**C**onclusion) format recommended throughout this text. The three sections contain some or all of the following information, depending on the specific report. Note that solutions to problems are not mentioned; this chapter deals separately with (1) problem analyses, whose main focus is problems; and (2) recommendation reports, whose main focus is solutions. Of course, be aware that during your career, you will be called on to write reports that combine both types.

ABC Format: Problem Analysis

Abstract

- Purpose of report
- Capsule summary of problems covered in report discussion

Body

- Background on source of problems
- Well-organized description of the problems observed
- Data that support your observations
- Consequences of the problems

Conclusion

- Brief restatement of main problems (unless report is so short that such restatement would seem repetitious)
- Degree of urgency required in handling problems
- Suggested next step

M&K case study for a problem analysis. Model 10-3 on pages 257–58 presents a sample problem analysis that follows this chapter's guidelines. Harold Marshal, a longtime M&K employee, supervises all technical work aboard the *Seeker II,* a boat that M&K leases during the summer. Staffed with several technicians and engineers, the boat is used to collect and test soil samples from the ocean floor. Different clients purchase these data—for example, oil companies that need to place oil rigs safely and telecommunications companies that need to lay cable.

After a summer on the *Seeker II,* Harold has severe reservations about the boat's safety and technical adequacy. Yet he knows that his supervisor, Jan Stillwright, will require detailed support of any complaints before she seriously considers negotiating a new boat contract next season. Given this critical audience, Harold focuses on specific problems that affect (1) the crew's safety, (2) the accuracy of the technical work performed, and (3) the crew's morale. He believes that this pragmatic approach, rather than an emotional appeal, will best persuade his boss that the problem is serious.

For Recommendation Reports

Most problem analyses contain both facts and opinions. You as the writer must make special efforts to separate the two, for this reason: most readers want the opportunity to draw their own conclusions about the problem. Also, be sure to support all opinions with facts. This guideline holds true especially for recommendation reports, for they include more personal views than other report types. Use the following working definition for recommendation report:

> **Recommendation report:** this informal report presents readers with specific suggestions that affect personnel, equipment, procedures, products, services, and so on. Although the report's main purpose is to persuade, every recommendation must be supported by objective data.

Recommendation reports can be either internal or external documents. Both follow the ABC format suggested here.

ABC format for recommendation reports. Problem analyses and recommendation reports sometimes overlap in content. You may recommend solutions in a problem analysis, just as you may analyze problems in a recommendation report. The

ABC format assumes that you want to mention the problem briefly before proceeding to discuss solutions.

ABC Format: Recommendation Report
Abstract
- Purpose of report
- Brief reference to problem to which recommendations respond
- Capsule summary of recommendations covered in report discussion

Body
- Details about problem, if necessary
- Well-organized description of recommendations
- Data that support your recommendations (with reference to attachments, if any)
- Main benefits of recommendations you put forth
- Any possible drawbacks

Conclusion
- Brief restatement of main recommendations (unless report is so short that restatement would seem repetitious)
- The main benefit of recommended change
- Your offer to help with next step

M&K case study for a recommendation report. Model 10-1 on pages 253–54 shows a typical recommendation report written at M&K. The reader is a client oil firm about to place an oil rig at an offshore site to the southeast of Newfoundland. Given the potential for risk to human life and to the environment, Shearwater Oil wants to take every precaution. Therefore, it has hired M&K to determine whether the preferred site is safe.

This example presents an important problem you may face in writing recommendation reports. Occasionally you may be asked to deliver recommendations sooner than you would prefer if you were working under ideal circumstances. In such cases, assume the cautious approach taken by Bartley Dowdell, the M&K writer in Model 10-1. That is, make sure to state that your report is preliminary and based on incomplete data. This approach is even more important in situations like this case study, in which there is risk to human life. Take pains to qualify your recommendations so that they cannot possibly be misunderstood by your audience.

For Equipment Evaluations

Every organization uses some kind of equipment, and someone has to help buy, maintain, and sometimes replace it. Because companies put so much money into this part of their business, evaluating equipment has become an important activity. Following is a working definition of equipment evaluation:

> **Equipment evaluation:** this informal report provides objective data about how equipment has, or has not, functioned. The report may cover topics such as machinery, tools, vehicles, office supplies, computer hardware, and computer software.

Like a problem analysis, an equipment evaluation may just focus on problems. Or like a recommendation report, it may go on to suggest a change in equipment. Whatever its focus, an equipment evaluation must provide a well-documented review of exactly how the equipment has performed. Follow the ABC format in evaluating equipment.

ABC format for equipment evaluations. Equipment evaluations that are informal reports should include some or all of the points listed here. Remember that in this type of report, the discussion must include the evaluation criteria most important to the readers, not you.

ABC Format: Equipment Evaluation
Abstract

- Purpose of report
- Capsule summary of what your report says about the equipment

Body

- Thorough description of the equipment being evaluated
- Well-organized critique, either analyzing the parts of one piece of equipment or contrasting several pieces of similar equipment according to selected criteria
- Additional supporting data, with reference to any attachments

Conclusion

- Brief restatement of major findings, conclusions, or recommendations

---

M&K case study for an equipment evaluation. Not only does M&K rely on word processing for all documents it generates, but it also is responsible for recommending software to its clients. Model 10-2 on pages 255–56 contains an evaluation of a new word-processing package used on a trial basis. Marta Cesta, office manager in Toronto, conducted the trial in her office and wrote the report to the assistant manager, Hank Worley. Note that she analyzes each of the software's five main features. Then she ends with a recommendation, much like a recommendation report.

Pay special attention to the tone and argumentative structure of this example. Cesta shows restraint in her enthusiasm, knowing that facts will be more convincing than opinions. Indeed, every claim about Best Choice software is supported either by evidence from her trial or by a logical explanation. For example, her praise of the file management feature is supported by the experience of a field engineer who used the system for three days. And her statement about the well-written user's guide is supported by the few calls made to the Best Choice support centre during the trial.

For Progress/Periodic Reports

Some short reports are intended to cover activities that occurred during a specific period of time. They can be directed inside or outside your organization and are defined in this way:

Progress report: this informal report provides your manager or client with details about work on a specific project. Often you agree at the beginning of a project to submit a certain number of progress reports at certain intervals.

Periodic report: this informal report, usually directed within your own organization, summarizes your work on diverse tasks over a specific time period. For example, as supervisor of company publications, you may be asked to submit periodic reports each month on new brochures, public relations releases, and product flyers.

Progress and periodic reports contain mostly objective data. Yet both of them, especially progress reports, sometimes may be written in a persuasive manner. (See Chapter 6 for argument guidelines.) After all, you are trying to put forth the best case for the work you have completed. The next section provides an ABC format for these two report types.

ABC format for progress/periodic reports. Whether internal or external, progress and periodic reports follow a basic ABC format and contain some or all of the following parts:

ABC Format: Progress/Periodic Report
Abstract
- Purpose of report
- Capsule summary of main project(s)
- Main progress to date or since last report

Body
- Description of work completed since last report, organized either by task or by time or by both
- Clear reference to any dead ends that may have taken considerable time but yielded no results
- Explanation of delays or incomplete work
- Description of work remaining on project(s), organized either by task or by time or by both
- Reference to attachments that may contain more specific information

Conclusion
- Brief restatement of work since last reporting period
- Expression of confidence, or concern, about overall work on project(s)
- Indication of your willingness to make any adjustments the reader may want to suggest

---

M&K case study for a progress report. As Model 10-4 on pages 259–60 indicates, Aziz Rashid, an M&K training officer and personnel manager, is in the middle of an internal project being conducted for Jacques Martin, M&K's president. Rashid's goal is to find ways to improve the company's training for technical employees. Having completed two of three phases, he is reporting his progress to Martin. Note that Rashid organizes the body sections by task. This arrangement helps to focus the reader's attention on the two main accomplishments—the successful phone interviews and the potentially useful survey. If, instead, Rashid had completed many smaller tasks, he might have wanted to organize the body of the report by time, not tasks.

Also note that Rashid adopts a persuasive tone at the end of the report. That is, he uses his solid progress as a way to emphasize the importance of the project. In this sense, he is "selling" the project to his "internal customer," Jacques Martin, who is in the position to make decisions about the future of technical training at M&K.

M&K case study for a periodic report. Model 10-5 on page 261 shows the rather routine nature of most periodic reports. Here Nancy Fairbanks is simply submitting her usual monthly report. The greatest challenge in such reports is to classify, divide, and label information in such a way that readers can quickly find what they need. Fairbanks selected the kind of substantive headings that help the reader locate information (e.g., "Jones Fill Project" and "Performance Reviews").

For Lab Reports

College and university students write lab reports for courses in science, engineering, psychology, and other subjects. Yet this report type also exists in technical organizations, such as hospitals, engineering firms, and computer companies. Perhaps more than any other type of informal report, the lab report varies in format from organization to organization (and from instructor to instructor, in the case of school courses). This chapter will present a format to use when no other instructions have been given. A working definition follows:

> **Lab report:** this informal report describes work done in any laboratory, with emphasis on topics such as purpose of the work, procedures, equipment, problems, results, and implications. It may be directed to someone inside or outside your own organization. Also, it may stand on its own or it may become part of a larger report that uses the laboratory work as supporting detail.

The next section shows a typical ABC format for lab reports, with the types of information that might appear in the three main sections.

ABC format for lab reports. Whether simple or complicated, lab reports usually contain some or all of the following parts:

ABC Format: Lab Report
Abstract

- Purpose of report
- Capsule summary of results

Body

- Purpose or hypothesis of lab work
- Equipment needed
- Procedures or methods used in the lab test
- Unusual problems or occurrences
- Results of the test with reference to your expectations (results may appear in conclusion instead)

Conclusion

- Statement or restatement of main results
- Implications of lab test for further work

M&K case study for a lab report. Model 10-6 on pages 262–63 shows a Martin & Koffman lab report that is not part of a larger document. In this case, the client sent M&K some soils taken from borings made into the earth. M&K has analyzed the samples in its company laboratory and then drawn some conclusions about the kind of rock the samples were taken from. The report writer, a geologist named Joanne Rappaport, uses the body of the report to provide background information, lab materials procedures, and problems encountered. Note that the report body uses process description, a main pattern of organization covered in Chapter 7.

Employability Skills

The Conference Board of Canada's *Employability Skills 2000+* indicates that the ability to communicate information effectively is critical to building a successful career. Relevant communication skills include the following:

- Read and understand information presented in a variety of forms (e.g., words, graphs, charts, diagrams).
- Write and speak so others pay attention and understand.*

Prepare a progress report in memo form in which you explain to your academic adviser what progress you have made in completing assignments and projects in your current semester and explain how you will manage your time and resources in order to complete all of the required work in the time allotted. The purpose of the report is to convince the client—your academic adviser—that you can successfully complete the work. Consider using a Gantt chart to help you produce an effective report.

* *Employability Skills 2000+* Brochure 2000 E/F (Ottawa: The Conference Board of Canada, 2000).

CHAPTER SUMMARY

This chapter deals exclusively with the short, informal reports you will write throughout your career. On the job, you will write them for readers inside your organization (as **memo reports**) and outside your organization (as **letter reports**). In both cases, follow these 10 basic guidelines:

1. Plan well before you write.
2. Use letter or memo format.
3. Make the text visually appealing.
4. Use the ABC format for organization.
5. Call the abstract an "Introductory Summary."
6. Put important details in the body.
7. Separate fact from opinion.
8. Focus attention in your conclusion.
9. Use attachments for details.
10. Edit carefully.

Although letter and memo reports come in many varieties, this chapter covered only five common types: problem analyses, recommendation reports, equipment evaluations, progress/periodic reports, and lab reports. Each follows its own type of three-part ABC format for organizing information.

ASSIGNMENTS

This chapter includes both short and long assignments. The short assignments in Part 1 are designed to be used for in-class exercises and short homework assignments. The assignments in Part 2 generally require more time to complete.

Part 1: Short Assignments

1. Problem analysis—critiquing a report. Using the guidelines in this chapter, analyze the level of effectiveness of the following M&K problem analysis.

April 16, 2006

Mr. Jay Henderson
Cornwall Community Centre
10 Proulx Dr.
Cornwall ON L2S 5R3

PROBLEM ANALYSIS
NEW COMMUNITY CENTRE BUILDING SITE

Introductory Summary

Last week your centre hired our firm to study problems caused by the recent incorporation of the centre's new building site into the city limits. Having reviewed the city's planning and zoning requirements, we have found some problems with your original site design, which initially was designed to meet the county's requirements only. My report focuses on problems with four areas on the site:

1. Landscaping screen
2. Signage for the centre
3. Detention pond
4. Fire truck access

Attached to this report is a site plan to illustrate these problems as you review the report. The plan was drawn from an aerial viewpoint.

Landscaping Screen

The city zoning code requires a landscaping screen along the west property line, as shown on the attached site illustration sheet. The former design does not call for a screen in this area. The screen will act as a natural barrier between the centre parking lot and the private residence adjoining the property. The code requires that the trees for this screen be a minimum height of 2 metres with a height maturity level of at least 6 metres. The trees should be an aesthetically pleasing barrier for all parties, including the resident on the adjoining property.

Signage for the Centre

After the site was incorporated into the city, the city decided to widen Woodstock Road and increase the setback to 15 metres, as illustrated on our site plan. With this change, the original location of the sign fell into the road setback. Its new location must be out of the setback and moved closer to the new building.

Detention Pond

The city's civil engineers reviewed the original site drawing and found that the detention pond was too small. If the detention pond is not increased, rainwater may build up and overflow into the building, causing a considerable amount of flood damage to property in the building and to the building itself. There is a sufficient amount of land in the rear of the site to enlarge and deepen the pond to handle all expected rainfall.

Fire Truck Access

On the original site plan, the slope of the ground along the back side of the new building is so steep that a city fire truck would not be able to gain access to the rear of the building in the event of a fire. This area is shown on our site illustration around the north and east sides of the building. The city enforces the building code, which states that all buildings within the city limits must provide a flat and unobstructed access path around the buildings. If the access is not provided, the safety of the building and its occupants would be in jeopardy.

Conclusion

The just-stated problems are significant, yet they can be solved with minimal additional cost. Once the problems are remedied and documented, the revised site plan must be approved by the zoning board before a building permit can be issued to the contractor.

I look forward to meeting with you and the centre's building committee next week to discuss any features of this study and its ramifications.

Sincerely,

Thomas K. Jones
Senior Landscape Engineer

Enc.

---

2. **Problem analysis—group project.** Divide into three- or four-person teams, as your instructor directs. In your group, share information about any problems that team members have encountered with services or facilities at the college or university you attend. Then select a problem substantive enough to be described in a short report. As a group, write a problem analysis in the format put forth in this chapter. Assume that your group represents a Martin & Koffman technical team that has been hired to investigate and then write a series of reports on problems at the school. Your report is one in the series. Select as your audience the appropriate administrators at the college or university.

3. **Recommendation report—critiquing a report.** Using the guidelines in this chapter, analyze the level of effectiveness of the following M&K recommendation report.

April 20, 2006

Northern RV Company
76 White Pine Road
Sudbury ON P1T 4T8

Attention: Mr. Ben Randall, Facilities Manager

EMERGENCY EXIT STUDY

Introductory Summary

As you requested, I have just completed a study of the emergency exits in your accounting office at the plant. My study indicates that you have two main problems: (1) easier access to exits is needed, and (2) more exit signs are needed, and they must be more visible. This report contains recommendations for rearranging the floor plan and improving signage.

Problems with Current Floor Plan

Two main problems cause the accounting office to fail to meet the county's guidelines for access to fire exits. First, the file cabinets on the north wall of the office are partially blocking the Reynolds Lane exit. Second, the office photocopier partially blocks the exit to the east hallway. In the first case, the file cabinets are so heavy that one person could not move them. In the second case, only a very strong individual could roll the photocopier out of the way. Obviously, both situations are unacceptable and violate the current code.

The other problem is signage. The Reynolds Lane exit has an exit sign, but it is not easily seen. The east hallway exit has no sign at all. In addition, the rest of the office lacks any maps that show people the location of the two fire exits.

Recommendations for Solving Exit Problem

Fortunately, the existing problems can be corrected with only minor cost to the company. The following recommendations should be implemented immediately upon your receipt of this report:

1. Move the file cabinets on the north wall to the east wall so that they no longer block the Reynolds Lane exit.
2. Relocate the photocopier to the office supply room or the cubicle adjacent to it.
3. Remove the undersized exit sign from the Reynolds Lane exit.
4. Purchase and install two province-approved exit signs above the two fire exits.
5. Draw up an emergency plan map and post a copy in every cubicle within the accounting office.

When you implement these recommendations, you will be in accordance with the province's current fire regulations.

Conclusion

I strongly suggest that my recommendations be put into action as soon as possible. By doing so you will greatly reduce the risk to your employees and your associated liability.

If you have any questions or need additional information, please call me at your convenience.

Sincerely,

Howard B. Manwell
Fire Prevention Technologist

---

4. **Writing a recommendation report.** Divide into groups of three or four students, as your instructor directs. Imagine your group is a technical team from M&K. Assume that the facilities director of your college or university has hired your team to recommend changes that would improve your classroom. Write a group report that includes the recommendations agreed to by your group. For example, you may want to consider structural changes of any kind, additions of equipment, changes in the type and arrangement of seating, and so forth.

5. **Writing an equipment evaluation.** Assume you are a supervisor at M&K's equipment development shop. The procurement office routinely asks you to write evaluations of new pieces of equipment being used in the shop. Such evaluations help the Canadian director of procurement, Brenda Seymour, decide on future purchases.

Write a brief memo to Seymour, evaluating the Brakoh cordless drills that your staff began using in the shop about a year ago. The Brakoh brand replaced a more expensive brand that the shop had used for the 10 previous years. In the past few months, your technicians have reported that the cheaper models have been falling apart after six or eight months of use. Information coming to you suggests that there are two main problems: (1) a grinding noise can be heard in the housing, resulting in the failure of the chuck (the piece that holds the drill bit) to rotate; and (2) drilling time between rechargings tends to decrease as the drill gets older. You believe that the manufacturer, in order to cut the cost of the drill, has substituted poorly made components in high-wear locations. For example, the gears responsible for turning the chuck are made of plastic. With a little wear, the gears tend to slip, which produces the grinding sound and the rotation failure. As for the recharging problem, the power cell just seems to hold less charge than the previous drill. In summary, the drill has broken down four times faster than the other model, causing many repair bills and a loss in productivity.

In writing your memo, remember that in this case your main job is to provide information to the director of procurement, not to make recommendations one way or the other. After receiving your memo, she probably will complete a cost analysis to determine if the problems with the cheaper drill outweigh the advantages of the initial cost savings.

Part 2: Longer Assignments—Individual or Group Work

While planning some of these assignments—especially #6—you may need to review information in Chapter 2 about M&K. Also, for each assignment you should complete a copy of the Planning Form (included in Chapter 1). These assignments can be completed as individual or group projects.

6. **Report based on project sheets.** The project sheets included in Chapter 2 contain summaries of five projects, in various topic areas. These summaries were written for marketing purposes, after the jobs were completed.

   Using the information on one of those sheets, write a brief informal report that summarizes the project for the client. If necessary, add details that are not on the sheet. *Caution:* Remember that marketing sheets may not be organized as reports are organized. Consider your purpose and audience carefully before writing.

7. **Report based on Internet "surfing."** Use the Internet to collect actual information, and/or a list of sources that may contain information, about a topic that relates to your academic major. Then write an informal equipment evaluation in which you analyze (1) the ease with which the Internet allowed you to collect information on your topic and (2) the quality of the sources or information you received. Your audience is your instructor, who will let you know the degree of knowledge you can assume he or she has on this topic.

8. **Problem analysis.** Assume you are an M&K field engineer working at the construction site of a nuclear power plant in southern Ontario. For the past three weeks, your job has been to observe the construction of a water cooling tower, a large cylindrical structure. As consultants to the plant's construction firm, you and your M&K crew were hired to make sure that work proceeds properly and on schedule. As the field engineer, you are supposed to report any problems in writing to your project manager, John Raines, at the Toronto office. Then he will contact the construction firm's office, if necessary.

   Write a short problem analysis in the form of a memo report to Raines. (Follow the guidelines in the "For Problem Analyses" section of this chapter.) Take the following randomly organized information and present it in a clear, well-organized fashion. If you wish, add information of your own that might fit the context.

   - Three cement pourings for the tower wall were delayed an hour each on April 21 because of light rain.
   - Cement-truck drivers need to slow down while driving through the site. Other workers complain about the excessive dust raised by the trucks.
   - Mary Powell, an M&K safety inspector on the crew, has cited 12 workers for not wearing their hard hats.
   - You just heard from one subcontractor, Allis Wire, Inc., that there will be a two-day delay in delivering some steel reinforcing wires that go into the concrete walls. That delay will throw off next week's schedule. Last Monday's hard rain and flooding kept everyone home that day.
   - It is probably time once again to get all the subcontractors together to discuss safety at the tower site. Recently two field hands had bad cuts from machinery.
   - Although there have not been any major thefts at the site, some miscellaneous boards and masonry pieces are missing each day—probably because nearby residents (doing small home projects) think that whatever they find at the site has been discarded. Are additional No Trespassing signs needed?
   - Construction is only two days behind schedule, despite the problems that have occurred.

9. **Problem analysis.** As a landscape engineer for M&K, one of your jobs is to examine problems associated with the design of walkways, the location of trees and garden beds, the grading of land around buildings, and any other topographical features. Assume that

a specific school, community, or company with which you are familiar has hired you. Your objective is to evaluate one or more landscaping problems at the site.

Write an informal report that describes the problem(s) in detail (follow the guidelines in the "For Problem Analyses" section of this chapter). Be specific about how the problem affects people—the employees, inhabitants, students, and so on. Here are some sample problems that could be evaluated:

- Poorly landscaped entrance to a major subdivision
- Muddy, unpaved walkway between dormitories and academic buildings on a university campus
- Unpaved parking lot far from main campus buildings
- Soil runoff into the streets from several steep, muddy subdivision lots that have not yet been sold
- City tennis courts with poor drainage
- Lack of adequate flowers or bushes around a new office building
- Need for a landscaped common area within a subdivision or campus
- Need to save some large trees that may be doomed because of proposed construction

10. **Recommendation report.** For this paper, choose a design problem at your college or company. Now put yourself in the position of an M&K employee hired by your school or company to recommend solutions to the problem.

Your ideas must be in the form of a report that gives one or more recommendations resulting from your study. (For this, consult the writing guidelines in the "For Recommendation Reports" section of this chapter.) Assume that the problem is well enough understood to require only a brief summary before you launch into your recommendations. Because this is a short report, it may not contain many technical details for implementing your recommendations. Also, you need to choose a topic limited enough that it can be covered in a short memo report. Following are some sample topics:

- Poor ventilation in an office or a classroom, such as one with sealed windows
- Inadequate space for quick exits during emergencies
- Poor visibility in a large auditorium
- Poor acoustics in a large classroom or training room
- Lack of, or improper placement of, lighting
- Energy inefficiency caused by structural flaws, such as poor insulation or high ceilings
- Rooms or walkways that are not handicap-accessible
- Failure to take advantage of solar heating
- Inefficient heating or air-conditioning systems

11. **Recommendation report.** This project will require some research. Assume that your college plans either to embark on a major recycling effort or to expand a recycling program that has already started. Put yourself in the role of an M&K environmental scientist or technologist who has been asked to recommend these recycling changes.

First, do some research about recycling programs that have worked in other organizations. A good place to start would be a periodical index or an online search. Either will lead you to some magazine articles of interest. Choose to discuss one or more recoverable resources, such as paper, aluminum, cardboard, plastic, or glass bottles. Be specific about how your recommendations can be implemented by the organization or audience you are writing about. (Consult the guidelines in the "For Recommendation Reports" section of this chapter.)

12. **Equipment evaluation.** For six months you have driven a new Ford 150 company truck at remote job sites. As lead field hand for M&K's Baltimore office, you have been asked to write an evaluation of the vehicle for Brenda Seymour, director of procurement at the corporate office in Toronto. Seymour will use your report to decide whether to recommend ordering five more F-150s for other offices. She has told you that you need to

discuss only major positive or negative features, not every detail. If she needs more information after reading your report, she will let you know.

Consider the list below to be your random notes. Use all this information to write a memo report that evaluates the truck. Make sure to follow the guidelines in this chapter.

- My 150 has been very reliable—it never failed to start, even during subzero ice storms last winter.
- The 302 engine, Ford's small V-8, has provided plenty of power to handle any hauling I have done. No need to order the more expensive and less fuel-efficient 350 V-8.
- Have been to 18 job sites with the truck, from marshes in Maine to mountains in New Hampshire. Have put about 19,000 kilometres on it, on all kinds of roads and in all conditions.
- Tires that came with the truck did not work well in muddy locations, even with four-wheel drive. Suggest we buy all-terrain tires for future vehicles. Continue to order four-wheel drive—it is necessary at over half our job sites.
- The short bed (0.5 metres) did not provide enough hauling room, once I put my toolbox across the truck bed near the back window. Suggest that company buy long-bed trucks with the added 0.5 metre of room.
- Given what I know now, I give the truck a good to excellent rating.
- Automatic transmission worked great. Am told by other owners that the automatic is better than the manual for construction jobs because the manual tends to burn out clutches, especially when the truck needs to be "rocked" back and forth to get out of mud holes. My automatic has taken a lot of abuse without problems.
- Have had some problems with front-end handling on rough roads. Suggest that future trucks be ordered with special handling package, which includes two shock absorbers—not just one—on each front wheel.
- Have had no major repairs, just the regular maintenance checks at the dealer.
- There was one recall from the manufacturer concerning an exhaust pipe hanger that might bend, but the dealer fixed the problem in 20 minutes.
- Really need to have another six months to see how well truck holds up.

13. **Equipment evaluation.** M&K has decided to make a bulk purchase of 20 personal computers. (For the purposes of this assignment, choose a computer that you are familiar with.) The machinery will go in a new department being set up in several months.

Assume that M&K now uses five different types of PCs. In the interests of a fair comparison/contrast, Marta Cesta, who manages the Toronto office, has asked you to evaluate the effectiveness of the system you use yourself. Several other employees are doing the same. Write a memo report that includes your evaluation. (Consult guidelines in the "For Equipment Evaluations" section of this chapter.) She will use the data and opinions in all the equipment evaluations she receives to make her choice for the bulk purchase. Your criteria for evaluation might include topics such as one or more of the following:

- Physical design of the equipment
- Quality of the supplied documentation
- Frequency and cost of maintenance
- Availability of appropriate software
- Length of coverage of warranty
- Proximity to a service centre
- Reputation of the manufacturer

14. **Progress or periodic report.** Assume that you have worked as a field hand at M&K's Montreal office for 15 years. Because of your reliability, good judgment, and intelligence, the company is paying for your enrollment at a local college. Also, you get half time off, with pay. Because of its investment in you, M&K expects you to report periodically on your college work. Choose one of the following two options for this assignment:

Progress report: Select a major project you are now completing in any college course. Following the guidelines in the "For Progress/Periodic Reports" section of this chapter, write a progress report on this project. Direct the memo report to the Montreal office's manager of engineering, Rodolfo Blades. Sample topics might include a major paper, laboratory experiment, field project, or design studio.

Periodic report: Assume that M&K requires you to submit periodic reports on your schooling every few weeks. Following the guidelines in the "For Progress/Periodic Reports" section of this chapter, write a periodic report on your recent course work (completed or ongoing classes or both). Direct the memo report to the manager of engineering, Rodolfo Blades. Organize the report by class, and then give specific updates on each one.

15. **Lab report.** For this assignment, you must be taking a lab course now or have taken such a course recently. As in assignment 14, assume you work as a field hand with M&K's Montreal office. The company is sponsoring your schooling and has requested that you report on a specific school lab.

    Following the guidelines in this chapter's "For Lab Reports" section, write a report to Rodolfo Blades, manager of engineering. The quality of your report may affect whether or not M&K continues to fund your schooling. Be specific about the goals, procedures, and results of your laboratory work—just as you would in an actual lab report.

16. **Informal report—international context.** Investigate features such as style, format, structure, and organization of short reports written in another country. For this assignment, it would be best to interview someone who does business in another country and, if possible, to get an actual report that you can submit. Write a memo report to your instructor that reports on the results of your research.

200 Fourth Ave. NW
Calgary AB T2N 0N3
(403) 555-7524

April 22, 2006

Shearwater Oil Inc.
12 Rankin St.
Edmonton AB T3L 2J3

ATTENTION: Mr. James Smith, Engineering Manager

NOTRE DAME BAY STUDY
BLOCK 15, AREA 43-B
OFFSHORE NEWFOUNDLAND

INTRODUCTORY SUMMARY

You recently asked our firm to complete a preliminary soils investigation at an offshore rig site. This report presents the tentative results of our study, including major conclusions and recommendations. A longer, formal report will follow at the end of the project.

On the basis of what we have learned so far, it is our opinion that you can safely place an oil platform at the Notre Dame Bay site. To limit the chance of a rig leg punching into the sea floor, however, we suggest you follow the recommendations in this report.

WORK AT THE PROJECT SITE

On April 16 and 17, 2006, M&K's engineers and technicians worked at the Block 15 site in the Notre Dame Bay region. Using M&K's leased drill ship, *Seeker II*, as a base of operations, our crew performed these main tasks:

• Seismic survey of the project study area, and
• Two soil borings of 40 feet each.

Both seismic data and soil samples were brought to our Calgary office the next day for laboratory analysis.

LABORATORY ANALYSIS

On April 18 and 19, our lab staff examined the soil samples, completed bearing capacity tests, and evaluated seismic data. Here are the results of that analysis.

Soil Layers

Our initial evaluation of the soil samples reveals a 2–3 metre layer of weak clay starting a half metre below the sea floor. Other than that layer, the composition of the soils seems fairly typical of other sites nearby.

Includes specific title.

Uses *optional* heading for abstract part of ABC format.

Draws attention to *main point* of report.

Gives on-site details of project—dates, location, tasks.

Uses *lead-in* to subsections that follow.

Highlights most important point about soil layer—that is the *weak clay*.

continues

Model 10-1 Recommendation report (letter format)

Notes *why* this method was chosen (that is, reliability).

Explains both *how* the mapping procedure was done and *what results* it produced.

Leads off section with major conclusion, for emphasis.

Restates points (made in body) that support conclusion.

Uses list to emphasize recommendations to *reduce risk*.

Again mentions tentative nature of information, to prevent misuse of report.

Maintains control and shows initiative by offering to *call* client.

James Smith
April 22, 2006
Page 2

Bearing Capacity

We used the most reliable procedure available, the XYZ method, to determine the soil's bearing capacity (that is, its ability to withstand the weight of a loaded oil rig). That method required that we apply the following formula:

$$Q = cNv + tY, \text{ where}$$

Q = ultimate bearing capacity
c = average cohesive shear strength
Nv = the dimensionless bearing capacity factor
t = footing displacement
Y = weight of the soil unit

The final bearing capacity figure will be submitted in the final report, after we repeat the tests.

Sea Floor Surface

By pulling our underwater seismometer back and forth across the project site, we developed a seismic "map" of the sea floor surface. That map seems typical of the flat floor expected in that area of the gulf. The only exception is the presence of what appears to be a small sunken boat. This wreck, however, is not in the immediate area of the proposed platform site.

CONCLUSIONS AND RECOMMENDATIONS

Based on our analysis, we conclude that there is only a slight risk of instability at the site. Though unlikely, it is possible that a rig leg could punch through the sea floor, either during or after loading. We base this opinion on (1) the existence of the weak clay layer, noted earlier, and (2) the marginal bearing capacity.

Nevertheless, we believe you can still place your platform if you follow careful rig-loading procedures. Specifically, take these precautions to reduce your risk:

1. Load the rig in 10-tonne increments, waiting one hour between loadings.
2. Allow the rig to stand 24 hours after the loading and before placement of workers on board.
3. Have a soils specialist observe the entire loading process, to assist with any emergency decisions if problems arise.

As noted at the outset, these conclusions and recommendations are based on preliminary data and analysis. We will complete our final study in three weeks and submit a formal report shortly thereafter.

M&K enjoyed working for Shearwater Oil at its offshore Newfoundland lease holdings. I will phone you this week to see if you have any questions about our study. If you need information before then, please give me a call.

Sincerely,

Bartley Dowdell

Bartley Dowdell, Project Manager
Martin & Koffman

hg

Model 10-1   *continued*

MEMORANDUM

DATE: July 26, 2006
TO: Marta Cesta, Office Manager
FROM: Hank Worley, Assistant Manager *HW*
SUBJECT: Evaluation of Best Choice Software

INTRODUCTORY SUMMARY

You asked us to evaluate Best Choice Software last month in order to determine whether it would be worth purchasing. Having used the package, I find it meets our performance specifications. I recommend that we use it in our office and that we recommend it to our clients.

HOW BEST CHOICE HAS HELPED US

Best Choice provides five primary features: word processing, file management, spreadsheet, graphics, and a user's guide. Here is my critique of all five.

Word Processing

The system contains an excellent word-processing package that the engineers as well as the secretaries have been able to learn easily. This package can handle both our routine correspondence and the lengthy reports that our group generates. Of particular help are the system's Canadian, American, and British dictionaries, which can be updated at any time. The spelling correction feature has already saved much effort that was previously devoted to mechanical editing.

File Management

The file manager function allows the user to enter information and then to manipulate it quickly. During one three-day site visit, for example, a field engineer recorded a series of problems observed in the field. Then she rearranged the data to highlight specific points I asked her to study, such as I-beam welds and concrete cracks.

Spreadsheet

Like the system's word-processing package, the spreadsheet is efficient and quickly learned. Because Best Choice is a multipurpose software package, spreadsheet data can be incorporated into letter or report format. In other words, spreadsheet information can be merged with our document format to create a final draft for submission to clients or supervisors, with a real savings in time. For example, the memo I sent you last week on budget projections for field equipment took me only an hour to complete; last quarter, the identical project took four hours.

Uses optional first heading for abstract section of ABC format. Gives background, main conclusion, and scope of menu.

Notes five main points to be covered.

Begins paragraph with most important point. Supports claim with evidence.

Uses specific example to document opinion.

Gives simple explanation of how spreadsheet works.

continues

Model 10-2   Equipment evaluation (memo format)

Marta Cesta
July 26, 2006
Page 2

Graphics

The graphics package permits visuals to be drawn from the data contained in the spreadsheet. For example, a pie chart that shows the breakdown of a project budget can be created easily by merging spreadsheet data with the graphics software. With visuals becoming such an important part of reports, we have used this feature of Best Choice quite frequently.

User's Guide

Eight employees in my group have now used the Best Choice user's guide. All have found it well laid out and thorough. Perhaps the best indication of this fact is that in 30 days of daily use, we have placed only three calls to the Best Choice customer-service number.

CONCLUSION

Best Choice seems to contain just the right combination of tools to help us do our job, both in the field and in the office. These are the system's main benefits:

- Versatility—it has diverse functions
- Simplicity—it is easy to master

The people in our group have been very pleased with the package during this 30-day trial. If you like, we would be glad to evaluate Best Choice for a longer period.

Marginal notes:

Shows relevance of graphics to current work.

Supplies strong supporting statistic.

Wraps up report by restating main points.

Offers follow-up effort.

Model 10-2   *continued*

MEMORANDUM

DATE: October 15, 2006
TO: Jan Stillwright, Vice President of Research and Training
FROM: Harold Marshal, Technical Supervisor *HW*
SUBJECT: Boat Problems during Summer Season

INTRODUCTORY SUMMARY

We have just completed a one-month project aboard the leased ship, *Seeker II*, in the North Atlantic Ocean. All work went just about as planned, with very few delays caused by weather or equipment failure.

However, there were some boat problems that need to be solved before we lease *Seeker II* again this season. This report highlights the problems so that they can be brought to the owner's attention. My comments focus on four areas of the boat: drill rig, engineering lab, main engine, and crew quarters.

DRILL RIG

Thus far the rig has operated without incident. Yet on one occasion, I noticed that the elevator for lifting pipe up the derrick swung too close to the derrick itself. A quick gust of wind or a sudden increase in sea height caused these shifts. If the elevator were to hit the derrick, causing the elevator door to open, pipe sections might fall to the deck below.

I believe the whole rig assembly needs to be checked over by someone knowledgeable about its design. Before we put men near that rig again, we need to know that their safety will not be jeopardized by the possibility of falling pipe.

ENGINEERING LAB

Quite frankly, it is a tribute to our technicians that they were able to complete all lab tests with *Seeker II's* limited facilities. Several weeks into the voyage, these four main problems became apparent:

1. Ceiling leaks
2. Poor water pressure in the cleanup sink
3. Leaks around the window near the electronics corner
4. Two broken outlet plugs

Although we were able to devise a solution to the window leaks, the other problems stayed with us for the entire trip.

Gives abstract (or *summary*) in first paragraph.

Provides *capsule listing* of problems discussed in report.

Opens with *most important point*—then qualifies it. Explains problem in *layperson's language*, indicating possible consequences.

Uses *listing* to draw attention to four main lab problems on board.

continues

Model 10-3 Problem analysis (memo format)

Jan Stillwright
October 15, 2006
Page 2

Uses *simple language* to describe technical problems.

MAIN ENGINE

On this trip, we had three valve failures on three different cylinder heads. From our experience on other ships, it is very unusual to have one valve fail, let alone three. Fortunately for us, these failures occurred between projects, so we did not lose time on a job. And fortunately for the owner, the broken valve parts did not destroy the engine's expensive turbocharger.

Closes section with opinion that flows from facts presented.

Only an expert will be able to tell whether these engine problems were flukes or if the entire motor needs to be rebuilt. In my opinion, the most prudent course of action is to have the engine checked over carefully before the next voyage.

CREW QUARTERS

Gives lead-in to three sections that follow.

When 15 men live in one room for three months, it is important that basic facilities work. On *Seeker II* we experienced problems with the bedroom, bathroom, and laundry room that caused some tension.

Bedroom

Describes three problem areas in great detail— knowing the owner will want facts to support complaints.

Three of the top bunks had such poor springs that the occupants sank 15 to 30 cm toward the bottom bunks. More important, five of the bunks are not structurally sound enough to keep from swaying in medium to high seas. Finally, most of the locker handles are either broken or about to break.

Bathroom

Poor pressure in three of the commodes made them almost unusable during the last two weeks. Our amateur repairs did not solve the problem, so I think the plumbing leading to the holding tank might be defective.

Laundry Room

We discovered early that the filtering system could not screen the large amount of rust in the old 45,000-litre tank. Consequently, undergarments and other white clothes turned a yellow-red colour and were ruined.

CONCLUSION

Briefly restates problem, with emphasis on *safety* and *profits*.

As noted at the outset, none of these problems kept us from accomplishing the major goals of this voyage. But they did make the trip much more uncomfortable than it had to be. Moreover, in the case of the rig and engine problems, we were fortunate that injuries and downtime did not occur.

Ends with specific recommendation.

I strongly urge that the owner be asked to correct these deficiencies before we consider using *Seeker II* for additional projects this season.

Model 10-3   *continued*

MEMORANDUM

DATE: June 11, 2006
TO: Jacques Martin, President, M&K
FROM: Aziz Rashid *AR*
SUBJECT: Progress Report on Training

INTRODUCTORY SUMMARY

On May 21 you asked that I study ways our firm can improve training for technical employees in all domestic offices. We agreed that the project would take about six or seven weeks and involve three phases:

Phase 1: Make phone inquiries to competing firms
Phase 2: Send a survey to our technical people
Phase 3: Interview a cross-section of our technical employees

I have now completed Phase 1 and part of Phase 2. My observation thus far is that the project will offer many new directions to consider for our technical training program.

WORK COMPLETED

In the first week of the project, I had extensive phone conversations with people at three competing firms about their training programs. Then in the second week, I wrote and sent out a training survey to all technical employees in M&K's offices.

Phone Interviews

I contacted three firms for whom we have done similar favours in the past: Simkins Consultants, Judd & Associates, and ABG Engineering. Here is a summary of my conversations:

1. Simkins Consultants
   Talked with Harry Rolak, training director, on May 23. Harry said that his firm has most success with internal training seminars. Each technical person completes several one- or two-day seminars every year. These courses are conducted by in-house experts or external consultants, depending on the specialty.

2. Judd & Associates
   Talked with Jan Tyler, manager of engineering, on May 24. Jan said that Judd, like Simkins, depends mostly on internal seminars. But Judd spreads these seminars over one or two weeks, rather than teaching intensive courses in one or two days. Judd also offers short "technical awareness" sessions at the lunch hour every two weeks. In-house technical experts give informal presentations on some aspect of their research or fieldwork.

Summarizes project, to refresh reader's memory and establish common ground.

Gives overview of report.

Summarizes two main tasks, as lead-in to subsections.

Organizes this section by the companies consulted.

Creates parallel form in organization of all three points.

continues

Model 10-4 Progress report (memo format)

Jacques Martin
June 11, 2006
Page 2

3. ABG Engineering
Talked with Newt Mosely, personnel coordinator, on May 27. According to Newt, ABG's training program is much as it was two decades ago. Most technical people at high levels go to one seminar a year, usually sponsored by professional societies or local colleges. Other technical people get little training beyond what is provided on the job. In-house training has not worked well, mainly because of schedule conflicts with engineering jobs.

Internal Survey

After completing the phone interviews noted, I began the survey phase of the project. Last week, I finished writing the survey, had it reproduced, and sent it with cover memo to all technical employees in our offices. The deadline for returning it to me is June 17.

WORK PLANNED

With phone interviews finished and the survey mailed, I foresee the following schedule for completing the project:

June 17:	Surveys returned
June 18–21:	Surveys evaluated
June 24–28:	Trips taken to all domestic offices to interview a cross-section of technical employees
July 3:	Submission of final project report to you

CONCLUSION

My interviews with competitors gave me a good feel for what technical training might be appropriate for our staff. Now I am hoping for a high-percentage return on the internal survey. That phase will prepare a good foundation for my on-site interviews later this month. I believe this major corporate effort will upgrade our technical training considerably.

I would be glad to hear any suggestions you may have about my work on the rest of the project. For example, please call if you have any particular questions you want asked during the on-site interviews (ext. 348).

Margin notes:

Gives important details about the survey.

Organizes section chronologically, making sure to stay within a six- or seven-week schedule.

Looks to future tasks.

Emphasizes major benefit, to "sell" the project internally.

Indicates flexibility and encourages response from reader.

Model 10-4 *continued*

MEMORANDUM

DATE: August 2, 2006
TO: Ralph Buzby, Manager of Engineering
FROM: Nancy Fairbanks, Project Manager *NF*
SUBJECT: Activity Report for July 2006

July has been a busy month in our group. Besides starting and finishing many smaller jobs, we completed the Jones Fill project. Also, the John Lewis Dam borings began just a week ago. Finally, I did some marketing work and several performance reviews.

SMALL PROJECTS

Last month, my group completed nine small projects, each with a budget under $20,000 and each lasting only a few days. These jobs were in three main areas:

1. Surveying subdivisions—five jobs
2. Taking samples from toxic sites—two jobs
3. Doing nearby soil borings—two jobs

All nine were completed within budget. Eight of the nine projects were completed on time. The Campbell County survey, however, was delayed for a day because of storms on July 12.

JONES FILL PROJECT

Our written report on this 12-month job was finally submitted to Trunk Engineering, Inc., on July 23. The delay was caused by Trunk's decision to change the scope of the project again. The firm wanted another soil boring, which we completed on July 22.

JOHN LEWIS DAM PROJECT

As you know, we had hoped to start work at the dam site last month. However, the client decided to make a lot of design changes that had to be approved by subcontractors. The final approval to start came just last week; thus our first day on site was July 29.

MARKETING

During July, my main marketing effort was to meet with some previous clients, acquainting them with some of our new services. I met with eight different clients at their offices, with two meetings occurring on each of these dates: July 15, 16, 22, and 23. There's a good possibility that several of these meetings will lead to additional waste-management work in the next few months.

PERFORMANCE REVIEWS

As we discussed last month, I fell behind on my staff's performance reviews in June. In July, I completed the three delayed reviews, as well as the four that were due in July. Copies of the paperwork were sent to your office and to the Personnel Department on July 19. This brings us up to date on all performance reviews.

Begins with overview of entire report.

Gives summary of small projects.

Uses list to highlight main types.

Indicates reasons for delays.

Again, gives *reasons* for delay.

Supports section with *specifics*— for example, the exact number of meetings.

Ralph Buzby
August 2, 2006
Page 2

CONCLUSION

July was a busy month in almost all phases of my job. Because of this pace, I haven't had time to work on the in-house training course you asked me to develop. In fact, I'm concerned that time I devote to that project will take me away from my ongoing client jobs. At our next meeting, perhaps we should brainstorm about some solutions to this problem.

Lays foundation for *next* meeting.

Model 10-5   Periodic report (memo format)

328 Ravin Road
Toronto ON   M2P 8J6
(416) 555-8438

December 12, 2006

Mr. Andrew Hawkes
Monson Coal Company
2139 Lasiter Dr.
Baltimore MD 21222

LABORATORY REPORT
BOREHOLE FOSSIL SAMPLES
BRAINTREE CREEK SITE, WEST VIRGINIA

INTRODUCTORY SUMMARY

Last week you sent us six fossilized samples from the Braintree Creek site. Having analyzed the samples in our lab, we believe they suggest the presence of coal-bearing rock. As you requested, this report will give a summary of the materials and procedures we used in this project, along with any problems we had.

As you know, our methodology in this kind of job is to identify microfossils in the samples, estimate the age of the rock by when the microfossils existed, and then make assumptions about whether the surrounding rock might contain coal.

LAB MATERIALS

Our lab analysis relies on only one piece of specialized equipment: a Piketon electron microscope. Besides the Piketon, we use a simple 400-power manual microscope. Other equipment is similar to that included in any basic geology lab, such as filtering screens and burners.

LAB PROCEDURE

Once we receive a sample, we first try to identify the exact kinds of microfossils that the rocks contain. Our specific lab procedure for your samples consisted of these two steps:

Step 1

We used a 400-power microscope to visually classify the microfossils that were present. Upon inspection of the samples, we concluded that there were two main types of microfossils: nannoplankton and foraminifera.

Gives overview of results.

Outlines procedure to be detailed in following paragraph.

Describes main equipment, in layperson's language.

Breaks down procedure into easy-to-read "chunks."

continues

Model 10-6   Lab report (letter format)

Andrew Hawkes
December 12, 2006
Page 2

Step 2

Next, we had to extract the microfossils from the core samples you provided. We used two different techniques:

Nannoplankton Extraction Technique
a. Selected a pebble-size piece of the sample
b. Thoroughly crushed the piece under water
c. Used a dropper to remove some of the material that floats to the surface
   (it contains the nannoplankton)
d. Dried the nannoplankton-water combination
e. Placed the nannoplankton on a slide

Foraminifera Extraction Technique
a. Boiled a small portion of the sample
b. Used a microscreen to remove clay and other unwanted material
c. Dried remaining material (foraminifera)
d. Placed foraminifera on slide

PROBLEMS ENCOUNTERED

The entire lab procedure went as planned. The only problem was minor and occurred when we removed one of the samples from the container in which it was shipped. As the bag was taken from the shipping box, it broke open. The sample shattered when it fell onto the lab table. Fortunately, we had an extra sample from the same location.

CONCLUSION

Judging by the types of fossils present in the sample, they come from rock of an age that might contain coal. This conclusion is based on limited testing, so we suggest you test more samples at the site. We would be glad to help you with this additional sampling and testing.

I will call you this week to discuss our study and any possible follow-up you may wish us to do.

Sincerely,

Joanne Rappaport

Joanne Rappaport
Senior Geologist

Model 10-6 *continued*

Provides smooth transitions.

Itemizes steps because of their importance in procedure.

Uses *parallel form* in describing this process.

Does not bury sampling error—gives it proper treatment.

Ends with wrap-up that reinforces main point of report.

Offers follow-up services.

CHAPTER 11

Formal Reports

M artin & Koffman's director of marketing was given an interesting assignment two months ago. Jacques Martin, the company president, asked the marketing director to take a long, hard look at the company's clients. Were they satisfied with the service they were receiving? Did they routinely reward M&K with additional work? Were there any features of the company, its employees, or its services that frustrated them? What did they want to see changed? In other words, the marketing director was asked to step back from daily events and evaluate the company's level of service. He tackled the project in four stages:

1. He designed and sent out a survey to all recent and current clients.
2. He followed up on some of the returned surveys with telephone and personal interviews.
3. He evaluated the data he collected.
4. He wrote a *formal report* on the results of his study. Besides going to all branch managers, the report later served as a basis for some in-house training sessions called "Quality at Martin & Koffman."

Like the marketing director, you will write a number of long, formal reports during your career. Most will be written collaboratively with colleagues; others will be your own creations. All of them will require major efforts at planning, organizing, drafting, and revising. Though informal reports are the most common reports in business writing, formal reports become a larger part of your writing as you move along in your career. This text uses the following working definition:

Formal report: this report covers complex projects and may be directed to readers at different technical levels. Although not defined by length, a formal report usually contains at least six to ten pages of text, not including appendices. It can be directed to readers either inside or outside your organization. Often bound, it usually includes the following separate parts: cover/title page, letter/memo of transmittal, table of contents, list of illustrations, glossary or list of symbols, executive summary, introduction, discussion sections, and conclusions and recommendations. (Appendices often appear after the report text.)

Remember that the measure of a report's success is not whether it meets the criteria established by the preceding definition. Students often have difficulty with the most important aspect of a report—its purpose. No employer will have anyone write a report as a learning exercise, nor will an employer demand a report that merely rephrases existing knowledge. In the world of work, reports are written for a *purpose*. That purpose can be many things, including to evaluate, to compare, and to report. In brief, the writer of a formal technical report uses the data available to produce a finding or conclusion that is unique to that report. Thus, the measure of a report's success is determined by *how well it achieves its purpose*.

To prepare you to write excellent formal reports, this chapter includes four main sections. The first briefly describes situations that would require formal reports, both in-house and external. The second outlines a strategy for organizing formal reports. The third provides guidelines for writing the main parts of a formal report. The final section introduces a complete long report from M&K that follows this chapter's guidelines. The actual report appears in Model 11-9 at the end of this chapter.

WHEN TO USE FORMAL REPORTS

Like most people, you probably associate formal reports with important projects. What else would justify all that time and effort? In comparison to informal reports, formal reports usually (1) cover more complicated projects and (2) are longer than their informal counterparts.

While length and the complexity of subject matter are the main differences between formal and informal reports, sometimes there is another distinction: formal reports may have a more diverse readership. In that case, readers who want just a quick overview can turn to the executive summary at the beginning or the conclusions and recommendations at the end. Technical readers who want to check your facts and figures can turn to discussion sections or appendices. And all readers can flip to the table of contents for a quick outline of what sections the report contains. You need to think about the needs of all these readers as you plan and write your formal reports.

The intended audience for formal reports can be inside or outside, though the latter is more common. Following are four situations at M&K where formal reports would be appropriate:

- **Salary study and recommendations (internal):** A supervisor at M&K's head office has just completed a study of technicians' and technologists' salaries among M&K's competitors throughout Canada. What prompted the study was the difficulty the supervisor was having hiring computer technicians and technologists. Lately some top applicants have been choosing other firms. Because M&K's policy has been that all its employees should be placed on the same salary scale, jobs at M&K are only appealing in areas where the cost of living is low. The supervisor wants to give the main office some data showing that starting salaries at some branch offices should be higher. She decides to submit a formal report, complete with data and recommendations for adjustments. Her main audience includes the president, Jacques Martin, and the vice president of Canadian operations.

- **Waste management survey (external):** For the past several years, the town of Lost River in Labrador has noticed increased fish kills on the Lost River, which flows through the town and serves as its main source of drinking water. Pollution has always been fairly well monitored on the river, so city officials are puzzled by the kills. M&K's Montreal office has been hired to analyze the problem and present its opinion about the cause. A team of chemists, environmental engineers, and field technicians has just completed a study and will present its formal report. The audience will be quite diverse—from the technical experts in the city's water department to the members of a special citizens' panel representing the residents.

- **Collapse of oil rig (external):** A 10-year-old rig in the Gulf of St. Lawrence recently collapsed during a mild storm. Several rig workers died, and several million dollars' worth of equipment was lost. Also, the accident created an oil spill that destroyed a significant amount of fish and wildlife before it was finally contained. M&K's Montreal office was hired to examine the cause of the structure's collapse, which supposedly was able to withstand hurricanes. After three months of on-site analysis and laboratory work, M&K's experts are ready to submit their report, which will be read by the firm's corporate managers, federal and provincial government agencies, and several major wildlife organizations' members. Also, the report may be used as the basis for some news reports throughout the world.

As these three situations show, formal reports are among the most difficult on-the-job writing assignments you will face in your career. You may write some yourself; you will write most as a member of a team of technical and professional people. In all cases, you need to (1) understand your purpose, (2) determine your readers' needs, and (3) design a report that responds to those needs. Guidelines in the next two sections will help you meet these goals.

Formal technical reports are, with rare exceptions, written by a group. Although in a group situation your expertise will not need to be as broad, and the amount of text you will be responsible for will obviously be smaller than if you worked by yourself, most people find it more difficult to work in a group. The fact that you may be responsible for only a part of the text does not relieve you of the responsibility for understanding the whole document. To successfully produce your section of the document, you must have an understanding of the entire document's structure and content. Only then can you produce work that can be integrated into the whole.

STRATEGY FOR ORGANIZING FORMAL REPORTS

You will encounter different report formats in your career, depending on your profession and your specific employer. Whichever format you choose, however, there is a universal approach to good organization that always applies. This approach is based on the following main principles, discussed in detail in Chapter 3:

Principle 1: Write different parts for different readers.
Principle 2: Emphasize beginnings and endings.
Principle 3: Repeat key points.

These principles apply to formal reports even more than they do to informal documents, for the following reasons:

1. A formal report may have a very mixed audience—from laypersons to highly technical specialists to executives.
2. The majority of readers of long reports focus on specific sections that interest them most, reading selectively each time they pick up the report.
3. Few readers have time to wade through a lot of introductory information before reaching the main point. They will get frustrated quickly if you do not place important information first.

This chapter responds to these facts about readers of formal reports by following the ABC format (for **A**bstract, **B**ody, **C**onclusion). As noted in Chapter 3, the three main rules are that you should (1) start with an abstract for decision makers, (2) put supporting details in the body, and (3) use the conclusion to produce action. This simple ABC format should be evident in all formal reports, despite their complexity.

ABC Format: Formal Report
Abstract

- Cover/title page
- Letter or memo of transmittal
- Table of contents
- List of illustrations
- Glossary (symbols)
- Executive summary
- Introduction

Body

- Discussion sections
- [Appendices—appear after text but support Body section]

Conclusion

- Conclusions
- Recommendations

Several features of this structure deserve special mention. First, note that the generic abstract section includes five different parts of the report that help give readers a capsule version of the entire report. As you will learn shortly, the executive summary is by far the most important section for providing this big picture. Second, appendices are placed within the body part of the outline, even though sequentially they come at the end of the report. The reason for this placement in the outline is that both appendices and body sections provide the report's supporting details. Third, remember that the generic conclusion section in the ABC format can contain conclusions, or recommendations, or both, depending on the nature of the report.

Before moving to a discussion of the specific sections that make up the ABC format, take note of the use of main headings in complex formal reports (see Chapter 4, Figure 4-5, pages 76–77). Much like chapter titles, these headings are often centred, in full caps, in bold type, and oversized. Also, they usually begin a new page. When treated this way, each major section of the formal report seems to exist on its own. Then you have three remaining heading levels for use within each section.

GUIDELINES FOR THE NINE PARTS OF FORMAL REPORTS

What follows is a description of nine parts of the formal report:

1. Cover/title page
2. Letter/memo of transmittal
3. Table of contents
4. List of illustrations
5. Glossary and list of symbols
6. Executive summary
7. Introduction
8. Discussion sections
9. Conclusions and recommendations

What could be considered a 10th part, appendices, is mentioned in the context of the discussion section.

Because formal reports can cover such a broad range of material, the guidelines here are rather general. For specific application of these guidelines, see the formal report in Model 11-9 on pages 289–310.

Cover/Title Page

Formal reports are usually bound, typically with a cover used for all reports in the writer's organization. (Reports prepared for college and university courses, however, are often placed in a three-tab folder, the outside of which serves as the report cover.) Since the cover is the first item the reader sees, it should be attractive and informative. Usually it contains the same four pieces of information mentioned in the following list with regard to the title page; sometimes it may have only one or two of these items.

Inside the cover is the title page, which should include the following four pieces of information:

- Project title (exactly as it appears on the letter/memo of transmittal)
- Your client's name ("Prepared for . . .")
- Your name and/or the name of your organization ("Prepared by . . .")
- Date of submission

To make your title page or cover distinctive, you might want to place a simple illustration on it. Do not clutter the page, of course. If the appearance of a project—an architectural proposal, for instance—is important, place an illustration on the title page. Otherwise, use a visual only if it reinforces a main point and if it can be simply and tastefully done. For example, assume that M&K has submitted a formal report to a coastal city in British Columbia, concluding that an industrial park can be built near the city's bird sanctuary without harming the habitat—*if* stringent guidelines are followed. The report writer decides to place the picture of a nesting bird on the title page, punctuating the report's point about the industrial park, as in Model 11-1 on page 281.

Letter/Memo of Transmittal

Letters or memos of transmittal have two possible functions. The more common one is to tell the readers who asked for the report that their request for information is satisfied in the report. The second, when the report is unsolicited, is to treat readers to an appetizer—a taste of what is ahead. If your formal report is to readers outside your own organization, write a letter of transmittal; if it is to readers inside your organization, write a memo of transmittal. Models 11-2 (page 282) and 11-3 (page 283) show examples of both. Follow these guidelines for constructing this part of your reports:

Transmittal Guideline 1: Place Letter/Memo Immediately after Title Page

This placement means that the letter or memo is placed in the document, to keep it from becoming separated. It is not, however, bound into the report. Some organizations paper-clip this letter or memo to the front of the report, making it a cover letter or memo. In so doing, however, they risk having it become separated from the report.

Transmittal Guideline 2: Include Major Points from Report

Remember that readers are heavily influenced by what they read first in reports. Therefore, take advantage of the position of this section by including the topics covered and the major findings, conclusions, or recommendations from the report—besides supplying necessary transmittal information.

Transmittal Guideline 3: Follow Letter and Memo Conventions

Like other letters and memos, letters and memos of transmittal should be easy to read, inviting readers into the rest of the report. Keep introductory and concluding paragraphs relatively short—no more than three to five lines each. Also, write in a conversational style that is free of technical jargon and clichés, such as "per your request" or "enclosed herewith." See the models at the end of Chapters 8 and 9 for more details concerning memo/letter format. For now, here are some highlights about the mechanics of format:

Letters and Memos

- Use single spacing and ragged-edge copy, even if the rest of the report is double-spaced and right-justified.
- Use only one page.

Letters

- Include company project number with the letter date.
- Correctly spell the reader's name.
- Be sure the inside address includes the mailing address to appear on the envelope.
- Use the reader's last name ("Dear Mr. Jamison:") in the salutation because of the report's formality—unless your close association with the reader would make it more appropriate to use first names ("Dear Bill:").
- Usually include a project title, as with letter reports. The title is treated like a main heading. Use concise wording that matches the wording on the title page.
- Use "Sincerely" as your closing.
- Include a line to indicate those who will receive copies of the report ("cc" for *carbon copy*, "pc" for *photocopy*, or just "c" or "copy" for *copy*).

Memos

- Give a clear description of the project in the memo's Subject line, including a project number if there is one.
- Include a distribution list to indicate those who will receive copies.

Table of Contents

Your contents page acts as an outline. Many readers go there right away to determine the report's structure, and then return again and again to locate report sections of most interest to them. Guidelines follow for assembling this important component of your report. See Model 11-4 on page 284 for an example.

Table of Contents Guideline 1: Make It Readable

The table of contents must be pleasing to the eye so that readers can find sections quickly and see how they relate to each other. Be sure to do the following:

- Space items well on the page.
- Use indenting to draw attention to subheadings.
- Include page numbers for every heading and subheading, unless there are many headings in a relatively short report, in which case you can delete page numbers for all of the lowest-level headings listed in the table of contents.

Table of Contents Guideline 2: Use the Contents Page to Reveal Report Emphases

Choose the wording of headings and subheadings with care. Be specific yet concise so that each heading listed in the table of contents gives the reader a good indication of what the section contains.

Readers associate the importance of report sections with the number of headings and subheadings listed in the table of contents. If, for example, a discussion section called "Description of the Problem" contains many more heading breakdowns than other sections, you are telling the reader that the section is more important. When possible, it is best to have about the same number of breakdowns for report sections of about the same importance. In short, the table of contents should be balanced. See Model 11-5 on page 285.

Table of Contents Guideline 3: Consider the Reader's Needs

Provide enough headings so that the readers can quickly and easily isolate the information that interests them. As you know from experience, it is irritating to have to read large sections of text in order to find what you need to know. At the same time, do not provide too many low-level headings: to fragment the body unnecessarily often destroys the logical development of your conclusions.

Table of Contents Guideline 4: Make the Table of Contents Self-Explanatory

Because your reader may only be scanning the table of contents, it is important to make the headings informative. A chapter titled "Design" does not inform a reader about the contents of the chapter. In contrast, the title "Design Options for the Front Forks" serves to give the reader a very good idea of the information available in the chapter.

Table of Contents Guideline 5: List Appendices

Appendices include items such as tables of data or descriptions of procedures that are inserted at the end of the report. Typically, they are listed at the end of the table of contents. Often no page numbers are given, since many appendices contain stand-alone material and are thus individually paged (for example, Appendix A might be paged A-1, A-2, A-3, etc.). Tabs on the edges of pages can help the reader locate these sections.

Table of Contents Guideline 6: Use Parallel Form in All Entries

All headings in one section, and sometimes even all headings and subheadings in the report, should have parallel grammatical form. Readers find mixed forms distracting. For example, "Subgrade Preparation" and "Fill Placement" are parallel, in that they are both the same type of phrase. However, if you were to switch the wording of the first item to "Preparing the Subgrade" or "How to Prepare the Subgrade," parallel structure would be lost.

Table of Contents Guideline 7: Proofread Carefully

The table of contents is one of the last report sections to be assembled; thus it often contains errors. Wrong page numbers and incorrect heading wording are two common mistakes. Another is the failure to show the correct relationship between headings and subheadings. Obviously, errors in the table of contents can confuse the reader and prove embarrassing to the writer. Proofread the section carefully.

List of Illustrations

Illustrations within the body of the report are usually listed on a separate page right after the table of contents. When there are few illustrations, another option is to list them at the bottom of the table of contents page rather than on a separate page. In either case, this list should include the *number, title,* and *page number* of every table and figure within the body of the report. If there are many illustrations, separate the list into tables and figures. See the example in Model 11-6 on page 286. (For more information on illustrations, see Chapter 5.)

Glossary and List of Symbols

A **glossary** should be provided if there is any terminology used in the report that the reader might not be familiar with. Generally you should try to avoid technical terminology if that is possible; however, that is usually impossible. You must define terms that may be unfamiliar to a reader (Example 1) as well as terms that the reader may misinterpret (Example 2).

Example 1:   **Gluconeogenesis** is the process by which the body produces small amounts of glucose.

Example 2:   The **apron** is the tool tray attached to the base of the machine.

The glossary may be located either after the list of illustrations or after the conclusions and recommendations. Ask your intended readers what they prefer.

A *list of symbols* may be necessary. Reports written in chemical, mechanical, and civil engineering often use symbols that must be explained so that the reader can understand the results. The list of symbols is placed after the glossary.

Executive Summary

No formal report would be complete without an executive summary. This short section provides decision makers with a capsule version of the report. Consider it a stand-alone section that should be free of technical jargon. See Model 11-7 on page 287 for an example. Follow these basic guidelines in preparing this important section of your formal reports:

Executive Summary Guideline 1: State the Conclusions or Findings in the Present Tense

You are attempting to convince the readers of the correctness of your conclusions. You want them to accept or act on your findings. Therefore, you must convince your readers that what you have decided is valid now. Readers may not be persuaded if the conclusion states, "The Chevrolet C-10 truck was the best truck tested." They may be more likely to react positively to a conclusion that reads, "Tests show that the Chevrolet C-10 is the better truck."

Executive Summary Guideline 2: Put It on One Page

The best reason to hold the summary to one page is that most readers expect and prefer this length. It is a comfort to know that somewhere within a long report there is one page to which they can turn for an easy-to-read overview. Moreover, a one-page length permits easy distribution at meetings. When the executive summary begins to crowd your page, it is acceptable to switch to single spacing if such a change helps keep the summary on one page—even though the rest of the report may be space-and-a-half or double-spaced.

Some extremely long formal reports may require that you write an executive summary of several pages or longer. In this case, you still need to provide the reader with a section that summarizes the report in less than one page. The answer to this dilemma is to write a brief abstract, which is placed right before the executive summary. Consider the abstract a condensed version of the executive summary, directed to the highest-level decision makers. (See Chapter 14 for further discussion of abstracts.)

Executive Summary Guideline 3: Avoid Technical Jargon

Include only that level of technical language the decision makers will comprehend. It makes no sense to talk over the heads of the most important readers.

Executive Summary Guideline 4: Include Only Important Conclusions and Recommendations

The executive summary mentions only the report's major points. An exhaustive list of findings, conclusions, and recommendations can come later, at the end of the report. If you have trouble deciding what is most important, put yourself in the readers' position. What information is most essential for them? If you want to leave them with one, two, or three points about the report, what will these points be? That is the information that belongs in the executive summary.

Executive Summary Guideline 5: Avoid References to the Report Body

Do not say that the report provides additional information. It is understood that the executive summary is only a general account of the report's contents. References to later sections do not provide the busy reader with further understanding.

An exception is those instances when you are discussing issues that involve danger or liability. Here you may need to add qualifiers in your summary—for example, "As noted in this report, further study will be necessary." Such statements protect you and the client in the event the executive summary is removed from the report and used as a separate stand-alone document.

Executive Summary Guideline 6: Use Paragraph Format

Whereas lists are often appropriate for body sections of a report, they can make executive summaries seem fragmented. The best summaries create unity with a series of fairly short paragraphs that flow together well. Within a paragraph, there can be a short listing of a few points for emphasis (see Model 11-7), but the listing should not be the summary's main structural element.

Occasionally, you may be convinced that the paragraph approach is not desirable. For example, a project may involve a series of isolated topics that would not mesh into unified paragraphs. In this case, use a modified list. Start the summary with a brief introductory paragraph, followed by a numbered list of three to nine points. Each numbered point should include a brief explanation (for example, "3. *Sewer Construction:* We believe that seepage influx can be controlled by . . . 4. *Geologic Fault Evaluation:* We found no evidence of surficial . . .).

Executive Summary Guideline 7: Write the Executive Summary Last

Only after finishing the report do you have the perspective to write a summary. Approach the task this way. First, sit back and review the report from beginning to end. Then ask yourself, "What would my readers really need to know if they had only a minute or two to read?" The answer to that question becomes the core of your executive summary.

Introduction

View this section as your chance to prepare both technical and nontechnical readers for the discussion ahead. You do not need to summarize the report, for your executive summary has accomplished that goal. Instead, give information on the report's purpose, scope, and format, as well as a project description. Follow these basic guidelines, which are reflected in Model 11-8 on page 288.

Introduction Guideline 1: State Your Purpose and Lead into Subsections

The purpose statement for the document should appear immediately after the main introduction heading (example: "This report presents Martin & Koffman's foundation design recommendations for the new Hilltop Building in Rimouski, Quebec"). Follow it with a sentence that mentions the introduction subdivisions to follow (example: "This introduction provides a description of the project site and explains the scope of activities we conducted").

Introduction Guideline 2: Include a Project Description

Here you need to be precise about the project. Depending on the type of project, you may be describing a physical setting, a set of problems that prompted the report study, or some other data. The information may have been provided to you or you may have collected it yourself. Accuracy in this section will help prevent any later misunderstandings between you and the reader. (If the project description is too long for the introduction, it can be placed in the body of the report.)

Introduction Guideline 3: Include Scope Information

This section must outline the study's precise objectives. Include all necessary details, using bulleted or numbered lists when appropriate. Your listing or description should parallel the order of the information presented in the body of the report. Like the project description, this subsection must be accurate in every detail. Careful, thorough writing here can prevent later misunderstandings about the tasks you were hired to perform.

Introduction Guideline 4: Consider Including Information on Report Format

Often the scope section lists information as it is presented in the report. If this is not the case, end the introduction with a short subsection on the report format. Here you can give readers a brief preview of the main sections that follow. In effect, the section acts as a condensed table of contents and may list the report's major sections and appendices.

Discussion Sections

Discussion sections compose the longest part of formal reports. In general, they are written for the most technically oriented members of your audience. You can focus on facts and opinions, demonstrating the technical expertise that the reader expects from you. General guidelines for writing the report discussion are listed here. For a complete example of the discussion component, see the formal-report example in Model 11-9 on pages 289–310.

Discussion Guideline 1: Move from Facts to Opinions

As you have learned, the ABC format requires that you start your formal report with a summary of the most important information. That is, you skip right to essential conclusions and recommendations the reader needs and wants to know. Once into the discussion section, however, you back up and adopt a strategy that parallels the stages of the technical project itself. You begin with hard data and move toward conclusions and recommendations—that is, those parts that involve more opinion.

The discussion should follow the order of a typical technical project, which usually involves the following stages:

First, you collect data (samples, interviews, records, etc.).

Second, you subject these data to verification or testing (lab tests or computer analyses, for example).

Third, you analyze all the information, using your professional experience and skills to form conclusions (or convictions based on the data).

Fourth, you develop recommendations that flow directly from the conclusions you have formed.

Thus, the body of your report gives technical readers the same movement from fact toward opinion that you experience during the project itself. There are two reasons for this approach, one ethical and the other practical. First, as a professional, you are obligated to draw clear distinctions between what you have observed and what you have concluded or recommended. Second, your reports will usually be more persuasive if you give readers the chance to draw conclusions for themselves. If you move carefully through the four-stage process just described, readers will be more likely to reach the same conclusions that you have drawn.

Discussion Guideline 2: Consider Numbering Headings and Subheadings

Headings help readers grasp the content of your report. They are especially needed in the body of the report, which presents the technical details. A system such as the decimal system will help to point out the importance of certain sections and to explain the report's structure to the reader. Alphabetical systems, although not often used in modern writing, will give your report a traditional feel that may appeal to certain readers.

Discussion Guideline 3: Use Listings to Break up Long Paragraphs

Long paragraphs full of technical details irritate readers. Use paragraphs for brief explanations, not for descriptions of processes or other details that could be listed.

Discussion Guideline 4: Use Illustrations for Clarification and Persuasion

A simple table or figure can sometimes be just the right complement to a technical discussion in the text. Incorporate illustrations into the report body to make technical information accessible and easier to digest.

Discussion Guideline 5: Place Excessive Detail in Appendices

Today's trend is to place cumbersome detail in appendices that are attached to formal reports, rather than weighing down the discussion with this detail. In other words, you give readers access to supporting information without cluttering up the text of the formal report. Of course, you need to refer to appendices in the body of the report and label appendices clearly so that readers can locate them easily.

Tabbed sheets are a good way to make all report sections, including appendices, accessible to the reader. Consider starting each section with a tabbed sheet so that the reader can "thumb" to it easily.

Conclusions and Recommendations

This final section of the report should give readers a place to turn to for a comprehensive description—sometimes in the form of a listing—of all conclusions and recommendations. The points may or may not have been mentioned in the body of the report, depending on the document's length and complexity. Conclusions are convictions or beliefs based on your study's findings; recommendations are actions you are suggesting based on your conclusions. For example, your conclusion may be that there are dangerous levels of toxic chemicals in a town's water supply. Your recommendation may be that the toxic site near the reservoir be immediately cleaned.

What distinguishes this last section of the report text from the executive summary is the level of detail and the audience. The conclusions and recommendations section provides an exhaustive list of conclusions and recommendations for technical and management readers. The executive summary provides a selective list or description of the most important conclusions and recommendations for decision makers, who may not have technical knowledge.

In other words, view the conclusions and recommendations section as an expanded version of the executive summary. It usually assumes one of the following three headings, depending of course on the content:

1. Conclusions
2. Recommendations
3. Conclusions and Recommendations

Another option for reports that contain many conclusions and recommendations is to separate this last section into two sections: (1) Conclusions and (2) Recommendations.

FORMAL REPORT EXAMPLES

Model 11-9 on pages 289–310 provides a long, formal technical report. It contains the main sections discussed earlier, excluding the list of illustrations.

The report results from a study that Martin & Koffman completed for the City of Ottawa (see Chapter 2, Project #2). Although most members of the intended audience have technical expertise, some do not. The audience comprises full-time professionals employed by the participating companies and local politicians who initiated the project. The professionals include engineers, environmental specialists, city planners, and architects.

Employability Skills

The Conference Board of Canada's *Employability Skills 2000+* shows that teamwork is an integral part of the working environment. Relevant teamwork skills include the following:

- Understand and work within the dynamics of a group.
- Ensure that a team's purpose and objectives are clear.
- Be flexible: respect, be open to and supportive of the thoughts, opinions and contributions of others in a group.
- Recognize and respect people's diversity, individual differences and perspectives.
- Accept and provide feedback in a constructive and considerate manner.

- Contribute to a team by sharing information and expertise.*

Select a group of between six and ten people to prepare a formal technical report. Choose a recent—within the last five years—innovation such as text messaging and prepare to write a formal report explaining how the innovation will have a positive impact on life or society. Remember to address the issues of those who do not agree with your point of view.

Divide the report into a series of tasks and have each person prepare an outline of what he or she plans to do in the assigned task.

* *Employability Skills 2000+* Brochure 2000 E/F (Ottawa: The Conference Board of Canada, 2000).

CHAPTER SUMMARY

In your career you will write formal reports for large, complex projects, either inside or outside your organization. In either case, you will be sending the report to people with different technical backgrounds. This complex audience will respond best to reports that subscribe to the ABC format, for it organizes information so that different readers can read different sections of the report. You are likely to engage in group writing in producing formal reports. Although long-report formats vary according to company and profession, most will have nine basic parts: cover/title page, letter/memo of transmittal, table of contents, list of illustrations, glossary and/or list of symbols, executive summary, introduction, discussion sections, and conclusions and recommendations. Follow the specific guidelines in this chapter for these sections. The annotated model, Model 11-9, can serve as your reference.

ASSIGNMENTS

Part 1 assignments ask you to evaluate a whole report, to write an individual section, or to evaluate an individual section. Part 2 assignments ask you to write complete formal reports. Remember to submit Planning Forms with the Part 2 assignments.

Part 1: Short Assignments

These assignments can be completed by individuals or by teams. If you are instructed to use teams, first review the guidelines for group writing found in Chapter 1.

1. **Evaluation—a formal report.** Use Model 11-9, the complete formal report example in this chapter, for this assignment. The audience for the report is described in the chapter section "Formal Report Examples." Although the writer directed the report to a mixed technical and nontechnical audience, some sections clearly are more technical than others.

   - Evaluate the likely audience for each section of the report.
   - Discuss ways that the writer addressed, or did not address, the needs of specific audience types.
   - Offer suggestions for improving the manner in which the report meets the needs of its intended audience.

2. **Evaluation—a formal report.** Locate a formal report written by a private firm or government agency *or* use a long report provided by your instructor. Determine the degree to which the example follows the guidelines in this chapter. Depending on the instructions given by your teacher, choose between the following options:

   - Present your findings orally *or* in writing.
   - Select part of the report *or* all of the report.

3. **Executive summary.** Choose one of the project sheets included in Chapter 2. Write a brief executive summary for the project. If necessary, provide additional information or transitional wording not included on the sheet, but do not change the nature of the information already provided.

4. **Evaluation—an introduction.** Review the chapter guidelines for writing an effective introduction to a formal report. Then evaluate the degree to which the following example follows or does not follow the guidelines presented.

INTRODUCTION

M&K has completed a three-week study of the manufacturing and servicing processes at King Radio Company. As requested, we have developed a blueprint for ways in which Computer-Aided Testing (CAT) can be used to improve the company's productivity and quality.

Project Description

Mr. Dan Mahoney familiarized our project team with the problems that prompted this study of computer-aided testing. According to Mr. Mahoney, the main areas of concern are as follows:

- Too many units on the production line are failing postproduction testing and thus returning to the repair line.
- Production bottlenecks are occurring throughout the plant because of the testing difficulties.
- Technicians in the servicing centre are having trouble repairing faulty units because of their complexity.
- Customers' complaints have been increasing, both for new units under warranty and repaired units.

Scope

From May 3–5, 2006, M&K had a three-person team of experts working at the King Radio Company plant. This team interviewed many personnel, observed all the production processes, and acquired data needed to develop recommendations.

Upon returning to the M&K office, team members met to share their observations and develop the master plan included in this report.

Report Format

This report is largely organized around the two ways that CAT can improve operation at the King Radio plant. Based on the detailed examination of the plant's problems in this regard, the report covers two areas for improvement and ends with a section that lists main conclusions and recommendations. The main report sections are as follows:

- Production and Servicing Problems at King Radio
- CAT and the Manufacturing Process
- CAT and the Servicing Process
- Major Conclusions and Recommendations

The report ends with two appendices. Appendix A offers detailed information on several pieces of equipment we recommend that you purchase. Appendix B provides three recent articles from the journal *CAT Today*. All three deal with the application of CAT to production and service problems similar to those you are experiencing.

Part 2: Longer Assignments

This section contains assignments for writing entire formal reports. Remember to complete the Planning Form for each assignment.

These assignments can be written by individual writers or by group-writing teams. If your instructor has made this a team assignment, review the guidelines on group writing in Chapter 1.

5. **Research-based formal report.** Complete the following procedure for writing a research-based report:

- Conduct either a computer-assisted search or a traditional library search on a general topic in a field that interests you. Do some preliminary reading to screen possible specific topics.
- Choose three to five specific topics that would require further research and for which you can locate information.
- Work with your instructor to select the one topic that would best fit this assignment, given your interests and the criteria set forth here.
- Develop a simulated context for the report topic, whereby you select a *purpose* for the report, a specific *audience* to whom it could be addressed (as if it were a "real" report), and a specific *role* for you as a writer.

   For example, assume you have selected "earth-sheltered homes" as your topic. You might be writing a report to the manager of a local design firm on the features and construction techniques of such structures. As a newly hired engineer or designer, you are presenting information so that your manager can decide whether the firm might want to begin building and marketing such homes. This report might present only data, or it could present data and recommendations.

- Write the report according to the format guidelines in this chapter and in consideration of the specific context you have chosen.
- Document your sources appropriately (see Chapter 14).

6. **Work-based formal report.** This assignment is based on the work experience that you may have had in the past or that you may be experiencing now.

- Choose five or ten report topics that are based on your current or past work experience. For example, you could choose "warehouse design" if you stock parts, "checkout procedure" if you work behind the counter at a video-rental store, "report-production procedures" if you work as a secretary at an engineering firm, and so on. In other words, find a subject that you know about or about which you can find more information, especially through interviews.
- Work with your instructor to select the one topic that holds out the best possibilities for a successful report, on the basis of the criteria given here.
- Develop a context for the report in which you give yourself a *role* in the company where you work(ed). This role should be one in which you would actually write a formal in-house or external report about the topic you have chosen, but the role does not have to be the exact one you had or have. Then select a precise *purpose* for which you might be writing the report and finally a set of *readers* who might read such a report within or outside the organization. Your report can be a presentation of data and conclusions *or* a presentation of data, conclusions, and recommendations.
- Follow the guidelines included in this chapter for format and organization.

7. **School-based formal report.** This assignment can be completed as an individual project or as a group project. As an individual project, it will rely on observations you have made during the time you spent at a high school, college, or university—either the one where you are taking this course or another you attended previously. As a group project, it will rely on either (1) group members from diverse majors using their varied backgrounds to examine a common campus problem or (2) group members majoring in the same field or working in the same department exploring a problem they have in common.

   Whether you write an individual or a group report, follow this general procedure:

   - Assemble a list of five or ten problems that you have observed at your school. These problems might concern (1) the physical campus (as in poor design of parking lots or inadequate lab space), (2) the curriculum (as in the need to update certain courses), (3) extracurricular activities (as in the need for more cultural or athletic events), or (4) difficulties with campus support services (as in red tape during registration).
   - Work with your instructor to choose the one topic for which you can find the most information and for which you can develop the context described here.
   - Collect information in whatever ways seem useful—for example, site observations, surveys of students, follow-up phone calls, or interviews.
   - Submit progress reports at intervals requested by your instructor. (Consult guidelines in the "For Progress/Periodic Reports" section of Chapter 10.)
   - Consider your *role* to be the one that you, in fact, have—a student or a group of students at the school. Then select as your *reader(s)* the school officials who would actually be in charge of solving the problem you have identified. (You may or may not end up sending the report. Follow the advice of your instructor in this matter.) The *purpose* of this report will be to explain, in great detail, all aspects of the problem *and* to form conclusions as to its cause. If it seems appropriate, you may take one further step and suggest recommendations for a solution—if your research has taken you this far. In any case, detail and also tact are important criteria.

8. **M&K-based formal report.** For this assignment you will assign to yourself a role of your choosing at M&K. Use the following procedure, which may be modified by your instructor:

   a. Review the section at the beginning of this chapter that lists M&K cases for formal reports to get a sense of when formal reports are used at companies like M&K.
   b. Review the M&K information in Chapter 2, especially with regard to the kinds of jobs people hold at the company and the kinds of projects that are undertaken.
   c. Choose a specific job that you could assume at M&K, based on your academic background, your work experience, or your career interests.
   d. Choose a specific project that (a) could conceivably be completed at M&K by someone in the role you have chosen, (b) would result in a formal report directed either

inside or outside the company, and (c) would be addressed to a complex audience at two or three of the levels indicated on the Planning Form in Chapter 1.

e. Be sure you have access to information that will be used in this simulated report—for example, from work experience, from a term paper or class project in another course, or from your interviews of individuals already in the field. (For this assignment, you may want to talk with a professional already in this field, such as a recent graduate in your major.)

f. Prepare a copy of the Planning Form found in Chapter 1 for your instructor's approval—*before* proceeding further with the project.

g. Complete the formal report, following the guidelines in this chapter.

An Assessment of Industrial Park on the Adjoining Bird Sanctuary

Prepared for: City Council
Esquimault, British Columbia

Prepared by: Martin & Koffman
Vancouver, British Columbia

Date: March 3, 2006

Model 11-1 Title page with illustration

Martin & Koffman

200 Fourth Avenue NW
Calgary AB T2N 0N3
(403) 555-7524

Report #82-651

July 19, 2006

Belton Oil Corporation
P.O. Box 301
Calgary AB T1X 9P6

Attention: Mr. Jorge Lopes

GEOTECHNICAL INVESTIGATION
DREDGE DISPOSAL AREA F
BELTON OIL REFINERY
CALGARY, AB

This is the second volume of a three-volume report on our geotechnical investigation concerning dredge materials at your Huff refinery. This study was authorized by Term Contract No. 604 and term Contract Release No. 20-6 dated May 6, 2006.

This report includes our findings and recommendations for Dredge Disposal Area F. Preliminary results were discussed with Mr. Lopes on July 16, 2006. We consider the soil conditions at the site suitable for limited dike enlargements. However, we recommend that an embankment test section be constructed and monitored before dike design is finalized.

We appreciate the opportunity to work with you on this project. We look forward to assisting you with the final design and providing materials-testing services.

Sincerely,

George Fursten

George H. Fursten
Geotechnical/Environmental Engineer

GHF/dnn

Model 11-2   Letter of transmittal

MEMORANDUM

DATE: March 18, 2006
TO: Jacques Martin, President
FROM: Alice Andrews, Personnel Assistant *aa*
SUBJECT: Report on Flex-Time Pilot Program at Vancouver Office

As you requested, I have examined the results of the six-month pilot program to introduce flex-time to the Vancouver office. This report presents my data and conclusions about the use of flexible work schedules.

To determine the results of the pilot program, I asked all employees to complete a written survey. Then I followed up by interviewing every fifth person off an alphabetical list of office personnel. Overall, it appears that flex-time has met with clear approval by employees at all levels. Productivity has increased and morale has soared. This report uses the survey and interview data to suggest why these results have occurred and where we might go from here.

I enjoyed working on this personnel study because of its potential impact on the way M&K conducts business. Please give me a call if you would like additional details about the study.

Model 11-3 Memo of transmittal

TABLE OF CONTENTS

ii

Model 11-4 Table of contents (all subheadings included)

TABLE OF CONTENTS

Model 11-5   Table of contents (third-level subheadings omitted)

Model 11-6 List of illustrations—formal report

EXECUTIVE SUMMARY

Martin & Koffman was asked to determine why there were traces of nickel in Well M-17 at the electric facility near Valleyfield, Quebec. As well, Martin & Koffman was asked to determine a remedy and to implement that remedy. Quarterly monitoring had shown that M-17 was the only well affected.

The project consisted of four main parts. First, we collected and tested 20 soil samples within a 50-metre radius of the well. Second, we collected groundwater samples from the well itself. Third, we removed the stainless steel well screen and casing and submitted them for metallurgical analysis. Finally, we installed a replacement screen and casing built with Teflon.

The findings from this project are as follows:

- The soil samples contained no nickel.
- We found significant corrosion and pitting in the stainless steel screen and casing that we removed.
- We detected no nickel in water samples retrieved from the well after replacement of the screen and casing.

The source of the nickel in the water was the corrosion of the screen and the casing. Since the screen and casing were replaced, there has been no nickel in the water. We recommend replacing the screens and casings in other wells.

Side notes:

Gives brief background of project.

Keeps verbs in active voice, for clarity and brevity.

Uses short list to emphasize major findings.

Emphasizes major conclusion in separate paragraph. (Note that this major point could have been placed after first paragraph, for a different effect.)

Model 11-7 Executive summary—formal report

Gives purpose
of report and
overview of
introduction (as
lead-in).

Describes the
task the writer
was given.

Denotes the
major activities
that were
accomplished.

Provides reader
with a preview of
main sections to
follow (as a sort
of "mini" table of
contents).

INTRODUCTION

This document examines the need for a Martin & Koffman <u>Human Resources Manual</u>. As background for your reading of this report, I have included (1) a brief description of the project, (2) the scope of my activities during the study, and (3) an overview of the report format.

Project Description

Three months ago, Jacques Martin met with the senior staff to discuss diverse human resources issues, such as performance appraisals and fringe benefits. After several meetings, the group agreed that the company greatly needed a manual to give guidance to managers and their employees. Shortly thereafter, I was asked to study and then report on three main topics: (1) the points that should be included in a manual, (2) the schedule for completing the document, and (3) the number of employees that should be involved in writing and reviewing policies.

Scope of Activities

This project involved seeking information from any M&K employees and completing some outside research. Specifically, the project scope involved:

- Sending a survey to all employees
- Tabulating the results of the survey
- Interviewing some of the survey respondents
- Completing library research on the topic of human resource manuals
- Developing conclusions and recommendations that were based on the research completed

Report Format

To fulfill the report's purpose of examining the need for an M&K <u>Human Resources Manual</u>, this report includes these main sections:

Section 1: Research Methods
Section 2: Findings of the Survey and Interviews
Section 3: Findings of the Library Research
Section 4: Conclusions and Recommendations

Appendices at the end of the text contain the survey form, interview questions, sample survey responses, and several journal articles of most use in my research.

Model 11-8 Introduction—formal report

LUNDY CONSTRUCTION

GEOTECHNICAL INVESTIGATION

PROPOSED PUBLIC LIBRARY ORLÉANS BRANCH OTTAWA, ONTARIO

continues

Model 11-9   Formal report
Barry Padolsky Architect Ltd.

The text of this report, based on an actual document, is presented without modification. For this reason there are some apparent contradictions between the format recommended in this book and the one used in the report. However, closer examination will show that the principles taught are utilized and the differences exist only in technology.

PROJECT NO. 10525

REPORT TO

LUNDY CONSTRUCTION

ON

PROPOSED PUBLIC LIBRARY
ORLÉANS BRANCH
OTTAWA, ONTARIO

Martin & Koffman
2219 Rue Decarie
Montreal, Quebec
H4T 1P9
Tel: (514) 555-6431
Fax: (514) 555-0825
August 19, 2006

continues

Model 11-9 *continued*

TABLE OF CONTENTS

Provides a detailed table of contents with descriptive titles.

continues

Model 11-9 *continued*

States the
project's
purpose.

States findings.

States
conclusion.

SUMMARY

Soil conditions at the site of the proposed Ottawa Library were examined in order
to determine how to guarantee the stability of the structure. The examination of
the soil conditions at the site revealed that there is a stable crust on top of a soft
layer of silty clay. The more solid layer at the top will, if not ruptured, support the
building securely. Since footings have to be located in the lower (softer) layer,
surcharge should be placed on the site in order to consolidate the silty clay prior
to loading.

iii

continues

Model 11-9   *continued*

1.0 INTRODUCTION

This report presents the results of a geotechnical investigation carried out for the proposed City of Ottawa Public Library, Orléans Branch, located on the east side of Orléans Boulevard, south of Beausejour Street, in Barrington Park, Ottawa, Ontario. Authorization to carry out the work was received from Mr. Enzo DiChiara, P.Eng., of Lundy Construction Limited.

This report has been prepared specifically and solely for the above noted project which is described herein. It contains all of our findings and includes geotechnical recommendations for the design and construction of the proposed library, parking area and access ways.

2.0 PROPOSED DEVELOPMENT

The site is located on the east side of Orléans Boulevard in Barrington Park, Ottawa, Ontario, as shown on Drawing 10525–1, Appendix 2. The layout of the proposed building and paved area is shown on Drawing 10525–2 in Appendix 2.

It is understood that the proposed building is to be a single storey structure with no basement, with a plan area of 1,500 m^2. It is understood that the finished floor will be a slab-on-grade at an elevation near existing grades. The building is to be surrounded mainly by grassed areas with a parking area for approximately 100 vehicles to the northeast. An access road to the parking lot will be provided from Orléans Boulevard.

3.0 SCOPE OF WORK

The scope of work for this investigation is as follows:

- Conduct a geotechnical investigation (minimum three building and two parking lot boreholes).
- Carry out laboratory testing required to define the characteristics of the subsurface soils.
- Provide geotechnical recommendations for the design and construction of the proposed building, parking structure, and access road.

Environmental-related issues are outside the scope of work of this investigation.

4.0 METHODS OF INVESTIGATION

4.1 Field Investigation

Prior to the commencement of the investigation, the borehole locations were cleared of underground utilities by Martin & Koffman (M&K) personnel. The field work for this investigation was carried out on August 11, 2006. A total of five boreholes, numbered BH 94–1 to 94–5, were put down using a track-mounted CME power

Describes report.

Describes limitations.

Provides background.

Delineates scope of the report.

Explains how the work was done.

1

continues

Model 11-9 *continued*

auger at the locations indicated on Drawing 10525–2 in Appendix 2. Three (3) boreholes were put down within the proposed building footprint and two (2) boreholes were put down within the area of the proposed paved parking lot.

The subsurface stratigraphy encountered in each borehole was recorded in the field by our personnel. Representative samples of each stratum encountered were collected by conducting Standard Penetration Tests. In situ vane shear tests were carried out at close intervals to assess the undrained shear strength of cohesive soils. All samples were stored in moisture-proof bags and were returned to our laboratory for detailed classification and testing. All boreholes were backfilled and compacted with the augered material.

Standpipe piezometers were installed in Boreholes 94–1, 94–2, and 94–3 for groundwater level monitoring. Groundwater levels were recorded on the day of drilling as well as on August 17, 2006, to confirm static water levels.

4.2   Survey

Borehole locations were laid out in the field by M&K personnel relative to existing site features. Ground surface elevations at the borehole locations were determined with reference to an elevation of 86.64 m for a catch basin located on Orléans Boulevard, across from the existing fire hydrant adjacent to the site. This benchmark elevation was taken from a topographical plan prepared by Annis, O'Sullivan, Vollebekk Limited for Lundy Construction Limited.

4.3   Laboratory Testing

All samples returned to the laboratory were subjected to detailed visual classification by a geotechnical engineer. Selected samples were tested for moisture content.

Samples remaining after testing will be stored for a period of three months after issuance of this report. Samples will then be discarded unless we are otherwise directed.

5.0   RESULTS OF INVESTIGATION

Reports what was found.

5.1   Surface Conditions

It is understood that the site of the proposed library has not been previously developed, although it has been used as a municipal park. The ground surface is generally flat. Grass is present at ground surface across the site with a few trees.

5.2   Subsurface Profile

The subsurface conditions observed in the boreholes are presented in detail on the Borehole Records provided in Appendix 1. An explanation of the symbols and terms used to describe the Borehole Records is also provided.

In general, the observed stratigraphy consists of topsoil overlying fill, sand or silt with some clay over silty clay. Boreholes were terminated within the silty clay layer. The observed soil conditions are briefly summarized below.

2

continues

Model 11-9   *continued*

5.2.1 Surficial Materials

A layer of topsoil 100 mm to 440 mm in thickness was encountered at the ground surface in all of the boreholes.

5.2.2 Fill

A layer of fill consisting of silty clay, trace gravel, trace sand, and trace asphalt was observed below the topsoil in Boreholes 94–4 and 94–5. The fill was found to range in thickness between 300 mm and 600 mm.

5.2.3 Sand

A layer of loose sand, trace silt was encountered below the fill in Borehole 94–5. The thickness of this layer was 600 mm.

5.2.4 Silt with Some Clay

A weathered layer of silt with some clay soil was encountered in Boreholes 94–1 and 94–2 beneath the topsoil. The unit was observed to range in thickness from 400 mm to 500 mm.

5.2.5 Silty Clay

Silty clay was encountered in all boreholes below the surficial materials. The silty clay layer can be subdivided into an upper, brown to grey, firm to stiff crust and underlying softer, grey materials.

The crust was consistently observed to extend to a depth of 2.9 m below existing grade in BH 94–1, 94–2, and 94–3. Boreholes 94–5 and 94–6 did not fully penetrate the crust. The moisture content of this layer ranged from 23% to 46% and averaged 38% for the 5 samples tested. In-situ shear vane values indicate the undrained shear strength of the crust in the areas tested ranges from 30 to 79 kPa, indicating a firm to stiff consistency. The remoulded strengths range from 5 to 24 kPa.

The deeper grey material is softer and has a higher moisture content than the overlying crust. The moisture content of the deeper grey silty clay ranged from 50% to 88% and averaged 73% in the samples tested. In-situ shear vane values indicate the undrained shear strength of the grey silty clay in the areas tested from 17 to 34 kPa, indicating a soft to firm consistency. The remoulded strengths were consistently under 5 kPa.

5.3 Groundwater

The groundwater table was not observed within the boreholes during drilling. Standpipe piezometers were installed in Boreholes 94–1, 94–2, and 94–3. Groundwater was observed in the standpipes at depths between 1.0 m and 1.2 m on August 17, 2006.

Fluctuations in the groundwater level due to seasonal variations or in response to a particular precipitation event should be anticipated.

3

continues

Model 11-9 *continued*

6.0   DISCUSSION AND RECOMMENDATIONS

6.1   General

The subsurface soils encountered at the site consist of fill, sand, or silt with clay overlying a stiff to firm silty clay crust overlying firm to soft silty clay. Based on the soil conditions determined and the expected loadings, it is anticipated that conventional spread footings founded on undisturbed silty clay could possibly be adequate in supporting the proposed structure. However, the presence of the soft, sensitive clays limits the size and type of structure that can be constructed at this site using conventional spread footings. Conventional spread footings may be used provided they are placed within the crust material and are limited in size to avoid overstressing the lower, weaker clay deposit. Furthermore, steps must be taken to ensure additional loads, such as those imposed by placement of additional fill, are limited to avoid long-term settlement problems. Recommendations for maximum footing pressures and footing size are provided in Section 6.3.

The following sections outline our recommendations for the design and construction of the proposed building, the parking lot pavement structure, and access road.

6.2   Site Grading and Preparation

Lists the recommendations.

The surficial vegetation, topsoil, fill, and other deleterious materials must be stripped from within the influence zone of the foundations for the building. The influence zone is defined by a line drawn at 1 horizontal to 1 vertical away and downward from the edge of the footings. Structural fill should be used to raise the grade to the underside of the footings as required.

Fill placement beneath or immediately adjacent to the building or paved areas should be limited to a maximum of 0.5 m above the original ground surface. This limitation was used in the calculation of bearing capacities in Section 6.3.

All surficial vegetation, topsoil, and rootmat should be removed from beneath the floor slab and paved areas. The exposed subgrade should be inspected and approved by a geotechnical engineer. Proof rolling using a large roller may be required to identify soft areas. All soft areas revealed under proof rolling must be removed and replaced with compacted fill. OPSS Select Subgrade Material may be used as fill below the subgrade line in paved areas.

Structural fill should consist of clean sand and gravel, such as OPSS Granular B, Type I. This material should be tested and approved by a geotechnical engineer prior to delivery to the site. Structural fill should be placed in lifts no thicker than 300 mm and compacted using suitable compaction equipment to at least 98% Standard Proctor maximum dry density.

The compaction requirement for Select Subgrade Material used as subgrade fill in paved areas should be at least 95% Standard Proctor maximum dry density.

The silty clay soils present at this site are generally suitable for re-use as grading fills only within landscaped areas.

4

continues

Model 11-9   *continued*

Earth removal should be inspected by a geotechnical engineer to ensure that all unsuitable materials are removed prior to placement of structural fill. Inspection and testing services will also be required to ensure that all fill is placed and compacted to the required degree.

6.3 Spread Footings

Spread footings may be placed directly on undisturbed silty clay crust or placed on a pad of engineered fill placed on undisturbed silty clay crust. The following bearing capacities are recommended for the design of the structure:

Bearing Elevation	Bearing Material	Factored Capacity at ULS	Capacity at SLS Type II
84.7 or higher	Silty clay or structural fill	100 kPa	75 kPa
Below 84.7	Grey silty clay	Not recommended	Not recommended

It has been assumed that regrading of the site will be limited to 0.5 m of fill above present grades and that floor loads will not be greater than 10 kPa on average. The total and differential settlements associated with the recommended bearing capacity under these conditions will be less than 25 mm for strip footings as wide as 1 m and square footings as large as 1 m by 1 m in size, provided the footings are not placed deeper than the above recommended elevation.

All exterior footings and footings located within 1 m distance from the exterior walls will require a minimum soil cover of 1.5 m for protection against frost action. Footings in unheated areas or exterior footings for signs or canopies should be founded at least 1.8 m below exterior grade to protect against frost action. Where adequate soil cover cannot be accommodated, insulation may be considered as a means of ensuring sufficient frost protection. Design of the insulation should be reviewed by the geotechnical engineer.

The base of all footing excavations should be inspected by a geotechnical engineer prior to placing concrete to confirm the above design pressures and to ensure there is no disturbance. Any disturbed material identified during the inspection will need to be removed and wasted.

Where construction is undertaken during winter conditions, footing subgrades should be protected from freezing and foundation walls and columns should be protected against heave due to soil adfreeze. It is understood that the construction schedule may result in construction of the earthworks and foundations during the fall of 2006 with the building remaining incomplete and unheated through the winter. Insulation must be provided for the footings and foundation walls in this circumstance.

5

continues

Model 11-9 *continued*

6.4 Floor Slab

A conventional slab-on-grade unit is suitable for use for the proposed building provided the site is prepared as outlined in Section 6.2. A layer of free-draining granular material should be placed immediately beneath the floor slab for levelling and support purposes. It is recommended that at least 200 mm of approved crushed stone be used, this material should be compacted to at least 98% Standard Proctor maximum dry density. Perimeter drains should be installed if the final grades around the building are higher than the underside of the slab.

The floor slab constructed as recommended above may be designed using a soil modulus of subgrade reaction, k, of 18 MPa/m. The slab-on-grade unit should float independently of all load-bearing walls and columns.

6.5 Excavation and Backfilling

The native sand and silty clay crust encountered at this site should be considered as Type 3 soils as defined by the Occupational Health and Safety Act and, therefore, excavation side slopes are required to be no steeper than 1 horizontal to 1 vertical from the bottom. Where excavations are required into the softer grey silty clay (Type 4 soil), the excavation slopes should be no steeper than 3 horizontal to 1 vertical from the bottom.

The groundwater level was encountered at a depth as shallow as 1 m one week after drilling. It has been our experience that the anticipated foundation soils are easily disturbed and are particularly sensitive to water softening. Excavation dewatering using conventional sumps and pumping techniques are expected to be applicable for this project based on the geotechnical information collected.

Foundation backfill should be placed and compacted in lifts. Care should be taken immediately adjacent to walls to avoid over-compaction of the soil resulting in damage to the walls.

Bedding for utilities should be placed in accordance with the pipe design requirements. It is recommended that a minimum of 150 mm to 200 mm OPSS Granular A be placed below the pipe invert as bedding material. Granular pipe backfill placed above the invert should consist of OPSS Granular A or Granular B. A minimum of 300 mm vertical and side cover should be provided. These materials should be compacted to at least 95% of Standard Proctor maximum dry density.

Backfill for service trenches in landscaped areas may consist of excavated material replaced and compacted in lifts. Where the service trenches extend below paved areas, the trench should be backfilled with OPSS Granular B from the top of the pipe backfill material to within 1.2 m of the proposed pavement surface. This material should be placed in lifts and compacted to at least 95% of Standard Proctor maximum dry density. The material used within the upper 1.2 m and below the subgrade line should be similar to that exposed in the trench walls to prevent differential frost heave. This material should be placed in lifts and compacted to at least 95% of Standard Proctor maximum dry density.

6

continues

Model 11-9   *continued*

6.6   Earthquake Considerations

As outlined in the National Building Code of Canada (NBCC), 2005, buildings and their foundations must be designed to resist a minimum earthquake force. The NBCC formula for obtaining the minimum earthquake force is dependent upon several factors, four of which are the Foundation Factor, Zonal Velocity Ration and the Acceleration and Velocity Related Seismic Zones. The recommended Foundation Factor, F, is 2.0 for the soils encountered at this site. The Zonal Velocity Ratio, v, of 0.10, the Acceleration Related Seismic Zone, Z_a, of 4, and the Velocity Related Seismic Zone, Z_v, of 2 are recommended for this site based on the NBCC.

6.7   Pavement Structure

The subgrade in paved areas should be prepared as described in Section 6.2 above. Assuming that the parking areas will be used mostly by passenger vehicles, and the access roads will be used by delivery trucks and fire vehicles, the following minimum pavement designs are recommended:

	Passenger Vehicle Parking Area	Access Roads
Asphaltic Concrete	50 mm	80 mm (2 lifts)
OPSS Granular A	150 mm	150 mm
OPSS Granular B	300 mm	450 mm

All materials should be tested and approved by a geotechnical engineer prior to delivery to the site. Both the OPSS Granular A and Granular B materials should be compacted to at least 100% Standard Proctor maximum dry density.

7.0   CLOSURE

The recommendations presented in the report are in accordance with our present understanding of the project. A soils investigation is a random sampling of a site. Should any condition at the site be encountered which differs from those at the test locations, we require that we be notified immediately in order to permit reassessment of our recommendations.

We trust the above information meets with your requirements. Should you have any questions or require further information, please do not hesitate to contact us.

Thank you for the opportunity to be of service to you.

Yours very truly,

Martin & Koffman
Michael A. Corbett, M.Sc., P.Eng.
Gloria J. Kack, M.E.Sc., P.Eng.

7

continues

Model 11-9 *continued*

APPENDIX I
SYMBOLS AND TERMS USED ON BOREHOLE AND TEST PIT RECORDS

SOIL DESCRIPTION

Terminology describing common soil genesis:

Topsoil	–	mixture of soil and humus capable of supporting good vegetation growth
Peat	–	fibrous aggregate of visible and invisible fragments of decayed organic matter
Till	–	unstratified glacial deposit which may range from clay to boulders
Fill	–	any materials below the surface identified as placed by humans (excluding buried services)

Terminology describing soil structure:

Desiccated	–	having visible signs of weathering by oxidation of clay minerals, shrinkage cracks, etc.
Fissured	–	having cracks, and hence a blocky structure
Varved	–	composed of regular alternating layers of silt and clay
Stratified	–	composed of alternating successions of different soil types, e.g., silt and sand
Layer	–	> 75 mm
Seam	–	2 mm to 75 mm
Parting	–	< 2 mm
Well Graded	–	having wide range in grain sizes and substantial amounts of all intermediate particle sizes
Uniformly Graded	–	predominantly of one grain size

Terminology describing soils on the basis of grain size and plasticity is based on the Unified Soil Classification System (USCS) (ASTM D-2488). The classification excludes particles larger than 76 mm (3 inches). This system provides a group symbol (e.g., SM) and group name (e.g., silty sand) for identification.

Terminology describing materials outside the USCS (e.g., particles larger than 76 mm, visible organic matter, construction debris) is based upon the proportion of these materials present:

Trace, or occasional	Less than 10%
Some	10–20%

The standard terminology to describe cohesionless soils includes the compactness (formerly "relative density"), as determined by laboratory test or by the Standard Penetration Test 'N' – value.

8

Provides raw data in appendices.

continues

Model 11-9 *continued*

Relative Density	'N' Value	Compactness %
Very Loose	< 4	< 15
Loose	4–10	15–35
Compact	10–30	35–65
Dense	30–50	65–85
Very Dense	> 50	> 85

The standard terminology to describe cohesive soils includes the consistency, which is based on undrained shear strength as measured by insitu vane tests, penetrometer tests, unconfined compression tests, or occasionally by standard penetration tests.

Consistency	Undrained Shear Strength		'N' Value
	kips/sq. ft.	kPa	
Very Soft	< 0.25	< 125	< 2
Soft	0.25–0.5	12.5–25	2–4
Firm	0.5–1.0	25–50	4–8
Stiff	1.0–2.0	50–100	8–15
Very Stiff	2.0–4.0	100–200	15–30
Hard	> 4.0	> 200	> 30

ROCK DESCRIPTION

Rock Quality Designation (RQD)

The classification is based on a modified core-recovery percentage in which all pieces of sound core over 100 mm long are counted as recovery. The smaller pieces are considered to be due to close shearing, jointing, faulting, or weathering in the rock mass and are not counted. RQD was originally intended to be done on NW core; however, it can be used on different core sizes if the bulk of the fractures caused by drilling stresses are easily distinguishable from in-situ fractures.

RQD	Rock Quality
90–100	Excellent, intact, very sound
75–90	Good, massive, moderately jointed or sound
50–75	Fair, blocky and seamy, fractured
25–50	Poor, shattered and very seamy or blocky, severely fractured
0–25	Very poor, crushed, very severely fractured

9

continues

Model 11-9 *continued*

Terminology describing rock mass:

Spacing (mm)	Bedding, Laminations, Bands	Discontinuities
2000–6000	*Very Thick*	*Very Wide*
600–2000	*Thick*	*Wide*
200–600	*Medium*	*Moderate*
60–200	*Thin*	*Close*
20–60	*Very Thin*	*Very Close*
< 20	*Laminated*	*Extremely Close*
< 6	*Thinly Laminated*	

Strength Classification	Uniaxial Compressive Strength (MPa)
Very Low	1–25
Low	25–50
Medium	50–100
High	100–200
Very High	> 200

Terminology describing weathering:

Slight	–	Weathering limited to the surface of major discontinuities. Typically iron stained.
Moderate	–	Weathering extends throughout rock mass. Rock is not friable.
High	–	Weathering extends throughout rock mass. Rock is friable.

Explains terms and symbols.

STRATA PLOT

Strata plots symbolize the soil or bedrock description. They are combinations of the following basic symbols:

Boulders Cobbles Gravel   Sand   Silt   Clay   Organics   Asphalt   Concrete   Fill   Igneous Bedrock   Meta-morphic Bedrock   Sedimentary Bedrock

WATER LEVEL MEASUREMENT

Borehole or Standpipe

Piezometer

10

continues

Model 11-9 *continued*

SAMPLE TYPE

SS	Split spoon sample (obtained by performing the Standard Penetration Test)
ST	Shelby tube or thin wall tube
PS	Piston sample
BS	Bulk sample
WS	Wash sample
HQ, NQ, BQ, etc.	Rock core samples obtained with the use of standard size diamond drilling bits

N - VALUE

Numbers in this column are the results of the Standard Penetration Test: the number of blows of a 140 pound (64 kg) hammer falling 30 inches (760 mm) required to drive a 2 inch (50.8 mm) O.D. split spoon sampler 1 foot (305 mm) into the soil. For split spoon samples where insufficient penetration was achieved and 'N' values cannot be presented, the number of blows are reported over sampler penetration in millimetres (e.g., 50/75).

OTHER TESTS

S	Sieve analysis	H	Hydrometer analysis
G_s	Specific gravity of soil particles	γ	Unit weight
k	Permeability (cm/sec)	C	Consolidation
	Single packer permeability test; test interval from depth shown to bottom of borehole	CD	Consolidated drained triaxial
		CU	Consolidated undrained triaxial with pore pressure measurements
	Double packer permeability test; test interval as indicated	UU	Unconsolidated undrained triaxial
		DS	Direct shear
	Falling head permeability test using casing	Q_u	Unconfined compression
		I_p	Point Load Index (I_p on Borehole Record equals
	Falling head permeability test using well point or piezometer		$I_p(50)$; the index corrected to a reference diameter of 50 mm)

11

continues

Model 11-9 *continued*

| JACQUES WHITFORD LIMITED | | | | | | | BOREHOLE RECORD | | | | | | | | 94-1 | | |

CLIENT	Lundy Construction													BOREHOLE No.	94-1
LOCATION	Proposed Library, Orléans Boulevard, Ottawa, Ontario											PROJECT No.	10525
DATES: BORING	06-08-11					WATER LEVEL	06-08-17			DATUM	Geodetic

| DEPTH (m) | ELEVATION (m) | SOIL DESCRIPTION | STRATA PLOT | WATER LEVEL | SAMPLES | | | | UNDRAINED SHEAR STRENGTH - kPa |
| | | | | | TYPE | NUMBER | RECOVERY | N-VALUE OR RQD | |

Undrained Shear Strength scale: 50, 100, 150, 200

WATER CONTENT & ATTERBERG LIMITS — Wp ─O─ W WL
DYNAMIC PENETRATION TEST, BLOWS/0.3m ★
STANDARD PENETRATION TEST, BLOWS/0.3m ●

Scale: 10 20 30 40 50 60 70 80 90 (mm)

Depth	Elev.	Description	Type	No.	Recovery	N
0	86.54					
	86.1	440 mm TOPSOIL				
	85.7	Stiff, light brown SILT with some clay	BS	1		
1		Stiff to firm, brown to grey SILTY CLAY, some sand, trace organics	SS	2	300	9
2			SS	3	200	8
3	83.6					
			SS	4	580	1
4		Firm to soft, grey SILTY CLAY				
5			SS	5	610	1
6	80.5					
7		End of Borehole Standpipe installed				
8						
9						
10						

◄ Proposed Pipe Invert

□ Field Vane Test, kPa
□ Remoulded Vane Test, kPa
△ Pocket Penetrometer Test, kPa

W/A/V

continues

Model 11-9 *continued*

JACQUES WHITFORD LIMITED

BOREHOLE RECORD

94-2

CLIENT **Lundy Construction**

LOCATION **Proposed Library, Orléans Boulevard, Ottawa, Ontario**

DATES: BORING **06-08-11**   WATER LEVEL **06-08-17**

BOREHOLE No. **94-2**

PROJECT No. **10525**

DATUM **Geodetic**

UNDRAINED SHEAR STRENGTH - kPa

WATER CONTENT & ATTERBERG LIMITS W_p W W_L

DYNAMIC PENETRATION TEST, BLOWS/0.3m ★

STANDARD PENETRATION TEST, BLOWS/0.3m ●

DEPTH (m)	ELEVATION (m)	SOIL DESCRIPTION	STRATA PLOT	WATER LEVEL	TYPE	NUMBER	RECOVERY	N-VALUE OR RQD
							mm	
0	86.51							
	86.3	200 mm TOPSOIL						
	85.8	Stiff, light brown SILT with some clay						
1		Stiff to firm, brown to grey SILTY CLAY, some sand, trace organics, occasional sand seam			SS	1	270	10
2					SS	2	140	12
3	83.6							
					SS	3	610	1
4		Firm to soft, grey SILTY CLAY						
5					SS	4	610	1
6	80.5							
		End of Borehole Standpipe installed						
7								
8								
9								
10								

◁ Proposed Pipe Invert

□ Field Vane Test, kPa
□ Remoulded Vane Test, kPa
△ Pocket Penetrometer Test, kPa

continues

Model 11-9 *continued*

JACQUES WHITFORD LIMITED	BOREHOLE RECORD	94-3

CLIENT **Lundy Construction** BOREHOLE No. **94-3**
LOCATION **Proposed Library, Orléans Boulevard, Ottawa, Ontario** PROJECT No. **10525**
DATES: BORING **06-08-11** WATER LEVEL **06-08-17** DATUM **Geodetic**

DEPTH (m)	ELEVATION (m)	SOIL DESCRIPTION	STRATA PLOT	WATER LEVEL	SAMPLES				UNDRAINED SHEAR STRENGTH - kPa
					TYPE	NUMBER	RECOVERY	N-VALUE OR RQD	

UNDRAINED SHEAR STRENGTH - kPa
50   100   150   200

WATER CONTENT & ATTERBERG LIMITS W_p — W — W_L
DYNAMIC PENETRATION TEST, BLOWS/0.3m ★
STANDARD PENETRATION TEST, BLOWS/0.3m ●

DEPTH (m)	ELEVATION	SOIL DESCRIPTION	TYPE	NUMBER	RECOVERY (mm)	N-VALUE OR RQD	10 20 30 40 50 60 70 80 90
0	86.86 86.8	100 mm TOPSOIL					
		Stiff to firm, brown to grey SILTY CLAY, trace sand, trace organics	BS	1			
1			SS	2	260	9	
2			SS	3	270	7	
3	84.0						
			SS	4	610	1	
4		Firm to soft, grey SILTY CLAY					
5			SS	5	610	1	
6	80.9						
		End of Borehole Standpipe installed					
7							
8							
9							
10							

◄ Proposed Pipe Invert

□ Field Vane Test, kPa
□ Remoulded Vane Test, kPa
△ Pocket Penetrometer Test, kPa

continues

Model 11-9 *continued*

JACQUES WHITFORD LIMITED

BOREHOLE RECORD

94-4

CLIENT __Lundy Construction__	BOREHOLE No. __94-4__
LOCATION __Proposed Library, Orléans Boulevard, Ottawa, Ontario__	PROJECT No. __10525__
DATES: BORING __06-08-11__ WATER LEVEL _____	DATUM __Geodetic__

DEPTH (m)	ELEVATION (m)	SOIL DESCRIPTION	STRATA PLOT	WATER LEVEL	SAMPLES				UNDRAINED SHEAR STRENGTH - kPa
					TYPE	NUMBER	RECOVERY	N-VALUE OR RQD	

UNDRAINED SHEAR STRENGTH - kPa
50   100   150   200

WATER CONTENT & ATTERBERG LIMITS w_p w w_L
DYNAMIC PENETRATION TEST,   BLOWS/0.3m   ★
STANDARD PENETRATION TEST,   BLOWS/0.3m   ●

mm

10 20 30 40 50 60 70 80 90

Depth	Elev.	Description	Type	No.	Recovery	N-Value
0	86.62					
	86.5	120 mm TOPSOIL				
	86.2	Dark brown silty clay, trace gravel, trace sand, trace asphalt: FILL	BS	1		
1		Stiff to firm, brown to grey SILTY CLAY	SS	2	170	10
			SS	3	300	3
2	84.5					
		End of Borehole				

▽ (Proposed Pipe Invert)

◄ Proposed Pipe Invert

□ Field Vane Test, kPa
□ Remoulded Vane Test, kPa
△ Pocket Penetrometer Test, kPa

continues

Model 11-9 *continued*

JACQUES WHITFORD LIMITED	BOREHOLE RECORD	94-5

CLIENT **Lundy Construction**
LOCATION **Proposed Library, Orléans Boulevard, Ottawa, Ontario**
DATES: BORING **06-08-11**   WATER LEVEL ___

BOREHOLE No. **94-5**
PROJECT No. **10525**
DATUM **Geodetic**

DEPTH (m)	ELEVATION (m)	SOIL DESCRIPTION	STRATA PLOT	WATER LEVEL	TYPE	NUMBER	RECOVERY	N-VALUE OR RQD
0	86.74							mm
	86.6	130 mm TOPSOIL			BS	1		
	86.0	Dark grey organic silty clay, trace gravel, trace sand, trace asphalt: FILL						
1	85.4	Loose, greyish brown SAND, trace silt			SS	2	90	10
2	84.6	Stiff to firm, brown to grey SILTY CLAY			SS	3	220	8
		End of Borehole						

UNDRAINED SHEAR STRENGTH - kPa

WATER CONTENT & ATTERBERG LIMITS   Wp ⊢—O—⊣ WL
DYNAMIC PENETRATION TEST, BLOWS/0.3m ★
STANDARD PENETRATION TEST, BLOWS/0.3m ●

▽ Proposed Pipe Invert

☒ Field Vane Test, kPa
☐ Remoulded Vane Test, kPa
△ Pocket Penetrometer Test, kPa

continues

Model 11-9 *continued*

APPENDIX II
DRAWING No. 10525–2 BOREHOLE LOCATION PLAN

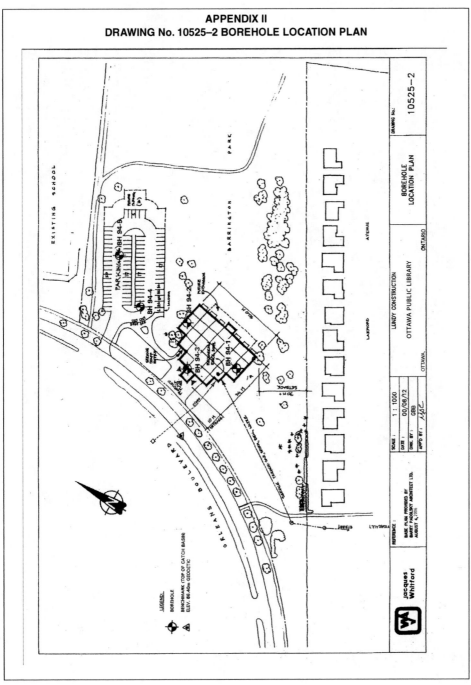

continues

Model 11-9 *continued*

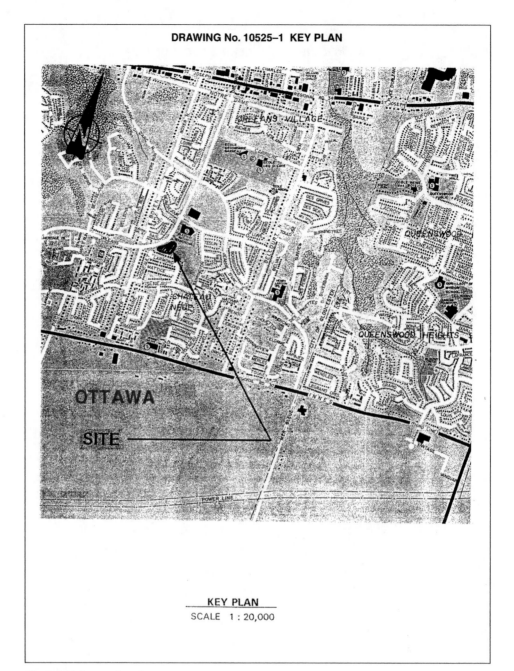

DRAWING No. 10525–1 KEY PLAN

KEY PLAN
SCALE 1 : 20,000

Model 11-9   *continued*

CHAPTER 12

Proposals and Feasibility Studies

Gina Harris, an engineer at M&K's Montreal office, recently had the opportunity to write her first major proposal. Anchor Productions, an American film company, asked M&K to design and build a replica of the fort at Annapolis Royal for a film about the Acadian experience in the Annapolis Valley. The film would have a number of scenes set in and around the fort. To write her proposal for Anchor, Gina had to consult both military and architectural historians.

M&K won the contract thanks to Gina's proposal. The work went so well that Gina asked her manager, Angela Koffman, if the company could start a technical group to work just on historical restoration/replication projects around the country. Intrigued by the idea, Koffman asked Gina to prepare a *feasibility study* that would focus on start-up costs, involvement of M&K offices, hiring needs, and potential profit during the first five years. If the feasibility study showed promise, Koffman would present the idea to Jacques Martin, the company's president, and Janice Kowalski, the president of American operations.

Although you probably won't write proposals to rebuild Fort York, you will write proposals and feasibility studies in your own field during your career. These modes of writing are crucial to most organizations. Indeed, many companies rely on them—especially on proposals—for their very survival. Proposals and feasibility studies are defined as follows:

> **Proposals:** documents written to convince your readers to adopt an idea, a product, or a service. They can be directed to colleagues inside your own organization (*in-house proposals*), to clients outside your organization (*sales proposals*), or to organizations that fund research and other activities (*grant proposals*).
>
> In all three cases, proposals can be presented in either a short, simple format (*informal proposal*) or a longer, more complicated format (*formal proposal*). Also, proposals can be either requested by the reader (*solicited*) or submitted without a request (*unsolicited*).

> **Feasibility studies:** documents written to show the practicality of a proposed policy, product, service, or other change within an organization. Often prompted by ideas suggested in a proposal, they examine details such as costs, alternatives, and likely effects. Though they must reflect the objectivity of a report, most feasibility studies also try to convince readers either (1) to adopt or reject the one idea discussed or (2) to adopt one of several alternatives presented in the study.
>
> Feasibility studies can be *in-house* (written to decision makers in your own organization) or *external* (requested by clients from outside your organization).

There are four main sections in this chapter. The first gives specific situations in which you might write proposals and feasibility studies at M&K. The second and third sections discuss informal and formal proposal formats, while also pointing out differences between in-house and sales versions of these formats. The fourth section covers feasibility studies.

PROPOSALS/FEASIBILITY STUDIES AT M&K

As the Annapolis Royal example shows, proposals and feasibility studies often work together. The proposal might suggest a topic upon which a feasibility study is then written. The flow chart in Figure 12-1 shows another possible communication cycle that would involve both a proposal and a feasibility study. Note that the diagram includes the term *RFP*, which stands for "request for proposal":

Request for proposal (RFP): a document sometimes sent out by organizations that want to receive proposals for a product or service. The RFP gives guidelines on (1) what the proposal should cover, (2) when it should be submitted, and (3) to whom it should be sent. As writer, you should follow the RFP religiously in planning and drafting your proposal.

RFPs generally are not used in the following situations:

- When the proposal is solicited from within your own organization
- When the proposal is requested less formally, as through a letter, phone call, or memo
- When the proposal is unsolicited, meaning that you are writing it without a request from the person who will read it

The sections that follow describe additional situations in which proposals and feasibility studies would be written at M&K. Reading through these brief cases will show you the varied contexts for persuasive writing.

M&K Proposals

Like many organizations, M&K depends on (1) in-house proposals to breathe new life into the company's internal operations, (2) sales proposals to request work from clients, and (3) occasional grant proposals to seek research funds from outside organizations. Proposals are a main activity in healthy, growing organizations.

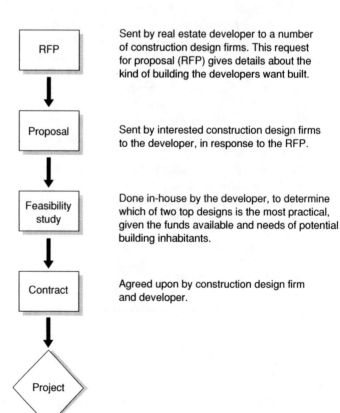

Figure 12-1 Flow chart showing the main documents involved in one possible construction project

RFP — Sent by real estate developer to a number of construction design firms. This request for proposal (RFP) gives details about the kind of building the developers want built.

Proposal — Sent by interested construction design firms to the developer, in response to the RFP.

Feasibility study — Done in-house by the developer, to determine which of two top designs is the most practical, given the funds available and needs of potential building inhabitants.

Contract — Agreed upon by construction design firm and developer.

Project

Of the five cases described here, the first and second are internal, requiring in-house proposals; the third and fourth are external, requiring sales proposals; and the fifth is external, requiring a grant proposal.

- **In-house proposal for computer drafting software:** Meg Strachan, a graphics expert at the M&K head office, writes an in-house proposal to Jacques Martin in which she proposes that M&K purchase new computer drafting software. Her proposal includes a schedule whereby the company can shift entirely to the new software in the next year.
- **In-house proposal for retaining legal counsel:** Jake Washington, an employment specialist in the Human Resources Department in the Baltimore office, writes an in-house proposal to Lynn Redmond, vice president of human resources in Toronto. In it he proposes that the company retain legal counsel on a half-time basis (20 hours a week). In his position at M&K, Jake needs outside legal advice in dealing with American regulations, including new hiring laws, unemployment compensation cases, affirmative action regulations, and occasional lawsuits by employees who have been fired. He is proposing that the firm retain regular half-time counsel, rather than dealing with different lawyers as is done now.
- **Sales proposal for asbestos removal:** Jane Ng, environmental technologist at M&K's Vancouver office, regularly talks with owners of buildings that may contain asbestos. After an initial discussion with the minister of First Street Church, she writes an informal sales proposal in which she offers M&K's services in performing an asbestos survey of the church building. Specifically, she explains how M&K will examine the structure for possible asbestos, gives a schedule for completing the survey and writing the final report, and proposes a lump-sum price for the project.
- **Sales proposal for work on wind turbine project:** A utility company in Saskatchewan plans to build 10 giant turbines in a semi-arid valley in the southern part of the province. The "free" power that is generated will help offset the large increases in fuel costs for the company's other plants. Although the firm has selected a turbine design and purchased the units, it needs to decide where to place them and what kind of foundations to use. Thus it has sent out a request for proposal to companies that have experience with foundation and environmental engineering. Louis Bergen, engineering manager at M&K's Calgary office, writes a proposal that offers to test the soils at the site, pinpoint the best locations for the heavy turbines, and design the most effective foundations.
- **Grant proposal for new equipment design:** Oilarus, Ltd., a British oil company, sometimes gives research and development funds to small companies. Such funding usually goes toward development of new technology or products in the field of petroleum engineering. Angela Isham, who works in M&K's Calgary office, decides to apply for some of the funding. Her proposed project, if successful, would provide a new piece of oil drilling safety equipment that would reduce the chance of offshore oil spills at production sites.

M&K Feasibility Studies

The next two examples show that feasibility studies often flow from proposals. They can be internal, to managers who need facts before making a decision, or they can be external, to clients who request a service.

- **In-house feasibility study about legal counsel:** Lynn Redmond, the vice president of human resources, recently received Jake Washington's proposal that M&K retain half-time legal counsel (see the second case in the previous section). The idea interests her, but she is not convinced of its practicality. She calls a meeting with Jake Washington and Scott Sampson, the personnel manager, who also uses legal counsel on a part-time basis. Because Lynn will have to sell her boss on this idea, she asks Jake and Scott to write a feasibility study on it. This study, unlike the proposal, must include a detailed comparison of the present mode of operating versus the proposed strategy of retaining a lawyer for 20 hours per week on a regular basis. The study must examine criteria such as current costs versus projected costs, current level of satisfaction versus projected level of satisfaction, and current level of services provided versus projected level of services provided. Lynn asks that the report include a clear recommendation, made on the basis of the data.

- **External feasibility study on plant site:** Tarnak, Inc., a large furniture manufacturing company in North Carolina, has decided to build a new plant in eastern Canada. After getting proposals from many cities that want the plant, the company has narrowed its choices to three spots that are about equal in cost of living, access to workers, standard of living, construction costs, transportation facilities, and access to raw materials. Yet the firm has not studied any site with respect to waste management. Specifically, Tarnak needs to know which of the three cities is best prepared to handle the solid and chemical wastes from the plant in a safe and economical manner. It hires M&K's Montreal office to write a feasibility study. The first goal of the study is to determine what sites, if any, meet Tarnak's criteria for waste management. If the first objective yields more than one site, M&K then must compare the sites and recommend the best one.

INFORMAL PROPOSALS

Like informal reports, informal proposals are short documents that cover projects with a limited scope. But how short is short? And just what does *limited* mean? Following are some specific guidelines that you can use if your employer or client has not provided others:

Use informal proposals when:

- The text of the proposal (excluding attachments) is no more than five pages
- The size of the proposed project is such that a long, formal proposal would appear to be inappropriate
- The client has expressed a preference for a leaner, less formal document

Use formal proposals when:

- The text of the proposal (excluding attachments) is 10 pages or more
- The size and importance of the project is such that a formal proposal would be appropriate
- The client has expressed a preference for a more formal document

These two formats can be used for proposals that are either **in-house** (to readers within your own organization) or **external** (to readers outside your organization). The rest of this section provides writing guidelines and an annotated model for informal proposals—the type of persuasive writing you will do most often in your career.

Guidelines for Informal Proposals

Informal proposals have two formats: (1) memos (for in-house proposals) and (2) letters (for external proposals). The guidelines recommended apply to both. With some variations, they are essentially the guidelines suggested in Chapter 10 for informal reports. The formats are much the same, though the content and tone are different: reports explain, whereas proposals persuade.

Informal Proposal Guideline 1: Plan Well Before You Write

Complete the Planning Form found in Chapter 1 for all proposal assignments in class, as well as for proposals you write on the job. Carefully consider your purpose, audience, and organization. Two factors make this task especially difficult in sales proposal writing:

1. You may know nothing more about the client than what is written on the RFP.
2. Proposals almost always are on a tight schedule that limits your planning time.

Despite these limitations, try to find out exactly who will be making the decision about your proposal. Many clients will tell you if you give them a call. In fact, they may be pleased that you care enough about the project to target the audience. Once you identify the decision makers, spend time brainstorming about their needs before you begin writing. Proposals that betray an ignorance of client needs often do so because the writer began writing too soon about the product or service.

Informal Proposal Guideline 2: Use Letter or Memo Format

Letter proposals, such as the example shown in Model 12-1 on pages 334–36, basically follow the format of routine business letters (see Chapter 9). This casual style gives readers the immediate impression that your document will be *approachable*—that is, easy to get through and limited in scope. Memo proposals, such as the example shown in Model 12-2 on pages 337–38, follow the format of an internal memorandum (see Chapter 8). Following are a few highlights:

- Line spacing is usually single, but it may be $1^1/_2$ or double, depending on the reader's or company's preference.
- The recipient's name, the date, and the page number appear on sheets after the first.
- Most readers prefer an uneven or ragged edge right margin, as opposed to an even or right-justified margin.

Your Subject line in a memo proposal (if you choose to use one) gives readers the first impression of the proposal's purpose. Choose concise yet accurate wording. Furthermore, the wording must match what you have used in the proposal text. See Model 12-2 for wording that gives the appropriate information and tries to engage the reader's interest.

Informal Proposal Guideline 3: Make the Text Visually Appealing

The page design of informal proposals must draw readers into the document. Remember—you are trying to *sell* a product, a service, or an idea. If the layout is unappealing, then you will lose readers before they even get to your message. Also, remember that your proposal may be competing with others. Put yourself in the place of the reader who is wondering which one to pick up first. How the text looks on the page can make a big difference. Following are a few techniques to help make your proposal visually appealing:

- Use lists (with bullets or numbered points) to highlight main ideas.
- Follow your readers' preferences as to font size, type, line spacing, and so forth. Proposals written in the readers' preferred format will gain a competitive edge.
- Use headings and subheadings to break up blocks of text.

These and other techniques help to reveal the proposal's structure and lead readers through the informal proposal. Given that there is no table of contents, you need to take advantage of such strategies.

Informal Proposal Guideline 4: Use the ABC Format for Organization

With its "hook" to gain the reader's attention, this structure makes good sense in proposal writing. Here are the main parts:

- **Abstract:** Gives the summary or "big picture" for those who will make decisions about your proposal. Usually includes some kind of hook or grabber—a point that will make the audience interested in reading further.
- **Body:** Gives the details about exactly what you are proposing to do.
- **Conclusion:** Drives home the main benefit and makes clear the next step.

Note: Beginning and ending sections should be easy to read and should stress just a few points. They provide short "buffers" on both ends of the longer, more technical sections in the middle. The next three guidelines give more specific advice for writing the main parts of an informal proposal.

Informal Proposal Guideline 5: Use "Introductory Summary" Heading for the Generic Abstract Section

Here you capture the client's attention with a capsule summary of the entire proposal. This one- or two-paragraph starting section permits space only for what the reader needs to know at the outset, such as the following:

- Proposal's *purpose*
- Reader's main *need*
- Main *features* and related *benefits*
- *Overview* of proposal sections to follow

As Models 12-1 and 12-2 show, the introductory summary appears immediately after the Subject line of the memo proposal, or after the salutation of the letter proposal. As with informal reports, you have the option of labelling the section "Introductory Summary" or leaving off the heading. In either case, keep this overview brief. Answer the one question clients are thinking: "Why should we hire this firm instead of another?" If you find yourself starting to give too much detail, move background into the first section of the discussion.

Informal Proposal Guideline 6: Put Important Details in the Body

The discussion of your proposal should address the following basic questions:

1. What problem are you trying to solve, and why?
2. What are the technical details of your approach?
3. Who will do the work, and with what?

4. When will it be done?

5. How much will it cost?

Discussion formats vary from proposal to proposal, but following are some sections commonly used to respond to these questions:

1. **Description of problem or project and its significance:** Give a precise technical description, along with any assumptions that you have made on the basis of previous contact with the reader. Explain the problems' importance or significance, especially to the reader of the proposal.

2. **Proposed solution or approach:** In a manner that is clear and well organized, describe the specific tasks you propose. If you are presenting several options, discuss each one separately—making it as easy as possible for the reader to compare and contrast information.

3. **Personnel:** If the proposal involves people performing tasks, it may be appropriate to state the participants' qualifications.

4. **Schedule:** Even the simplest proposals usually require some sort of information about the schedule for delivering goods, performing tasks, and so on. Be both clear and realistic in this portion of the proposal. Use graphics when appropriate (see Chapter 5 for guidelines on Gantt and milestone charts).

5. **Costs:** Place complete cost information in the body of the proposal unless you have a table that would be more appropriately placed in an attachment. Above all, do not bury dollar figures in paragraph format. Instead, highlight these figures with indented or bulleted lists, or at least place them at the beginnings of paragraphs. Because your reader will be looking for cost data, it is to your advantage to make that information easy to find.

Informal Proposal Guideline 7: Give Special Attention to Establishing Need in the Body

A common complaint about proposals is that writers fail to establish the need for what is being proposed. As any good salesperson knows, customers must feel that they need your product, service, or idea before they can be convinced to purchase or support it. In other words, do not simply try to dazzle readers with the good sense and quality of what you are proposing. Instead, lay the groundwork for acceptance by first showing the readers that a strong need exists.

Establishing need is most crucial in unsolicited proposals, of course, since readers may not be psychologically prepared to accept a change that will cost them money. Even in proposals that have been solicited, however, you should give some attention to restating readers' basic needs. If nothing else, this special attention shows your understanding of the problem.

Informal Proposal Guideline 8: Focus Attention in Your Conclusion

Called the *conclusion* or *closing*, this section gives you the opportunity to control the reader's last impression. It also helps you avoid the awkwardness of ending proposals with the statement of costs, which is usually the last section in the discussion. In this closing section you can include the following:

- Emphasize a main benefit or feature of your proposal.
- Restate your interest in doing the work.
- Indicate what should happen next.

Regarding the last point, sometimes you may ask readers to call if they have questions. In other situations, however, it is appropriate to say that you will follow up the proposal with a phone call. This approach leaves you in control of the next step.

Incidentally, for informal sales proposals, there is a special technique that can push the proposal one step closer to approval. After the signature section, place an "acceptance block." As shown in the following example, this item makes it as easy as a signature for the reader to accept your proposal.

ACCEPTED BY LMN DEVELOPMENT, INC.

By: _____

Title: _____

Date: _____

Informal Proposal Guideline 9: Use Attachments for Less Important Details

Remember that the text of informal proposals is usually no more than five pages. That being the case, you may have to put supporting data or illustrations in attachments following the conclusion. Cost and schedule information, in particular, is best placed at the end in well-labelled sections.

Make sure that the proposal text includes clear references to these visuals. If you have more than one attachment, give each one a letter and a title (for example, "Attachment A: Project Costs"). If you have only one attachment, include the title but no letter (for example, "Attachment: Résumés").

Informal Proposal Guideline 10: Edit Carefully

In the rush of completing proposals, some writers fail to edit carefully. That is a big mistake. Make sure to build in enough time for a series of editing passes, preferably by different readers. There are two reasons why proposals of all kinds deserve this special attention:

1. They can be considered contracts in a court of law. If you make editing mistakes that alter meaning (such as an incorrect price figure), you could be bound to the error.
2. Proposals often present readers with their first impression of you. If the document is sloppy, they may make assumptions about your professional abilities as well.

FORMAL PROPOSALS

Sometimes the complexity of the proposal may be such that a formal response is best. As always, the final decision about format should be based on your readers' needs. Ask yourself questions like the following in deciding whether to write an informal or a formal proposal:

- Is there too much detail for a letter or memo?
- Is a table of contents needed so that sections can be found quickly?
- Will the professional look of a formal document lend support to the cause?

- Are there so many attachments that a series of lengthy appendices would be useful?
- Are there many different readers with varying needs, such that there should be different sections for different people?

If you answer yes to one or more of these questions, give careful consideration to writing a formal proposal. This long format is most common in external sales proposals; however, important in-house proposals may sometimes require the same approach, especially in large organizations in which you may be writing to unknown persons in distant departments. Both in-house and sales examples follow the writing guidelines given next.

Formal proposals can be long and complex, so this part of the chapter treats each proposal section separately, from title page through conclusion. Two points will become evident as you use these guidelines. First, formal reports and formal proposals are a lot alike. A quick look at the last chapter will show you the similarities in format. Second, a formal proposal—like all technical writing described in this text—follows the basic ABC format described in Chapter 3. Specifically, the parts of the formal proposal fit the pattern in this way:

ABC Format: Formal Proposal
Abstract

- Cover/title page
- Memo/letter of transmittal
- Table of contents
- List of illustrations
- Executive summary
- Introduction

Body

- Technical information
- Management information
- Cost information
- [Appendices—appear after text but support Body section]

Conclusion

- Conclusion

As you read through and apply these guidelines, refer to Model 12-3 on pages 339–47 for an annotated example of the formal proposal. Note that each major section in the model proposals starts on a new page. Another alternative is to run most sections together, changing pages only at the end of the letter of transmittal and executive summary. Minor format variations abound, of course, but this chapter's guidelines will stand you in good stead throughout your career.

Cover/Title Page

Like formal reports, formal proposals usually are bound documents with a cover. The cover will include one or more of the items listed below on the title page. Just as important, the cover should be designed to attract the reader's interest, with good page layout and perhaps even a graphic. Remember that proposals are sales documents. No one *has* to read them.

Inside the cover is the title page, which contains the following four pieces of information:

- **Project title,** preceded by "Proposal for" or similar wording
- **Your reader's name** ("Prepared for . . .")
- **Your name or the name of your organization,** spelled out in full ("Prepared by . . .")
- **Date of submission**

The title page gives clients their first impression of you. For that reason, consider using some tasteful graphics to make the proposal stand out from those of your competitors. For sales proposals, a particularly persuasive technique is to place the logo of the *client's company* on the cover or title page. In this way, you imply your interest in linking up with that firm and your interest in satisfying its needs, rather than simply selling your products or services.

Memo/Letter of Transmittal

Internal proposals have memos of transmittal; external sales proposals have letters of transmittal. These letters or memos must grab the reader's interest. The guidelines for format and organization presented here will help you write attention-getting prose. In particular, note that the letter or memo should be in single-spaced, ragged-right format, even if the rest of the proposal is double-spaced with right-justified margins.

For details of memo and letter format, see Chapters 8 and 9. The guidelines for the memo/letter of transmittal for formal reports also apply to formal proposals (see Transmittal Guideline 3 in Chapter 11). For now, here are some highlights of format and content that apply especially to letters and memos of transmittal:

1. Use short beginning and ending paragraphs (about three to five lines each).
2. Use a conversational style, with little or no technical jargon. Avoid stuffy phrases, such as "per your request."
3. Use the first paragraph for introductory information, mentioning what your proposal responds to (for example, a formal RFP, a conversation with the client, or your perception of a need).
4. Use the middle of the letter to emphasize one main benefit of your proposal, though the executive summary and proposal proper will mention benefits in detail. Stress what you can do to solve a problem, using the words *you* and *your* as much as possible (rather than *I* and *we*).
5. Use the last paragraph to retain control by orchestrating the next step in the proposal process. When appropriate, indicate that you will call the client soon to follow up on the proposal.
6. Follow one of the letter formats described in Chapter 9. Following are some exceptions, additions, and restrictions:
   - Use single-spaced, ragged-right copy to make your letter stand out from the proposal proper.
   - Keep the letter on one page; a two-page letter loses that crisp, concise impact you want a letter to make.
   - Place the company proposal number (if there is one) at the top, above the date. The exact placement of number and date depends on your letter style.
   - Include the client's company name or personal name on the first line of the inside address, and follow it with the mailing address that will be on the enve-

lope. If you use a company name, place an "Attention" line below the inside address. Include the full name (and title, if appropriate) of your contact person at the company; then use a conventional greeting ("Dear Mr. Adams:").
- (Optional) Include the project title below the Attention line, using the exact wording that appears on the title page.
- Close with "Sincerely" and your name at the bottom of the page. Also include your company affiliation.

Table of Contents

Create a very readable table of contents by spacing items well on the page. List all proposal sections and subsections, and their page references. At the end, list any appendices that may accompany the proposal.

Given the tight schedule on which most proposals are produced, errors can be introduced at the last minute because of additions or revisions. Therefore, take time to proofread the table of contents carefully. In particular, make sure to follow these guidelines:

- Wording of headings should match the proposal text.
- Page references should be correct.
- All headings of the same order should be parallel in grammatical form.

List of Illustrations

When there are many illustrations, the list of illustrations appears on a separate page after the table of contents. When there are few entries, however, the illustrations may be listed at the end of the table of contents page. In either case, the list should include the number, title, and page number of every illustration appearing in the body of the text. (If there is only one illustration, a number need not be included.) You may divide the list into tables and figures if many of both appear in your proposal.

Executive Summary

Executive summaries are the most frequently read parts of proposals. That fact should govern the time and energy you put into their preparation. Often read by decision makers in an organization, the summary should present a concise one-page overview of the proposal's most important points. Make note of the following guidelines as well:

- Avoid technical language.
- Make it as self-contained as possible.
- Make brief mention of the problem, proposed solution, and cost.
- Emphasize the main benefits of your proposal.

Start the summary with one or two sentences that command readers' attention and engage their interest. Then focus on just a few main selling points (three to five is best). You might even want to highlight these benefits with indented lead-ins such as "Benefit 1 . . . Benefit 2 . . ." When possible, use the statement of benefits to emphasize what is unique about your company or your approach so that your proposal will attract special attention. Finally, remember to write the summary after you have completed the rest of the proposal. Only at this point do you have the perspective to sit back and develop a reader-oriented overview.

Introduction

The introduction provides background information for both nontechnical and technical readers. Although the content will vary from proposal to proposal, some general guidelines apply. Basically, you should include information on (1) the purpose, (2) the problem to which you are responding, (3) the scope of the proposed study, and (4) the format of the proposal. (A lengthy problem or project statement should be placed in the proposal's first discussion section, not in the introduction.)

- Use subheadings if the introduction goes over a page. In this case, begin the section with one or two lead-in sentences that mention the sections to follow.
- Start with a purpose statement that concisely states the reason you are writing the proposal.
- Include a description of the problem or need to which your proposal is responding. Use language directly from the request for proposal or other document the reader may have given you so that there is no misunderstanding. For longer problem or need descriptions, adopt the alternative approach of including a separate needs section or problem description after the introduction.
- Include a scope section in which you briefly describe the range of proposed activities covered in the proposal, along with any research or pre-proposal tasks that have already been completed.
- Include a proposal format section if you feel the reader would benefit from a listing of the major proposal sections that will follow.

Discussion Sections

Aim the discussion or body toward readers who need supporting information. Traditionally, the discussion in a formal sales proposal contains three basic types of information: (1) technical, (2) management, and (3) cost. Following are some general guidelines for presenting each type. Remember that the exact wording of headings and subheadings will vary, depending on proposal content.

1. Technical sections

- Respond thoroughly to the client's concerns, as expressed in writing or in meetings.
- Follow whatever organization plan can be inferred from the request for proposal.
- Use frequent subheadings with specific wording.
- Back up all claims with facts.

2. Management sections

- Describe who will do the work.
- Explain when the work will be done.
- Display schedule information graphically.
- Highlight personnel qualifications (but put résumés in appendices).

3. Cost section

- Make costs extremely easy to find.
- Use formal or informal tables when possible.
- Emphasize value received for costs.
- Be clear about add-on costs or options.
- Always total your costs.

Conclusion

Formal proposals should always end with a section labelled *Conclusion* or *Closing*. This final section of the text gives you the chance to restate a main benefit, summarize the work to be done, and assure clients that you plan to work with them closely to satisfy their needs. Just as important, this brief section helps you end on a positive note. You come full circle back to what you stressed at the beginning of the document—benefits to the client and the importance of a strong personal relationship. (Without the conclusion, the client's last impression would be of the cost section in the discussion.)

Appendices

Because formal proposals are so long, readers sometimes have trouble locating information they need. Headings help, but they are not the whole answer. Another way you can help readers is by transferring technical details from the proposal text into appendices. The proposal still will contain detail—for technical readers who want it—but detail will not intrude into the text. This technique can save you and your employer considerable time, since it allows you to develop standard appendices (also called **boilerplate**) to be used in later proposals.

While any supporting information can be placed in appendices, the following items are most commonly included there:

- Résumés
- Organization charts
- Company histories
- Detailed schedule charts
- Contracts
- Cost tables
- Detailed options for technical work
- Summaries of related projects already completed
- Questionnaire samples

Boilerplate is often taken right off the shelf and thus is not paged in sequence with your text. It is best to use individual paging within each appendix. For example, pages in an Appendix B would be numbered B-1, B-2, B-3, and so on.

FEASIBILITY STUDIES

Much like recommendation reports (see Chapter 10), feasibility studies guide readers toward a certain line of action. Another similarity is that both report types can be either in-house or external. Yet most feasibility studies have the following five distinctive features that justify their being considered separately here:

1. They *always* are solicited by the reader, usually for the purpose of deciding on the best course of action.
2. They *always* assume one of the following two patterns of organization:
    - An analysis of the advantages and disadvantages of one course of action, product, or idea
    - A comparison of two or more courses of action, products, or ideas
3. They *always* are intended to help managers and other decision makers vote for or against an idea or select among several alternatives.

4. They *usually* nudge (as opposed to urge or push) the reader toward a decision. That is, they are supposed to be written in such a way that the facts speak for themselves.

5. They *often* are preceded by a proposal.

In some ways, feasibility studies could be viewed as a cross between technical reports and proposals. As a writer, you are expected to deal with the topic objectively and honestly, yet you are also expected to express your point of view. The *Oxford Canadian Dictionary* defines *feasible* in this way: "practicable; easily or conveniently done." Thus, a feasibility study determines if a particular course of action is practical. For example, it may be *desirable* for a student to quit work and return to school full-time. Yet if that same student has hefty car and apartment payments, the only *feasible* alternative may be part-time course work.

Guidelines for Feasibility Studies

The following guidelines will help you prepare the kinds of feasibility studies requested by your boss (if the study is in-house) or by your client (if the study is external). In either case, your study may be used as the basis for a major decision. Refer to Model 12-4 on pages 348–49 as you read and apply these guidelines to your own writing.

Feasibility Study Guideline 1: Choose Format Carefully

In deciding whether to use the format of an informal (letter or memo) or formal document, apply the same criteria mentioned earlier in the chapter with regard to proposals. As always, the central questions concern your readers:

- What format will give them easiest access to the data, conclusions, and recommendations of your study?
- Are there enough pages to suggest the need for a table of contents (that is, a formal report)?
- What is your readers' format preference?
- What has been the format of previous feasibility studies written for the same organization?

Feasibility Study Guideline 2: Use the ABC Format

Like other forms of technical writing, good feasibility studies have this basic three-part structure: **A**bstract, **B**ody, and **C**onclusion. As with other documents, the exact headings you choose may vary from report to report. Yet the overall structure should be as follows:

ABC Format: Feasibility Study

Abstract
- Capsule summary of information for the most important readers (for example, the decision makers)

Body
- Details that support whatever conclusions and recommendations the study contains, working logically from fact toward opinion

Conclusion
- Wrap-up in which you state conclusions and recommendations resulting from study

---

The following guidelines examine specific sections of feasibility studies, along with details of content and tone.

Feasibility Study Guideline 3: Call Your Abstract an Introductory Summary

This section provides information that the most important readers would want if they were in a rush to read your study. With that criterion in mind, consider including the following items:

- Brief statement about who has authorized the study and for what purpose
- Brief mention of the criteria used during the evaluation
- Brief reference to your recommendation

The last item is important, for it saves readers the frustration of having to wade through the whole document in search of the answers to the questions "Is this a practical idea?" or "Which alternative is best?" It is best to mention the recommendation up front, as this gives readers a frame through which to see the entire report.

Feasibility Study Guideline 4: Organize the Body Well

More than anything else, readers of feasibility studies expect an unbiased presentation. That means the midsection of your report must clearly and logically work from facts toward recommendations. Here is one approach that works:

1. **Describe evaluation criteria used during your study,** if readers need more detail than was presented in the introductory summary.
2. **Describe exactly** *what* **was evaluated and** *how*, especially if you are comparing several items.
3. **Choose criteria that are most meaningful to the readers,** such as:
   - Cost
   - Practicality of implementing idea
   - Changes that may be needed in personnel
   - Effect on growth of organization
   - Effects on day-to-day operations

     Of course, exact criteria are going to depend on the precise topic you are investigating.
4. **Discuss both advantages and disadvantages** when you are evaluating just one item. Move from advantages to disadvantages. The conclusion will allow you to come back around to supporting points.
5. **Follow organization guidelines for comparisons** when evaluating several alternatives (see Chapter 6). You can discuss one item at a time or you can discuss one criterion at a time.

Feasibility Study Guideline 5: Use the Conclusion for Detailed Conclusions and Recommendations

Here you get the opportunity to state (or restate) the conclusions evident from data you have presented in the discussion. First state conclusions, and then state your recommendations. Use listings for three or more points, to make this last section of the study as easy as possible to read.

Feasibility Study Guideline 6: Use Graphics for Comparisons

When comparing several items, you need to consider that most readers prefer tabulated information. Tables can appear either in the discussion section or in attachments. Whichever the case, follow graphics guidelines explained in Chapter 5.

Feasibility Study Guideline 7: Offer to Meet with the Readers

Most readers have many questions after reading a feasibility study, even if that study has been quite thorough. You score points for eagerness and professionalism if you anticipate needs and express your willingness to meet with readers later. Such meetings give you another opportunity to demonstrate your understanding of the topic.

Employability Skills

The Conference Board of Canada's *Employability Skills 2000+* suggests that the critical skills needed in the workplace are not limited to the technical, physical, or intellectual skills needed to perform specific work tasks. Rather, workers require a wide variety of fundamental, personal management, and teamwork skills, including the following:

Fundamental Skills

- Communicate.
- Manage information.
- Use numbers.
- Think and solve problems.

Personal Management Skills

- Demonstrate positive attitudes and behaviours.
- Be responsible.
- Be adaptable.
- Learn continuously.
- Work safely.

Teamwork Skills

- Work with others.
- Participate in projects and tasks.*

Instead of purely monetary contributions to charity, a number of companies have provided charitable organizations with the services of one of their executives. The companies have paid their executive's salary. The executives have worked outside of their fields of technical expertise, yet they have made a dramatic, positive difference in the charities' abilities to provide for their clients' needs.

Referring to the skills identified in *Employability Skills 2000+* (see Figure 1-11 in Chapter 1), write a proposal to a local firm suggesting that it provide this kind of donation, and explain why the loan of the executives would constitute a valuable contribution to charitable organizations.

* *Employability Skills 2000+* Brochure 2000 E/F (Ottawa: The Conference Board of Canada, 2000).

CHAPTER SUMMARY

Proposals and feasibility studies aim to *convince* readers. In the case of proposals, you are writing to convince someone inside or outside your organization to adopt an idea, a product, or a service. In the case of feasibility studies, you are marshalling facts to support the practicality of one approach to a problem, sometimes in comparison with other approaches. Either document can be informal or formal, depending on its length and complexity, as well as reader preferences.

This chapter included lists of writing guidelines for informal proposals, formal proposals, and feasibility studies. For informal proposals, follow these basic guidelines:

1. Plan well before you write.
2. Use letter or memo format.
3. Make the text visually appealing.
4. Use the ABC format for organization.
5. Use "Introductory Summary" heading for the generic abstract section.
6. Put important details in the body.
7. Give special attention to establishing need in the body.
8. Focus attention in your conclusion.
9. Use attachments for less important details.
10. Edit carefully.

In formal proposals, abide by the same general format as presented in Chapter 11 for formal reports. To be sure, formal proposals have a different tone and substance because of their more persuasive purpose. Yet they do have the same basic parts, with minor variations: cover/title page, memo/letter of transmittal, table of contents, list of illustrations, executive summary, introduction, discussion sections, conclusion, and appendices.

Feasibility studies demonstrate that an idea is or is not practical. Also, they may compare several alternatives. Follow these basic writing guidelines:

1. Choose format carefully.
2. Use the ABC format.
3. Call your abstract an introductory summary.
4. Organize the body well.
5. Use the conclusion for detailed conclusions and recommendations.
6. Use graphics for comparisons.
7. Offer to meet with the readers.

ASSIGNMENTS

The assignments in Part 1 and Part 2 can be completed either as individual projects or as group-writing projects. If your instructor assigns group projects, review the information on group writing in Chapter 1.

Part 1: Short Assignments

The following short assignments require either that you write parts of informal or formal proposals or that you evaluate the effectiveness of an informal proposal included here.

1. **Introductory summary.** For this assignment, select one of the projects that appear at the end of Chapter 2. Now assume that you were responsible for writing the proposal that resulted in the project. In other words, work backward from the project to the informal proposal that was used to get the work. Write a short introductory summary for the original proposal. Focus on what you think would be the client's main reason for hiring M&K. If necessary, invent additional information to complete this assignment successfully.

2. **Needs section.** As this chapter suggests, informal proposals—especially those that are unsolicited—must make a special effort to establish the need for the product or service being proposed. Assume that you are writing an informal proposal to suggest a change in procedures or equipment at your school. Keep the proposal limited to a small change;

you may even see a need in the room where you attend class (audiovisual equipment? lighting? heating or air systems? aesthetics? soundproofing?). Write the needs section that would appear in the body of the informal proposal.

3. **Conclusion or closing.** For this assignment, as with assignment 1, select a project from the project sheets in Chapter 2. Assume that you were the M&K employee responsible for writing the informal proposal that resulted in the work described in the project. Write an effective conclusion or closing for the proposal.

4. **Evaluation—informal proposal.** Review the informal proposal that follows, submitted by MainAlert Security Systems to the M&K office in Montreal. Evaluate the effectiveness of every section of the proposal.

---

200 Atwater Street
Montreal PQ H1Q 9B5
(514) 555-2000

September 15, 2006

Ms. A. Koffman
Martin & Koffman
2219 rue Decarie
Montreal PQ H4T 1P9
(514) 555–5688

Dear Angela,

Thank you for giving MainAlert Security Systems an opportunity to submit a proposal for installation of an alarm system at your new office. The tour of your nearly completed office in Montreal last week showed me all I need to know to provide you with burglary and fire protection. After reading this proposal, I think you will agree with me that my plan for your security system is perfectly suited to your needs.

This proposal describes the burglary and fire protection system I've designed for you. This proposal also describes various features of the alarm system that should be of great value. To provide you with a comprehensive description of my plan, I have assembled this proposal in several main sections:

1. Burglary Protection System
2. Fire Protection System
3. Arm/Disarm Monitoring
4. Installation Schedule
5. Installation and Monitoring Costs

BURGLARY PROTECTION SYSTEM

The burglary protection system would consist of a 46-zone MainAlert alarm control set, perimeter protection devices, and interior protection devices. The alarm system would have a strobe light and a siren to alert anyone nearby of a burglary in progress. Our system also includes a two-line dialer to alert our central station personnel of alarm and trouble conditions.

Alarm Control Set

The MainAlert alarm control set offers many features that make it well suited for your purposes. Some of these features are as follows:

1. Customer-programmable keypad codes
2. Customer-programmable entry/exit delays
3. Zone bypass option

4. Automatic reset feature
5. Point-to-point annunciation

I would like to explain the point-to-point annunciation feature, since the terminology is not as self-explanatory as the other features are. Point-to-point annunciation is a feature that enables the keypad to display the zone number of the point of protection that caused the alarm. This feature also transmits alarm-point information to our central station. Having alarm-point information available for you and the police can help prevent an unexpected confrontation with a burglar.

Interior and Perimeter Protection

The alarm system I have designed for you uses both interior and perimeter protection. For the interior protection, I plan to use motion detectors in the hallways. The perimeter protection will use glass-break detectors on the windows and door contacts on the doors.

There are some good reasons for using both interior and perimeter protection:

1. Interior and perimeter protection used together provide you with two lines of defence against intrusion.
2. A temporarily bypassed point of protection will not leave your office vulnerable to an undetected intrusion.
3. An employee who may be working late can still enjoy the security of the perimeter protection while leaving the interior protection off.

Although some people select only perimeter protection, it is becoming more common to add interior protection for the reasons I have given. Interior motion detection, placed at carefully selected locations, is a wise investment.

Local Alarm Signalling

The local alarm-signalling equipment consists of a 40-watt siren and a powerful strobe light. The siren and strobe will get the attention of any passerby and unnerve the most brazen burglar.

Remote Alarm Signalling

Remote alarm signalling is performed by a two-line dialer that alerts our central station to alarm and trouble conditions. The dialer uses two telephone lines so that a second line is available if one of the lines is out. Any two existing phone lines in your office can be used for the alarm system. Phone lines dedicated for alarm use are not required.

FIRE PROTECTION SYSTEM

My plan for the fire protection system includes the following equipment:

1. Ten-zone fire alarm panel
2. Eight smoke detectors
3. Water flow switch
4. Water cutoff switch
5. Four Klaxon horns

The 10-zone fire alarm panel will monitor one detection device per zone. Because each smoke detector, the water flow switch, and the water cutoff switch have a separate zone, the source of a fire alarm can be determined immediately.

To provide adequate local fire alarm signalling, this system is designed with four horns. Remote signalling for the fire alarm system is provided by the MainAlert control panel. The fire alarm would report alarm and trouble conditions to the MainAlert control panel. The MainAlert alarm control panel would, in turn, report fire alarm and fire trouble signals to our central station. The MainAlert alarm panel would not have to be set to transmit fire alarm and fire trouble signals to our central station.

ARM/DISARM MONITORING

Since 20 of your employees would have alarm codes, it is important to keep track of who enters and leaves the office outside office hours. When an employee would arm or disarm the alarm system, the alarm would send a closing or opening signal to our central station. The central station would keep a record of the employee's identity and the time the signal was received. With the arm/disarm monitoring service, our central station would send you opening/closing reports on a semi-monthly basis.

INSTALLATION SCHEDULE

Given the size of your new office, our personnel could install your alarm in three days. We could start the day after we receive approval from you. The building is now complete enough for us to start anytime. If you would prefer that the construction be completed before we start, that would not present any problems for us. To give you an idea of how the alarm system would be laid out, I have included an attachment to this proposal showing the locations of the alarm devices.

INSTALLATION AND MONITORING COSTS

Installation and monitoring costs for your burglary and fire alarm systems as I have described them in this proposal will be as follows:

- $8,200 for installation of all equipment
- $75 a month for monitoring of burglary, fire, and opening/closing signals under a two-year monitoring agreement

The $8,200 figure covers the installation of all the equipment I have mentioned in this proposal. The $75-a-month monitoring fee also includes opening/closing reports.

CONCLUSION

The MainAlert control panel, as the heart of your alarm system, is an excellent electronic security value. The MainAlert control panel is unsurpassed in its ability to report alarm status information to our central station. The perimeter and interior protection offers complete building coverage that will give you peace of mind.

The fire alarm system monitors both sprinkler flow and smoke conditions. The fire alarm system I have designed for you can provide sufficient warning to allow the fire department to save your building from catastrophic damage.

The arm/disarm reporting can help you keep track of employees who come and go outside office hours. It's not always apparent how valuable this service can be until you need the information it can provide.

I'll call you early next week, Angela, in case you have any questions about this proposal. We will be able to start the installation as soon as you return a copy of this letter with your signature in the acceptance block.

Sincerely,

Anne Rodriguez Evans

Anne Rodriguez Evans, Commercial Sales

Enc.

ACCEPTED by Martin & Koffman

By: _____   Date: _____

Title: _____

ALARM SYSTEM LAYOUT FOR
MARTIN & KOFFMAN—MONTREAL, PQ

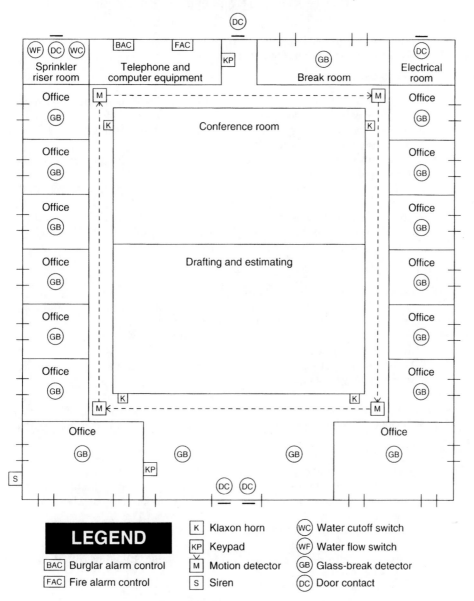

LEGEND		
BAC Burglar alarm control	K Klaxon horn	WC Water cutoff switch
FAC Fire alarm control	KP Keypad	WF Water flow switch
	M Motion detector	GB Glass-break detector
	S Siren	DC Door contact

Part 2: Longer Assignments

For each of these assignments, complete a copy of the Planning Form included in Chapter 1 (Figure 1-5).

5. **Informal proposal—M&K.** Choose Option A or Option B. Remember that informal proposals should be fairly limited in scope, given their length and format.

Option A: In-house

- Use your past or present work experience to write a memo proposal suggesting a change at M&K. Possible topic areas include changes in operating procedures, revisions to company policies, additions to the workforce, alterations of the physical plant, and purchase of products or services.
- Place yourself in the role of an employee of M&K. The proposal may be solicited or unsolicited, whichever best fits your situation.
- Make sure your proposal topic is limited enough in scope to be covered fully in an informal proposal with memo format.
- Choose at least two levels of readers who could conceivably be decision makers about a proposal such as the one you are writing—for example, branch or corporate managers. Review Chapter 2 if necessary.

Option B: Sales

- Select a product or service (1) that you are reasonably familiar with (on the basis of your work experience, research, or other interests) and (2) that could conceivably be purchased by a company like M&K.
- Put yourself in the role of someone representing the company that makes the product or provides the service.
- Write an informal sales proposal in which you propose purchase of the product or service by a representative of M&K.

6. **Formal proposal—M&K.** Choose Option A, B, or C. Make sure that your topic is more complex than the one you would choose for the preceding informal proposal assignments.

Option A: Community-related

- Write a formal proposal in which you propose a change in (1) the services offered by a city or town (for example, mass transit or waste management) or (2) the structure or design of a building, garden, parking lot, shopping area, school, or other civic property.
- Select a topic that is reasonably complex yet one that you can locate information about.
- Place yourself in the role of an outside consultant with a division of M&K, who is proposing the change.
- Choose either an unsolicited or a solicited context.
- Write to an audience that could actually be the readers. Do enough research to identify at least two levels of audience.

Option B: School-related

- Write a proposal in which you propose a change in some feature of a school you attend or have attended.
- Choose from topics such as operating procedures, personnel, curricula, activities, and physical plant.
- Select an audience that would actually make decisions on such a proposal.
- Give yourself the role of an outside consultant working for M&K.

Option C: Work-related

- Write a proposal in which you, as a representative of M&K, propose the purchase of a product or service by another firm.
- Choose a topic for which you have work experience, research knowledge, or a keen interest—and one that could conceivably relate to one of M&K's project areas. Make sure you have good sources of information.
- Choose either a solicited or an unsolicited context.

7. Informal or formal proposal—international context.

- Assume you are a consultant asked to propose a one-week training course to one of M&K's offices outside Canada. Most or all seminar participants will be residents native to the country you choose—not Canadian citizens working overseas.
- Choose a seminar topic familiar to you—for example, from college or university courses, work experience, or hobbies—or one that you are willing to learn about quickly through some study.
- Research the work habits, learning preferences, social customs, and other relevant topics concerning the country where the M&K office you have chosen is located.
- Write M&K an informal or a formal proposal that reflects your understanding of the topic, your study of the country, and your grasp of the proposal-writing techniques presented in this chapter.

Optional group approach: If this assignment is done by groups within your class, assume that members of your team work for M&K proposing training seminars at M&K offices around the world. Each group member has responsibility for one of M&K's offices outside Canada.

Different sections of the proposal will be written by different group members, who may be proposing the same seminar for all offices or different seminars. Whatever the case, the document as a whole should be unified in structure, format, and tone. It will be read by (1) the vice president for international operations at the M&K corporate office; (2) the vice president for research and training at the M&K corporate office; (3) the three branch managers in Venezuela, Saudi Arabia, and Japan; and (4) the training coordinator at M&K's office in Toronto.

8. Feasibility study—M&K.

- Choose any one of the proposal assignments that you completed as part of the preceding assignments. (Or for this assignment, you can use a proposal completed by one of your classmates.)
- Take yourself out of the role of proposal writer. Instead, consider yourself someone assigned (or hired) to complete the task of evaluating the practicality of the proposal, after it has been received.
- If appropriate, choose several alternatives to evaluate.

328 Ravine Road, Toronto, Ontario M2P 8J6
(416) 555-8438

January 15, 2006

Mr. David Barker
Technical Communications Manager
Real Big Professional Software
12 Nepean Drive
Ottawa ON K2P 0X7

Dear David:

I enjoyed meeting with you and learning about your new General Ledger software product. Because you require a March release, I can understand why you want to choose an approach to documentation and get the project started.

This proposal describes a strategy for completing the documentation in the 10 weeks between now and your March deadline. Included are these main sections:

1. Selection of the Best Format
2. Adoption of a Publication Plan
3. Control of Costs
4. Conclusion

SELECTION OF THE BEST FORMAT

I think your customers will be best served by a combination installation and user's guide. It uses a functional approach to show how General Ledger works. My assessment results from these completed steps:

- Interviews with support staffers responsible for providing technical support to customers using the company's other accounting products
- Interviews with programmers developing General Ledger, who have an intimate knowledge of how it works
- Conversations with you that clarified your organization's general expectations for the documentation

The assessment is also based on my experience developing documentation for other products. I strive to use clear, concise prose and ample white space to provide a visually appealing text. The text will be enhanced and supplemented with graphics depicting General Ledger's feature screens. The screens themselves will be captured directly

continues

Model 12-1 Letter proposal

Margin notes:

Shows understanding of client's main concern—*scheduling.*

Asserts ability to meet scheduling need.

Gives helpful overview of sections to follow.

Uses list to itemize important points—that is, the *basis* for his assessment.

David Barker
January 15, 2006
Page 2

from the program and inserted into the text by your staff using your in-house publishing system.

This approach will yield a thorough and easy-to-use document that will allow your customers to take full advantage of General Ledger's many innovative features.

As you know, writing documentation is a cooperative effort. Each member of the General Ledger product team will play key roles during the development process. To keep us all on track, I have put together a publication plan that shows how the project will progress from beginning to end.

ADOPTION OF A PUBLICATION PLAN

The publication plan shows how we can have the documentation ready for General Ledger's March unveiling. The four major steps are described here.

Define the Project

Much of this work has already been accomplished as a result of doing the research for this proposal. As a preliminary step, we will meet and review the project's scope and priority within the organization. We will detail the resources that will be available to complete the project. Most important, we will look at expectations: management's, yours, and the customers'.

Develop a Schedule

This step is the key to the publication process and ensures a common understanding of what has to be done and in what period of time. It has three basic steps:

- We define the tasks that are part of the project.
- We define the resources we have available to deal with the identified task.
- We assign tasks to the most appropriate individuals.

Manage the Project

What is good project management? In this plan, good management is essentially good communications. In the first three steps, we define the information that project members must have to understand how the document will be produced and their roles in that process. Ongoing management of the project will be a matter of keeping the channels of communication open.

Perform a Post-mortem

The last step is an evaluation of the effectiveness of the publication plan. It provides the opportunity for us to learn how to do future documentation better. It is important to look back at what went right and what went wrong during a project and to share this information with the others. You will get a complete postmortem report from me after the project is completed.

Continues emphasis on benefits to reader.

Leads in smoothly to next section.

Starts with *overview* of sections to follow.

Organizes paragraph around three *main points*.

Uses bulleted list for primary *steps* in project.

Introduces section with *question* to attract attention to passage.

continues

Model 12-1 *continued*

David Barker
January 15, 2006
Page 3

Shows interest in *following through*.

Throughout the project, this management system will guide us in completing General Ledger's documentation on time and within budget.

Places benefit in heading.

CONTROL OF COSTS

Good documentation helps to sell software. By working smart, we can develop documentation that will enhance General Ledger's appeal, and we can do it at a reasonable cost.

Shows he can meet project criteria—but also *clarifies* the *assumptions* he is making.

My experience in this area and the management system described here will reduce waste and duplication of effort, two factors that affect cost. This savings means I can bring the project in within the 200-hour cap you mentioned.

This estimate assumes that three of the program's four main features are in a complete, or "fixed," state and that the fourth main feature is about 50% complete. This estimate also assumes that all programming will be finished by March 5, which will allow time to put the guide through final review and production.

Returns to *main concern* of reader— scheduling.

CONCLUSION

The functional approach, which describes a product in terms of its operations, is the documentation format that will best serve General Ledger customers. Your goal of having the documentation ready by March will be aided by adopting a four-step publication plan. The plan will define the strategy for writing the documentation and will help keep costs down.

Retains *control* of next step.

I'll call you in a few days, David, to answer any questions you might have about this proposal. I can begin work on the documentation as soon as you sign the acceptance block and return a copy of this letter to me.

Sincerely,

Steven Nickels

Steven Nickels
Documentation Specialist

Enclosure

Includes acceptance block to simplify approval process.

ACCEPTED by Real Big Professional Software

By: _____

Title: _____

Date: _____

Model 12-1   *continued*

DATE: October 4, 2006
TO: Gerri le Bon
FROM: Jeff Bilstrom *JB*
SUBJECT: Creation of Logo for Montrose Service Centre

Part of my job as director of public relations is to get the Montrose name firmly entrenched in the minds of Montreal Urban Community residents. Having recently reviewed the contacts we have with the public, I believe we are sending a confusing message about the many services we offer retired citizens in this area.

To remedy the problem, I propose we adopt a logo to serve as an umbrella for all services and agencies supported by the Montrose Service Centre. This proposal gives details about the problem and the proposal solution, including costs.

The Problem

The lack of a logo presents a number of problems related to marketing the centre's services and informing the public. Here are a few:

- The letterhead mentions the organization's name in small type, with none of the impact that an accompanying logo would have.
- The current brochure needs the flair that could be provided by a logo on the cover page, rather than just the page of text and headings that we now have.
- Our 14 vehicles are difficult to identify because there is only the lettered organization name on the sides without any readily identifiable graphic.
- The sign in front of our campus, a main piece of free advertising, could better spread the word about Montrose if it contained a catchy logo.
- Other signs around campus could display the logo, as a way of reinforcing our identity and labelling buildings.

It's clear that without a logo, the Montrose Service Centre misses an excellent opportunity to educate the public about its services.

The Solution

I believe a professionally designed logo could give the Montrose Service Centre a more distinct identity. Helping to tie together all branches of our operation, it would give the public an easy-to-recognize symbol. As a result, there would be a stronger awareness of the centre on the part of potential users and financial contributors.

Gives concise view of problem—*and* his proposed solution.

Includes effective lead-in.

Uses bulleted list to highlight main difficulties posed by current situation.

Ends section with good *transition* to next section.

Starts with *main point*—need for logo.

continues

Model 12-2   Memo proposal

Gerri le Bon
October 4, 2006
Page 2

The new logo could be used immediately to do the following:

- Design and print letterhead, envelopes, business cards, and a new brochure
- Develop a decal for all company vehicles that would identify them as belonging to Montrose
- Develop new signs for the entire campus, to include a new sign for the entrance to the campus, one sign at the entrance to the Blane Workshop, and one sign at the entrance to the Administration Building

Focuses on *benefits* of proposed change.

Cost

Developing a new logo can be quite expensive. However, I have been able to get the name of a well-respected graphic artist in Montreal who is willing to donate his services in the creation of a new logo. All that we must do is give him some general guidelines to follow and then choose among eight to ten rough sketches. Once a decision is made, the artist will provide a camera-ready copy of the new logo.

Emphasizes *benefit* of possible price break.

- Design charge $0.00
- Charge for new letterhead, envelopes, business cards, and brochures
  (min. order)   545.65
- Decal for vehicles 14 @ $50.00 + 7.5%   752.50
- Signs for campus   415.28

  Total Cost $1,713.43

Uses *listing* to clarify costs.

Conclusion

As the retirement population of Montreal increases in the next few years, there will be a much greater need for the services of the Montrose Service Centre. Because of that need, it's in our best interests to keep this growing market informed about the organization.

I'll stop by later this week to discuss any questions you might have about this proposal.

Closes with major benefit to reader and urge to action.

Keeps control of next step.

Model 12-2   *continued*

PROPOSAL FOR SUPPLYING
TEAK CAM CLEAT SPACERS

Prepared by
Totally Teak, Inc.

Prepared for
John L. Riggini
Bosun's Locker Marine Supply

August 22, 2006

continues

Model 12-3 Formal proposal (external)

In this example, the letter of transmittal appears immediately following the title page. It can also appear before the title page.

Establishes *link* with previous client contact.

Stresses two main benefits.

Says he will *call* (rather than asking client to call).

Totally Teak, Inc.
6543 Amster Avenue, N.W.
Atlanta, Georgia 30308
(404) 555-9425

August 22, 2006

John L. Riggini, President
Bosun's Locker Marine Supply
24 Harbour Crescent
Vancouver BC V6Y 4S2

Dear Mr. Riggini:

I enjoyed talking with you last week about inventory needs at the 10 Bosun's stores. In response to your interest in our products, I'm submitting this proposal to supply your store with our Teak Cam Cleat Spacers.

This proposal outlines the benefits of adding Teak Cam Cleat Spacers to your line of sailing accessories. The potential for high sales volume stems from the fact that the product satisfies two main criteria for any boat owner:

1. It enhances the appearance of the boat.
2. It makes the boat easier to handle.

Your store managers will share my enthusiasm for this product when they see the response of their customers.

I'll give you a call next week to answer any questions you have about this proposal.

Sincerely,

William G. Rugg

William G. Rugg,
President
Totally Teak, Inc.

WR/rr

continues

Model 12-3   *continued*

TABLE OF CONTENTS

Organizes entire proposal around *benefits.*

LIST OF ILLUSTRATIONS

continues

Model 12-3 *continued*

Briefly mentions main *need* to which proposal responds.

Reinforces main points mentioned in *letter* (*selective repetition* of crucial information is acceptable).

EXECUTIVE SUMMARY

This proposal outlines features of a custom-made accessory designed for today's sailors—whether they be racers, cruisers, or single-handed skippers. The product, Teak Cam Cleat Spacers, has been developed for use primarily on the *Catalina 22,* a boat owned by many customers of the 10 Bosun's stores. However, it can also be used on other sailboats in the same class.

The predictable success of Teak Cam Cleat Spacers is based on two important questions asked by today's sailboat owners:

- Will the accessory enhance the boat's appearance?
- Will it make the boat easier to handle and, therefore, more enjoyable to sail?

This proposal answers both questions with a resounding affirmative by describing the benefits of teak spacers to thousands of people in your territory who own boats for which the product is designed. This potential market, along with the product's high profit margin, will make Teak Cam Cleat Spacers a good addition to your line of sailing accessories.

1

continues

Model 12-3   *continued*

INTRODUCTION

The purpose of this proposal is to show that Teak Cam Cleat Spacers will be a practical addition to the product line at the Bosun's Locker Marine Supply stores. This introduction highlights the need for the product, as well as the scope and format of the proposal.

Background

Sailing has gained much popularity in recent years. The high number of inland impoundment lakes, as well as the vitality of boating on the Great Lakes, has spread the popularity of the sport. With this increased interest, more and more sailors have become customers for a variety of boating accessories.

What kinds of accessories will these sailors be looking for? Accessories that (1) enhance the appearance of their sailboats and (2) make their sailboats easier to handle and, consequently, more enjoyable to sail. With these customer criteria in mind, it is easy to understand the running joke among boat owners (a profitable joke among marine supply dealers): "A boat is just a hole in the water that you pour your money into."

The development of this particular production originated from our designers' first-hand sailing experiences on the *Catalina 22* and knowledge obtained during manufacture (and testing) of the first prototype. In addition, we conducted a survey of owners of boats in this general class. The results showed that winch and cam cleat designs are major concerns.

Proposal Scope and Format

The proposal focuses on the main advantages that Teak Cam Cleat Spacers will provide your customers. These six sections follow:

1. Practicality
2. Suitability for a Variety of Sailors
3. High-Quality Construction and Appearance
4. Dealer Benefits
5. Sizable Potential Market
6. Affordable Price

Annotations (right margin):

- Makes clear the proposal's purpose.
- Gives lead-in about section to follow.
- Establishes *need* for product.
- Shows his understanding of *need* (personal experience of designing owner survey).
- Gives list of sections to follow, to reinforce organization of proposal.

2

Model 12-3 *continued*

continues

Uses main heading that *engages reader's interest.*

Phrases each side heading in "benefit-centred" language.

FEATURES AND BENEFITS

Teak Cam Cleat Spacers offer Bosun's Locker Marine Supply the best of both worlds. On the one hand, the product solves a nagging problem for sailors. On the other, it offers your store managers a good opportunity for profitability. Described here are six main benefits for you to consider.

Practicality

This product is both functional and practical. When installed in the typical arrangement shown in the figure below, the Teak Cam Cleat Spacer raises the height of the cam cleat, thereby reducing the angle between the deck and the sheet as it feeds downward from the winch. As a result of this increased height, a crew member is able to cleat a sheet with one hand instead of two.

SIDE VIEWS OF CLEATING ARRANGEMENT

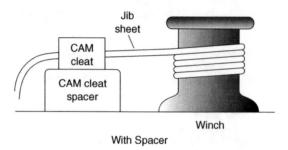

With Spacer

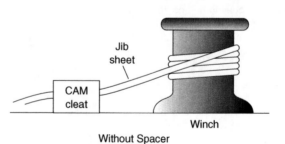

Without Spacer

3

continues

Model 12-3   *continued*

Such an arrangement allows a skipper to maintain steerage of the boat, keeping one hand on the helm while cleating the sheet with the other. Securing a sheet in this manner can be done more quickly and securely. Also, this installation reduces the likelihood of a sheet "popping out" of the cam cleat during a sudden gust of wind.

Explains exactly how product will work.

Suitability for a Variety of Sailors

For the racer, cruiser, and single-handed sailor, sailing enjoyment is increased as sheets and lines become easier to handle and more secure. In a tight racing situation, these benefits can be a deciding factor. The sudden loss of sail tension at the wrong moment as a result of a sheet popping out of the cam cleat could make the difference in a close race.

Moves logically from racing *to* cruising *to* single-handed sailing—*all to show usefulness of product.*

A cruising sailor is primarily concerned with relaxation and pleasure. A skipper in this situation wants to reduce his or her workload as much as possible. In the instance of a sheet popping loose, the sudden chaos of a sail flapping wildly interrupts an otherwise tranquil atmosphere. Teak Cam Cleat Spacers reduce the chance of this happening.

A cruising sailor often has guests aboard. In this situation, as well as in a race, the skipper wants to maintain a high level of seamanship, especially where the control of the boat and the trim of its sails are concerned.

The single-handed sailor derives the greatest benefit from installing Teak Cam Cleat Spacers. Without crew nearby to assist with handling lines or sheets, anything that makes work easier for this skipper is welcome.

High-Quality Construction and Appearance

The teakwood frame from which this product is manufactured is well suited for use around water, since teak will not rot. It also looks nice when oiled or varnished.

Stresses quality.

The deck of most sailboats is made primarily of fibreglass. The appearance of such a boat can be significantly enhanced by the addition of some teak brightwork.

Each spacer is individually handcrafted by Totally Teak, Inc., to guarantee a consistent level of high quality.

Dealer Benefits

Teak Cam Cleat Spacers make a valuable addition to the dealer's product line. They complement existing sailing accessories as well as provide the customer with the convenience of a readily available prefabricated product.

Appeals to self-interest of individual *Bosun's dealers.*

A customer who comes in to buy a cam cleat is a ready prospect for the companion spacer. Such a customer will likely want to buy mounting hardware as well.

With this unique teak product readily available, a dealer can save the customer the time and trouble of fabricating makeshift spacers.

4

continues

Model 12-3 *continued*

Includes number
of owners to
emphasize
potential sales.

Sizable Potential Market

These Teak Cam Cleat Spacers are designed with a large and growing potential market in mind. They are custom-made for the *Catalina 22*, one of the most popular sailboats in use today. Over 13,000 of this model of sailboat have been manufactured to date. These spacers are also well suited for other similar-class sailboats.

Keeps price
information
short and *clear.*

Affordable Price

The Teak Cam Cleat Spacers made by Totally Teak, Inc., wholesale for $3.95/pair. Suggested retail is $6.95/pair. This low price is easy on the skipper's wallet and should help this product move well. And, of course, the obviously high profit margin should provide an incentive to your store managers.

5

continues

Model 12-3 *continued*

CONCLUSION

Why should a marine supply dealer consider carrying Teak Cam Cleat Spacers? This product satisfies two common criteria of sailboat owners today: it enhances the appearance of any sailboat, and it makes the boat easier to handle. The potential success of this product is based on its ability to meet these criteria and the following features and benefits:

1. It is practical, allowing quick, one-handed cleating.

2. It is ideally suited for a variety of sailors, whether they are racing, cruising, or sailing single-handedly.

3. It is a high-quality, handcrafted product that enhances the appearance of any sailboat.

4. It is a product that benefits the dealer by making a valuable addition to her or his product line. It complements existing sail accessories and satisfies a customer need.

5. It is geared toward a sizable potential market. Today there are thousands of sailboats in the class for which this accessory is designed.

6. It is affordably priced and provides a good profit margin.

Links list of *benefits* with order of same in discussion— drives home advantages of product to *user* and *dealer.*

6

continues

Model 12-3   *continued*

MEMORANDUM

DATE: July 22, 2006
TO: Nizar Bhindi
FROM: Mike Tran *MT*
SUBJECT: Replacement of In-House File Server

INTRODUCTORY SUMMARY

    The purpose of this feasibility study is to determine if the NTR PC905 would make a practical replacement for our in-house file server. As we agreed in our weekly staff meeting, our current file-serving computer is damaged beyond repair and must be replaced by the end of the week. This study shows that the NTR PC905 is a suitable replacement that we can purchase within our budget and install by Friday afternoon.

FEASIBILITY CRITERIA

    There are three major criteria that I addressed. First, the computer we buy must be able to perform the tasks of a file-serving computer on our in-house network. Second, it must be priced within our $4,000 budget for the project. Third, it must be delivered and installed by Friday afternoon.

Performance

    As a file server, the computer we buy must be able to satisfy these criteria:

- Store all programs used by network computers
- Store the source code and customer-specific files for Xtracheck
- Provide fast transfer of files between computers while serving as host to the network
- Serve as the printing station for the network laser printer

    The NTR PC905 comes with a 10.0 GB hard drive. This capacity will provide an adequate amount of storage for all programs that will reside on the file server. Our requirements are for 2 GB of storage for programs used by network computers and 2.5 GB of storage for source code and customer-specific programs. The 10.0 GB drive will leave us with 5.5 GB of storage for future growth and work space.

    The PC905 can transfer files and execute programs across our network. It can perform these tasks at speeds up to five times faster than our current file server. Productivity should increase because the time spent waiting for transfer will decrease.

Gives context for feasibility study.

Summarizes conclusion of report.

Pinpoints three criteria to be discussed.

Shows how NTR PC905 will fulfill performance criteria.

Only covers advantages because there are *no* disadvantages to buying PC905.

continues

Model 12-4 Feasibility study (one alternative)

Nizar Bhindi
July 22, 2006
Page 2

The computer we choose as the file server must also serve as the printing station for our network laser printer. The PC905 is compatible with our Hewy Packer laser printer. It also has double the memory of our current server. As a result, it can store larger documents in memory and print them with greater speed.

Budget

The budget for the new file server is $4,000. The cost of the PC905 is as follows:

PC905 with 10.0 GB Hard Drive	$2,910
Keyboard	112
Monitor	759
Total	$3,781

No new network boards need to be purchased because we can use those that are in the current server. We also have all additional hardware and cables that will be required for installation. Thus the PC905 can be purchased for $200 under budget.

Time Frame

Our sales representative at NTR guarantees that we can have delivery of the system by Friday morning. Given this assurance, we can have the system in operation by Friday afternoon.

Additional Benefits

We are currently using NTR PCs at our customer sites. I am very familiar with the setup and installation of these machines. By purchasing a brand of computer currently in use, we will not have to worry about additional time spent learning new installation and operation procedures. In addition, we know that all our software is fully compatible with NTR products.

The warranty on the PC905 is for one year. After the warranty period, the equipment is covered by the service plan that we have for all our other computers and printers.

CONCLUSION

I recommend that we purchase the NTR PC905 as the replacement computer for our file server. It meets or exceeds all criteria for performance, price, and installation.

Marginal notes:

Makes costs easy to find with simple table.

Highlights major goal—quick installation.

Ends with "extras"—that is, benefits not among major criteria but still useful.

Restates significant point already noted in introductory summary.

Model 12-4 *continued*

CHAPTER 13

Oral Communication

Your career will present you with many opportunities for oral presentations, both formal and informal. You may not, however, consider them as "opportunities," but, rather, as stressful obstacles. That response is normal. The purpose of this chapter is to provide you with the appropriate tools so that oral presentations will contribute to your self-esteem and career success. You will find guidelines for preparation and delivery, techniques for dealing with anxiety, and an example of a technical presentation. Also, the chapter addresses the related topic of running effective meetings.

The entire chapter is based on one simple principle: *almost anyone can become an excellent speaker*. Put aside the myth that competent speakers are born with that talent—that "either they have it or they don't." Certainly some people have more natural talent at thinking on their feet or have a more resonant voice. But success at speaking can come to all speakers, whatever their talent, if they follow the "3 Ps":

Step 1: Prepare carefully.
Step 2: Practise often.
Step 3: Perform with enthusiasm.

These steps form the foundation for all specific guidelines that follow. Before presenting these guidelines, this chapter examines specific ways that formal and informal presentations become part of your professional life.

PRESENTATIONS AND YOUR CAREER

Some oral presentations you will choose to give; others will be "command performances" thrust upon you. Presented next are some situations where the ability to speak well can lead to success for you and for your organization:

- **Getting hired:** As a job applicant with a business degree, you are asked to present several M&K managers with a 10-minute summary of your education, previous experience, and career goals.
- **Getting customers:** As coordinator for an M&K proposal team, you have just been informed that M&K has made the shortlist of companies bidding on the contract to develop a customer information system for a large insurance firm. You and your three-member team must deliver a 20-minute presentation that highlights the written proposal. The presentation, which will be held in the firm's Toronto head office, will begin and end with comments by you in your role as coordinator. Your colleagues are expected to contribute short talks on their areas of expertise.
- **Keeping customers:** As a field engineer at M&K's Montreal office, you recently submitted a report evaluating a 30-year-old dam in Labrador. Now your client, Newfoundland and Labrador's Mines and Energy ministry, which owns the dam, has asked you to attend a committee meeting to present an overview of your findings and respond to questions.
- **Contributing to your profession:** As a laboratory supervisor for M&K, you belong to a professional society that meets yearly to discuss issues in your field.

This year you have been asked to deliver a 15-minute presentation on new procedures for testing toxic-waste samples in the laboratory.

- **Contributing to your community:** As a computer systems technologist, you have been asked to speak to a support group for single-parent families. You have been asked to explain how computer technology could reduce their office overhead, speed up the organization's response time, and help publicize the group's services. The group has given you 10 minutes to speak. You have accepted the invitation because of M&K's commitment to the community and willingness to provide services at cost to struggling charitable organizations.

As you can see from this list, oral presentations are defined quite broadly. Usually they can be classified according to criteria like the following:

1. **Format:** from informal question/answer sessions to formal speeches
2. **Length:** from several-minute overviews to long sessions of an hour or longer
3. **Number of presenters:** from solo performances to group presentations
4. **Content:** from a few highlights to detailed coverage

Throughout your career, you will speak to different-sized groups, on diverse topics, and in varied formats. The next two sections provide some common guidelines on preparation, delivery, and graphics.

PREPARATION AND DELIVERY

The goal of most oral presentations is quite simple: you must present a few basic points, in a fairly brief time, to an interested but usually impatient audience. Simplicity, brevity, and interest are the keys to success. By delivering what *you* expect when *you* hear a speech, you will be giving a good presentation.

Guidelines for Preparation and Delivery

Although the guidelines here apply to any presentation, they relate best to those that precede or follow a written report, proposal, memo, or letter. Few career presentations are isolated from written work. With this connection in mind, you will note many similarities between the guidelines for good speaking and those for good writing covered in earlier chapters—especially the importance of analyzing the needs of the audience.

Presentation Guideline 1: Know Your Listeners

The following features are common to most listeners:

- They cannot rewind the tape of your presentation; contrast this with the text of a report, through which readers can skip back and forth.
- They are impatient after the first few minutes, particularly if they do not know where a speech is going.
- They will daydream and often need to have their attention brought back to the matter at hand (expect a 30-second attention span).
- They have heard so many disappointing presentations that they may not have high expectations for yours.

To respond to these realities, you must learn as much as possible about your listeners. For example, you can (1) consider what you already know about your audience, (2) talk with colleagues who have spoken to the same group, and (3) find out which listeners make the decisions.

Most important, make sure not to talk over anyone's head. If there are several levels of technical expertise represented by the group, find the lowest common denominator and decrease your presentation's technical level accordingly. Remember that decision makers are often the ones without current technical experience. They may want only highlights. Later they can review written documents for details or solicit more technical information during the question-and-answer session that follows your presentation.

Presentation Guideline 2: Use the Preacher's Maxim

The well-known preacher's maxim goes like this:

> First you tell 'em what you're gonna tell 'em, then you tell 'em, and then you tell 'em what you told 'em.

Why should most speakers follow this plan? Because it gives the speech a simple three-part structure that most listeners can grasp easily. Here is how your speech should be organized (note that it corresponds to the ABC format used throughout this text for writing):

1. **Abstract (beginning of presentation):** Right at the outset, you should (1) get the listeners' interest (with an anecdote, a statistic, or other technique), (2) state the exact purpose of the speech, and (3) list the main points you will cover. Do not try the patience of your audience with an extended introduction. Use no more than a minute. For example:

   > Last year, Jones Engineering had 56 percent more field accidents than the year before. This morning, I'll examine a proposed safety plan that aims to solve this problem. My presentation will focus on three main benefits of the new plan: lower insurance premiums, less lost time from accidents, and better morale among the employees.

2. **Body (middle of presentation):** Here you discuss the points mentioned briefly in the introduction, in the same order that they were mentioned. Provide transitions to help your listeners stay on track. For example:

   > The final benefit of the new safety plan will be improved morale among the field workers at all our job sites . . .

3. **Conclusion (end of presentation):** In the conclusion, review the main ideas covered in the body of the speech and specify actions that you want to occur as a result of your presentation. For example:

   > Jones Engineering can benefit from this new safety plan in three main ways . . . If Jones implements the new plan next month, I believe you will see a dramatic reduction in on-site accidents during the last half of the year.

This simple three-part plan for all presentations gives listeners the handle they need to understand your speech. First, there is a clear "road map" in the introduction so that they know what lies ahead in the rest of the speech. Second, there is an organized pattern in the body, with clear transitions between points. And third, there is a strong finish that brings the audience back full circle to the main thrust of the presentation.

Presentation Guideline 3: Stick to a Few Main Points

Our short-term memory holds limited items. It follows that listeners are most attentive to speeches organized around a few major points. In fact, a good argument can be made for organizing information in groups of *threes* whenever possible. For reasons that are not totally understood, listeners seem to remember groups of three items more than they do any other size groupings—perhaps because of the following:

- The number is simple.
- It parallels the overall three-part structure of most speeches and documents (beginning, middle, end).
- Many good speakers have used triads (Winston Churchill's "Blood, sweat, and tears," Caesar's "I came, I saw, I conquered," etc.).

Whatever the reason, groupings of three make your speech more memorable.

Presentation Guideline 4: Put Your Outline on Cards, Paper, or Overheads

The best presentations are *extemporaneous*, meaning the speaker shows great familiarity with the material and uses notes only for occasional reference. Avoid the extremes of (1) reading a speech verbatim, which many listeners consider the ultimate insult, or (2) memorizing a speech, which can make your presentation seem somewhat wooden and artificial.

Ironically, you appear more natural if you refer to notes during a presentation. Such extemporaneous speaking allows you to make last-minute changes in phrasing and emphasis that may improve delivery; it frees you from having to rely on specific phrasing that is memorized or written out word for word.

Depending on your personal preference, you may choose to write speech notes on (1) index cards, (2) a sheet or two of paper, or (3) overhead transparencies or computer-generated slides. Following are the main advantages and disadvantages of each:

1. Notes on Cards (3" × 5" or 4" × 6")

Advantages

- Are easy to carry in a shirt pocket, coat, or purse
- Provide a way to organize points, through ordering of cards
- Can lead to smooth delivery in that each card contains only one or two points that are easy to view
- Can be held in one hand, allowing you to move away from lectern while speaking

Disadvantages

- Keep you from viewing outline of entire speech
- Require that you flip through cards repeatedly in speech
- Can limit use of gestures with hands
- Can cause confusion if they are not in correct order

2. Notes on Sheets of Paper

Advantages

- Help you quickly view outline of entire speech
- Leave your hands free to use gestures
- Are less obvious than note cards, for no flipping is needed

Disadvantages

- Tend to tie you to the lectern, where the sheets lie
- May cause slipups in delivery if you lose your place on page

3. Notes on Computer-Generated Slides or Transparencies

Advantages

- Introduce variety to audience
- Give visual reinforcement to audience
- Can be turned on and off

Disadvantages

- Require you to bring a second set of more complete notes
- May cause you to look at the screen and lose eye contact
- May cause you to read from the screen
- Cannot be altered as easily at last minute
- Must be presented neatly and in parallel style
- Involve the usual risks that relying on machinery always introduces into your presentation

Presentation Guideline 5: Practise, Practise, Practise

Many speakers prepare a well-organized speech but then fail to add the essential ingredient: practice. Constant practice distinguishes superior presentations from mediocre ones. It also helps eliminate the nervousness that most speakers feel at one time or another.

In practising your presentation, make use of four main techniques. They are listed here, from least effective to most effective:

- **Practise before a mirror:** This old-fashioned approach allows you to hear and see yourself in action. The drawback, of course, is that it is difficult to evaluate your own performance while you are speaking. Nevertheless, such run-throughs definitely make you more comfortable with the material.
- **Audiotape your voice:** Most presenters have access to a tape player, so this approach is quite practical. The machine's portability allows you to practise almost anywhere. Although taping a presentation will not improve gestures, it will help you discover and eliminate verbal distractions such as filler words (*uh, um, ya know*).
- **Practise before a live audience:** Groups of your colleagues, friends, or family—simulating a real audience—can provide the kinds of responses that approximate those of a real audience. In setting up this type of practice session, however, make certain that observers understand the criteria for a good presentation and are prepared to give an honest, forthright critique.
- **Videotape your presentation:** This practice technique allows you to see and hear yourself as others do. A careful review of the tape, particularly with another qualified observer, allows you to identify and eliminate problems with posture, eye contact, vocal patterns, and gestures. At first it can be a chilling experience, but soon you will get over the awkwardness of seeing yourself on tape.

Presentation Guideline 6: Speak Vigorously and Deliberately

Vigorously means "with enthusiasm"; *deliberately* means "with care, attention, and appropriate emphasis on words and phrases." The importance of this guideline becomes clear when you think back to how you felt during the last speech you heard. At the very least, you expected the speaker to show interest in the subject and to demonstrate enthusiasm. Good information is not enough. You need to arouse the listeners' interest.

You may wonder, "How much enthusiasm is enough?" The best way to answer this question is to hear or (preferably) watch yourself on tape. Your delivery should incorporate just enough enthusiasm that it sounds and looks a bit unnatural to you. Few if any listeners ever complain about a speech being too enthusiastic or a speaker being too energetic. But many, many people complain about dull speakers who fail to show that they themselves are excited about the topic. Remember that every presentation is, in a sense, "show time."

Presentation Guideline 7: Avoid Filler Words

Avoiding filler words presents a tremendous challenge to most speakers. When thinking about what comes next or encountering a break in the speech, people tend to fill the gap with filler words and phrases such as these:

uh . . .

ya know . . .

okay . . .

well . . . uh . . .

like . . .

I mean . . .

umm . . .

These gap fillers are a bit like spelling errors in written work: once your listeners find a few, they start looking for more and are distracted from your presentation. To eliminate such distractions, follow these three steps:

Step 1:   **Use pauses to your advantage.** Short gaps or pauses inform the listener that you are shifting from one point to another. By signalling a transition, a pause draws attention to the point you make right afterward. Note how listeners look at you when you pause. Do not fill these strategic pauses with filler words.

Step 2:   **Practise with tape.** Tape is brutally honest: when you play it back, you will become instantly aware of fillers that occur more than once or twice. Keep a tally sheet of the fillers you use and their frequency. Your goal will be to reduce this frequency with every practice session.

Step 3:   **Ask for help from others.** After working with tape machines in step 2, give your speech to an individual who has been instructed to stop you after each filler. This technique provides immediate benefits.

Presentation Guideline 8: Use Rhetorical Questions

Showing enthusiasm is, of course, the best technique for capturing your audience's attention. Another technique is to use rhetorical questions at pivotal points in your presentation.

Rhetorical questions are those you ask to get listeners thinking about a topic, not those that you would expect them to answer out loud. Rhetorical questions prod listeners to think about your point; they also set up an expectation that important information will follow. In addition, they break the monotony of standard declarative sentences. For example, following is a rhetorical question an M&K consultant used in proposing a purchase to a client:

> I've discussed the three main advantages that a centralized word-processing centre would provide your office staff. But is this an approach that you can afford at this point in the company's growth?

The speaker followed the question with remarks supporting the position that the system was affordable.

"What if" scenarios are another way to introduce rhetorical questions. They gain listeners' attention by having them envision a situation that might occur. For example, a safety engineer could use this kind of rhetorical question in proposing M&K's asbestos removal services to a regional bank:

> What if you repossessed a building that contained dangerous levels of asbestos? Do you think that your bank would then be liable for removing all the asbestos?

Again, the question pattern heightens listener interest.

Rhetorical questions do not come naturally. You must make a conscious effort to insert them at points when it is most important to gain or redirect the audience's attention. Three particularly effective uses follow:

1. **As a grabber at the beginning of a speech:** "Have you ever wondered how you might improve the productivity of your word-processing staff?"

2. **As a transition between major points:** "We've seen that centralized word processing can improve the speed of report production, but will it require any additions to your staff?"

3. **As an attention-getter right before your conclusion:** "Now that we've examined the features of centralized word processing, what's the next step you should take?"

Presentation Guideline 9: Maintain Eye Contact

Your main goal—always—is to keep listeners interested in what you are saying. This goal requires that you maintain control, using whatever techniques you can to direct the audience's attention. Frequent eye contact is one good strategy.

The simple truth is that listeners pay closer attention to what you are saying when you look at them. Think how you react when a speaker makes constant eye contact with you. If you are like most people, you feel as if the speaker is speaking to you personally—even if there are 100 people in the audience. Also, you tend to feel more obligated to listen when you know that the speaker's eyes will be meeting yours throughout the presentation. Here are some ways you can make eye contact a natural part of your own strategy for effective oral presentations:

- **With audiences of about 30 or fewer:** Make regular eye contact with everyone in the room. Be particularly careful not to ignore members of the audience who are seated to your far right and far left (see Figure 13-1). Many speakers tend to focus on the listeners within Section *B*. Instead, make wide sweeps so that listeners in Sections *A* and *C* get equal attention.

- **With large audiences:** There may be too many people or it may be too large a room for you to make individual eye contact with all listeners. In this case, focus on just a few people in all three sections of the audience noted in Figure 13-1. This approach gives the appearance that you are making eye contact with the entire audience.

- **With any size audience:** Occasionally look away from the audience—either to your notes or toward a part of the room where there are no faces looking back. In this way, you avoid the appearance of staring too intensely at your audience. These breaks also give you the chance to collect your thoughts or check your notes.

Presentation Guideline 10: Use Appropriate Gestures and Posture

Speaking is only one part of giving a speech; another is adopting appropriate posture and using gestures that will reinforce what you are saying. Note that good speakers are much more than "talking heads" before a lectern. Instead, they do the following:

1. Use their hands and fingers to emphasize major points
2. Stand straight, without leaning on or gripping the lectern
3. Avoid remaining behind the lectern, to decrease the distance to the audience
4. Point toward visuals on screens or charts, without losing eye contact with the audience

The audience will judge you by what you say *and* what they see—a fact that again makes videotaping a crucial part of your preparation. By working on this facet of your presentation, you can avoid problems such as keeping your hands constantly in your pockets, rustling change (remove pocket change and keys beforehand), tapping a pencil, scratching nervously, slouching over a lectern, and shifting from foot to foot.

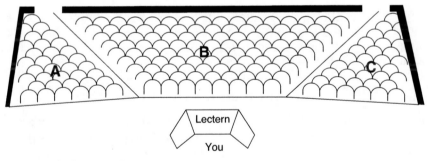

Figure 13-1 Audience sections

PRESENTATION GRAPHICS

More than ever before, listeners expect good graphics during oral presentations. Much like gestures, graphics transform the words of your presentation into true communication with the audience. To emphasize the importance of speech graphics, we present the following incident, which actually happened:

Several years ago the competitors for designing a large city's football stadium had been narrowed down to three firms. Firm A, a large and respected company, had done some preliminary design work on the project and was expected to get the contract. Firm B, another large and respected firm, was competing fiercely for the job. And Firm C, a small and fairly new company, was considered by all concerned to be a genuine long shot. Yet it had submitted an interesting-enough proposal to be chosen as a finalist.

All three firms were invited to make 10- or 15-minute presentations on their proposals. The presentations by Firms A and B were professional, conventional, and predictable. Firm C took a different and riskier approach. Its presentation was barely five minutes long and was given simultaneously with a videotape. As expected, the speech itself stressed the benefits of Firm C's design for the stadium. The accompanying videotape, however, was quite unconventional. It interspersed drawings of Firm C's design with highlights of that city's football team scoring touchdowns, catching passes, and making game-winning tackles.

Firm C's effort to associate the winning football team with its proposed design worked. Shortly after the presentations, the selection committee chose the dark horse, Firm C, to design the new stadium.

The lesson here is not that fancy visuals always win a contract. Rather, the point is that innovative graphics, in concert with a solid proposal presentation, can set you apart from the competition. Firm C had a sound stadium design reinforced by an unusual visual display. Granted, it walked the fine line between effective and manipulative graphics. Yet even the fanciest visuals cannot disguise a bad idea to a discerning audience. The Firm C presenters won because they found an effective way to present their proposal. They incorporated graphics into their presentation to reinforce main selling points.

Guidelines for Presentation Graphics

Graphics Guideline 1: Discover Listener Preferences

Modern audiences expect to see computer-generated graphics displayed by a data projector. On increasingly rare occasions you may be required to use other visuals, such as flip charts and transparencies. It is wise to use these only if your audience has specifically requested them.

Graphics Guideline 2: Think about Graphics Early

Graphics added as an afterthought usually look it. Plan graphics while you prepare the text so that the final presentation will seem fluid. This guideline holds true especially if you rely on specialists to prepare your visuals. These professionals need some lead time to do their best work. Also, they can often provide helpful insights as to how visuals will enhance the presentation—if you consult them early enough and if you make them a part of your presentation team.

The goal is to use graphics that you can be proud of. Never put yourself in the position of having to apologize for the quality of your graphic material. If an illustration is not up to the quality your audience would expect, do not use it.

Graphics Guideline 3: Use Appropriate Visual Support

The visuals you use should be appropriate for (1) the subject of your presentation, (2) the size of the audience, and (3) the characteristics of the room. For example, a presentation that has something to do with computers should include computer-visuals. Do be careful, however, because older audiences tend to react unfavourably to presentations that use multiple media. For example, a presentation that uses slides, video, *and* audio may well be deemed disorganized. Furthermore, when presenting material to an audience of more than 20 people, use projection-sized visuals. As well, the brightness of the room may dictate which kinds of visuals you can use effectively.

Graphics Guideline 4: Make Any Wording Brief and Visible

The best graphics rely on visual images, not words. Avoid cluttering graphics with language. Instead, provide necessary explanations during the presentation. When you do need to add words to a visual—perhaps in a list of major points—pare them down to the bare minimum. Single words or phrases can then be elaborated on in your speech text.

Equally important, be certain that all wording is visible from the back of the room. Nothing is more irritating than a poster, an overhead, or a slide that that audience cannot read. Avoid this problem by asking beforehand about the room size and arrangement; then adjust letter size and thickness accordingly. Incidentally, standard type is too small to use effectively on overhead transparencies. When using overheads, prepare them with oversized type.

Graphics Guideline 5: Use Colours Carefully

Colours can add flair to visuals. Follow these simple guidelines to make colours work for you:

- Have a good reason for using colour (such as the need to highlight three different bars on a graph with three distinct colours).
- Use only dark, easily seen colours, and be sure that the colour contrasts with its background (for example, yellow on white would not work well).
- Use no more than three or four colours in each graphic (to avoid a confused effect).
- For variety, consider using white on a dark or blue–green background.

Graphics Guideline 6: Leave Graphics up Long Enough

Because graphics reinforce text, they should be shown only while you address the particular point at hand. For example, reveal a graph just as you are saying, "As you can see from the graph, the projected revenue reaches a peak in 2002." Then pause and leave the graph up a bit longer for the audience to absorb your point.

How long is too long? A graphic outlives its usefulness when it remains in sight after you have moved on to another topic. Listeners will continue to study it and ignore what you are now saying. If you plan to return to a graphic, take it down after its first use and show it again later.

Graphics Guideline 7: Avoid Handouts

Because timing is so important in your use of speech graphics, handouts are usually a bad idea. Readers move through a handout at their own pace, rather than at the pace the speaker might prefer. Thus handouts cause you to lose your audience's attention. Use handouts, therefore, only if (1) no other visual will do, (2) your listener has requested them, or (3) you distribute them as reference material *after* you have finished talking.

Graphics Guideline 8: Maintain Eye Contact While Using Graphics

Do not stare at your visuals while you speak. Maintain control of the listeners' responses by looking back and forth from the visual to faces in the audience. When pointing to the graphic aid, use the hand closest to it. When you use the other, you force yourself to turn away from the audience.

Graphics Guideline 9: Include All Graphics in Your Practice Sessions

The dry run you make before the actual presentation should include every graphic you plan to use, in its final form. This is a good reason to prepare graphics at the same time as you prepare text, rather than as an afterthought. Running through a final practice without graphics would be much like doing a dress rehearsal for a play without costumes and props—you would be leaving out the parts that require the greatest degree of timing and orchestration. Practising with graphics helps you improve transitions.

Graphics Guideline 10: Use Your Own Equipment

Murphy's Law always seems to apply when you use another person's audiovisual equipment—that is, whatever can go wrong, will. For example, a new bulb burns out, the resolution is inadequate, an extension cord is too short, the screen does not stay down, the data projector won't focus—all these problems, and others, must be anticipated. Even if the equipment works, it often operates differently from the way you are used to. The only sure way to put the odds in your favour is to carry your own equipment and set it up in advance.

However, most of us have to rely on someone else's equipment at least some of the time. Following are a few ways to ward off disaster:

- Find out exactly who will be responsible for providing the equipment, and contact that person in advance.
- Have some easy-to-carry backup supplies with you—an extension cord, another disk with a copy of the show, felt-tip markers, and chalk, for example.
- Bring handout versions of your visuals, as a last resort.

In short, you want to avoid putting yourself in the position of having to apologize. Plan well.

OVERCOMING NERVOUSNESS

The problem of nervousness deserves special mention because it is so common. Virtually everyone who gives speeches feels some degree of nervousness before the event. For the many people who have an absolute dread of presentations, an instinctive "fight or flight" response kicks in. Surveys have determined that most of us rate public speaking at the top of our list of fears—even above sickness and death!

Given this common response, this chapter considers the problem and offers suggestions for overcoming it.

Why Do We Fear Presentations?

Most of us feel comfortable with informal conversations, when we can voice our views to friends and indulge in impromptu exchanges. We are used to this type of casual presenting of our ideas. Formal presentations, however, place us in a more structured, more awkward, and thus more tense environment. Even though we may know the audience is friendly and interested in our success, the formal context triggers nervousness that is sometimes difficult to control.

This nervous response is normal and, to some degree, useful. That adrenaline pumping through your body can generate a degree of enthusiasm that propels the presentation forward and creates a lively performance. Veteran actors say that some nervousness improves their performance; excellent speakers usually say the same.

A Strategy for Staying Calm

Nervousness becomes a problem, however, when it becomes so overwhelming that it affects the quality of the presentation. And because sympathy is the last thing a speaker wants the audience to feel, following are some techniques to combat nervousness.

No Nerves Guideline 1: Know Your Speech

The most obvious suggestion is also the most important one. If you prepare your speech well, your command of the material will help conquer any queasiness you feel, particularly at the beginning of the speech, when nervousness is usually at its peak. Be so sure of the material that your listeners will overlook any initial discomfort you may feel.

No Nerves Guideline 2: Prepare Yourself Physically

Your physical well-being before the speech can have a direct bearing on anxiety. More than ever before, most cultures understand the essential connection between mental and physical well-being. This connection suggests that you should take the following precautions before your presentation:

- **Avoid caffeine or alcohol for at least several hours before you speak.** You do not need the additional jitters brought on by caffeine or the false sense of ease brought on by alcohol.
- **Eat a light, well-balanced meal within a few hours of speaking.** However, do not overdo it—particularly if a meal comes right before your speech. If you are convinced that any eating will increase your anxiety, wait to eat until after speaking.
- **Practise deep-breathing exercises before you speak.** Inhale and exhale slowly, making your body slow down to a pace you can control. If you can control your breathing, you can probably keep the butterflies under control.
- **Exercise normally the same day of the presentation.** A good walk will help invigorate you and reduce nervousness. However, do not wear yourself out by exercising more than you would normally.

No Nerves Guideline 3: Picture Yourself Giving a Great Presentation

Many speakers become nervous because their imaginations are working overtime. They envision the kinds of failure that almost never occur. Instead, speakers should imagine success and confidence. Mentally take yourself through the following steps of the presentation:

- Arriving at the room
- Feeling comfortable at your chair
- Getting encouraging looks from your audience
- Giving an attention-getting introduction
- Presenting your supporting points with clarity and smoothness
- Ending with an effective wrap-up
- Fielding questions with confidence

Sometimes called *imaging*, this technique helps you program success into your thinking and control those negative feelings that haunt even the best speakers.

No Nerves Guideline 4: Arrange the Room as You Want

To control your anxiety, assert some control over the physical environment as well. You need everything going for you if you are to feel at ease. Make sure that chairs are arranged to your satisfaction, that the lectern is positioned to your taste, that the lighting is adequate, and so on. These features of the setting can almost always be adjusted if you make the effort to ask. Again, it is a matter of your asserting control so that your overall confidence is increased.

No Nerves Guideline 5: Have a Glass of Water Nearby

Extreme thirst and a dry throat are physical symptoms of nervousness that can affect delivery. There is nothing to worry about as long as you have water available. Think about this need ahead of time so that you do not have to interrupt your presentation to pour a glass of water.

No Nerves Guideline 6: Engage in Casual Banter before the Speech

If you have the opportunity, chat with members of the audience before the speech. This ice-breaking technique will reduce your nervousness and help start your relationship with the audience.

No Nerves Guideline 7: Remember That You Are the Expert

As a final "psyching-up" exercise before you speak, remind yourself that you have been invited or hired to speak on a topic about which you have useful knowledge. Your listeners are eager to hear what you have to say. So tell yourself, "I'm the expert here!"

No Nerves Guideline 8: Do Not Admit Nervousness to the Audience

No matter how anxious you may feel, never admit it to others. First of all, you do not want listeners to feel sorry for you—that is not an emotion that will lead to a positive critique of your speech. Second, nervousness is almost never apparent to the audience. Even when your heart is pounding, your knees are shaking, and your throat is dry, few if any members of the audience will see these symptoms. Why draw attention to the problem by admitting to it? Third, you can best defeat initial anxiety by simply pushing right on through.

No Nerves Guideline 9: Slow Down

Some speakers who feel nervous tend to speed through their presentations. If you have prepared well and practised the speech on tape, you are not likely to let this happen. Having heard yourself on tape, you will be better able to sense that the pace is too quick. As you speak, constantly remind yourself to maintain an appropriate pace. If you have had this problem before, you might even write "Slow down!" in the margin of your notes.

No Nerves Guideline 10: Join a Speaking Organization

The previous nine guidelines will help reduce your anxiety about a particular speech. To help solve the problem over the long term, however, consider joining an organization like Toastmasters International, which promotes the speaking skills of all its members. Like some other speech organizations, Toastmasters has chapters that meet at many companies and campuses. These meetings provide an excellent, supportive environment in which all members can refine their speaking skills.

EXAMPLE OF M&K ORAL PRESENTATION

This section presents the text and visuals of a short presentation given by Robert Laroche, an environmental expert at M&K's Montreal office. He has been invited to speak at the monthly lunch meeting of an organization of building owners in the Montreal region. The agreed-upon topic is the problem of asbestos contamination.

The members of Robert's audience have an obvious interest in the problem: they own buildings that are at risk. Yet they know little about asbestos except that it is a health issue they must consider when they renovate. Robert's job is to inform them and heighten their awareness. He needs to cover only the highlights, however, because the presentation will be followed by a detailed question-and-answer session. Although some of these owners have been, and will be, clients of M&K, he has an ethical obligation to avoid promoting M&K while making his presentation.

> Good evening. My name is Robert Laroche, and I work on asbestos abatement for M&K. I've been asked to give a short presentation on the problem of asbestos and then to respond to your questions about the importance of removing it from buildings. I'll focus on three main reasons why you, as building owners, should be concerned about the asbestos problem. (SLIDE 1 [see Figure 13-2])
>
> 1. To prevent future health problems of your tenants
> 2. To satisfy regulatory requirements of the government
> 3. To give yourself peace of mind for the future
>
> Again, my comments will provide just an overview, serving as a basis for the question session that follows in a few minutes. (SLIDE 2 [see Figure 13-3])
> *Question:* What is the most important reason you need to be concerned about asbestos? *Answer:* The long-term health of the tenants, workers, and other people in buildings that contain asbestos. Research has clearly linked asbestos with a variety of diseases, including lung cancer, colon cancer, and asbestosis (a debilitating lung

Figure 13-2 Slide 1 for sample presentation

Figure 13-3 Slide 2 for sample presentation

disease). Although this connection was first documented in the 1920s, it has only been taken seriously in the last few decades. Unfortunately, by that time asbestos had already been commonly used in many building materials that are part of many structures today.

Here's a list of some of the most common building products containing asbestos. (SLIDE 3 [see Figure 13-4]) As you can see, asbestos was used in materials as varied as floor tiles, pipe wrap, roof felt, and insulation around heating systems. An abundant and naturally occurring mineral, asbestos was fashioned into construction materials through processes such as packing, weaving, and spraying. Its property of heat resistance, as well as its availability, was the main reason for such widespread use.

While still embedded in material, asbestos causes no real problems. However, when it deteriorates or is damaged, fibres may become airborne. In this state, they can enter the lungs and cause the health problems mentioned a minute ago. This risk prompted Environment Canada in the mid-1970s to ban the use of certain asbestos products in most new construction. But today the decay and renovation of many asbestos-containing building materials may put many of our citizens at risk for years to come. (SLIDE 4 [see Figure 13-5])

After your concern for occupants' health, what's the next best reason to learn more about asbestos? It's the *law*. The law requires that you follow certain procedures when structures you own could endanger tenants and asbestos-removal workers with contamination. For example, when a structure undergoes renovation that will involve any asbestos-containing material (ACM), the ACM must be removed by following approved engineering procedures. Also, the contaminated refuse must be disposed of in approved landfills. Considering the well-documented potential for health problems related to airborne asbestos, this legislative focus on asbestos contamination makes good sense.

By the way, regulations require removal of asbestos by licensed contractors. These contractors, however, will assume liability only for what they have been told to remove. They may or may not have credentials and training in health and safety. Therefore, building owners should hire a firm with a professional who will (1) survey the building and present a professional report on the degree of asbestos contamination and (2) monitor the work of the contractor in removing the asbestos. By taking this approach, you as an owner stand a good chance of eliminating all problems with your asbestos.

Yes, it is *your* asbestos. As owner of a building, you also legally own the asbestos associated with that building—*forever*. For example, if a tenant claims to have been exposed to asbestos because of your abatement activity and then brings a lawsuit, you must have documentation showing that you contracted to have the work performed in a "state-of-the-art" manner. If, as recommended, you have hired a qualified monitoring firm and a reputable contracting firm, liability will be focused on the contractor and the monitoring firm—*not* on you. (SLIDE 5 [see Figure 13-6])

Which brings me to the last reason for concerning yourself with any potential asbestos problem: *peace of mind*. If you examine and then effectively deal with any asbestos contamination that exists in your buildings, you will sleep better at night. For one thing, you will have done your level best to preserve the health of your tenants. For another, as previously noted, you will have shifted any potential liability from you to the professionals you hired to solve the problem—assuming you hired professionals. Your monitoring firm will have continuously documented the contractor's operations and will have provided you with reports to keep in your files, in the event of later questions by lawyers or regulatory agencies.

In just these few minutes, I have given only highlights about asbestos. It poses a considerable challenge for all of us who own buildings or work in the abatement business. Yet the current diagnostic and cleanup methods are sophisticated enough to suggest that this problem, over time, *will* be solved. Now I would be glad to answer questions.

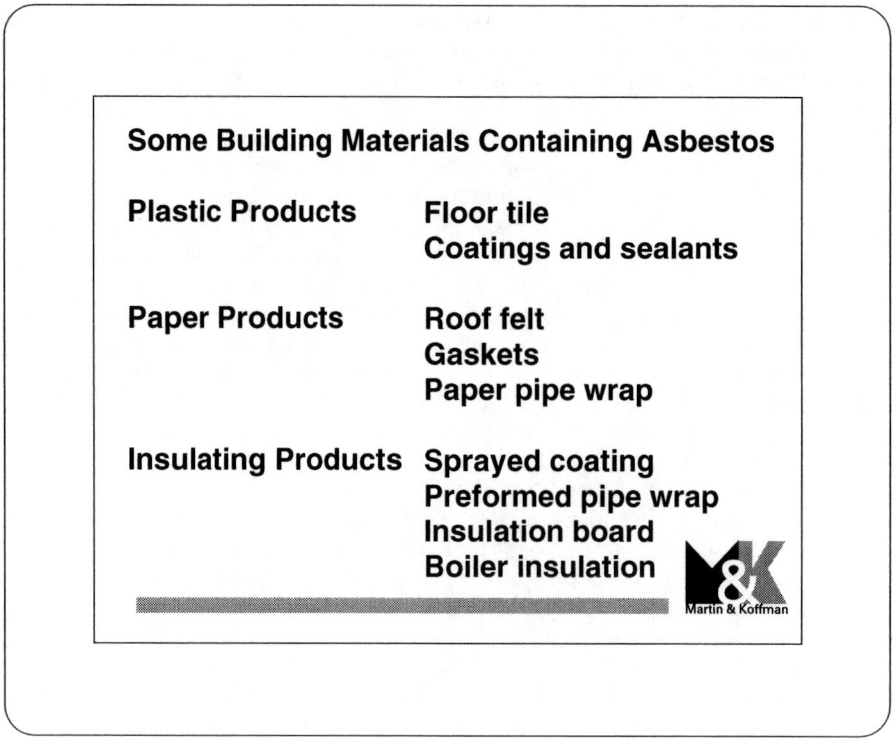

Figure 13-4 Slide 3 for sample presentation

Figure 13-5 Slide 4 for sample presentation

RUNNING EFFECTIVE MEETINGS

Like formal presentations, meetings are a form of spoken communication, which goes hand in hand with written work. Important reports and proposals—and even many routine ones—often are followed or preceded by a meeting. For example, you may meet with your colleagues to prepare a group-written report, with your clients to discuss a proposal, or with your department staff to outline recommendations to appear in a yearly report to management. This section will make you a first-class meeting leader by (1) highlighting some common problems with meetings, along with their associated costs to organizations, and (2) describing 10 guidelines for overcoming these problems.

Common Problems with Meetings

Following are six major complaints about meetings held in all types of organizations:

1. They start and end too late.
2. Their purpose is unclear.
3. Not everyone in the meeting really needs to be there.
4. Conversations get off track.
5. Some people dominate while others do not contribute at all.
6. Meetings end with no sense of accomplishment.

Figure 13-6 Slide 5 for sample presentation

As a result of these frustrations, career professionals waste much of their time in poorly run meetings.

Because they waste participants' time, bad meetings also waste a lot of money. To find out what meetings cost an organization, do the following rough calculation. Use information about an organization for which you work, or for which a friend or family member works.

1. Take the average weekly number of meetings in an office.
2. Multiply that number by the average length of each meeting, in hours.
3. Multiply the result of step 2 by the average number of participants in each meeting.
4. Multiply the result of step 3 by the average hourly salary or billable amount of the participants.

The result, which may surprise you, is the average weekly cost of meetings in the office that you investigated. With these heavy costs in mind, the next section presents some simple guidelines for running good meetings.

Guidelines for Good Meetings

When you choose (or are chosen) to run a meeting, your professional reputation is at stake, as well as the costs just mentioned. Therefore, it is in your own best interests to make sure meetings run well. When you are a meeting participant, you also have an obligation to speak up and help accomplish the meeting's goals.

The guidelines that follow will help create successful meetings. They fall into three main stages:

Stage 1:   Before the meeting (Guidelines 1–4)

Stage 2:   During the meeting (Guidelines 5–9)

Stage 3:   After the meeting (Guideline 10)

These 10 guidelines apply to **working** meetings—that is, those in which participants use their talents to accomplish specific objectives. Such meetings usually involve a lot of conversation. The guidelines do not apply as well to **informational** meetings, where a large number of people are assembled only to listen to announcements.

Meeting Guideline 1: Involve Only Necessary People

Necessary means those people who, because of their position or knowledge, can contribute to the meeting. Your goal should be a small working group—four to six people is ideal. If others need to know what occurs, send them a copy of the minutes after the meeting.

Meeting Guideline 2: Distribute an Agenda before the Meeting

To be good participants, most people need to think before the meeting about the session's objectives. The agenda also gives you, as leader, a way to keep the meeting on schedule. If you are worried about having time to cover the agenda items, consider attaching time limits to each item. That technique helps the meeting leader keep the discussion moving.

Meeting Guideline 3: Distribute Readings before the Meeting

Jealously guard time at a meeting, making sure to use it for productive discussion. If any member has reading materials that committee members should review as a basis for these discussions, such readings should be handed out ahead of time. Do not use meeting time for reading. Even more important, do not refer to handouts that all members have not had the opportunity to go over.

Meeting Guideline 4: Have Only One Meeting Leader

To prevent confusion, one person should always be in charge. The meeting leader should be able to perform the following tasks:

- **Listen carefully** so that all views get a fair hearing
- **Generalize accurately** so that earlier points can be brought back into the discussion when appropriate
- **Give credit to participants** so that they receive reinforcement for their efforts
- **Move toward consensus** so that the meeting does not involve endless discussion

Meeting Guideline 5: Start and End on Time

Nothing deadens a meeting more than a late start, particularly when it is caused by people arriving late. Tardy participants are given no incentive to arrive on time when a meeting leader waits for them. Even worse, prompt members become demoralized by such delays. Latecomers will mend their ways if you make a practice of starting right on time.

It is also important to set an ending time for meetings so that members have a clear view of the time available. Concerning meeting length, most people do their best work in the first hour. After that, productive discussion reaches a point of diminishing returns. If working meetings must last longer than an hour, make sure to build in short breaks and stay on the agenda.

Meeting Guideline 6: Keep Meetings on Track

By far the biggest challenge for a meeting leader is to encourage open discussion while still moving toward resolution of agenda items. As a leader, you need to be assertive, yet tactful, in your efforts to discourage these three main time-wasters:

- Long-winded digressions by the entire committee
- Domination by one or two outspoken participants
- Interruptions from outside the meeting

Meeting Guideline 7: Strive for Consensus

Consensus means agreement by all those present. Your goal should be to orchestrate a meeting so that all members, after a bit of compromise, feel comfortable with a decision. Such a compromise, when it flows from healthy discussion, is far preferable to a decision generated by voting on alternatives. After all, you are trying to reach a conclusion that everyone helped produce, rather than one that only part of the committee embraces.

Meeting Guideline 8: Use Visuals

Graphics help make points more vivid at a meeting. They are especially useful for recording ideas that are being generated rapidly during a discussion. Using a computer to show slides will allow you to add and save information. Flip charts and transparencies can be useful when others are recording ideas.

Meeting Guideline 9: End with a Summary

Before the meeting adjourns, take a few minutes to summarize what items have been discussed and agreed to. This wrap-up gives everyone the opportunity to clarify any points brought up during the meeting. Also, each member will know exactly which actions come next.

Meeting Guideline 10: Distribute Minutes Soon

Write and send out minutes within 48 hours of the meeting. For even routine meetings, it is important that there be a record of the meeting's accomplishments. Also, if any discussion items are particularly controversial, consider having committee members approve minutes with their signature and return them to you, before final distribution.

Employability Skills

The Conference Board of Canada's *Employability Skills 2000+* states that the ability to communicate orally is one of the most important skills that you can bring to your place of work. As well, the ability to contribute effectively to the efforts of a team is critical to your success in the workplace. Relevant communication and teamwork skills include the following:

- Write and speak so others pay attention and understand.
- Listen and ask questions to understand and appreciate the points of view of others.
- Understand and work within the dynamics of a group.
- Ensure that a team's purpose and objectives are clear.
- Accept and provide feedback in a constructive and considerate manner.

- Contribute to a team by sharing information and expertise.*

In one group, prepare a telephone survey for local small businesses. In another, prepare one for medium-sized businesses, and in another prepare one for larger businesses. You can find information about developing questionnaires in Chapter 14.

Each group will attempt to determine how often the businesses they've targeted convey information orally, in both formal and informal settings. Also, each group should ascertain whether the employers have specific expectations for the language and style of speech used in formal and informal presentations.

Orally present the information to your classmates. Remember to use appropriate visual support.

* *Employability Skills 2000+* Brochure 2000 E/F (Ottawa: The Conference Board of Canada, 2000).

CHAPTER SUMMARY

The main theme of this chapter is that anyone can become a good speaker by preparing well, practising often, and giving an energetic performance. This effort pays off richly by helping you deal effectively with employers, customers, and professional colleagues.

Ten guidelines for preparation and delivery will lead to first-class presentations:

1. Know your listeners.
2. Use the preacher's maxim.
3. Stick to a few main points.
4. Put your outline on cards, paper, or overheads.
5. Practise, practise, practise.
6. Speak vigorously and deliberately.
7. Avoid filler words.
8. Use rhetorical questions.
9. Maintain eye contact.
10. Use appropriate gestures and posture.

You should also strive to incorporate illustrations into your speeches by following these 10 guidelines:

1. Discover listener preferences.
2. Think about graphics early.
3. Use appropriate visual support.
4. Make any wording brief and visible.
5. Use colours carefully.
6. Leave graphics up long enough.
7. Avoid handouts.
8. Maintain eye contact while using graphics.
9. Include all graphics in your practice sessions.
10. Use your own equipment.

A major problem for many speakers is fear of giving presentations. You can control this fear by following these guidelines:

1. Know your speech!
2. Prepare yourself physically.
3. Picture yourself giving a great presentation.
4. Arrange the room as you want.
5. Have a glass of water nearby.
6. Engage in casual banter before the speech.
7. Remember that you are the expert.
8. Do not admit nervousness to the audience.
9. Slow down.
10. Join a speaking organization.

Besides conventional presentations, you often will be required to speak in meetings, as either a leader or a participant. Given the effect that poor meetings have on morale and profits, it is important to develop a strategy for running them well. Following are 10 guidelines:

1. Involve only necessary people.
2. Distribute an agenda before the meeting.
3. Distribute readings before the meeting.
4. Have only one meeting leader.

5. Start and end on time.
6. Keep meetings on track.
7. Strive for consensus.
8. Use visuals.
9. End with a summary.
10. Distribute minutes soon.

ASSIGNMENTS

1. **Two- to three-minute presentation based on M&K projects.** Select one of the projects in the Chapter 2 project sheets. Use information from the project and, if you wish, additional details you invent that could relate to the project. For this presentation, assume you are an M&K marketing specialist talking to a group of potential clients in a meeting. They may hire M&K for a similar project and thus want a summary of the job described in the project sheets.

2. **Two- to three-minute presentation based on your academic major.** Give a presentation in which you discuss (a) your major field, (b) reasons for your interest in this major, and (c) specific career paths you may pursue. Assume your audience is a group of students, with as yet undecided majors, who may want to select your major.

3. **Five- to six-minute presentation based on short report.** Select any of the short written assignments in chapters that you have already completed. Prepare a presentation based on the report you have chosen. Assume your main objective is to present the audience with the major highlights of the written report, which they have all read. Use at least one visual aid.

4. **Five- to six-minute presentation based on proposal.** Prepare a presentation based on a proposal assignment at the end of Chapter 12. Assume that your audience wants highlights of your written proposal, which they have read.

5. **Ten- to twelve-minute presentation based on formal report.** Prepare a presentation based on any of the long-report assignments at the end of Chapter 11. Assume your audience has read or skimmed the report. Your main objective is to present highlights, along with some important supporting details. Use at least three visual aids.

6. **Group presentation.** Prepare a group presentation in the group sizes indicated by your instructor. The presentation may be related to a collaborative writing assignment in an earlier chapter, or it may be done as a separate project. Review the Chapter 1 guidelines for group writing. Though related to writing, some of those suggestions apply to any group work.

   Your instructor will set time limits for the entire presentation and perhaps for individual presentations. Make sure your group's members move smoothly from one speech to the next. The individual presentations should work together for a unified effect.

7. **Group presentation: Internet search.** Prepare a group presentation that results from research your group does on the Internet. Your task is to retrieve information about one or more businesses and/or careers in a particular country. Once you have split up the group's initial tasks, conduct some of your business by email. Then present the results of your investigation in a panel presentation to the class. For example, your topic could be the computer software industry in England, the tourist industry in Costa Rica, or the textile industry in Malaysia.

CHAPTER 14

Technical Research

Research does not end with the last college term paper. In fact, your career often will require you to gather technical information from libraries, interviews, questionnaires, the Internet, and other sources. Such on-the-job research will produce documents as diverse as reports, proposals, conference presentations, published papers, newspaper articles, Web sites, or essays in company magazines. Your professional reputation may depend on your ability to locate information, evaluate it, and use it effectively in everyday research tasks.

This chapter takes you through the research process used in college courses and practised on the job. Specifically, the chapter has eight main sections:

- Getting started
- Searching online catalogues
- Searching the library
- Searching the Web
- Using questionnaires and interviews
- Using borrowed information correctly
- Selecting and following a documentation system
- Writing research abstracts

A common thread throughout the chapter is an M&K case study. Tanya Grant, who works in marketing at M&K, is searching for information to complete a project for Jacques Martin, the president of the firm. We'll observe Tanya as she gathers research material.

Like Tanya, later you will have to apply the research process to a specific technical-writing task in college or on the job. It is one thing to read about doing research; it is quite another to dive into your project and work directly with the books, periodicals, electronic databases, Web sites, and other resources in the library and on the Internet. You should seek first-hand research experience as soon as you can.

Finally, remember that the best research writing smoothly merges the writer's ideas with supporting data. Such writing should (1) impress the reader with its clarity and simplicity and (2) avoid sounding like a strung-together series of quotations. These two goals present a challenge in research writing.

GETTING STARTED

In Chapter 1 you learned about the three phases of any writing project: planning, drafting, and revising. Research can occur in the planning stage, right before you complete an outline, but it can also occur again and again throughout the project. Before starting your research, ask yourself questions like the following, to give direction to your work:

- What *questions* must be answered during the research phase?
- What *print, multimedia,* and *electronic sources* would be most useful?
- What is the nature and extent of information that is needed? Should it be scholarly or popular? Current or historical?
- What are the best strategies and research tools for locating information?
- Whom can you talk to who might have expertise on the topic?
- What are the best criteria for critically evaluating information for reliability, validity, accuracy, timeliness, or point of view or bias?
- What *format* must be used to document material borrowed from sources, and what copyright permissions must be acquired to use the information?

Let's take a look at the way Tanya Grant answers these questions during her project.

Tanya has just been given an important task. The company president, Jacques Martin, wants her to examine the feasibility of the company's switching to hybrid electric-powered cars in their urban offices. Success with hybrid electric cars could help address serious air-quality issues and offset escalating petroleum prices. Also, he hopes his firm becomes a major player in refining the technology and fostering its use. In short, this move could serve as a public relations effort, a budgetary control, and a marketing tool for M&K products.

Jacques told Tanya she should write a report investigating the successes and failures of hybrid electric cars. Upper-level management at an upcoming meeting will review the report. She should study the impending tax and other legislation affecting fuel-efficient vehicles. In addition, she should investigate the potential of hybrid vehicles. Some of her report will look at start-up costs for switching the vehicle fleet, employee needs, and other in-house matters. The following outline shows how Tanya would probably answer the questions previously noted, as she begins her research:

1. Main question: Should M&K switch to hybrid electric vehicles?
2. Main types of information needed:

   - What are the advantages and disadvantages of this technology?
   - What is the research saying about the outlook for hybrid electric vehicles?
   - What tax and other legislation is pending at both provincial and federal levels?
   - Who are the current and potential consumers and what do they think about hybrid electric cars?
   - What are the real costs in maintaining a fleet?
   - What could Martin & Koffman gain by the switch? What would they lose?
   - What impact would such a switch have on the competition, potential clients, or employees?

3. Possible sources:

   - Directories (of periodicals, newsletters, newspapers, electronic journals, organizations)
   - Indexes and abstracts to journals, periodicals, newspapers
   - Bibliographies
   - Government documents
   - Books
   - Web sites
   - Actual copies of environmental magazines or Web pages
   - Questionnaires
   - Interviews with some potential readers, such as current clients

4. Format for documentation: Tanya will submit a short report to Jacques Martin, documenting her research using the author-date system of citing borrowed information (the same format used by M&K engineers and scientists in their research reports).

With this basic plan in mind, Tanya can begin her work. Her first decision is where to start her research. Choices include the following:

- The public library
- Her corporate library

- The university library
- The Internet—specifically, the Web

She eliminates the public library and the M&K corporate library—the first is too general and the second is too specialized. The remaining options are the Web and the local university library. Tanya will need to use both to do a thorough job of research. She knows about the university's extensive print collections in science and technology, their Web-based online catalogue, and the electronic databases. In addition, the staff in the reference department and interlibrary loan office will help her identify and track down sources. She also uses the Web regularly for finding business information, news, entertainment, and discussion on just about anything. The Web and the library work amazingly well together—they intersect, overlap, and complement one another, and each contributes unique sources, provided you know the basic research techniques and tools. A good researcher uses both the Web and the library to take advantage of the strengths, and overcome the weaknesses, of each.

Deciding whether to start in the library or on the Internet can depend on personal factors, such as the following:

- Your current knowledge of the topic
- The speed of your Internet connection and computer
- Your experience and skill in using effective search strategies
- Your ability to stay focused
- Your ability to critically evaluate the materials you locate
- Your schedule and the blocks of time you have for research

A planning trip to the library can save you hours of time searching the Web in unfamiliar subject areas. On the other hand, a few hours' preparation online—for example, searching a library's Web-based catalogue—can make your trip to the library more productive.

Tanya schedules two days this week and one next week to work in the library and begins her research from her computer in the office. The next section introduces some of the strategies, tools, and basic concepts you need for searching library online catalogues, searching in the library, and searching on the Web.

SEARCHING ONLINE CATALOGUES

Both the library and the Internet can seem intimidating when you first start a project. Once you learn a few basics, however, you will become comfortable, and even confident about, using these amazing resources. This section includes information on using online library catalogues to locate books, journals, and other resources. We will look at the basics as well as at more advanced techniques that you will need for searching not only library catalogues but also most Web search engines and databases.

Books provide well-supported, tested information about a topic, but, by definition, the information is often dated. Even a book just published has information that is one to two years old, given the time it takes to put a book-length manuscript into print. Keep this limitation in mind as you search.

Most college libraries organize their collections by the Library of Congress (LC) system (see Figure 14-1) or by the Dewey decimal system (see Figure 14-2). The library's catalogue is a road map to its collection of books, periodicals, and other material; it is an alphabetical list by author, title, and subject. These days, the majority of college and university libraries offer sophisticated online catalogues that can be searched at the library or remotely from home or office. The online catalogue, unlike the manual card catalogue, often has additional features such as keyword and *Boolean searching* (outlines the relationship of words and phrases using simple *and*, *or*, *not* statements) and information about whether a book is available or checked out.

The current trend in university and college libraries is to provide access to the library's catalogue through the Internet and usually the Web. Now you can search

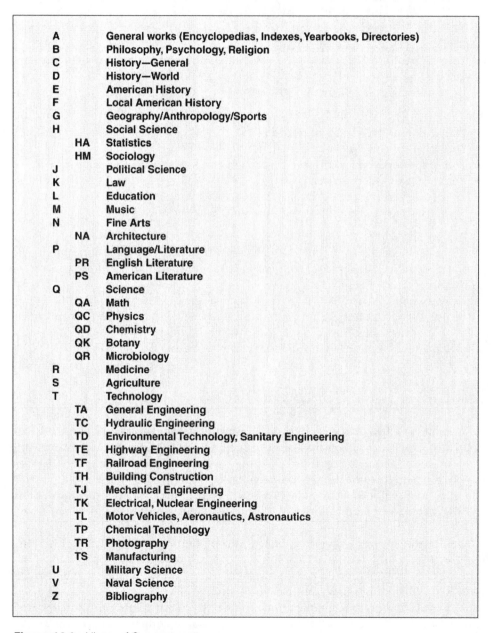

A		General works (Encyclopedias, Indexes, Yearbooks, Directories)
B		Philosophy, Psychology, Religion
C		History—General
D		History—World
E		American History
F		Local American History
G		Geography/Anthropology/Sports
H		Social Science
	HA	Statistics
	HM	Sociology
J		Political Science
K		Law
L		Education
M		Music
N		Fine Arts
	NA	Architecture
P		Language/Literature
	PR	English Literature
	PS	American Literature
Q		Science
	QA	Math
	QC	Physics
	QD	Chemistry
	QK	Botany
	QR	Microbiology
R		Medicine
S		Agriculture
T		Technology
	TA	General Engineering
	TC	Hydraulic Engineering
	TD	Environmental Technology, Sanitary Engineering
	TE	Highway Engineering
	TF	Railroad Engineering
	TH	Building Construction
	TJ	Mechanical Engineering
	TK	Electrical, Nuclear Engineering
	TL	Motor Vehicles, Aeronautics, Astronautics
	TP	Chemical Technology
	TR	Photography
	TS	Manufacturing
U		Military Science
V		Naval Science
Z		Bibliography

Figure 14-1 Library of Congress system

General Breakdown and Sample Subdivisions

000	General Works
100	Philosophy
200	Religion
300	Social Science
400	Language
500	Science
600	Technology
700	The Arts
800	Literature
900	History

510 Mathematics
    511 Arithmetic
    512 Algebra
    513 Geometry
       513.1 Plane Geometry

Figure 14-2 Dewey decimal system

not only your library's catalogue for the best books and periodicals on your topic but also the catalogues of many other libraries around the world. A useful resource is the Canadian National Library's catalogue list. For the Web address, see "Weblinks" on the text enrichment site. Your library's Web site often provides additional helpful information about services and hours, electronic databases, access to other library catalogues, and links to important Web sites. One of the easiest ways to locate the address for your library's Web site is to telephone the library staff and ask.

The rules for searching online catalogues vary depending on the computer program the library uses. The online catalogue's Help screen is the best guide to search techniques. Following are some general strategies for effective searching.

Author or Title Search

If you know specific authors or titles of potentially useful books, conduct an author or title search to locate the call numbers. Study the catalogue entry, especially the subject heading; similar books can be found if you search by subject using these terms.

Subject Search

When you know the subject headings assigned to books or journals on your topic, searching by subject can be very efficient. Libraries select the subject headings from a set of books entitled *The Library of Congress Subject Headings*. Knowing exactly which subject words to use can be a matter of trial and error, but once found, these headings can serve as powerful tools to gather information on your topic.

Keyword Search

This strategy is probably your best choice, for it allows you to scan through all the fields in a book's library record—author field, title, subject headings, dates, notes, publishers, etc.—to locate books that match your request. Searching by keyword permits use of natural language instead of rigid subject headings. Pay close attention to the catalogue's rules for keyword searches; you can often improve your results by limiting searches to particular fields. See Figure 14-3 for a typical keyword search.

Advanced Search Techniques

A library catalogue may also include advanced strategies, such as *Boolean searching,* *positional operators,* and *truncation.* Many times you may not be aware that you are using these tools. Learning to use these techniques is important because they are used in library catalogues, most periodical databases, and Web search engines. Look for the Help screens in your catalogue that describe the advanced search options, and practise using them whenever possible; they can save you time and produce excellent results. Following is a brief description of some of the most common:

- A **Boolean search** outlines the relationship of words and phrases using simple *and, or, not* statements. See Figure 14-4 for examples.
- **Positional operators** stipulate the relative location of each term within the record. For example, you can often specify that terms must be adjacent or within a certain number of words.
- **Truncation** allows for variant spelling or plurals. For example, in some catalogues entering *wom*n* would retrieve records with either the words *woman* or *women.*

Searching other library catalogues can sometimes be as simple as selecting a link from your library's Web site to a library consortium or union catalogue of university and college libraries within your region. Searching libraries close to home has the

Library Catalog - Basic Search Page

For database status and news, see GTEC News

Need help? Check our Search Tips page. Please logout when you are done. [Logout]

For more options, go to our Advanced Search page.

Search Tip: Do not use stop words in a search. Stop words are A, AN, BY, FOR, IN, OF, ON, THE, TO.
To search a title such as *"IBM Journal of Research and Development"* enter "ibm journal research development."

[hybrid electric cars]   [Search Everything ▾]
[Start Search] [Clear Form]

No. of Records to display per page: [20 ▾]

View Search History: [▾]

| about us | architecture library | ask a librarian | contact us | site map | help |

continues

Figure 14-3 Results of a typical keyword search
Source: GIL Across Georgia Union Catalog. Used by permission.

Library Catalog
Search Results for:
S1:
6 Record(s) found. (This page: 1 ~ 6)

Please logout when you are done. [Logout]

[search] [prev. group] [next group]

Results are sorted by Year, newest-oldest.
Want to change sort order?
[Year ▼] [Descending ▼] Sort by in order [Re-Sort]

[Format for printing]

[Select marked records]

1 ☐	**Title:** Forward drive : the race to build "clean" cars for the future / Jim Motavalli. **Author:** Motavalli, Jim. **Call Number:** TL221.15 .M68 2000. **Year:** 2000.	
2 ☐	**Title:** Electric vehicles : socio-economic prospects and technological challenges / edited by Robin Cowan, Staffan Hulten. **Author:** **Call Number:** TL220 .E4485X 2000. **Year:** 2000.	
3 ☐	**Title:** History of the electric automobile : hybrid electric vehicles / Ernest Henry Wakefield. **Author:** Wakefield, Ernest Henry, 1915-. **Call Number:** TL220 .W343 1998. **Year:** 1998.	
4 ☐	**Title:** Evaluation of a Toyota prius hybrid system (THS) [[microform] /] Karl H. Hellman, Maria R. Peralta, Gregory K. Piotrowski. **Author:** Hellman, Karl H. **Call Number:** EP6.2:P93. **Year:** 1998.	
5 ☐	**Title:** The household market for **electric** vehicles : testing the **hybrid** household hypothesis-- reflexively designed survey of new-**car**-buying, multip **Author:** Turrentine, Thomas. **Call Number:** TL220 .T88X 1995. **Year:** 1995.	
6 ☐	**Title:** **Electric and hybrid** vehicles : selected papers through 1980 / prepared under the auspices of the **Electric** Vehicle Committee, Passenger **Car** Act **Author:** **Call Number:** TL220 .E37 1981. **Year:** 1981.	

continues

Figure 14-3 *continued*

Library Catalog
Search Results for:
S2:
Record 3 out of 6

Please logout when you are done. [Logout]

[search] [result list] [prev. group] [next group] [first record] [last record]
[prev. record] [next record]

[Request Document Delivery]

Call Number: **TL220 .W343 1998.**
Main Author: Wakefield, Ernest Henry, 1915-.
Main Title: **History of the electric automobile : hybrid electric vehicles / Ernest Henry Wakefield.**
Pub Info: Warrendale, Pa. : Society of Automotive Engineers, c1998.
Physical Desc: xxii, 332 p. : ill. ; 26 cm.
Notes: Includes bibliographical references and index.
Subject: Automobiles, Electric--History.
Subject: Hybrid electric cars--History.
Record Type: MON.
Language: ENG.
ISSN/ISBN: 0768001250.
Voyager Number: 461227.
OCLC: 38566039.
LCCN: 8003420.

Location and availability:

1) TL220 .W343 1998
Location 1: Currently checked out--to recall, ask at Circulation desk, 1st floor West

---

[search] [result list] [prev. group] [next group] [first record] [last record]
[prev. record] [next record]

Figure 14-3 *continued*

---

advantage of easier access to their collection whether you visit in person or gain access through your library's interlibrary loan service. If you want to see what's out there in larger or more specialized libraries, try searching for library catalogues on the Web or ask the reference librarian if your library provides access to OCLC's WorldCat, a comprehensive database.

Following are two Web directories of library catalogues that have been around for some time. (Keep in mind, however, that the nature of the Web is such that they may have disappeared since this book was written.)

- **Libcat-Metronet:** www.librarysites.info/

    or

- **Libweb: Library Servers:** http://lists.webjunction.org/libweb/

BOOLEAN SEARCHING

AND: Example: periodicals AND directories.
Locates only those records where both terms are present.
Use this to narrow your search and reduce the number of matches.

OR: Example: periodicals OR journals OR zines.
Locates records in which any one of these terms can appear.
Use this to broaden or enlarge your search.

NOT: Example: periodicals NOT magazines.
Eliminates records containing the excluded term.
Use this sparingly to narrow your search.

Figure 14-4 Boolean search examples

When you use the Web for searching catalogues, remember to evaluate what you find as you search. Begin thinking critically as soon as you start, and work to keep this perspective throughout your research. For example, when looking at a reference to a book, a journal, an article, or a Web site, ask yourself the following questions:

- What are the author's academic qualifications?
- Who is the publisher and what is its reputation?
- What are the scope and content of the work?
- What are the trends in information on this topic and how does this book, article, journal, or Web site fit in?
- How current is this information?

Finally, use your library's online catalogue to find out what research databases are available to you. You may be able to search important research databases, such as periodical indexes and abstracts, encyclopedias, dictionaries, directories, and other reference sources (see Figure 14-5). Many of these databases can be searched remotely from your home or office, but some are restricted to in-library searching only. Policies governing who can search, from where, passwords, whether searching is fee-based or free vary widely depending on the contracts between the library and the database vendor. You will learn more about using research databases in the next section, but for now keep in mind that the quality of information you will retrieve from research databases is usually superior to the material you may locate searching the vast Web. In addition, online catalogues may provide links to recommended, high-quality Web sites you might not otherwise locate. Explore your online options and discuss your needs with the reference staff at your library.

Tanya Grant's M&K Project

Tanya Grant, for example, rightly thinks that books will not be her main source of information about hybrid electric cars, since the topic has developed relatively recently. Yet she at least wants to see what range of sources the catalogue offers. Tanya does a keyword search and determines that the correct subject heading is "hybrid electric vehicles." Her own library's holdings are somewhat limited, but one item is worth reviewing. She decides to search the online catalogue from another local university with an automotive engineering school. Here she finds a better selection of books, and, because her library card gives her borrowing privileges at all university system libraries, she decides to take a trip to this library. Her final search is in OCLC's WorldCat; this comprehensive database leads her to a few more noteworthy titles that she will borrow through her library's interlibrary loan department.

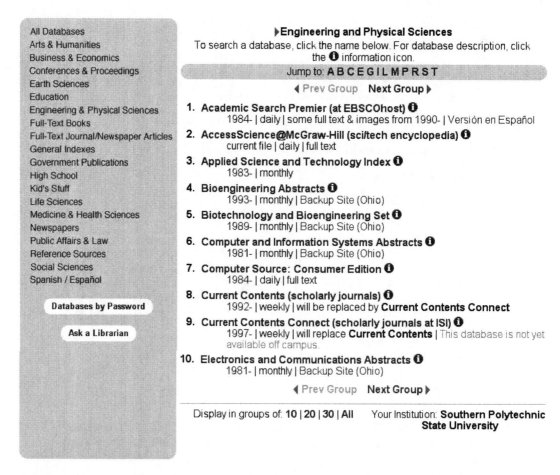

Figure 14-5   Research databases available on one library's Web site
Source: Galileo–Georgia Library Learning Online. Courtesy of the Board of Regents of the University System of Georgia.

SEARCHING THE LIBRARY

At some point during your search for secondary resources, you will need to visit your academic library. The library's services and collections of books, journals, microforms, and reference materials, while complex, will support your research and help you locate information. Fortunately, academic and research libraries are organized along similar principles, and the skills you gain from using one library can generally be transferred to other libraries. This section will highlight some of the services and resources you can expect to find as you conduct your research in the library.

Library Services

The services that your library can provide during the research process are many. The three most important ones are (1) reference and information, (2) interlibrary loan, and (3) circulation.

  1. Reference and information. Discussing your research topic with a reference librarian can be a productive first step. The librarian can recommend reference books; provide instruction on how to search indexes, abstracts, and electronic databases; and guide you to collections, such as government documents, microform sets, and noteworthy Web sites that you may not have found on your own. Make the most of your time with the reference staff by asking specific questions and returning whenever you need more help in locating or using sources.

2. **Interlibrary loan.** In the course of research you will identify excellent sources not owned by your library. Fortunately, in most libraries you can arrange to borrow or photocopy these sources through the interlibrary loan service. Be aware that the lending process can take a number of weeks and may require payment for the service. Interlibrary loan and other document delivery services have become increasingly accepted as the popularity of computer networks and electronic databases grows.

3. **Circulation.** The circulation department is responsible for the lending and returning of library materials. In addition, the department may register library users, provide access to reserve materials, recall checked-out books, renew materials to extend the loan, and search for material not on the shelf. Circulation services are generally highly automated with a growing trend toward self-service checkout.

Library Resources

This section includes information on the following resources: books; periodicals; newspapers; company directories; and dictionaries, encyclopedias, and other general references.

Resource 1: Books

As previously discussed, the library catalogues these days are generally automated, and very few traditional wooden card catalogues remain. Books are arranged in an alphanumeric call number order in the library stacks, generally by Library of Congress number or Dewey decimal number (see Figures 14-1 and 14-2). Once you locate the exact book you are searching for, browse through the books located beside this title. You will likely find other useful and related material. Ask for assistance at the reference desk or circulation desk if you cannot locate the books on your topic.

Resource 2: Periodicals

A periodical is a publication issued at regular intervals. The term encompasses the following:

- Popular magazines that take commercial advertising, such as *Maclean's, Science,* and *National Geographic*
- Professional and scholarly journals such as *IEEE Transactions on Professional Communication*

Most library visitors are familiar with the section that houses current periodicals, either in alphabetical order or by call number. Yet they are less familiar with the part of the library containing back issues. Libraries keep back issues of the periodicals considered most important to its users. They may be in the form of bound volumes, microfilm or microfiche, or full-text electronic versions of periodicals.

Your key to locating information in periodicals is a periodical index or abstract. By looking up your subject in the index, you can find articles that provide the information you need. Some indexes and abstracts, such as *Readers' Guide to Periodical Literature,* deal with popular periodicals, while others, such as the *Engineering Index,* deal with a broad range of technical information. Still others, such as *Mechanical Engineering Abstracts,* focus on periodicals, books, Web sites, and papers in specialized technical fields. The periodicals covered in the index or abstract are listed in the volumes or on the online Information screen, along with the inclusive dates of the issues indexed.

A periodical abstract has the added advantage of providing a brief description of articles so that you can decide whether or not the entire article is worth finding. Abstracts are especially useful when the article being summarized is not available in your library. The abstract can help you decide whether to (1) visit another library, (2) order an article through the interlibrary loan service, or (3) disregard an article altogether.

Most periodical indexes and abstracts are available as electronic databases that can be searched quickly and thoroughly once you know the basics. Your library may subscribe to these sources in a variety of ways—CD-ROMs, locally mounted online files, or, now more commonly, as a Web site linked from the library's online catalogue. Many electronic databases provide extensive abstracts or even full-text copies of articles. Some libraries permit you to search these databases from your home or office, while other libraries, because of licence requirements with the database vendors, permit searching within the library only. Still other libraries provide professional search services where, for a fee, the research staff conducts the search for you.

The rules for searching electronic indexes and abstracts vary widely. Each database has unique features and searching requirements. You must invest time and energy to learn these rules to take full advantage of the information the database offers. Start your search by reading the Help screens and the instructional materials about the database or any support materials that the library provides. You will save yourself time and improve your search results if you understand the basic search strategies and have a grasp of the scope of the database. At a minimum, make sure that you know the rules for printing, emailing, or saving to disk the results of your search before you get too far into your research.

Most of the electronic databases have search strategies similar to what you may have encountered when searching the online catalogue for books. The strategies will likely include subject, keyword searching, Boolean search techniques, positional operators, truncation options, and language and date limiting options. The more you practise, the better your searching will become and the more precise your results will be.

Once you have evaluated and narrowed the list of articles on your topic that you wish to read, your next step is to determine which are owned by the library, which need to be requested through interlibrary loan, and which are owned by other nearby libraries. Libraries are often able to flag their holdings in the online database. Also, database vendors sometimes provide online full-text copies of articles that can be printed immediately or emailed to your home or office. Keep in mind, however, that many excellent periodical articles are not available electronically. Try to avoid the trap of arbitrarily limiting your research only to those periodicals with readily available full text. Be aware that the process of getting copies of the article can be tedious and time-consuming; be sure to reserve sufficient time for this important step.

Hundreds of indexes and abstracts are available. Many libraries provide handouts or guides to their print and electronic databases in their online catalogues. Ask the reference staff to help you locate the indexes and abstracts that are most appropriate for your topic. Following are a few of the well-known indexes and abstracting services available in print and/or computer format:

- *ABI/Inform Global* (business and trade journals)
- *Academic Search Premier*
- *Applied Science and Technology Abstracts* (print title: *Applied Science and Technology Index*)
- *Biological Abstracts*
- *Cambridge Scientific Abstracts*
- *Chemical Abstracts*
- *Computer Abstracts International Database*
- *Current Contents*
- *Engineering Index* (electronic title: *Ei Tech Index or COMPENDEX*)
- *Findex*
- *General Science Abstracts* (print index: *General Science Index*)
- *GPO Monthly Catalog* (index to government documents)
- *Lexis-Nexis Academic*
- *Periodical Abstracts*
- *Psychological Abstracts* (electronic title: *PsycINFO*)
- *Public Affairs Information Service* (electronic title: *PAIS International*)
- *Science Citation Index, Social Sciences Citation Index, Arts & Humanities Citation Index* (online through the *Web of Science*)

Tanya Grant's M&K Project

Tanya decided to consult a few of the electronic databases recommended by the reference librarian.

1. She conducted a search using *Environmental Engineering Abstracts,* which the library subscribed to electronically through *Cambridge Scientific Abstracts.* The abstract's scope and content were exactly what she wanted since they targeted the technological and engineering aspects of hybrid electric vehicles. Because the database was new to her, Tanya spent time learning how to conduct a search and save her results. She limited her search to articles from the past few years. The search not only retrieved useful articles, but also provided links to six high-quality Web sites. Scanning the results, she selected the most promising articles and Web site and emailed a copy to herself and printed a copy of the list to use for locating the periodicals in the library. See Figure 14-6 for Tanya's search.

2. Next she consulted *ABI/Inform Global,* an online database that covers business and management trade journals produced by ProQuest. She was interested in looking at business viewpoints on hybrid vehicles. Her search produced 72 items published since 1999, many of which had full-text copies of the articles available for her to read immediately. After sampling a few articles, she flagged those she wanted and emailed them to herself. Tanya decided to redo her search and narrow it to "peer-reviewed" articles only. The 14 articles she retrieved in her second search have undergone review and evaluation by experts in the field prior to publishing. These articles will be particularly noteworthy. See Figure 14-7 for Tanya's search.

3. Finally, Tanya consulted *Academic Search Premier,* a comprehensive, general-purpose database created by EBSCO, a database company. *Academic Search Premier* covers almost 4,000 periodicals, 2,300 of which are scholarly. Again, Tanya was able to narrow her search to peer-reviewed articles and located some very current and useful information. One of the full-text articles referred to an organization she wanted to investigate further, the Partnership for a New Generation of Vehicles.

Resource 3: Newspapers

If your research topic demands the most current information, newspapers provide an excellent source. One disadvantage of newspapers, however, is that information

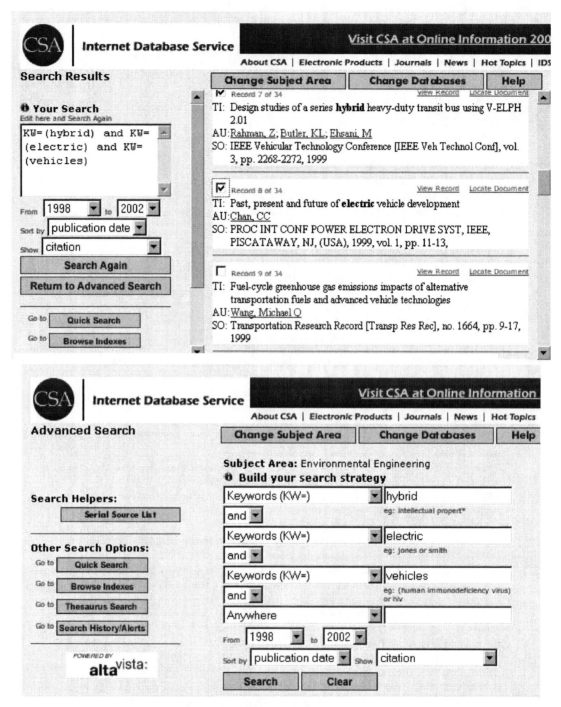

Figure 14-6   Results of a search conducted in CSA through a library's Web site
Source: *Cambridge Scientific Abstracts.* Used by permission.

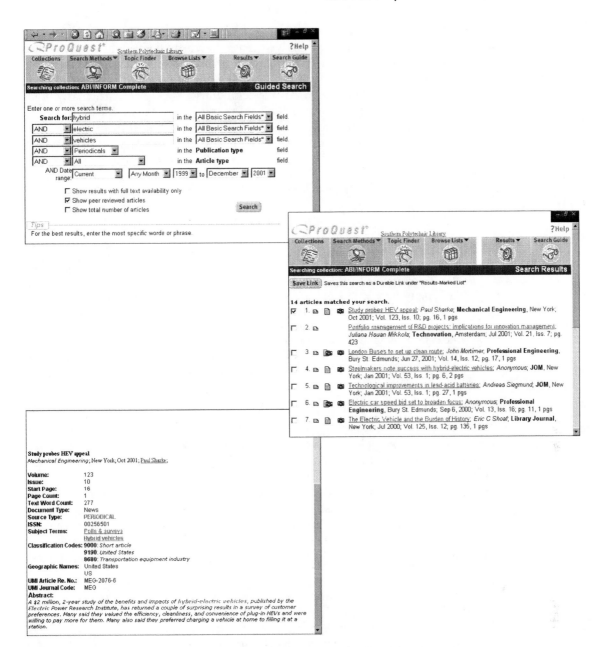

Figure 14-7   Results of a search conducted in *ABI/Inform* database through a library's Web site

Source: Image published with permission of ProQuest Information and Learning Company. Further reproduction is prohibited without permission. Image produced by ProQuest Information and Learning Company. Inquiries may be made to: ProQuest Information and Learning Company, 300 North Zeeb Road, Ann Arbor, MI 48106-1346 USA. Telephone (734) 761-7400; Email: info@il.proquest.com; Web page: www.il.proquest.com.

has not stood the test of time to the same extent as information in journals and books, due to the short-duration analysis necessitated by daily publication and to the lack of in-depth evaluation that would result from analyzing an event in the context of subsequent events. Despite this drawback, newspaper articles can give you insight, facts, and opinion on many contemporary issues. Two particularly noteworthy newspapers are the *Globe and Mail* and the *Wall Street Journal,* well-respected newspapers with a long tradition of high-quality journalism. Both titles are thoroughly indexed from the earliest issues to the present, and many libraries keep microfilm or microfiche back issues for these and other significant national and regional newspapers. Check your library's online catalogue to see if it provides additional links to some of the Web-based news services.

Tanya Grant's M&K Project

Tanya decided to see what kind of newspaper coverage hybrid electric cars were receiving and to uncover some of the tax legislation being proposed by each province. Her first search located hundreds of articles—some written just the previous week. Reading through a few full-text articles convinced her that this would be her best approach to get the consumer perspective she needed. With her second search, Tanya added the concept *tax* and uncovered 14 articles from major newspapers from around the country describing various tax legislation efforts underway. These articles served as a starting point for studying the complex tax legislation being proposed by various provincial legislatures. See Figure 14-8 for Tanya's first search results.

Resource 4: Company Directories

Often your research needs may require that you find detailed information about specific firms. For example, you could be completing research about a company that may hire you, or you may seek information about companies that compete with your own. There are many options these days for finding company information, ranging from traditional printed directories to online and Web-based products. Most companies now produce sophisticated Web sites about their services and products. While not without bias, these can be an excellent source of information. The following is a small sample of some useful directories that are available; ask the reference librarian to recommend others and to assist you in using the online versions of these and other directories:

- *Compact D/SEC* (generally on compact disc or online)
- *Corp Tech Directory of Technology Companies*
- *D & B Million Dollar Directory*
- *Moody's Industrial Manuals* (and other Moody products)
- *Standard & Poor's Register of Corporations, Directors, and Executives*
- *Who's Who in Science and Engineering*

Resource 5: Dictionaries, Encyclopedias, and Other General References

Sometimes you may need some general information to help you get started on a research project. In this case, you may wish to consult specialized dictionaries, handbooks, or encyclopedias. Most general encyclopedias are available in some electronic format, such as CDs or Web-based products. For example, the *Encyclopedia Britannica* is currently available in print, on interactive CD, and online at its own Web site

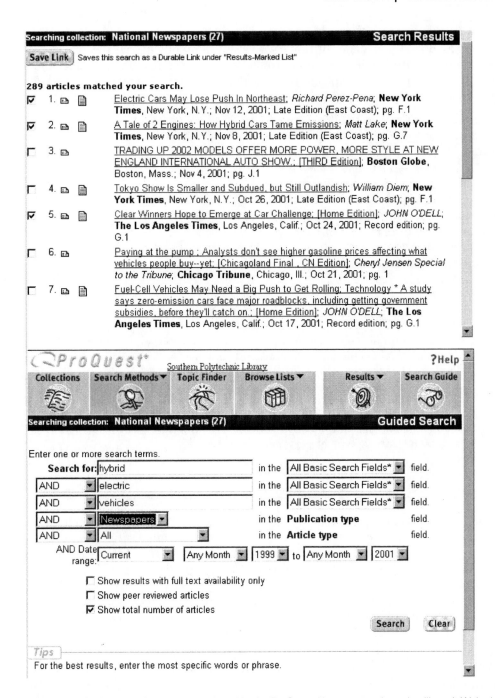

Figure 14-8 Results of a search conducted in the ProQuest Newspapers through a library's Web site
Source: Image published with permission of ProQuest Information and Learning Company. Further reproduction is prohibited without permission. Image produced by ProQuest Information and Learning Company. Inquiries may be made to: ProQuest Information and Learning Company, 300 North Zeeb Road, Ann Arbor, MI 48106-1346 USA. Telephone (734) 761-7400; Email: info@il.proquest.com; Web page: www.il.proquest.com.

(**www.britannica.com**). There are, however, advantages to using a specialized subject-based encyclopedia or dictionary over a general one in that the articles target a more scholarly audience, assume greater subject expertise, and reference more scholarly materials in their bibliographies. Following is a list of a few specialized dictionaries, handbooks, and encyclopedias you may find in the reference collection:

- *Blackwell Encyclopaedia of Management*
- *Cambridge Encyclopaedia of Life Sciences*
- *CRC Handbook of Chemistry and Physics*
- *Dictionary of Business and Economics*
- *Dictionary of the History of Science*
- *Encyclopaedia of Associations*
- *Encyclopaedia of Business Information Sources*
- *Handbook of Industrial Engineering*
- *International Business Information*
- *McGraw-Hill Encyclopaedia of Science and Technology*
- *Van Nostrand's Scientific Encyclopaedia*

Tanya Grant's M&K Project

At this point, Tanya has spent many hours examining the library's online catalogue, searching in online periodical indexes and abstracts, and newspaper indexes. She has located books and articles in scholarly and technical periodicals, as well as articles in popular magazines and newspapers. She requested a few promising items not locally owned through interlibrary loans. In the meantime she has plenty to read and begins creating notes. She has a couple of leads to reliable Web sites from the library's online catalogue and an organization she wants to research. She has a good start, and plenty of work ahead.

SEARCHING THE WEB

Throughout this chapter you have seen references to the Internet and the Web. This vast global computer network has changed the way we communicate, market services and products, and collect and distribute information. The Web is the largest and fastest-growing portion of the Internet with its appealing graphic interface that incorporates text, images, and sound, and its ability to let you move from one Web page to another through hyperlinks. This section will highlight some of the terms and concepts, challenges, and strategies associated with using the Web.

Fundamentals of Web Searching

Mining the Web for useful resources is always challenging and frequently frustrating, but it can yield terrific results. Why is searching such a challenge?

- The Web is huge; it contains tens of millions of documents and is growing at an astounding rate.
- The Web is constantly changing—sites are added, altered, moved, and disappear without warning.
- Search engines and subject directories don't work very well—they retrieve too much, they don't cover the entire Web, the relevancy ranking defies logic, and no two search engines work alike.

- The content of the Web is unregulated; anyone can add anything—fact, fiction, or fiction that looks like fact.
- There is no central index to the Web and few rules for describing Web pages.
- The process of searching, sifting through results, downloading pages, and critically evaluating each Web page is time-consuming.
- The Web is full of distractions that make it difficult to stay focused.

Despite these challenges, the Web offers access to extraordinary resources that often have no print counterpart. Because of the Web's sheer size, a search will usually find something on any topic—possibly something of value or perhaps something useless. Some studies have estimated that scholarly sites represent only 10%–20% of the Web, but this number is still significant. Most people agree that the Web's strength lies in its information on current events, business and industry, popular culture, the government, computing, and technology, but all disciplines are represented in some way. Some resources you can find on the Web include the following:

1. Directories of people, businesses, and organizations
2. Government documents
3. Periodicals, newspapers, and magazines
4. Books
5. Conference proceedings and reports
6. Reference tools, such as guides, indexes to periodicals, dictionaries
7. An increasing number of "by subscription only" information sources
8. Sound and video clips
9. Illustrations
10. Raw data

Using Your Evaluation Skills

When you search the Web, be prepared to invest time and effort in critically evaluating what you find. Unlike books and articles that undergo a rigorous editing and review process, any Web site can be loaded directly onto the Internet. You will encounter misinformation, grossly biased content, and poor text and graphic design. Evaluate Web sources using the criteria discussed earlier in this chapter.

As well, because Web sources do not generally follow standard publishing practices, be prepared to invest your valuable research time determining the authority, timeliness, reliability, accuracy, point of view, and validity of the source. Once you develop a systematic approach to evaluating sources, you will quickly be able to recognize both high- and low-quality Web sources. Be particularly alert to the following:

- **Obscured authorship:** Often a Web designer is credited as the author when in fact an organization or a corporation is the real source.
- **Out-of-date information:** The Web is littered with abandoned and non-maintained Web sites. A high-quality Web site will prominently display the date.
- **Subtle and obvious bias:** Many Web sites are elaborate advertisements promoting products, services, causes, or points of view. Data manipulation, false arguments, and unsubstantiated opinions are common.
- **Poor-quality links:** Links from a high-quality Web site usually lead you to other valuable sites; links from a poor-quality site usually lead you to other poor-quality sites. Spending time examining the links will help you determine the site's quality.

- **Flawed style and design:** Well-organized and accessible Web sites support the research process. While there are many cases of good research in poorly designed sites, be aware that extracting the information from overly complex sites drains away your research time.

Spend time evaluating the source up front before you spend time reading the document. If you cannot determine the scope, authority, or date of the Web site, don't use it.

Learning the Basics

The Web is made up of millions of *Web pages*. A Web site is a collection of Web pages that generally start with a *home page* (the introductory first page) with links to additional pages within the site or to other Web sites. A Web page is uniquely identified by a *URL*, or *Uniform Resource Locator;* this is the key to locating and documenting the Web page. A URL address includes the following elements:

- Letters that indicate the method of access. For Web sites, *http://* indicates that *hypertext transfer protocol* is used.
- The computer's *address* and *domain*. The domain defines the country of origin or the type of computer the document is stored on.
- The directory paths that will lead to the specific page being referenced.

See Figure 14-9 for a list of common domains and examples.

Web browsers, such as Microsoft Internet Explorer and Netscape, are software applications for viewing Web documents and navigating the Web. Both share similar features: a line for entering URLs, options for creating *bookmarks* (or favourite sites), basic navigational features for moving forward and backward and stopping, and options for setting preferences to customize the browser.

com	Commercial organization (for profit)
edu	Educational institution
gov	Government organization (nonmilitary)
int	International nonprofit organizations
mil	Military organization (U.S.)
net	Networking organization
org	Nonprofit organization
ca	Canada (country of origin)
uk	United Kingdom (country of origin)

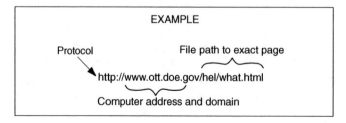

Figure 14-9 Common domains and examples

Web Search Options

Options for searching the Web include the following:

- Searching by URL when you know the specific address
- Searching by keyword in an index-type *search engine* or *meta-search engine*
- Searching by subject category using a *subject directory*
- Using guides to reviewed and recommended Web sites

Figure 14-10 lists some of the most popular search engines. Keep in mind that Web address changes or improved applications may have appeared since this list was created.

Searching by URL: Uniform Resource Locator

Searching by a URL—Uniform Resource Locator—is the most effective strategy, provided you have complete information and the Web page still exists. URLs are regularly included in books, journals, television and radio broadcasts, and marketing and advertising literature. One good URL may lead you to other well-written and maintained Web sites. Take care when recording and entering a URL—the punctuation, special marks, and abbreviations can be complex and lead to frustrating Cannot Locate messages if entered incorrectly.

Searching by Keywords Using Search Engines and Meta-Search Engines

Hundreds of companies on the Web have created massive catalogues or databases of Web sites and provide keyword "search engines." These companies are actually in the business of selling advertising, and the search engines attract potential customers.

The databases are built without human intervention using computer programs called **robots** or **spiders** that move throughout the Web searching for new sites. No single search engine indexes the entire Web, and there is fierce competition among companies for the distinction of having the largest, most current, or most useful database.

AltaVista	www.altavista.com	Keyword
AskJeeves	www.askjeeves.com	Keyword & subject prompting
BUBL Information Service	bubl.ac.uk	Subject guide plus
Dogpile	www.dogpile.com	Meta-search engine
Excite	www.excite.com	Keyword & subject directory
Google	www.google.ca	Keyword results based on links
HotBot	www.hotbot.com	Keyword & subject directory
Internet Public Library	www.ipl.org	Subject guide plus
Lycos	www.lycos.com	Keyword & subject directory
Northern Light	www.northernlight.com	Keyword & subject directory
WebCrawler	www.webcrawler.com	Keyword & subject directory
Yahoo!	www.yahoo.com	Keyword & subject directory

Figure 14-10 Popular search engines and subject guides

The value of a search engine depends on quality, quantity, and currency of the information it retrieves. However, just as important are indexing, speed, basic and advanced search options, and relevancy ranking of the results. The best search engines will provide simple, clear instructions and explain their criteria for building the database and ranking sites. Look for these instructions and pay particular attention to the advanced search features.

Most search engines use a combination of keyword and Boolean searching and often provide options for positional operators and truncation. An identical set of keywords entered into different search engines will produce entirely different information. This inconsistency can be attributed to variations in the search rules, the content, and the characteristics of the database. Experienced searchers recommend using two to four search engines to do a search.

Meta-search engines (or multi-search engines) use the databases of a number of search engines at once to respond to a request. A request is forwarded to a variety of search engines; then the results are collected and displayed. You can save time using a meta-search engine, particularly in narrow, well-defined topics, but you lose the ability to refine searches using the features of individual search engines.

Hundreds of search engines now exist, and a new and better one is always on the way. Second-generation search engines feature **intelligent agents** designed to help refine your question by providing suggestions and alternative lines of inquiry. Other second-generation search engines provide continual updating services using **push technology** that store your search profile, run searches, and report results automatically. Some newer search engines retrieve Web sites based on keywords and the number of links to and from that site.

Keeping up with developments in search engines is a challenge. Periodically search for new ones or ask colleagues to recommend one. Keep trying different ones until you find a few that meet your needs.

Searching with Subject Directories

Searching the Web with a subject directory is similar to browsing in a library; it can be very useful when you are not exactly sure what you are looking for or just want to get a feel for where sources are located. *Yahoo!* is the best-known subject directory. The distinction between a subject directory and a true keyword search engine is disappearing as companies rush to add both features to attract potential customers and advertisers.

The strength of a subject directory lies in how selective it is and how well it classifies Web sites into subject categories. Subject directories are generally compiled by people who review and index sites, although robots are used to retrieve potential additions. Web site authors can also request their sites be added. Subject directories, unlike robot-driven search engines, do not attempt to be comprehensive indexes to the Web. Instead, they try to capture a segment of the Web that appeals to their customers and advertisers. Generally, the goal is to attract customers. Adding the keyword search feature to subject directories has improved access, eliminating endless searching through multiple layers of information.

Using Reviewed and Recommended Subject Guides

Finding reviewed and recommended guides to Web sites is the most efficient route to high-quality information. A list of recommended sources compiled and maintained by an expert could be all you need to do a thorough job of research. Naturally, the reviewer's reliability and authority, the scope and criteria for what is included, and the timeliness of the list determine its value. The best guides will publish a clear statement of their criteria, background information on their reviewers, and a "last updated" statement. Many lists have been compiled by librarians, scholars, and other subject experts associated with professional organizations or government agencies. You may discover your library's online catalogue includes links to such lists. Figure 14-11 shows an example of a guide to recommended Web sites found in an online catalogue.

Tanya Grant's M&K Project

Tanya began her Web search using a URL that one of M&K's engineers had given to her, which led her to a Web site maintained by the U.S. Department of Energy's Office of Transportation Technology. This comprehensive site helped her organize the issues, policies, and research trends, as well as locate articles, reports, and other information sources on the subject. Next, she followed up on a reference to an organization she found mentioned in a journal article. Using *Google's* advanced search feature, she entered the organization's name as a phrase and located the Web site immediately. It was here that she located a number of useful Canadian and international documents. She spent three to four hours reviewing the sites and following up the links.

Tanya spent half an hour searching for a guide to recommended and reviewed Web sites on the topic. First she checked the library's online catalogue subject guide to the Web. While she did find a few useful guides on more general topics, she did not find anything specific. She next checked *BUBL Information Service* and *Internet Public Library* for prepared guides; neither one had anything on target. Finally, she

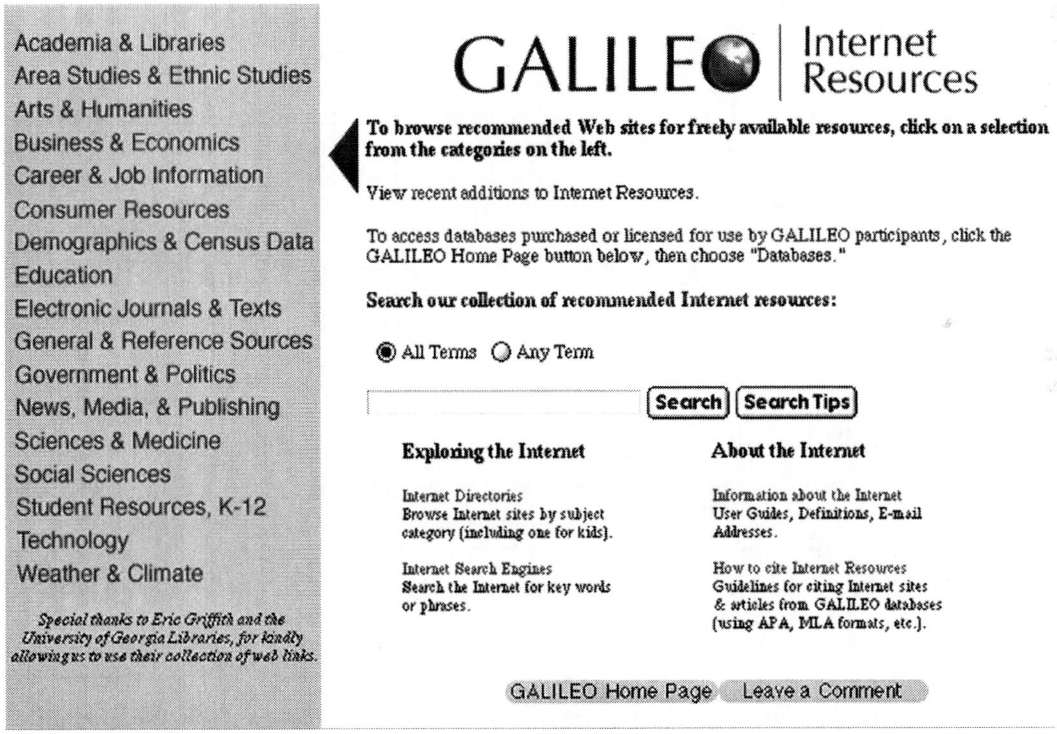

Figure 14-11   Recommended Web sites found in one library's online catalogue
Source: Galileo–Georgia Library Learning Online. Courtesy of the Board of Regents of the University System of Georgia.

tried *AskJeeves* and had better results. From there she was guided to the Web sites of a number of government agencies, private companies, and universities conducting hybrid vehicle studies. She came across a Web site for a local research centre at a nearby university. She bookmarked the page and made a note to contact the centre later that day.

Tanya needed current and specific information on hybrid vehicles and tax incentives. This narrow search worked well using the advanced search features of *Google, Excite,* and, particularly, *HotBot,* which allowed multiple domain limits, such as *.gov, .edu,* and *.org.* Just to double-check, Tanya tried *Dogpile,* a meta-search engine; the results were mixed and she found she was spending too much time trying to evaluate sources. Ultimately, since she needed to be confident she had located the most accurate and current information, Tanya returned to her library's online catalogues for a guide to government documents on the Web and was referred to the Canadian government portal at **www.canada.gc.ca**. Her search here was uncluttered and produced information that she could confidently use.

Tanya's final search used the popular subject directory *Yahoo!* After a few false starts using the subject tree, she used the keyword feature to locate appropriate sites. Although she found a few new sites, most of them were familiar. This was a sure sign that she had completed her Web research and should move on.

USING QUESTIONNAIRES AND INTERVIEWS

Sometimes, your research project may require that you collect first-hand information yourself, using research tools such as questionnaires or personal interviews. In this section, you will learn how to (1) prepare, send out, and report the results of a questionnaire, and (2) prepare, conduct, and summarize a personal interview.

Tanya Grant's M&K Project

You will recall that Tanya Grant, who works in marketing at Martin & Koffman, has been asked by the company president to write a report that examines the successes and failures of hybrid electric cars. This report will look at start-up costs for switching the vehicle fleet, tax and other incentives, and the technology's potential.

Now, before reporting her findings to Jacques Martin, Tanya wants to find out what corporate users of the technology think of its potential. She believes her best approach would be to (1) send a questionnaire to companies that have hybrid vehicle fleets and (2) personally interview three or four respondents who will help management decide on the company's direction.

Questionnaires

Tanya Grant faces the same challenges you would in developing a questionnaire. Like you, she receives many questionnaires herself—most of which she tosses in the recycle bin because (1) they don't warrant her time, (2) are too long, or (3) seem confusing. Now that the shoe is on the other foot, however, she wants to design a questionnaire that attracts readers' attention and entices them to complete it. To accomplish this feat, Tanya goes through the following three-stage process:

Step 1: Preparing the Questionnaire

Obviously, your questionnaire is useful only if readers complete and return it. You must focus as much on your readers' needs as you do on your own objectives.

Before readers complete a form, they must perceive that (1) it benefits them personally or professionally and (2) it is easy to fill out and return. Keep these two points in mind as you design the form and the cover letter. Following are some specific guidelines for preparing a reader-focused document:

1. **Write a precise purpose statement.** As in other documents, a one-sentence statement of purpose can also provide a good lead-in for the cover letter that will accompany your survey (see "Step 2: Conducting the Project"). For example, Tanya Grant has prepared the following purpose statement for her survey concerning hybrid electric vehicles: "The purpose of this survey is to find out ways in which your experience with hybrid cars can benefit others." As obvious as that statement sounds, it will help busy readers who don't have time to wade through long rationales.

2. **Limit the number of questions.** Every question must draw out information that relates to your purpose statement. For example, Tanya Grant knows her questions must focus on the readers' experiences with hybrid electric vehicles. She must resist the temptation to clutter the questionnaire with irrelevant questions on other alternative fuel vehicles, such as natural gas or electric cars.

3. **Ask mostly objective questions.** You need to design your form so that (1) questions are easy to answer and (2) responses are easy to compile. Although open-ended questions yield more detailed information, the answers take time to write and are difficult to analyze. Instead, your goal is breadth, not depth, of response. With the exception of one or two open-ended questions at the end of your questionnaire, reserve long-answer responses for personal interviews you conduct with a select audience. For example, Tanya Grant has decided to include an optional open-ended question at the end of her questionnaire: she will ask hybrid users to recommend design improvements for hybrid electric vehicles.

   Objective questions come in several forms. Following are four common types, along with examples of each.

   - *Either/or questions:* Such questions give the reader a choice between two options, such as *yes* or *no.* They are useful only when your questions present clear, obvious choices. Example: "Do you believe your hybrid vehicles accelerate well in all driving situations?" (followed by Yes and No blocks), or "The hybrid accelerates well in all driving situations" (followed by Yes and No blocks).
   - *Multiple-choice questions:* These questions expand the range of possibilities for the reader to three or more, thereby requiring a longer response time. Example: "If you answered 'yes' to the preceding question [a question asking if the hybrid vehicle accelerates well], what is your typical driving terrain: (a) flat, (b) hilly, (c) combination of flat and hilly, (d) mountainous?"
   - *Graded-scale questions:* By permitting degrees of response, these questions help gauge the relative strength of the reader's opinion. Example: "Use of hybrid vehicles has met our day-to-day driving needs: (a) strongly agree, (b) agree, (c) disagree, (d) strongly disagree, or (e) have no opinion."
   - *Short-answer questions:* Use these questions when the possible short answers are too numerous to list on your form. Example: "List the makes of vehicles that your company has purchased in the past five years."

4. **Provide clear questions that are easy to answer.** Like other forms of technical writing, questionnaires can frustrate readers when questions are unclear. Four

common problems are (1) bias in phrasing, (2) undefined terms, (3) more than one variable, and (4) questions that require too much homework. Following are some examples of right and wrong ways to phrase questions, along with a brief comment on each problem:

- Biased question:
  Original question: "Are the federal and provincial governments' excessive tax credits for purchasing alternative fuelled vehicles affecting your purchasing decision?" (Words like *excessive* reflect a bias in the question, pushing a point of view and thus skewing the response.)
  Revised question: "Do you believe that the federal and provincial tax credits affected your purchasing decision?"

- Undefined technical terms:
  Original question: "Are you familiar with the work of the PNGV on AFVs?" (Your reader may not know that PNGV is short for Partnership for a New Generation of Vehicles or that AFV stands for "alternative fuel vehicles." Thus some "no" answers may be generated by confusion about terminology.)
  Revised question: "Are you familiar with the work of the Partnership for a New Generation of Vehicles on alternative fuel vehicles?"

- Mixed variables:
  Original question: "Were the dealer's maintenance technicians prompt and thorough in their work?" (There are two questions here: one deals with promptness and the other with thoroughness.)
  Revised question (two separate questions): "Were the dealer's maintenance technicians prompt?" "Were the dealer's maintenance technicians thorough?"

- Question that requires too much homework:
  Original question: "What other alternative fuel vehicles has your company researched, tested, or purchased in the past 10 years?" (This question asks readers to conduct research for an accurate answer. If they do not have the time for that research, they may leave the answer blank or provide an inaccurate guess. In either case, you are not getting valid information.)
  Revised question: "Has your company tried other alternative fuel vehicles?"

5. **Include precise and concise instructions at the top of the form.** Your instructions can be in the form of an easy-to-read list of points that start with action verbs, such as the following list:

- Answer Questions 1–20 by checking the correct box.
- Answer Questions 21–30 by completing the sentences in the blanks provided.
- Return the completed form in the envelope provided by October 15, 2006.

Or, if instructions are brief, they can be written as a short, action-centred paragraph, like this: "After completing this form, please return it in the enclosed stamped envelope by October 15, 2006."

6. **Apply principles of document design.** Although you must strive for economy of space when designing a questionnaire, use adequate white space and other design principles to make the document attractive to the eye.

7. **Test the questionnaire on a sample audience.** Some sort of "user test" is a must for every questionnaire. For example, after completing her survey, Tanya decided to test it on three people:

- A fellow marketing colleague at M&K, who has conducted several questionnaires for the firm
- A psychologist Tanya knows through a local professional association
- A vehicle fleet manager whom she knows well enough to ask for constructive criticism

Thus, Tanya's user test will solicit views from people with three quite different perspectives.

Step 2: Conducting the Project

When you have designed a good form, the next task is to distribute it. Following are guidelines for selecting a good sampling of potential respondents, introducing the questionnaire to your audience, and encouraging a quick response from a high percentage of readers.

1. **Choose an appropriate audience.** Selecting your audience depends on the purpose of your questionnaire. If you manage a 100-employee engineering firm and want to gauge customer satisfaction with recent construction jobs, you might send your questionnaire to all 156 clients you have served in the past two years. Restricting the mailing list would be unnecessary because you have a small sample.

   However, if you are in Tanya Grant's position at M&K, with a mailing list totalling about 3,200 corporations that have purchased hybrid vehicles in 2003 and 2004, you will need to select a random sample. Tanya's research suggests that she will receive about a 25% rate of return on her questionnaires. (Actually, this rate would be quite good for an anonymous questionnaire.) Given that she wants about 200 returned forms, she must send out about 800 questionnaires in expectation of the 25% return rate.

   With a client list of 3,200, she simply selects every fourth name from the alphabetized list to achieve a random list of 800 names. Note that the selection of client names from an alphabetized list preserves what is essential—that is, the process's random nature.

   Of course, you can create more sophisticated sampling techniques if necessary. For example, let's assume Tanya wants an equal sampling of companies that purchased in each of the two years—2003 (with 1,200 names) and 2004 (with 2,000 names). In other words, she wants to send an equal number of forms to each year's hybrid owners, even though the number of corporate hybrid owners varies from year to year. In this case, first she would select 400 names—or every third name—from the 1,200 alphabetized names for 2003. Then she would select the other 400 names—or every fifth name—from the 2,000 alphabetized names for 2004. As a result, she has done all she can do to equalize the return rate for two years.

   This strategy will help you choose the audience for simple questionnaire projects. You may want to consult a specialist in statistics if you face a sophisticated problem in developing an appropriate sampling.

2. **Introduce the questionnaire with a clear, concise cover letter.** In 15 or 20 seconds, your letter of transmittal must persuade readers that the question-

naire is worth their time. Toward this end, the cover letter should include three main sections (which correspond to the letter pattern presented in Chapter 9):

- *Opening paragraph:* Here you precisely state the questionnaire's purpose and perhaps indicate why this reader was selected.
- *Middle paragraph(s):* Here you state the project's importance. Strive to emphasize ways that the project might benefit the reader.
- *Concluding paragraph:* Specify when the questionnaire should be returned, even though this information will be included in the directions on the questionnaire itself.

3. Encourage a quick response. If your questionnaire is not anonymous, you may need to offer an incentive for respondents to submit the form by the due date. For example, you can offer to send them a report of survey results, a complimentary pamphlet or article related to their field, or even something more obviously commercial, when appropriate. Clearly, any incentive must be fitting for the context. Keep in mind also that some experts believe an incentive of any kind introduces a bias to the sample.

If the questionnaire is anonymous or if complimentary gifts are inappropriate or impractical, then you must encourage a quick response simply by making the form as easy as possible to complete. Clear instructions, frequent use of white space, a limited number of questions, and other design features mentioned earlier must be your selling points.

Step 3: Reporting the Results

After you tabulate results of the survey, you must return to the needs of your original audience—the people who asked you to complete the questionnaire. They expect you to report the results of your work. Described next are the major features of such a report.

First, you want to show your audience that you did a competent job of preparing, distributing, and collecting the questionnaire. Thus, the body of your report should give details about your procedures. Appendices may include a sample form, a list of respondents, your schedule, extensive tabulated data, and other supporting information.

Second, you want to reveal the results of the survey. Here is where you need to be especially careful. You should present only those conclusions that flow clearly from data. Choose a tone that is more one of suggesting than declaring. In this way, you give readers the chance to draw their own conclusions and to feel more involved in final decision making. Graphs are an especially useful way to present statistical information (see Chapter 5, "Graphics").

Finally, remember that your report and the completed questionnaires may remain on file for later reference by employees who know nothing about your project. Be sure that your document is self-contained. Later readers who uncover your project should be able to understand its procedures and significance from the report you have written.

Interviews

Interviews are another common way to gather primary research. Often they are conducted after a questionnaire has been completed, as a follow-up activity with selected respondents. Interviews also may be used as primary research independent of questionnaires. In either case, you need to follow some common guidelines to achieve success in the interview. Following are a few basic pointers for preparing, conducting, and recording the results of your interviews:

Step 1: Preparing for the Interview

You should put at least as much effort into planning the interview as you do into conducting it. Good planning will put you at ease and show interviewees that you value their time. Specifically, follow these guidelines:

1. **Develop a list of specific objectives for the interview.** Know exactly what you want to accomplish so that you can convey this significance to the person you interview.

2. **Make clear your main objectives when you make contact for the interview.** This conversation should (1) stress the uniqueness of the person's contribution, (2) put him or her at ease with your goals and the general content of the proposed discussion, and (3) set a starting time and approximate length for the interview. If handled well, this preliminary conversation will serve as a prelude to the interview, giving it direction.

3. **Prepare an interview outline.** People you interview understand your need for written reference during the interview. Indeed, they will expect it of any well-prepared interviewer. A written outline should include (1) a sequential list of topics and subtopics you want to cover and (2) specific questions you plan to ask.

4. **Show that you value your interviewee's time.** You can do this first by showing up a few minutes early so that the interview can begin on time. You also show this courtesy by staying on track and ending on time. Never go beyond your promised time limit unless it is absolutely clear that the person being interviewed wants to extend the conversation longer than planned.

Step 2: Conducting the Interview

Your interview will be successful if you stay in control of it. Maintaining control has little to do with force of personality, so don't worry if you are not an especially assertive person. Instead, keep control by sticking to your outline and not letting time get away from you. If you find your speakers straying from the topic, for example, gently bring them back to the point with another question from your list. Following are additional pointers for conducting the interview:

1. **Ask mostly "open" questions.** Open questions require your respondent to say something other than "yes," "no," or other short answers. They are useful to the speaker because they offer an opportunity to clarify an opinion or a fact. They are useful to you because you get the chance to listen to the speaker, to digest information, and to prepare for the next question.

    For example, M&K's Tanya Grant may ask questions like the following: "Could you describe two or three ways in which your expectations for hybrid vehicles have been met?" or "For what purposes is your company currently using its fleet of hybrid vehicles?" or "I've been told that your company has a high commitment to environmental issues in the Calgary area. How has purchasing and using hybrid vehicles been part of that commitment?"

2. **Ask closed questions when you need to nail down an answer.** For example, Tanya Grant may ask people she interviews, "Would you be willing to meet with our fleet supervisor to discuss your experience with maintaining hybrid vehicles?" A "yes" or "perhaps" answer will give her an opening for calling this person several months later. A closed question works when commitment is needed.

3. **Use summaries throughout the interview.** Brief and frequent summaries serve as important resting points during the conversation. They give you the chance to make sure you understand the answers that have been given. They give your counterpart the chance to amplify or correct previous comments. For example, Tanya Grant may comment to her speaker, "So, in other words, you are saying that hybrid vehicles make most sense right now for in-city driving where only one or two people share the vehicle." This summary will elicit either a "yes" or a clarification, either of which will help Tanya record the interview accurately.

Step 3: Recording the Results

Throughout the interview you will have taken notes. The actual mechanics of this process may influence the accuracy of your note taking. Following are three possible approaches:

Option 1: **Number reference:** Using this approach, you will begin the interview with a list of numbered questions on your outline page. Then when you are taking notes, simply list the number of the question, followed by your notes. This approach gives you as much space as you want to write questions, but it does require that you move back and forth between your numbered question list and note page.

Option 2: **Combined question-and-answer page:** Here you place a major question or two on each page, leaving the rest of the page to record answers to these and related questions that may be discussed. While this strategy requires considerably more paper and separates your prepared list of questions, it does help you focus quickly on each specific question and answer.

Option 3: **Split page:** Some interviewers prefer to split each page lengthwise, writing questions in the left column and corresponding answers in the right column. Some questions may have been prepared ahead of time, as in Option 2. Others may be written as they are asked. In either case, you have a clear visual break between questions on one side and answers on the other. The advantage over Option 2 is that you have a visual map that shows you your progress during the conversation. Questions and answers are woven together into the fabric of your interview.

USING BORROWED INFORMATION CORRECTLY

Most errors in research papers occur in accurately transferring borrowed information to your report, paper, or other document. This section has two goals: (1) to explain why you must acknowledge sources you have used and (2) to outline a research process, from the point at which you identify possible sources of information to the point at which you have written the first draft.

Avoiding Plagiarism

One basic rule underlies the mechanical steps described in the rest of this chapter:

> With the exception of "common knowledge," you should cite sources for *all* borrowed information used in your final document—including quotations, paraphrases, and summaries.

"Common knowledge" is information generally available from basic sources in the field. In the case of Tanya Grant's research project, common knowledge would be a definition of hybrid electric vehicles. When you are uncertain whether or not a piece of borrowed information is common knowledge, go ahead and cite the source. It is better to err on the side of excessive documentation than to leave out a citation and risk a charge of *plagiarism* (the intentional or unintentional use of others' ideas as your own). Following are three main reasons for documenting sources thoroughly and accurately:

1. **Ethics:** You have an *ethical* obligation to show your reader where your ideas stop and those of another person begin. Otherwise you would be passing off the ideas of others as your own.
2. **Law:** You have a *legal* obligation to acknowledge information borrowed from a copyrighted source. In fact, you should seek written permission for the use of borrowed information that is copyrighted when you plan to publish your document or when you are using your document to bring in profit to your firm (as in a proposal or report). If you need more specific information about copyright laws or about the legalities of documentation, see a research librarian.
3. **Courtesy:** You owe readers the *courtesy* of citing sources where they can seek additional information on the subject. Presumably, sources for quotations, paraphrases, and summaries would provide such a reference point.

Certainly some plagiarism occurs when unscrupulous writers intentionally copy the writing of others without acknowledging sources. However, most plagiarism results from sloppy work during the research and writing process. Described here are two common types of unintentional plagiarism. Though the errors are unintentional—that is, the writer did not intend to "cheat"—both result in the inappropriate use of another person's work—and that constitutes plagiarism.

Mike Pierson, a supervisor at M&K, has been asked to deliver a presentation at an upcoming conference on hybrid electric vehicles. In his last-minute rush to complete the presentation—which will be published in a collection of papers from the meeting—Mike is taking notes from a source in the company library. He hurriedly writes a note on a note card but fails to indicate the source. Later, when he is writing the paper draft, he finds the card and does not know whether it contains information that was borrowed from a source or ideas that came to him during the research process. If he incorporates the passage into his paper without a source, he will have committed plagiarism.

In our second case, Mike transfers a direct quotation from a source onto a note card. He remembers to place source data on the card, but he forgets to include quotation marks. If later he were to incorporate the quotation into his presentation, with the source citation but without quotation marks, he would be plagiarizing. Why? Because he would be passing the exact words of another writer as his own paraphrase. The passage would give the appearance of being in his own words but supported by the ideas of another, when in fact the passage would be a direct quote. Again, remember that the test for plagiarism is not one's intent—it is the result.

The next section shows you how to avoid plagiarism by completing the research process carefully. In particular, this section focuses on a methodical process that involves (1) bibliography cards, (2) a rough outline, (3) note cards of three main kinds, (4) a final outline, and (5) drafts.

Following the Research Process

Like most other technical tasks, if you carefully attend to the following five-step procedure, you can avoid problems at the end of the research process.

Step 1: Write Complete Bibliography Cards

You should write a complete bibliography card for each source that may help you later. You can do this either by using 3'' × 5'' index cards, or electronically by building a database. Called a *working bibliography*, this batch of cards becomes the foundation for the rest of your research. (Figure 14-12 shows a bibliography card that Tanya Grant might have collected in her research on hybrid vehicles.)

Errors made at this stage—in transferring information from sources to your cards—can easily work their way into a final document. In writing your cards, therefore, be sure to take the following precautions:

1. **Include all information needed for the final-copy citation in your paper.** Use the exact wording for titles and publication information. Common errors are to leave off articles (*a, an, the*) and to abbreviate words in titles, with the writer thinking there will be time later to double-check the original source. In fact, that final check often does not occur, leading to errors in the final citation. Also, for Internet sources you must include the names of online databases, the exact citation for Uniform Resource Locators (URLs), and the date the Internet source was consulted.

GALILEO
Academic Search Premier

Henry E. and C. McGrath (2000).
    Coast to coast on four fill-ups. Kiplinger's
Personal Finance Magazine, 548 (August), 160.

Mentions the Insight Cult and "fudoexia nervosa"

Figure 14-12 Sample bibliography card

2. **Save space at the bottom of the card for a reminder to yourself about the source's usefulness.** For example, a notation such as "includes excellent chapter on water resources" may help you later as you begin your research. While they are mainly to record source information, bibliography cards can also provide some guidance in the next stage of note taking.

3. **Include information in the exact format in which it will appear in your final bibliography, down to the indenting, punctuation, and capitalization.** Tanya Grant's card in Figure 14-12, for example, follows the capitalization guidelines for the APA system. Again, do not assume that you will have time later to transcribe every card into another format. That time will not be there. Also, using the same format ensures that you will make sure to take down all information needed later for the source page.

Step 2: Develop a Rough Outline

This outline is not the one you will use to write the first draft. Instead, it is essentially a list of topics in the approximate sequence in which they will be covered in the paper. It serves to direct your note-card writing during the next step.

Step 3: Take Careful Notes on Large Note Cards

Most plagiarism results from sloppy note taking. This important stage requires that you attend to detail and follow a rigorous procedure. The procedure suggested here divides note cards into three types: summary, paraphrase, and quotation. Figure 14-13 gives examples of all three types.

- **Summary cards** are written in your words and reduce a good deal of borrowed information to a few sentences. They are best written by reading a section of source material, looking away from the source, and summarizing the passage in your own words. In this way, you can later use any of this information with confidence in your paper, without worrying about the absence of quotation marks. Of course, a summary card may contain a few quoted passages, but the card's main purpose is to reduce considerable source material to a short summary.
- **Paraphrase cards** include a close rephrasing of material from your sources. Unlike summary cards, which condense a considerable amount of information, paraphrase cards usually include more of the original text. Thus they demand even more attention than summary cards to the problem of plagiarism. Like summary cards, they are best written by looking away from the source for a moment and then rewriting the passage in your own words. You can use a few keywords from the passage, but do not duplicate exact phrasing or sentence structure. Using the "look away" technique will help you avoid creating a paraphrase that too closely resembles the original.
- **Quotation cards** include only words taken directly from the source. Your main concern should be the care with which you transfer sentences from source to card—with absolute accuracy. Even include grammatical or spelling errors that the original source may contain (and, in so doing, use the word *sic*—see the Handbook at the end of this book). Also, as shown in Figure 14-13, you should use ellipses (spaced dots) when you leave out words that you deem unnecessary. When using ellipses, however, be sure not to alter the meaning of the passage you are quoting.

SUMMARY CARD   Henry + McGrath

The Insight has modest power but can't carry much weight.

PARAPHRASE CARD   Henry + McGrath

The Insight won't win any races, but it will get you safely on the freeway. Its load weight (165.56 kg) is poor, however. Honda says that it wouldn't damage the car to overload it, but that performance and mileage would suffer.

QUOTATION CARD   Henry + McGrath

"Although the car [Insight] will never lead the pack at Indy, you won't fear for your life getting on the freeway . . . But note this: The Insight's 165.56 kg payload capacity means a couple of hefty passengers can overload [sic] the car. Honda says that wouldn't damage the vehicle but would impede performance and mileage."

Figure 14-13   Sample note cards on same passage

Step 4: Organize Research in an Outline

With note cards in hand, you are now ready to render order from chaos—to create an outline that flows from the technical research related in your note cards. (See outline suggestions in Chapter 1.) Key your note cards to the outline by placing one or both of these items at the top of the card: (1) the wording of the related topic, as it appears on the outline, or (2) the letter and/or number that exists on the outline for the related topic. Then place your cards in the order that you will use them in writing your first draft.

Step 5: Write the Draft from the Outline and the Cards

This step poses the greatest challenge. Here you must incorporate borrowed information with your own ideas to create fluid prose. Your goal should be to demonstrate (1) a smooth transition between your ideas and those you have borrowed and (2) absolute clarity about when borrowed ideas and quotations start and end.

SELECTING AND FOLLOWING A DOCUMENTATION SYSTEM

Documentation refers to the mechanical system you use to cite sources from which you borrow information. This section briefly compares documentation styles from three important style manuals—APA, MLA, and CBE—and provides examples for the most common citations. For complete details about a particular documentation system, consult one of the manuals in the list that follows or consult the Web site of the organization that publishes the manual. Pay special attention to new guidelines these manuals may provide for documenting information from online databases and the Internet.

Varieties of Documentation

There are almost as many systems as there are professional organizations. Yet all have the same goal—to show readers the sources from which you gathered information. One of your early steps in research is to determine which style manual you will use. In school, often your instructors will select a discipline-specific style manual. Style manuals guide the writer through the editorial rules governing everything from headers and pagination, graphic and text layout, to data display, and, of course, documentation of sources. Be sure to check the edition of the style manual you are using to make sure it is the latest available: style manuals are regularly revised by the organizations that publish them, in large part to keep pace with the rapid evolution of electronic resources.

Following are just a few documentation manuals commonly used in business, industry, and the professions. You will find useful tips and examples at the Web sites that each of these organizations maintains as well as information on how to purchase the style manual.

American Psychological Association (APA)

Publication Manual of the American Psychological Association. 5th ed. 2001. Web site: **www. apastyle.org**

Also useful from APA:

Electronic Reference Formats Recommended by the American Psychological Association. Web site: **www.apastyle.org/elecref.html**

Council of Biology Editors (CBE)

Scientific Style and Format: The CBE Manual for Authors, Editors, and Publishers. 6th ed. 1994. The much-anticipated 7th edition will soon be published by the Council of Science Editors. Check the following for updates: **www.councilscienceeditors. org/publications/style.cfm**

Modern Language Association (MLA)

MLA Handbook for Writers of Research Papers. 6th ed. 2003. Web site: **www.mla. org/style**

University of Chicago Press

Chicago Manual of Style. 15th ed. 2003. Web site: **www.chicagomanualofstyle.org/ tools.html**

University of Wisconsin's Writing Center

Writer's Handbook Web site: **www.wisc.edu/writing/Handbook**

You can find helpful hints about other documentation manuals by searching the Web by the name of the documentation style. In addition, many libraries, writing centres, and universities have posted reliable and useful sample style sheets. Remember—you must carefully evaluate the quality, currency, and authorship of the Web site before using it.

Figure 14-14 compares APA, MLA, and CBE documentation styles for citing works. The three systems share some common characteristics. Each uses parenthetical references in the body of the report that lead the reader to a separate works-cited or reference page. Each system cites the author's name and either the publication year (APA and CBE) or, if using MLA, the relevant page number where the fact, quote, or observation can be located. Frequently, the content of the parenthetical references is blended into the text with perhaps only the date or page in parentheses. The works-cited or reference page is arranged alphabetically by the author's last name for APA, MLA, and CBE.

CBE offers a second style choice, where each parenthetical reference in the body of the report is numbered. Each number corresponds to a numbered reference on a separate reference or works-cited page arranged numerically (see third page of Figure 14-14). When using CBE, you must determine which system is preferred—the name-year system or the citation-sequence system. Check with your instructor or editor.

See Model 14–1 at the end of this chapter for Tanya Grant's complete memo report that cites research.

APA Parenthetical References and Works-Cited Examples

The American Psychological Association (APA) uses the parenthetical author and year system within the text, which leads the reader to an alphabetically arranged works-cited page at the end of the text. Anonymous works are cited using the first few title words and year.

Parenthetical Reference	Entry in Works-Cited List
1.1 **Book, one author** (Wakefield, 1998)	Wakefield, E. (1998). *History of the electric automobile: Hybrid electric vehicles.* Warrendale, PA: Society of Automotive Engineers.
1.2 **Book, two or more authors** (Hodkinson & Fenton, 2001)	Hodkinson, R., & Fenton, J. (2001). *Lightweight electric/hybrid vehicle design.* Woburn, MA: Butterworth-Heinemann.
1.3 **Edited book** (Johnson, 1993)	Johnson, A.E. (Ed.). (1993). *Future of vehicle transportation.* London: Sage.
1.4 **Work in an anthology** (Seal, 1993)	Seal, M. (1993). Feasibility studies of solar electric hybrids. In A. Johnson (Ed.), *Future of Vehicle Transportation* (pp. 321–332). London: Sage.
1.5 **Encyclopedia article (unsigned)** ("Alternative," 2003)	Alternative automobiles. (2003). In K. Kramer (Ed.), *Encyclopedia of automotive history.* (3rd ed. Vol. 2, pp. 235–239). New York: Harper.
1.6 **Newspaper article** (Kiley & Healey, 2004)	Kiley, D., & Healey, J.R. (2004, May 14). Hybrid SUV getting big response Ford says 30,000 want to buy one. *USA Today,* p. A1.
1.7 **Magazine article** (Wouk, 1997)	Wouk, V. (1997, October). Hybrid electric vehicles. *Scientific American, 277,* 70–74.
1.8 **Journal article** (Kim, Jung, & Nam, 2004)	Kim, J., Jung, J., & Nam, K. (2004). Dual-inverter control strategy for high-speed operation of EV induction motors. *IEEE Transactions on Industrial Electronics, 51*(2), 312–321.
1.9 **Article from an electronic database** (Einstein, 1999)	Einstein, P. (1999). The benefits of Insight. *Professional Engineering, 12*(19), 23. Retrieved August 3, 2001, from Academic Search Premier database at EBSCOhost.
1.10 **WWW site (no author)** ("Toyota Prius," 2001)	Toyota Prius. (2001). *Cartalk.com.* Retrieved August 19, 2001, from http://cartalk.cars.com/Info/Testdrive/Reviews/toyota-prius-2001.html

continues

Figure 14–14 Sample list of references

MLA Parenthetical References and Works-Cited Examples

The Modern Language Association (MLA) uses an author and page reference system. The author and specific page number where the fact, quote, or reference can be located are referenced in the text, either in parentheses or as part of the text. The works-cited page is arranged alphabetically by author. Titles may be underlined or italicized with title words generally capitalized.

Parenthetical Reference	**Entry in Works-Cited List**
1.1 **Book, one author** (Wakefield 125)	Wakefield, Earl. *History of the Electric Automobile: Hybrid Electric Vehicles.* Warrendale, PA: Society of Automotive Engineers, 1998.
1.2 **Book, two or more authors** Hodkinson and Fenton in their 2001 book (311)	Hodkinson, Richard, and John Fenton. *Lightweight Electric/Hybrid Vehicle Design.* Woburn, MA: Butterworth-Heinemann, 2001.
1.3 **Edited book** Johnson argues (225)	Johnson, Arthur, ed. *Future of Vehicle Transportation.* London: Sage, 1993.
1.4 **Work in an anthology** (Seal 321)	Seal, Martin. "Feasibility Studies of Solar Electric Hybrids." *Future of Vehicle Transportation.* Ed. Arthur Johnson. London: Sage, 1993. 321–32.
1.5 **Encyclopedia article (lesser-known encyclopedia)** (Murray 325)	Murray, Kim L. "Alternative Automobiles." *Encyclopedia of Automotive History.* Ed. K. Kramer. 3rd ed. 2 vols. New York: Harper, 2003.
1.6 **Newspaper article** (Kiley and Healey 1A)	Kiley, Dan, and John Healey. "Hybrid SUV Getting Big Response Ford Says 30,000 Want to Buy One." *USA Today* 14 May 2004:A1.
1.7 **Magazine article** (Wouk 71)	Wouk, V. "Hybrid Electric Vehicles." *Scientific American* Oct. 1997: 70–74.
1.8 **Journal article** (Kim and Nam 314–15)	Kim, J., J. Jung, and K. Nam. "Dual-inverter Control Strategy for High-Speed Operation of EV Induction Motors." *IEEE Transactions on Industrial Electronics* 51 (2004): 312–21.
1.9 **Article from an electronic database** (Einstein)	Einstein, Paul. "The Benefits of Insight." *Professional Engineering.* 12.19 (1999): 23. *Academic Search Premier* EBSCOhost. GALILEO. 3 Aug. 2001 <http://www.galileo.usg.edu>.
1.10 **WWW site (no author)** ("Toyota Prius")	"Toyota Prius." *Cartalk.com.* 2001. 19 Aug. 2001 <http://cartalk.cars.com/Info/Testdrive/Reviews/toyota-prius-2001.html>.

continues

Figure 14–14 *continued*

CBE References and Works-Cited Examples

The *CBE Manual for Authors, Editors, and Publishers* (6th edition), prepared by the Council of Biology Editors Style Manual Committee, offers a choice in parenthetical systems—the name-year or the citation-sequence system. You need to decide early on which CBE system to use. Ask the instructor or the editor. Each system is demonstrated here. The much-anticipated 7th edition refines the method for citing electronic sources.

CBE's Citation-Sequence System

Parenthetical Reference	**Entry in Works-Cited List**
1.1 **Book, one author** As Wakefield[1] claims	1. Wakefield E. History of the electric automobile: hybrid electric vehicles. Warrendale, PA: Society of Automotive Engineers; 1998. 223p.
1.2 **Book, two or more authors** Hodkinson and Fenton[2]	2. Hodkinson R, Fenton J. Lightweight electric/hybrid vehicle design. Woburn, MA: Butterworth-Heinemann; 2001. 253p.
1.3 **Edited book** As described by Johnson[3]	3. Johnson AE, editor. Future of vehicle transportation. London: Sage; 1993. 345p.
1.4 **Work in an anthology** Early experiments demonstrated[4]	4. Seal M. Feasibility studies of solar electric hybrids. In Johnson A, editor. Future of vehicle transportation 1993. London: Sage; p 321–332.
1.5 **Encyclopedia article (unsigned)** Alternatives[5]	5. Alternative automobiles. Encyclopedia of automotive history. 3rd ed. 2 volumes. New York: Harper, 2003, 2: 235–239.
1.6 **Newspaper article** Kiley and Healey[6]	6. Kiley D, Healey JR. Hybrid SUV getting big response Ford says 30,000 want to buy one. USA Today 2004, May 14; Sect A; 1.
1.7 **Magazine article** Wouk[7]	7. Wouk V. Hybrid electric vehicles. Scientific American 1997 October, 277, (4): 70–74.
1.8 **Journal article** The breakthrough in the power system[8]	8. Kim J, Jung J, Nam, K. Dual-inverter control strategy for high-speed operation of EV induction motors. IEEE Transactions on Industrial Electronics 2004; 51: 312–321.

1.9 **Article from an electronic database**

The following example reflects the anticipated changes in the 7th edition for citing electronic resources.

Einstein[9]	9. Einstein P. The benefits of Insight. Professional Engineering. 1999 12 (19): 23. Available from Academic Search Premier EBSCOhost. (Accession No.: 2479269).

1.10 **WWW site (no author)**

The following example reflects the anticipated changes in the 7th edition for citing electronic resources.

The performance of the Toyota Prius[10]	10. Toyota Prius. Cartalk.com <http://cartalk.cars.com/Info/Testdrive/Reviews/toyota-prius-2001.html>. Accessed 2001 Aug 19.

continues

Figure 14–14   *continued*

CBE's Name-Year System

Parenthetical Reference	Entry in Works-Cited List
1.1 **Book, one author** As demonstrated by Wakefield (1998)	Wakefield E. 1998. *History of the electric automobile: Hybrid electric vehicles.* Warrendale, PA: Society of Automotive Engineers. 223p.
1.2 **Book, two or more authors** (Hodkinson and Fenton 2001)	Hodkinson R, Fenton J. 2001. *Lightweight electric/hybrid vehicle design.* Woburn, MA: Butterworth-Heinemann. 253.p
1.3 **Edited book** (Johnson 1993)	Johnson AE, editor. 1993. *Future of vehicle transportation.* London: Sage. 345p.
1.4 **Work in an anthology** Seal argues (1993)	Seal M. 1993. Feasibility studies of solar electric hybrids. In Johnson, A, editor, *Future of vehicle transportation.* London: Sage. p. 321–332.
1.5 **Encyclopedia article (unsigned)** HEV are defined as (Alternative 2003)	Alternative automobiles. (2003) In Kramer K, editor *Encyclopedia of automotive history.* 3rd ed. New York: Harper; p. 235–239.
1.6 **Newspaper** (Kiley and Healey 2004)	Kiley D, Healey JR. 2004, May 14. Hybrid SUV getting big response Ford says 30,000 want to buy one. *USA Today* A1.
1.7 **Magazine article** (Wouk 1997)	Wouk V. 1997. Hybrid electric vehicles. *Scientific American* 277(4): 70–74.
1.8 **Journal article** (Kim and others 2004)	Kim J, Jung J, Nam, K. 2004. Dual-inverter control strategy for high-speed operation of EV induction motors. IEEE *Transactions on Industrial Electronics* 51: 312–321.

1.9 **Article from an electronic database**
The following example reflects the anticipated changes in the 7th edition for citing electronic resources.
(Einstein 1999)

> Einstein P. 1999. The benefits of Insight. *Professional Engineering.* 12(19): 23. Available from: Academic Search Premier EBSCOhost (Accession No.: 2479269).

1.10 **WWW site (no author)**
The following example reflects the anticipated changes in the 7th edition for citing electronic resources.
(Toyota Prius, 2001)

> Toyota Prius, 2001. Cartalk.com. Available from: http://cartalk.cars.com/Info/Testdrive/Reviews/toyota-prius-2001.html. Accessed 2001 Aug 19.

Figure 14–14   *continued*

Online Documentation

Because information found in online sources is also borrowed, it deserves the same level of care in documentation as print sources. After all, borrowed information is borrowed information, whatever the source.

However, documenting electronic sources presents some special problems, and the rules are not completely settled. Most important and perhaps most obvious, you do not have the assurance with online information—as you do with print sources—that material will stay the same each time it is used. Thus documentation format must include information that clearly notes the date of access and the exact location. Generally, your entry should include the same kind of data used for print sources, with the addition of the following information:

- The name of the database or information service provider you consulted to locate the article, newspaper, electronic source, etc.

- The URL address of the database, information service provider, or specific electronic source
- The date you used the online source

If the electronic source you are citing is also available in print, you must provide a reference to the print format. Take care to present URL addresses completely and accurately. When you must break the address, do so at a logical point.

See Model 14-1 at the end of this chapter for Tanya Grant's complete memo report that cites research.

WRITING RESEARCH ABSTRACTS

The term **abstract** has been used throughout this book to describe the summary component of any technical document. As the first part of the ABC format, it gives decision makers the most important information they need. However, here we use *abstract* for a narrower purpose. It is a stand-alone summary that provides readers with a capsule version of a piece of research, such as an article or a book. This section (1) describes the two main types of research abstracts, with examples of each, and (2) gives five guidelines for writing research abstracts.

Types of Abstracts

There are two types of abstracts: informational and descriptive. As the following definitions indicate, informational abstracts include more detail than descriptive abstracts.

Informational Abstract

- **Format:** This type of abstract includes the major points from the original document.
- **Purpose:** Given their level of detail, informational abstracts give readers enough information to grasp the main findings, conclusions, and recommendations of the original document.
- **Length:** Though longer than descriptive abstracts, informational abstracts are still best kept to one to three paragraphs.
- **Example:** A sentence from such an abstract might read, "The article notes that functional résumés should include a career objective, academic experience, and a list of the applicant's skills." (See corresponding example in definition of a descriptive abstract.)

Descriptive Abstract

- **Format:** This type of abstract gives only main topics of the document, without supplying supporting details such as findings, conclusions, or recommendations.
- **Purpose:** Given their lack of detail, descriptive abstracts can only help readers decide whether they want to read the original document.
- **Length:** Their lack of detail usually ensures that descriptive abstracts are no longer than one paragraph.
- **Example:** A sentence from such an abstract might read, "The article lists the main parts of the functional résumé." (See corresponding example in definition of an informational abstract.)

You may wonder when you'll need to write abstracts during your career. First, your boss may ask you to summarize some research, perhaps because he or she lacks your technical background. Second, you may want to collect abstracts as part of your own research project. In either case, you need to write abstracts that accurately reflect the tone and content of the original document.

Assume, for example, that your M&K supervisor has asked you to read some current research on strategies for negotiating. Later your boss plans to use your abstracts to get an overview of the field and to decide which, if any, of the original full-length documents he or she should read in full. The examples that follow show both informational and descriptive abstracts of the section of Chapter 15 that covers negotiating. Note that the informational abstract actually lists the guidelines contained in the chapter, whereas the descriptive abstract notes only that the article includes the guidelines.

Informational Abstract: "Guidelines for Negotiating"

This article suggests that modern negotiations should replace "I win, you lose" thinking with a "we can both win" attitude. To achieve this change, these six main guidelines are prescribed: (1) think long-term, (2) explore many options, (3) find the shared interests, (4) listen carefully, (5) be patient, and (6) do look back. Although this strategy applies to all types of negotiation, this article focuses on a business context. It includes an extended example that involves establishing an appropriate entry salary for a job applicant in computer systems engineering.

Descriptive Abstract: "Guidelines for Negotiating"

This article describes six main guidelines that apply to all types of negotiations. The emphasis is on strategies to be used in the context of business. All the suggestions in the article support the need for a "we both win" attitude in negotiating, rather than an "I win, you lose" approach.

Guidelines for Writing Research Abstracts

The guidelines given here will help you (1) locate the important information in a document written by you or someone else and (2) present it with clarity and precision in an abstract. In every case, you must present a capsule version of the document in language the reader can understand. The ultimate goal is to save the reader time.

Abstracting Guideline 1: Highlight the Main Points

This guideline applies whether you are abstracting a document written by you or someone else. To extract information that will be used in your abstract, follow these steps:

- Find a purpose statement in the first few paragraphs.
- Skim the entire piece quickly, getting a sense of its organization.
- Read the piece more carefully, underlining main points and placing comments in margins.
- Pay special attention to information gained from headings, first sentences of paragraphs, listings, graphics, and beginning and ending sections.

Abstracting Guideline 2: Sketch Out an Outline

From the notes and marginal comments gathered in Guideline 1, write a brief outline that contains the piece's main points. If you are dealing with a well-organized piece of writing, it will be an easy task. If you are not, it will be a challenge. Following is an outline for the negotiation section of Chapter 15, as abstracted in the previous examples:

Purpose: to provide rules that help readers adopt a "we both win" strategy

I. Think long-term.
    A. Focus on building mutual trust.
    B. Project the long-term attitude into every part of the negotiation process.

II. Explore many options.
    A. Get away from thinking there are only two choices.
    B. Put diverse options on the table early in the negotiation.

III. Find the shared interests.
    A. Stress points of agreement, rather than conflict.
    B. Use mutual concerns to defuse contentious issues.

IV. Listen carefully.
    A. Ask questions and listen, rather than talk.
    B. Use probing questions to move discussion along in salary discussion.
        1. Break out of attack/counterattack cycle.
        2. Uncover motivations.
        3. Expose careless logic and unsupported demands.
        4. Move both sides closer to objective standards.

V. Be patient.
    A. Avoid the mistakes that come from hasty decisions.
    B. Avoid the bad feeling that results when people feel pressured.

VI. Do look back.
    A. Keep a journal in which you reflect on your negotiations.
    B. Analyze the degree to which you followed the previous five guidelines.

Abstracting Guideline 3: Begin with a Short Purpose Statement

Both descriptive and informational abstracts should start with a concise overview sentence. This sentence acquaints the reader with the document's main purpose. Stylistically, it should include an action verb and a clear subject. Following are three options that can be adapted to any abstract:

- The article "Recycle Now!" states that Ontario must intensify its effort to recycle all types of waste.
- In "Recycle Now!" Laurie Hellman claims that Ontario must intensify its effort to recycle all types of waste.
- According to "Recycle Now!" Ontario residents must intensify their efforts to recycle all types of waste.

Abstracting Guideline 4: Maintain a Fluid Style

One potential hazard of the abstracting process is that you may produce disjointed, awkward paragraphs. You can reduce the possibility of this stylistic flaw by following these steps:

- Write in complete sentences, without deleting articles (*a, an, the*).
- Use transitional words and phrases between sentences.
- Follow the natural logic and flow of the original document itself.

Abstracting Guideline 5: Avoid Technical Terms Readers May Not Know

Another potential hazard is that the abstract writer, in pursuit of brevity, will use terms unfamiliar to the abstract's readers. This flaw is especially bothersome to readers who do not have access to the original document. As a general rule, use no technical terms that may be unclear to your intended audience. If a term or two are needed, provide brief definitions in the abstract itself.

Note, also, that abstracts that might become separated from the original document should include a bibliographical citation.

Employability Skills

The Conference Board of Canada's *Employability Skills 2000+* states that part of your value as an employee depends on the personal values that you bring to the job. Relevant personal management skills include the following:

- Deal with people, problems, and situations with honesty, integrity and personal ethics.*

Prepare a short bulletin for first-year students explaining how the proper use of researched materials from print, public media, and the Web is a demonstration of personal honesty, integrity, and personal ethics. Remember not to focus on the possible punishment exacted by the school; rather, explain how these actions do damage to their own character and credibility.

* *Employability Skills 2000+* Brochure 2000 E/F (Ottawa: The Conference Board of Canada, 2000).

CHAPTER SUMMARY

This chapter highlights the process of conducting technical research and writing about the results. Much of the information is presented within the context of a research project conducted at M&K.

Before starting your search for information, you need to decide what main question you are trying to answer. Also, think about the types of information you need, the types of sources that would be useful, and the format required for the final document. Once in the library, you have many sources—both online and in print—available to you: books, periodicals, newspapers, company directories, general references such as dictionaries and encyclopedias, and abstracts. You can also search the Internet, the Web, and use questionnaires and interviews.

As you begin to locate sources, be sure to use your borrowed information correctly by following this five-step research process: (1) write complete bibliography cards, (2) develop a rough outline, (3) take careful notes on large note cards, (4) organize research in an outline, and (5) write the draft from the outline and the cards. For the final paper, choose a documentation system appropriate for your field or organization, taking particular care with your online documentation. Today the preferred approach is to use some form of parenthetical citations, such as the author-date system outlined in this chapter.

Another research skill is writing research abstracts (summaries) of articles, books, or other sources of information. Abstracts can be either descriptive (quite brief) or informational (somewhat more detailed).

ASSIGNMENTS

If your instructor considers it appropriate, use a copy of the Planning Form found in Chapter 1 for completing the following assignments.

1. **General research paper.** Using a topic approved by your instructor, follow the procedure suggested in this chapter for writing a paper that results from some technical research. Be sure that your topic (1) relates to a technical field in which you have an interest, by virtue of your career or academic experience, and (2) is in a field that you can find information about in nearby libraries.

2. **Research paper—your major field.** Write a research paper on your major field. Consider some of the following questions in arriving at your paper's thesis: what is the history of your major? What types of jobs do majors in your discipline pursue? Do their job responsibilities change after 5, 10, or 15 years in the field? What kinds of professional organizations exist to support your field?

3. **Research paper—M&K.** As an M&K engineer or scientist, you have been asked to write a research paper for M&K's upper management. Choose your topic from one of the technical fields listed below. Assume that your readers are gathering information about the topic because they may want to conduct consulting work for companies or government agencies involved in these fields. Focus on advantages and disadvantages associated with the particular technology you choose. Follow the procedure outlined in this chapter.

   - Artificial intelligence
   - Chemical hazards in the home
   - Fibre optics
   - Forestry management
   - Geothermal energy
   - Human-powered vehicles
   - Lignite-coal mining
   - Organic farming
   - Satellite surveying
   - Solar power
   - Wind power

4. **Abstract—one article or several articles.**
   Option A: Visit your college library and find a magazine or journal in a technical area, perhaps your major field. Then photocopy a short article (about five pages) that does not already contain a separate abstract or summary at the beginning of the article. Using the guidelines in this chapter, write both an informative and a descriptive abstract for a nontechnical audience. Submit the two abstracts, along with the copy of the article.
   Option B: Follow the instructions in Option A, but use a short article that has been selected or provided by your instructor.
   Option C: Read three to five current articles in your major field. Write an abstract that summarizes all of them on one page.

5. **Questionnaire—analysis.** Using the guidelines in this chapter for questionnaires, point out problems posed by the following questions:

   a. Is the state of the economy changing your opinion about the current government?
   b. Do you think the company's severe morale problem is being caused by excessive layoffs?
   c. Was the response of our salespeople both courteous and efficient?
   d. Of all the computer consultants you have used in the past 15 years, which category most accurately reflects your ranking of our firm: (a) the top 5 percent, (b) the top 10 percent, (c) the top 25 percent, (d) the top 50 percent, or (e) the bottom 50 percent?
   e. In choosing your next writing consultant, would you consider seeking the advice of a professional association such as the STC or the CPTSC?
   f. Other than the position just filled, how many job openings at your firm have been handled by Dowry Personnel Services?

6. **Questionnaire—writing.** Design a brief questionnaire to be completed by students on your campus. Select a topic of general interest, such as the special needs of evening students or the level of satisfaction with certain college facilities or services. Administer the questionnaire to at least 20 individuals (in classes, at the student union, in dormitories, etc.). After you analyze the results, write a brief report that summarizes your findings. *Note:* before completing this exercise, make sure that you gain any necessary approvals of college officials, if required.

7. **Interviews—simulation and analysis.** Divide into groups of three or four students, as your instructor directs. Two members of the group will take part in a simulated interview between a placement specialist at your school and a personnel representative from an area company. Assume that the firm might have a number of openings for your school's graduates in the next few years.

   As a group, create some questions that would be useful during the simulated interview. Then have the two members perform the role-playing exercise for 15 to 20 minutes. Finally, as a group, critique the interview according to the suggestions in this chapter and share your findings with the entire class.

8. **Interview—real-world.** Select a simple research project that would benefit from information gained from an interview. (Your project may or may not be associated with a written assignment in this course.) Using the suggestions in this chapter, conduct the interview with the appropriate official.

9. **Ethics assignment.** This assignment is best completed as a group exercise. Assume your group has been chosen to develop a Web-based course in technical communication. Team members are assembling materials on a Web site that can be used by students like you—materials such as (1) guidelines and examples from this book, (2) scholarly articles on communication, (3) newspaper articles and graphics from print and online sources, and (4) examples of technical writing that have been borrowed from various engineering firms.

   Your team has been told that, generally speaking, the "fair use" provision of the copyright law permits use of limited amounts of photocopied material from copyrighted sources without the need to seek permission from, or provide payment to, the authors—as long as use is related to a non-profit organization, such as a college. Your tasks are as follows:

   1. Research copyright law to make sure you understand its application to conventional classroom use. If possible, also locate any guidelines that relate to the Internet.
   2. Develop a list of some specific borrowed materials your group would want to include on the site for the technical communication course. These materials may fall inside or outside the four general groupings noted previously.

3. Discuss how the medium of the Internet may influence the degree to which the "fair use" provision would apply to your Web course. Be specific about the various potential uses of the material.

4. Consult an actual Web-based college course in any field and evaluate the degree to which you think it follows legal and ethical guidelines for usage.

5. Prepare a report on your findings (written or oral, depending on the directions you have been given by your instructor).

10. **International communication assignment.** Using interviews, books, periodicals, or the Internet, investigate the degree to which writers in one or more cultures other than your own acknowledge borrowed information in research documents. For example, you might want to seek answers to one or more of the following questions: Do you believe acknowledging the assistance of others is a matter of absolute ethics? Or should such issues be considered relative and therefore influenced by the culture in which they arise? For example, would a culture that highly values teamwork and group consensus take a more lenient attitude toward acknowledging the work of others? These are not simple questions. Think them through carefully.

MEMORANDUM

DATE: March 12, 2002
TO: Jacques Martin, President
FROM: Tanya Grant, Technical Writer
SUBJECT: Hybrid-Electric Vehicle Research and Recommendations

INTRODUCTORY SUMMARY

When you heard that our Tokyo office had purchased some Toyota minivans powered by a combination gasoline-electric engine, you asked me to research hybrid-electric vehicles (HEVs) and recommend whether or not M&K should use them. After making several phone calls, checking useful Web sites, and reviewing related books and articles, I recommend M&K not switch to HEVs at this time. However, we should consider the idea again when HEVs similar to the trucks and SUVs we now use in our offices are available. This report highlights advantages and disadvantages of HEVs, costs, and facts about the current and future HEV market.

ADVANTAGES

HEVs offer five main advantages: excellent fuel economy, low emissions, long range, conventional fuelling, and adequate power.

Excellent Fuel Economy

HEVs are able to approach double the fuel economy of the current conventional car. The subcompact Toyota Prius is rated by the U.S. Environmental Protection Agency (2000) at 22 litres/100 km city driving, and at 19 litres/100 km highway. That's right: the Prius gets better mileage in the city, in part because it makes better use of regenerative braking to capture energy for its battery (Garretson, 2001) and has an electric motor–gasoline engine configuration that favours slower stop-and-go traffic (Traeger). The two-seat Honda Insight gets even better mileage, rating 26 litres/100 km city and 29 litres/100 km highway. Because the gasoline engine gets a boost when needed from the electric motor, the engine needn't be large.

Another gas saver is the fact that the gasoline engine shuts down when at a stoplight, to be restarted immediately by the electric motor when you engage the clutch. However, having the engine shut off can be unnerving. One new Insight owner turned the ignition key every time the engine cut out, continuing to do so for two weeks until her husband figured out that the car would start back up by itself (Anderton, 2001).

Low Emissions

In an HEV, the electric motor releases no emissions, and the small gasoline engine recharges the battery and has to work less often, so its emissions are much lower. The California Air Resources Board (2001) rates the Honda Insight as an Ultra-Low Emissions Vehicle (ULEV), which means that the Insight is at least 50% cleaner than the average 2001 model car. The Prius does even better, rating as a Super-Ultra-Low Emissions Vehicle (SULEV) because its emissions are 90% below the average.

continues

Model 14-1 Memo report citing research

Long Range

Because the gasoline engine automatically recharges the electric motor, HEVs can go many hundreds of kilometres before refuelling due to their excellent fuel economy. With fuel tanks of 45 and 40 litres, respectively, both the Toyota Prius and the Honda Insight can easily go over 800 km between gas stations. Henry and McGrath (2000) estimate that the Insight could cross the continent on only four tanks of gas.

Conventional Fuelling

HEVs run on gasoline, so fuelling is no different than for a standard automobile. This feature greatly increases their ease of use for those who may be concerned about making the transition from conventional vehicles.

Adequate Power

For their size, the existing HEVs have decent power. The Toyota Prius can go from 0 to 100 km in 14.0 seconds and achieve a top speed of 160 km/hr. The Honda Insight has somewhat better power, going to 100 km in 11 seconds with a top speed of 170 km/hr. ("Road Test," 2001). Anderton (2001) admits, however, that the Insight can "lag a bit on hills."

DISADVANTAGES

The three main disadvantages of HEVs are as follows: small selection, low load capacity, and complexity.

Small Selection

Presently, only two HEVs are available: the Honda Insight and the Toyota Prius. Both are small cars. The Insight seats only two, and the Prius supposedly five, but three of them had better be children. The only company vehicles used in our offices are pickup trucks and SUVs. Currently there are no HEVs on the market that meet M&K's immediate needs.

Low Load Capacity

The Toyota Prius has the cab room and trunk space of a Corolla, and the Honda Insight has much less. The total load of the Insight is only 165 kg, so two engineers of 75 kg each would nearly weigh it to capacity, even without any equipment. The trunk space is so small that Henry and McGrath (2000) complain that a golf bag doesn't even fit. Though the Prius can carry a greater load, it still would not come close to meeting the needs we have for our current fleet vehicles.

Complexity

Although electric motors are relatively simple, gasoline engines are quite complex. Add the fact that the two engines must be linked, and you end up with a very complex system. Einstein (1999) warns that "with two powertrains, hybrids are far more complex than conventional cars and that could mean more down time and higher maintenance costs."

COST CONSIDERATIONS

There remain important issues regarding HEV purchase and maintenance costs that also may influence your decision.

continues

Model 14-1 *continued*

Purchase

HEVs are more expensive than conventional gasoline vehicles. The Toyota Prius costs about $30,000, which is about $6,000 more than the cost of the comparable Toyota Corolla. The even smaller Honda Insight sells for as much as the Prius. Though neither of the current HEVs on the market is cheap, both Honda and Toyota are selling their hybrids at a significant loss, estimated to be between a few thousand dollars and $45,000 per vehicle by industry analysts (Swoboda & Brown, 2001). Neither company is commenting on the cost of production.

Daimler-Chrysler has announced plans to market an HEV Dodge Durango SUV in 2003, and when it does, the company says that it will cost about $5,000 more than the current gasoline model (Glynn, 2001).

Maintenance

Both the Insight and the Prius have standard 3-year/58,000 km warranties with 8-year/160,000 km warranties on the $3,000 batteries. Many mechanics are wary, however, including Tom and Ray Magliozzi of *Cartalk:* "[D]on't delude yourself," they warn. "There's no doubt that buying a vehicle such as this [the Prius] places you squarely among the ranks of the hybrid pioneers" ("Toyota Prius," 2001).

Because the technology is so new, it's difficult to find maintenance data. I phoned two fleet mechanics for the city of Calgary, which recently used a federal grant to acquire 40 Priuses. Harry Stone, of the Calgary Fire Department, says that he's "afraid to touch" the 10 HEVs in his fleet until he gets more training. Dan Ramsey of the Calgary Public Works Department, which has had 30 of the Priuses for three months now, said that they've had a few problems with the cars. Five had dead batteries, though Ramsey admits that they were sitting on the lot for two months without being started. One Prius had a check-engine light come on, which was fixed by the dealer, who is contracted to do all maintenance "They're pretty hush-hush about it," Ramsey says of the Toyota dealer's maintenance.

THE HEV MARKET

Manufacturers are not yet sure about the target market for HEVs, which has been characterized as "greenies, techno-geeks, tightwads, urban commuters, hip kids?" (Morgan, 2000). What is certain is that production is low and that the size of cars produced runs counter to the current popularity of SUVs.

Low Production

Partly because they're losing money with every Insight and Prius sold, Honda and Toyota have kept the number of these first HEV models small. Only 9,360 were sold in North America last year (Miller & Plungis, 2001), and only about 16,000 to 20,000 are expected to sell this year (Trapps, 2001; Stutzman, 2001). HEVs are responsible for only 0.01% of new cars sold in North America. While both companies report waiting lists for the cars (Henry & McGrath, 2000; Swoboda & Brown, 2001), the case seems to be one of small demand and even smaller supply.

continues

Model 14-1 *continued*

Small Cars

Another reason HEVs have not sold well yet is that both models on the market are small cars, and data indicate that North Americans like big vehicles. A survey by the Alliance for Automobile Manufacturers shows that the 50 vehicle models that get 13 litres/100 km or better make up only 2% of North American auto sales (Bodipo-Memba, 2001). "It's not the case of 'If you build it, they will come,'" says Steve Douglas, director of environmental affairs for the Alliance's Sacramento office, about smaller, more energy-efficient cars. "We build it, but they haven't come." Meanwhile, SUV sales were up 9% last year, despite fluctuating gas prices and the fact that the total new car and truck market declined by 7%. The fuel economy figures for new North American cars were the worst since 1980 (Stutzman, 2001).

OUTLOOK FOR HEVS

This section describes the near-term outlook for the manufacture of North American and Japanese HEVs, as well as long-term prospects in the industry.

Short-Term: American Automakers

North Americans may be willing to buy HEVs if they're similar to the big cars, trucks, and SUVs that are currently in demand. The Big Three automakers have been reluctant to rush a small hybrid to a market that isn't demanding it; instead, they've been developing HEV trucks and SUVs similar to the models that consumers are buying.

Both Ford and Dodge plan to market a hybrid SUV in 2003. The Ford Escape should get about 64 km/hr. and cost less than $40,000 (McDiarmid, 2000). Estimates are not yet publicly available for the HEV Dodge Durango. In 2004, General Motors should have out a hybrid SUV that can go from 0 to 100 in just over 7 seconds ("GM Announces," 2001), the first of its many vehicles planned for their ParidiGM gas-electric system. That year or next, Dodge plans to introduce its Ram Contractor Special, allowing its owner to "take it to a job site and plug in the power tools. And if the power goes out at home he can just plug his house into the truck's 220-volt system to watch television" (Swoboda & Brown, 2001).

Short-Term: Japanese Automakers

Toyota and Honda have been making further HEV plans too. Toyota plans to market a hybrid with a modified HEV power system this fall. The new system is less expensive than that used in the Prius and is more adaptable, so Toyota can use it in pre-existing models. However, it is not as stingy on gas, and it reduces emissions by only 50%—40% less than the Prius (Tanikawa, 2001). Just this year Toyota has been selling an HEV minivan in Japan—the ones that our Tokyo office is using—but it is unclear when the automaker might bring it to North America. Honda should have an HEV Civic on the market by March 2002, hoping to triple its HEV sales in North America ("Honda Plans," 2001).

continues

Model 14-1 *continued*

Long-Term Prospects

Five years ago engineer Victor Wouk called HEVs "the car of the near future" (1997). It looks as if he was right, though HEV sales are not expected to be overwhelming. The Office for the Study of Automotive Technology at the University of Michigan predicts that only 3%–4% of the market will consist of hybrids by 2010 (Morgan, 2000). Ford Motor Company Chairman William Clay Ford Jr., however, believes that hybrids could make up 20% of new auto sales by then (McCracken, 2001).

In the same speech, Ford also said that fuel cells could "be the predominant automotive power source in 25 years" (McCracken, 2001). Nearly all other industry analysts agree, and many believe that fuel cell vehicles, which use hydrogen as fuel and emit only water as a waste product, will be in production by the end of the decade. GM President G. Richard Wagoner Jr., referring to fuel cells as "the Holy Grail for the pollution-free car," has set a goal for his company to have 10% of its vehicles using fuel cells by 2010 (Jones, 1999). Not to be outdone, Honda and Toyota have both developed fuel cell prototypes. So the HEV may be only a brief chapter in automotive history.

CONCLUSION

In my view, M&K should not add HEVs to its fleet at present—mainly because the available HEVs are smaller than what the company needs. When larger HEVs come to the market in a few years, however, M&K will probably want to buy several. Though the vehicles should be more expensive, we probably can recoup the initial expense in saved fuel costs and tax savings. Furthermore, we can continue buying vehicles using our discount arrangement with Ford, as Ford will probably be the first to offer a hybrid SUV. Furthermore, because M&K is well known for its environmental services, having part of the fleet go "green" in the long term would reinforce our positive image in the minds of customers.

continues

Model 14-1   *continued*

REFERENCES

Anderton, F. (2001, June 21). Green dream comes true. *Los Angeles Times*, p. E1. Retrieved August 3, 2001, from ProQuest database.

Bodipo-Memba, A. (2001, May 17). Incentives appeal to automakers. *Detroit Free Press.* Retrieved August 6, 2001, from Newspaper Source database.

California Air Resources Board. (2001, April 20). *2001 model year guide to passenger cars.* Retrieved August 10, 2000, from http://www.arb.ca.gov/msprog/ccbg/2001pc.htm

Einstein, P. (1999, October 29). The benefits of Insight. *Professional Engineering, 12*(19), 23. Retrieved August 3, 2001, from ProQuest database.

Garretson, C. (2001, May 10). In an era of gas-gulpers, hybrid cars get by on sip. *The Cincinnati Post.* Retrieved August 10, 2001, from http://www.cincypost.com/2001/may/10/hybrid051001.html

Glynn, M. (2001, January 19). Automakers will offer "2 for the price of 1": Many major manufacturers are hoping gas-electric hybrids can power future sales. *Seattle Times,* p. F1. Retrieved August 4, 2001, from ProQuest database.

GM announces hybrid production plans. (2001, January 9). *PR Newsline.* Retrieved August 3, 2001, from ProQuest database.

Henry, E., & McGrath, C. (2000, August). Coast to coast on four fill-ups. *Kiplinger's Personal Finance Magazine, 54*(8), 160. Retrieved August 3, 2001, from Academic Search Premier database.

Honda plans to unveil gasoline-electric Civic. (2001, June 26). *Toronto Star,* p. BU12. Retrieved August 4, 2001, from Newspaper Source database.

Jones, T. (1999, October 18). Whose car is greenest? *Forbes, 164*(18), 60+.

McCracken, J. (2001, January 9). GM promises gas-electric hybrid for 2004 will get 35 m.p.g. *Detroit Free Press.* Retrieved August 3, 2001, from ProQuest database.

McDiarmid, H. (2000, October 21). Auto representatives in Michigan say demand will drive need for hybrid cars. *Detroit Free Press.* Retrieved August 3, 2001, from Newspaper Source database.

Miller, J., & Plungis, J. (2001, January 9). GM cuts output 21%: Automaker plans to sell gas-electric SUV in 2004. *Detroit News,* p. A1. Retrieved August 3, 2001, from ProQuest database.

Morgan, C. (2000, October 20). "Green mobiles" are slowly catching on as Honda, Toyota models hit showrooms. *The Miami Herald.* Retrieved August 6, 2001, from Newspaper Source database.

Road test digest. (2001). *Car and Driver.com.* Retrieved August 10, 2001, from http://www.caranddriver.com/xp/Caranddriver/road_test_digest_current.xml

Stutzman, E. (2001, June 4). Hybrid owners testify to vehicles benefits, drawbacks. [Boulder] *Daily Camera.* Retrieved August 3, 2001, from Newspaper Source database.

Swoboda, F., & Brown, W. (2001, May 16). Easing off the gas: Unsure of demand, big 3 move slowly on hybrid cars. *The Washington Post,* p. E1. Retrieved August 3, 2001, from ProQuest database.

continues

Model 14-1 *continued*

Tanikawa, M. (2001, June 13). Toyota to introduce another hybrid engine. *New York Times*, p. W1. Retrieved August 8, 2001, from ProQuest database.

Toyota Prius. (2001). *Cartalk.com.* Retrieved August 19, 2001, from http://cartalk.cars.com/Info/ Testdrive/Reviews/toyota-prius-2001.html

Traeger, C. (n.d.). The will of the Prius. *Carlist.com.* Retrieved August 10, 2001, from http://www. carlist.com/newcars/2001/toyotaprius.html

Trapps, T. (2001, June 21). Scientists urge accelerated pace to greater auto fuel efficiency. *Los Angeles Times.* Retrieved August 3, 2001, from ProQuest database.

U.S. Environmental Protection Agency. (2000, November 22). *Model year 2001 fuel economy guide.* Retrieved August 10, 2000, from http://fueleconomy.gov/feg/FEG2001.pdf

Wouk, V. (1997, October). Hybrid electric vehicles. *Scientific American, 277*(4), 70–74.

Model 14-1   *continued*

CHAPTER 15

The Job Search

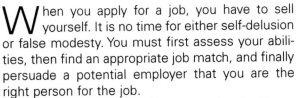

When you apply for a job, you have to sell yourself. It is no time for either self-delusion or false modesty. You must first assess your abilities, then find an appropriate job match, and finally persuade a potential employer that you are the right person for the job.

This chapter offers suggestions for landing a job in your profession. You'll find information on the following main activities:

- Researching occupations and companies
- Writing job letters
- Writing résumés
- Succeeding in job interviews
- Negotiating on the job

RESEARCHING OCCUPATIONS AND COMPANIES

Before writing a job letter and résumé, you may need information about (1) career fields that interest you (if you have not already chosen one), (2) specific companies that hire graduates in your field, and, obviously, (3) specific jobs that are available. Following are some pointers for finding such information—both from traditional sources and via your computer.

Pointers

Do Basic Research

Libraries and placement centres offer good starting points for getting information about professions. Following are a few well-known handbooks and bibliographies that you can find in reference collections and that either give information about occupations or provide names of other books that supply such information:

Job Futures

Canadian Classification Dictionary of Occupations and the new *National Occupations Code (NOC)*

Provincial and federal publications, such as *Careers Ontario* and *Careers Canada*

The following American publications also may be useful to you:

Career Choices Encyclopedia: Guide to Entry-Level Jobs

Dictionary of Occupational Titles

Directory of Career Training and Development Programs

Encyclopedia of Business Information Sources

Encyclopedia of Careers and Vocational Guidance

High-Technology Careers

Occupational Outlook Handbook

Professional Careers Sourcebook: An Information Guide for Career Planning

Also, a great deal of information about jobs is available on the Internet, in job banks, placement services, and company Web sites. Each provides valuable information, and the listings are more current than those in hard-copy reference material.

Interview Someone in Your Field of Interest

To get the *most* current information, arrange an interview with someone working in an occupation that interests you. This abundant source of information often goes untapped by students, who mistakenly think such interviews are difficult to arrange. In fact, usually you can locate people to interview through (1) your placement office, (2) your alumni association, or (3) your own network of family and friends. Another possibility is to call a reputable firm in the field and explain that you wish to interview someone in a certain occupation. Make it clear, however, that you are not looking for a job—only information about a profession.

Once you set up the interview, prepare well by listing your questions in a notebook or on a clipboard that you take with you to the interview. This preparation will keep you on track and show the people being interviewed that you value their time and information. Following are some questions to ask:

- How did you prepare for the career or position you now have?
- What college or university course work or other training was most useful?
- What types of activities fill your typical working day?
- What features of your career do you like the most? The least?
- What personality characteristics are most useful to someone in your career?
- How would you describe the long-term outlook of your field?
- How do you expect your career to develop in the next five years, ten years, or fifteen years?
- Do you know any books or periodicals that might help me find out more about your field?
- Do you know any individuals who, like you, might permit themselves to be interviewed about their choice of a profession?

Although this interview may lead to a discussion about job openings in the interviewer's organization, the main purpose of the conversation is to retrieve information about an occupation.

Find Information on Companies in Your Field

Once you have focused on a profession, you can begin screening companies that employ people in your chosen field. First, determine what information you want to find—for example, location, net worth, number of employees, number of workers in your specific field, number of divisions, types of products or services, financial rating, and names and titles of company officers. Following are some sources that might have such information:

Association and trade journals

Canada Employment Centres

Canadian Trade Index

CATAlog (Ottawa, Canadian Advanced Technology Association)

Chamber of Commerce

Commercial and Industrial Development Corporation Directory

Financial Post "100 Best Companies in Canada to Work For"

Local economic councils

Scott's Industrial Directories

Do Intensive Research on a Selected List of Potential Employers

The previous steps help get you started finding information on occupations and firms. Ultimately, you will develop a selected list of firms that interest you. Your research may have led you to these companies, or your placement office may have told you that openings exist there. Now you need to conduct an intensive search to learn as much as you can about the firms. Following are a few sources of information, along with the kinds of questions each source will help to answer.

- **Annual reports** (often available in your library or placement office): How does the firm describe its year's activities to shareholders? What are its products or services?
- **Media or press kits** (available from public relations offices): How does the firm portray itself to the public?
- **Personnel manuals and other policy guidelines:** What are features of the firm's "corporate culture"? How committed is the firm to training? What are the benefits and retirement programs? Where are its branches? What are its customary career paths?
- **Graduates of your college or university now working for the firm:** What sort of reputation does your school have among decision makers at the firm?
- **Company newsletters and in-house magazines:** How open and informative is the firm's internal communication?
- **Business sections of newspapers and magazines:** What kind of news gets generated about the firm?
- **Professional organizations or associations:** Is the firm active within its profession?
- **Stock reports:** Is the firm making money? How has it done in the past five years?
- **Accrediting agencies or organizations:** How has the firm fared during peer evaluations?
- **Former employees of the company:** Why have people left the firm?
- **Current employees of the company:** What do employees like, or dislike, about the company? Why do they stay?

Other good sources include the Better Business Bureau, Chamber of Commerce, and local newspapers. In other words, you should thoroughly examine an organization from the outside. The information you gather will help you decide where to apply and, if you later receive a job offer, where to begin or continue your career.

Use Your Computer to Gather Data

In addition to traditional sources, you can use your computer to find information about professions, organizations, graduate schools, and job openings. Between the time this book is written and the time it is published, the names and number of online resources will have changed dramatically. Generally, the following kinds of information are available:

- College and university catalogues
- Web sites of companies, organizations, and schools
- Employment listings from local and national sources
- Online discussion forums composed of recent graduates of colleges and universities.

In other words, the Internet will help you locate a variety of information during your job search. Moreover, you can use your computer to search for openings and respond to job ads, as mentioned in the next section.

WRITING JOB LETTERS

Job letters and résumés must grab the attention of busy readers, who may spend only 60 seconds deciding whether to consider you further. The following sections give you the tools to write a successful letter and résumé. *Successful*, of course, means a letter and résumé that will get you an interview. After that, your interpersonal skills will help you land the job. The letter and résumé aim only to get you to the next step—the personal interview.

Most job letters and résumés still get sent through the mail. However, a growing number of applicants use the Internet to apply for jobs.

Whether you use online techniques like email and résumé services or stick with the traditional approach, the same basic writing guidelines apply. Your letter, no longer than one page, should be specific to the job you seek and to your main selling points.

In preparing to write a job letter, consider the point of view of the people to whom you are writing. What criteria will they use to evaluate your credentials? How much or how little do they want in the letter? What main points will they be hunting for as they scan your résumé? This section first examines the needs of those readers and then gives guidelines for you, the writer. Models 15-1 and 15-2 on pages 447–50 include sample job letters and résumés.

The Readers' Needs

You probably will not know personally the readers of your job letter, so you must think hard about what they may want. Your task is complicated by the fact that often there are several readers of your letter and résumé, who may have quite different backgrounds.

Following is one possible scenario:

Step 1: The letter may go first to the personnel office, where a staff member specializing in employment selects letters and résumés that meet the criteria stated in the position announcement. (In some large employers, letters and résumés may even be stored in a computer, where they are scanned for keywords that relate to specific jobs.)

Step 2: Applications that pass the screening in step 1 are sent to the department manager who will supervise the employee who is hired. This manager will interview applicants and ultimately hire the employee. The manager may then select a group to be interviewed.

One variation of this process has the personnel department doing an interview as well as screening letters and résumés—before the department manager even hears about any applications. Another variation, as noted earlier, has the employer relying on an online résumé service for the initial screening.

Sooner or later, an actual person will read your letter and résumé. And most readers, whatever their professional background, have the following five characteristics in common:

Feature 1: They Read Job Letters in Stacks

Most search-and-screen processes are arranged in such a way that letters get filed until there are many to evaluate. Your reader faces this intimidating pile of paper, from which you want your letter to stand out.

Feature 2: They Are Tired

Some employment specialists may save job letters for their fresher moments, but many people who do the hiring get to job letters at the end of a busy day or at home in the evening. So they have even less patience than usual for flowery wording or hard-to-read print.

Feature 3: They Are Impatient

Your readers expect major points to jump right out at them. In most cases, they will not dig for information that cannot be found quickly. It is your responsibility to keep the letter short and well organized.

Feature 4: They Become Picky Grammarians

Readers of all professional and academic backgrounds expect good writing when they read job letters. There is an unspoken assumption that a letter requesting a chance at a career should reflect solid language use with no typographical errors. If the letter does contain a typo or grammatical error, the reader will assume that you will also be careless in your work.

Feature 5: They Want Attention-Grabbers but Not Slickness

You want your letter and résumé to stand out but to avoid gimmicks. Most readers prefer a tasteful, reserved format that does not draw too much attention to itself. For example, white or off-white stationery is still the standard, along with traditional fonts with lots of white space for easy reading. If you want to attract attention in a professional manner, consider attaching a business card to your letter so that the reader has your name and number handy. Many college and university computer labs provide software that allows students to design and print their own business cards.

Of course, likes and dislikes vary. An advertising director, who works all day with graphics, would probably want a bolder format design than an engineering manager, who works with documents that are less flashy. If you cannot decide, it is best to use a conservative format and style.

The Letter's Organization

The job letter format that follows relates to the features mentioned about readers. Your goal is to tantalize the reader enough to want to interview you. That is all.

With that goal and the reader's needs in mind, your job letter should follow this ABC format:

ABC Format: Job Letter
Abstract

- Apply for a specific job.
- Refer to ad, mutual friend, or other source of information about the job.
- (Optional) Briefly state how you can meet the main need of your potential employer.

Body

- Specify your understanding of the reader's main needs.
- Provide main qualifications that satisfy those needs (but only *highlight* points from résumé—do not simply repeat all résumé information).
- List personal characteristics that allow you to function well in the workplace (for example, interpersonal skills, dependability, supervisory skills).
- Avoid mentioning weak points or deficiencies.
- Keep body paragraphs to six or fewer lines.
- Use a bulleted or numbered list if it helps draw attention to three or four main points.
- Maintain the "you" attitude throughout.

Conclusion

- Tie the letter together with one main theme or selling point, as you would a sales letter.
- Refer to your résumé.
- Explain how and when the reader can contact you for an interview.

This pattern gives you a starting point, but it is not the whole story. There is one feature of application letters that cannot be placed easily in a formula. That feature is style. Work hard with your draft to develop a unity and flow that, by itself, will set you apart from the crowd. Your attention-grabber will engage interest. But the clarity of your prose will keep readers attentive and persuade them that you are an applicant who should be interviewed.

WRITING RÉSUMÉS

Résumés usually accompany application letters. The résumé—one page or two at most—should simply, specifically, and neatly highlight your background.

An increasing number of companies post blank résumés on the Internet. In order to apply, you simply fill in the blanks and submit. As well, there are online services available that can place résumés into a bank used by hundreds, perhaps thousands, of companies. The résumés will be scanned, using software that searches for keywords that reflect abilities needed for specific jobs; then the program sends selected résumés to companies. If you use this kind of service, remember one point: when you send credentials into cyberspace, you cannot be sure where they will land. Do not expect the level of confidentiality and security that you have with personal mail.

Three points make writing résumés a challenge:

1. **Emphasis:** You should select just a *few major points of emphasis* from your personal and professional life. Avoid the tendency to include school and employment details best left for the interview.

2. **Length:** Usually you should use only *one page*. For individuals with extensive experience, a two-page résumé is acceptable, if it is arranged evenly over both pages.
3. **Arrangement:** You should arrange information so that it is *pleasing to the eye and easy to scan.* (Typically, prospective employers spend less than a minute assessing your application.) You may even want to include an appropriate, simple illustration.

There is no easy formula for writing excellent résumés. Stylistic preferences vary greatly. This section distills the best qualities of many formats into three basic patterns: (1) the chronological résumé, which emphasizes employment history, (2) the functional résumé, which emphasizes the skills you have developed, and (3) the combined résumé, which merges features of both the chronological and functional formats. To learn when to use each format, see the "Experience" section that follows. Choose the pattern that best demonstrates your strengths.

The following paragraphs describe the main parts of the résumé. The "Experience" section explains the differences between chronological, functional, and combined résumés. Refer to the following models on pages 447–57 for résumé examples:

Model 15-1: Job letter and chronological résumé

Model 15-2: Job letter and chronological résumé

Model 15-3: Job letter and functional résumé

Model 15-4: Job letter and functional résumé

Model 15-5: Combined résumé

Model 15-6: Combined résumé

Model 15-7: Résumé with innovative format

Objective

Personnel directors and other people in the employment cycle often sort résumés by the Objective statement. Writing a good one is hard work, especially for new graduates, who often just want a chance to start working at a firm at any level. Despite this eagerness to please, do not make the mistake of writing an all-encompassing statement such as "Seeking challenging position in innovative firm in civil engineering field." Your reader will find such a general statement of little use in sorting your application. It gives the impression that you have not set clear professional goals.

Most objectives should be short—preferably one sentence. They should be detailed enough to show that you have prepared for, and are interested in, a specific career, yet open-ended enough to reflect a degree of flexibility. If you have several quite different career options, you may want to design a different résumé for each job description instead of trying to write a job objective that takes in too much territory. Word processing allows you to tailor résumé objectives to the particular employer to whom you are writing.

Note: Some employers prefer that you not include an objective. For example, you may be applying for an entry-level job for which an objective would be inappropriate. As always, consider your reader's needs as you make decisions about objectives.

Education

Whether you follow the objective with the education or experience section depends on the answer to one question: which topic is most important to the reader? Most recent graduates lead off with education, particularly if the completion of the degree prompted the job search.

This section seems simple at the outset. Obligatory information includes your school, school location, degree, and date of graduation. However, it is what you include beyond the bare details that most interests employers. Following are some possibilities:

- **Grade point average:** Include it if you are proud of it; do not if it fails to help your case.
- **Honours:** List anything that sets you apart from the crowd—such as dean's list or individual awards in your major department. If you have many, include a separate Recognitions heading toward the end of the résumé.
- **Minors:** Highlight any minors or degree options, whether they are inside or outside your major field. Employers place value on this specialized training, even if (and sometimes especially if) it is outside your major field.
- **Key courses:** When there is room, provide a short list of the courses you took that you consider most appropriate for the kind of position you are seeking. Because the employer probably will not look at your transcripts until a later stage of the hiring process, use this brief listing as an attention-grabber.

Experience

This section poses a problem for many recent graduates. Students often comment that experience is what they are looking for, not what they have yet. Depending on the amount of work experience you have gained, consider three options for completing this section of the résumé: (1) emphasize specific positions you have held (chronological résumé), (2) emphasize specific skills you have developed in your experience (functional résumé), or (3) emphasize both experience and skills (combined résumé).

Option 1: Chronological Format

This option works best if your job experience leads logically toward the job you now seek. Follow these guidelines:

- List relevant full-time or part-time experience, including co-op work, in *reverse* chronological order.
- Be specific about your job responsibilities, while still being brief.
- Be selective if you have had more jobs than can fit on a one-page résumé.
- Include nonprofessional tasks (e.g., working on the campus custodial staff) if they will help your case (e.g., the employer might want to know that you worked your way through school).
- Remember that if you leave out some jobs, the interview will give you the chance to expand on your work experience.
- Select a readable format, with appropriate white space.
- Use action verbs and lists to emphasize what you did or what you learned at jobs—for example, "Provided telephone support to users of System/23." Use parallel form in each list.

Option 2: Functional Format

This approach works best if (1) you wish to emphasize the skills and strengths you have developed in your career, rather than specific jobs you have had, or (2) you have had "gaps" in your work history, which would be obvious if you used the chronological format. Although this format is sometimes used by those whose job experience is not a selling point, valid reasons do exist for adopting the functional format. Sometimes, for example, the skills you have built up over time may be your best argument, even if your job experience is also strong. For example, you may have five years' experience in responsible positions at four different retailers. Thus, you decide to write a functional résumé that focuses on the three skill areas you have developed: sales, inventory control, and management.

If you write a functional résumé that stresses skills, you may still want to follow this section with a brief employment history (see Option 3). Most potential employers will want to know where and when you worked, even though this issue is not a high priority. *Note:* if you decide to leave out the history, bring it with you to the interview on a separate sheet.

Option 3: Combined Format

The combined format uses features of both the chronological and the functional formats. This format works best when you want to emphasize the skills you have developed, while still giving limited information on the chronology of your employment.

Models 15-5 and 15-6 on pages 455 and 456 show two variations of the combined format. In Model 15-5 the experience section looks exactly as it would in a functional résumé, with subheadings giving the names of skills. However, the writer adds a brief skeleton work history near the end of the page; she believes the reader will want some sort of chronological work history, even if it is not the writer's strength. Model 15-6 integrates chronological information into the skills section. The positions held may not be prestigious, but together they show that the applicant has considerable experience developing the two sets of skills listed: Editing/Writing and Teaching/Research.

Activities, Recognitions, Interests

Most résumés use one or two of the following headings to provide the reader with additional background information. The choice of which ones, if any, to use depends on what you think will best support your job objective. Here are some possibilities:

- **Activities:** selected items that show your involvement in your school or your community, or both.
- **Recognitions:** awards and other specific honours that set you apart from other applicants. (Do not include awards that might appear obscure, meaningless, or dated to the reader, such as most high school honours.)
- **Interests:** hobbies or other interests that give the reader a brief look at the "other" you.

However you handle these sections, they should be fairly brief and should not detract from the longer, more significant sections described earlier.

References

Your résumé opens the door to the job interview and later stages of the job process, when references will be called. There are two main approaches to the references section of the résumé:

1. Writing "Available upon request" at the end of the page
2. Listing names, addresses, and phone numbers at the end of the résumé

The first approach assumes that the reader prefers the intermediate step of contacting you before references are sent or solicited. The second approach assumes that the reader prefers to call or write references directly, without having to contact you first. Use the format most commonly used in your field or, most important, the one most likely to meet the needs of a particular employer. As always, be ready to tailor your letter and résumé each time you put it in the mail.

Your goal is to write an honest résumé that emphasizes your good points and minimizes your deficiencies. To repeat a point made at the outset, you want your résumé and job letter to open the door for later stages of the application process. Look upon this writing task as your greatest persuasive challenge. Indeed, it is the ultimate sales letter, for what you are selling is the potential you offer to change an organization and, perhaps, the world as well. Remember that the possibilities are heady, and make sure to spend the time necessary to produce first-rate results.

SUCCEEDING IN JOB INTERVIEWS

Your job letter and résumé have only one purpose: to secure a personal interview with the personnel director or other official who screens applicants for a position.

Much has been written about job interviews. Fortunately, most of the good advice about interviewing goes back to just plain common sense about dealing with people. Following are some suggestions to show you how to prepare for a job interview, perform at your best, and send a follow-up letter.

Preparation

Do Your Homework on the Prospective Employer

You have learned how to locate data about specific companies. Once you have been selected for an interview, review whatever information you have already gathered about the employer. Then go one step further by searching for the *most current* information you can find. Your last source may be someone you know at the organization, or a "friend of a friend."

If you don't have personal contacts, use your research skills again. For large firms, locate recent periodical or newspaper articles by consulting general indexes, such as the *Business Periodicals Index, Readers' Guide to Periodicals,* or the index for any newspaper in a large metropolitan area. For smaller firms, consult recent issues of local newspapers for announcements about the company. Being aware of current company issues will demonstrate your initiative and show your interest in the firm.

As noted earlier in the chapter, the Internet can also be a good source of current information about an organization.

Write Out Answers to the Questions You Consider Likely

Although you probably would not take written answers with you to the interview, writing them out will give you a level of confidence unmatched by candidates who only ponder possible questions. This technique resembles the manner in which some people prepare for oral presentations: first they write out a speech, then they commit it to notes, and finally they give an extemporaneous presentation that reflects confidence in themselves and knowledge of the material. This degree of preparation will place you ahead of the competition.

There are few, if any, original questions asked in job interviews. Most interviewers simply select from some standard questions to help them find out more about you and your background. Following are some typical questions, along with tips for responses:

1. **Tell me a little about yourself.** Keep your answer brief and relate it to the position and company—do not wander off into unrelated issues, like hobbies, unless asked to do so.

2. **Why did you choose your college or university?** Be sure your main reasons relate to academics—for example, the academic standing of the department, the reputation of the faculty, or the job placement statistics in your field.

3. **What are your strengths?** Focus on two or three qualities that would directly or indirectly lead to success in the position you are applying for.

4. **What are your weaknesses?** Choose weaknesses that, if viewed from another perspective, could be considered strengths—for example, your perfectionism or over-attention to detail.

5. **Why do you think you would fit into this company?** Using your research on the firm, cite several points about the company that correspond to your own professional interests—for example, the firm may offer services in three fields that relate to your academic or work experience.

6. **What jobs have you held?** Use this question as a way to show that each previous position, no matter how modest, has helped prepare you for this position—for example, part-time employment in a fast-food restaurant developed teamwork and interpersonal skills.

7. **What are your long-term goals?** Be ready to give a five- or ten-year plan that, preferably, fits within the corporate goals and structure of the firm to which you are applying. For example, you may want to move from the position of technical field engineer into the role of a project manager, to develop your management skills.

8. **What salary range are you considering?** Avoid discussing salary if you can. Instead, note that you are most interested in criteria such as job satisfaction and professional growth. If pushed, give a salary range that is in line with the research you did on the career field in general and this company in particular; see the last section of this chapter on negotiating.

9. **Do you like working in groups or do you prefer working alone?** Most employers want to know that you have interest and experience in group work, whether in school courses or previous jobs. But they also admire and reward individual accomplishment. In deciding which part of your background to emphasize, consider the "corporate culture" of the organization interviewing you.

10. Do you have any questions to ask me? Always be ready with questions that reinforce your interest in the organization and your knowledge of the position—for example, "Given the recent opening of your Edmonton warehouse, do you plan other expansions in the West?" or "What types of in-house or off-site training do you offer new engineers who are moving toward project management?" Other questions can concern issues such as (a) benefits, (b) promotions, (c) availability of personal computers, and (d) travel requirements.

Do Mock Interviews

You can improve your chances considerably by practising for job interviews. One of the easiest and best techniques is role-playing. Ask a friend to serve as the interviewer, and give him or her a list of questions. Also, inform that person about the company so that he or she can improvise during the session. In this way you will be prepared for the real thing.

You can get additional information about your interviewing abilities by videotaping your role-playing session. Reviewing the videotape will help you highlight (1) questions that pose special problems for you and that you need to prepare further for and (2) mannerisms that need correction. This preparation technique is especially useful if you are one of the growing number of applicants who take part in a video interview with a recruiter.

Be Physically Prepared for the Interview

Like oral presentations, job interviews work best when you are physically at your best. Thus all the old standbys apply:

- Get a good night's rest before the interview.
- Avoid caffeine or other stimulants.
- Eat about an hour beforehand so that you are not distracted by hunger pangs during the session.
- Take a brisk walk to dispel excess nervous energy.

Performance

Good planning is your best assurance of a successful interview. Of course, there are always surprises. Remember, however, that most interviewers are seriously interested in your application and want you to succeed. Help them by selling *yourself*; doing so will give them a reason to hire you. Following are some guidelines for the interview.

Dress Appropriately

Much has been written on the topic of appropriate attire for interviews. Here are some practical suggestions that are often emphasized:

- Dress conservatively. Avoid drawing attention to your dress—for example, do not use the interview as an opportunity to break in a garment in the newest style.
- Consider the organization—for example, an interview at a brokerage firm may require a dark suit for a man and a tailored suit for a woman, whereas an interview at a construction firm may require less-formal attire.
- Avoid excessive jewellery.
- Pay attention to the fine points—for example, wear shined shoes and carry a tasteful briefcase or notebook.

Take an Assertive Approach

Either directly or indirectly, use everything you say to make the case for your hiring. Be positive, direct, and unflappable. Use every question as a springboard to show your capabilities and interests, instead of waiting for point-blank questions about your qualifications. To be sure, the degree to which you assert yourself partly depends on your interpretations of the interviewer's preference and style. Although you do not want to appear "pushy," you should take the right opportunities to sell yourself and your abilities.

Use the First Few Minutes to Set the Tone

What you have heard about first impressions is true: interviewers draw conclusions quickly. Having given many interviews, they are looking for an applicant who injects vitality into the interview and makes their job easier. Within a minute or two, establish the themes and the tone that will be reinforced throughout the conversation—that is, your relevant background, your promising future, and your eagerness (not pushiness). In this sense, the interview follows the preacher's maxim mentioned in Chapter 13: "First you tell 'em what you're gonna tell 'em, then you tell 'em, and then you tell 'em what you told 'em."

Maintain Eye Contact While You Speak

Although you may want to look away occasionally, much of the time your eyes should remain fixed on the person interviewing you. In this way you show interest in what she or he is saying.

If you are being interviewed by several people, make eye contact with *all* of them throughout the interview. No one should feel ignored. You are never quite certain exactly who may be the decision maker in your case.

Be Specific in the Body of the Interview

In every question you should see the opportunity to say something specific about yourself and your background. For example, rather than simply stating that your degree program in computer science prepared you for the open position, cite three specific courses and briefly summarize their relevance to the job.

Do Not Hesitate

A job interview is no time to hesitate, unless you are convinced the job is not for you. If the interviewer notes that the position involves 40% travel, quickly respond that the prospect of working around the country excites you. The question is this: do you want the job or not? If you do, then accept the requirements of the position and show excitement about the possibilities. You can always turn down the job if you receive an offer and decide later that some restrictions, like travel, are too demanding.

Reinforce Main Points

The interviewer has no text for the session other than your résumé. Therefore, you should drive home main points by injecting short summaries into the conversation. After a five-minute discussion of your recent work experience, take 15 seconds to present a capsule version of relevant employment. Similarly, orchestrate the end of the interview so that you have the chance to summarize your interest in the position and your qualifications. Here is your chance to follow through on the "tell 'em what you told 'em" part of the preacher's maxim.

Follow-up Letters

Follow up *every* personal contact with a letter to the person you spoke with. Send it within 24 hours of the interview or meeting so that it immediately reinforces the person's recollection of you. This simple strategy gives you a powerful tool for showing interest in a job.

Follow-up letters abide by the same basic letter pattern discussed in Chapter 9. In particular, follow these guidelines:

- Write no more than one page.
- Use a short first paragraph to express appreciation for the interview.
- Use the middle paragraph(s) to (a) reinforce a few reasons why you would be the right choice for the position or (b) express interest in something specific about the organization.
- Use a short last paragraph to restate your interest in the job and to express hope that a job offer will be forthcoming.

See Chapter 9 for the various formats appropriate for all types of business letters. Following is sample text of a thank-you letter:

> Dear Ms. Ferguson:
>
> I enjoyed meeting with you yesterday about the career possibilities at Klub Kola's district headquarters. The growth that you are experiencing makes Klub an especially exciting company to join.
>
> As I mentioned, my marketing background at Bow River College has prepared me for the challenge of working in your new Business Development Department. Several courses last semester focused specifically on sales strategies for consumer goods. In addition, an internship this semester has given me the chance to try out marketing strategies in the context of a local firm.
>
> Again, thank you for the chance to learn about your firm's current success and promising future. I remain very interested in joining the Klub Kola team.
>
> Sincerely,
>
> *Marcia B. Mahoney*
>
> Marcia B. Mahoney

When your audience might appreciate a less formal response, consider writing your interviewer a personal note instead of a typed letter. This sort of note is most appropriate when you plan a short message.

NEGOTIATING ON THE JOB

We negotiate every day. Both on the job and in our personal lives, we constantly find ourselves in give-and-take discussions to negotiate issues as diverse as those that follow:

- Major and minor purchases
- Relationships with spouses and friends

- Performance evaluations—with bosses and with subordinates
- Salaries—with those to whom we report and with those who report to us

Because negotiating will become an important part of your career, this final section gives some brief background information and then focuses on six guidelines that will steer you toward successful negotiations—when you are hired and also at other points in your career. The main example used in this section is a salary negotiation for an entry-level position.

How has the art of negotiating changed recently? In the past, the process was often characterized by words like *trickery, intimidation,* and *manipulation.* In this game's lexicon there were "winners" and "losers" and lots of warlike imagery. Participants, seen as battlefield adversaries, took up extreme positions, defended and attacked each other's flanks, finally agreed reluctantly to some middle ground, and then departed wounded and usually uncertain of who had won the battle.

Today, the trend is away from this war-zone approach with its "I win, you lose" mentality. As a negotiator, you must enter the process searching for common ground for a very practical reason: long-term relationships are at stake. In later negotiations, you are much more likely to achieve success if the present negotiation helps both parties. This goal—"we both win"—requires a new set of practices at the negotiation table.

Guidelines for Negotiating on the Job

Specifically, six guidelines should drive the negotiation process. All of them embody the point of view that successful negotiations involve honest communication wherein both parties benefit. Try to weave these six guidelines into the style of negotiating that you develop.

Negotiating Guideline 1: Think Long-Term

Enter every negotiation with a long-term strategy for success. You need to establish and nurture a continuing relationship with the person on the other side of the table. Later dealings may depend on mutual understandings and goodwill that result from your first meeting. First impressions *do* count.

How might such long-term thinking apply to actual contract discussions for jobs, especially for your first position after graduating? If you are fortunate enough to be in demand in the job market, you will have the leverage to discuss salary expectations and other benefits during an interview. Such discussions often are characterized by you and the employer sharing details about your expectations and the employer's offer. You should enter such sessions with a realistic idea of what you can command in the marketplace. Neither sell yourself short nor harbour inflated ideas of your worth. Your college or university placement office should be able to provide information about salary ranges and benefit options for graduates in your field and organizations in your region.

Of course, the "real world" of the job hunt is such that the supply of new talent may overshadow the demand. You may be so glad to receive a good offer that you hesitate to jeopardize it by attempting to negotiate. Yet, ironically, you can damage your long-term interests in an organization by being overly timid before accepting an offer. Even if there is little or no room for salary negotiation, you should engage in a wide-ranging discussion that allows you to explore options for your contract and learn about features of the position. This dialogue helps you learn about the organization. It also gives the employer a healthy respect for your ability to ask serious questions about your career.

Whatever your bargaining position, take advantage of the opportunity to discuss features of your job and the organization. Questions like the ones that follow may yield important information for you *and* show your interest in developing a long-term relationship with the employer:

- What philosophy underlies the firm's approach to management?
- What is the general timetable for career advancement?
- Where will your specific job lead?
- What opportunities exist for company-sponsored training?
- How will you be evaluated and how often?

Employers respect applicants who have done enough homework to ask informed questions about the firm's employment practices. Both parties benefit from a frank, detailed discussion. You get what you need to make an informed decision about the firm; and your potential employer can showcase the organization and observe your ability to ask perceptive questions.

Negotiating Guideline 2: Explore Many Options

The negotiation process sometimes begins with only two options—your salary objective and the employer's offer—with seemingly little room for movement. You can escape this "either/or" trap by working to explore many options in the early stages of contract negotiation. This technique opens both parties to a variety of possible solutions and keeps the discussion rolling.

For example, assume that M&K recently decided to add a new computer systems technologist to the staff at its Vancouver office. As a student in the final semester of a computer systems program, you have applied for the job and have had a good first interview. The next week you are called back for a second interview and are offered a job, with a starting salary of $29,000. You are told this firm offer reflects the standard salary for new engineers with no experience. However, your research suggests that entry-level jobs in your field should pay closer to $32,000 a year—a full $3,000 more than the M&K offer. While this difference concerns you, you have heard good things about the working environment at M&K and would like to join the firm.

If you immediately were to state your need for a $32,000 starting salary, the negotiation might be thrown into the "either/or" trap that leaves little room for agreement. Instead, you should keep the conversation going by putting additional options on the table and asking open-ended questions (that is, questions that require more than a yes or no answer). For example, you could temporarily put aside your salary objective and ask how M&K arrived at the offer figure. While giving the M&K representative the chance to get facts on the table, this strategy also gives you opportunities to develop and then offer alternatives other than the two salary figures. The discussion might lead to options like these: (1) starting at $29,000 but moving to a higher figure after a successful 90-day trial period, (2) starting at the $29,000 figure but receiving an enhanced stock-option package upon being hired, or (3) starting at $31,000 but giving up the standard $2,000 moving allowance offered to entry-level employees.

The point is that you must be careful to avoid rigidity. Consider possibilities other than the two ideal goals both parties brought to the negotiation table.

Negotiating Guideline 3: Find the Shared Interests

If you succeed in keeping options open during the negotiation process, you will discover points on which you agree. Psychologically, it is to your advantage to draw attention to these points rather than to points of conflict. Finding shared interests helps establish a friendship that, in turn, makes your counterpart more willing to compromise.

Let's go back to the preceding M&K example. Assume you are continuing to discuss a number of salary options but have reached no agreement. Chances for closure may increase if you temporarily stop discussing salary and instead search for points, however minor, upon which you agree. For example, you could ask about job tasks in the position. When you learn that you will spend about 25% of your workday writing reports, you comment that your training included two electives in technical writing, along with a senior-level research report. The M&K representative praises the extra effort you made to prepare for the communication tasks in a technical profession.

This discussion about writing, though brief, has highlighted information that might have been missed during M&K's early reviews of your application. The company's interest in good writing overlaps with the extra effort you gave to this discipline in university. That shared interest may motivate the company to offer a salary figure closer to what you desire. At the very least, you will have reinforced the decision M&K officials made to offer you the job over three other finalists.

Negotiating Guideline 4: Listen Carefully

Despite shared interests, negotiations often return to basic differences. An effective technique at this point is to seek information on the rationale behind your counterpart's views. It furthers the negotiation and, in fact, your own case to ask questions and then listen carefully to the answers coming from the other side of the table.

How are we helped by asking questions? Let's return to the M&K example. When you are confronted with the salary offer, ask how M&K arrived at that figure. Your question may uncover what is really behind the offer. Did M&K recently make similar offers to other applicants? Is M&K aware of national salary surveys that tend to support your request? Asking such questions benefits both you and the entire negotiation process in four ways:

- You give your counterparts the opportunity to explain their views (thus breaking out of the either/or cycle).
- You discover what motivates them (making it more likely that you will reach consensus).
- You expose careless logic and unsupported demands.
- You move closer to objective standards on which to base negotiations.

From your persistent questioning, careful listening, and occasional responses, information may emerge that would otherwise have remained buried. You may discover, for example, that M&K is basing its salary offer on data pertaining to another part of the country, where both salaries and costs of living are lower. That would give you the opportunity to argue for a higher starting salary, on the basis of regional differences in compensation.

Negotiating Guideline 5: Be Patient

In the old hard-sell negotiations, participants frequently pushed for quick decisions, often to the regret of at least one of the parties. The better approach is to slow down the process. For example, you might want to delay agreement on a final salary figure until a later meeting, giving both yourself and your counterpart the chance to digest the conversation and consider options.

The main benefit of slowing down the process is to prevent basing decisions on the emotionalism of the moment. When objectivity takes a backseat to emotions in any negotiation—with an applicant, a client, a spouse, or a vendor—it is always best to put on the brakes, for two reasons:

- Good negotiated settlements should stand the test of time. When one party feels pressured, mistakes are made.
- Well-thought-out decisions are likely to produce better long-term relationships—a major goal of your negotiations.

Negotiating Guideline 6: *Do* Look Back

Conventional wisdom has it that once you negotiate an agreement, you should not look back to second-guess yourself, since it will only make you less satisfied with what cannot be changed. That kind of thinking assumes that negotiations are spontaneous phenomena that cannot be analyzed, which is not true. If you have conducted your negotiations methodically, you will have much to gain from post-mortems—particularly if they are in writing. Keep a negotiation journal to review before every major negotiation starts. Besides reminders, this journal should contain a short summary of previous negotiations. Make these entries immediately after a session ends, being sure to answer these questions:

- What options were explored before a decision was made?
- What shared interests were discovered?
- Did you emphasize those shared interests?
- What questions did you ask?
- How did you show that you were listening to responses?

So *do* look back. Analyze every negotiation to discover what went right and what went wrong during the proceedings. Like other communication skills, such as writing and speaking, the ability to negotiate improves with use. With a few basic guidelines in mind and a journal to reflect in, you will discover the power of friendly persuasion.

Employability Skills

The Conference Board of Canada's *Employability Skills 2000+* identifies personal management skills as critical to success in the workforce. Relevant skills include the following (see the complete *Employability Skills 2000+*—in Chapter 1, Figure 1-11—for specific details within each of the following categories):

- Demonstrate positive attitudes and behaviours.
- Be responsible.
- Be adaptable.
- Learn continuously.
- Work safely.*

Complete the Web site that you developed in Chapter 4 by developing a personal profile for the Web. In it you will need to show how you have demonstrated the personal characteristics identified by the *Employability Skills 2000+*. For example, if you have assumed a leadership role in a project, you will have demonstrated the ability to be accountable for action you have undertaken.

* *Employability Skills 2000+* Brochure 2000 E/F (Ottawa: The Conference Board of Canada, 2000).

CHAPTER SUMMARY

This chapter surveyed the entire process of searching for a job, from performing initial research to negotiating a contract. As a first step in the process, use the library and other sources of information to learn about occupations and specific employers that interest you. Second, write letters and résumés that get attention and respond to employers' specific needs. You can choose from chronological, functional, combined, or more innovative résumé formats, using the patterns of organization and style that best highlight your background. Third, prepare carefully for your job interview, especially in anticipating the questions that may be asked. Then perform with confidence. Also, do not forget to send a thank-you letter soon after the interview. Finally, use the negotiation phase of the job search process to begin building a long-term relationship with your new employer.

ASSIGNMENTS

1. **Job letter and résumé.** Find a job advertisement in the newspaper, on the Internet, or at your college or university placement office. The ad should match either qualifications you have now or those you plan to have after you complete the academic program on which you are now working. Write a job letter and résumé that respond to the ad. Submit the letter, résumé, and written advertisement to your instructor.

   If useful for this assignment and if permitted by your instructor, you may fictionalize part of your résumé so that it lists a completed degree program and other experience not yet acquired. In this way, the letter and résumé will reflect the background you would have if you were applying for the job. Choose the résumé format that best fits your credentials.

2. **Job interview.** Pair up with another classmate for this assignment. First, exchange the letters, résumés, and job ads referred to in assignment 1. Discuss the job ads so that you are familiar with the job being sought by your counterpart, and vice versa. Then perform a role-playing exercise during which you act out the two interviews, one person as applicant and the other as interviewer.

   Option: Include a third member in your group. Have this person serve as a recorder, providing an oral critique of each interview at the end of the exercise. Then collaborate among the three of you in producing a written critique of the role-playing exercise. Specifically, explain what the exercise taught you about the main challenges of the job interview.

3. **Follow-up letter.** Write a follow-up letter to the interview that resulted from assignment 2.

4. **Follow-up letter.** Last month you submitted a job letter and résumé for a position with the Barlow Group in Windsor, Ontario. Now the firm has written to express interest in your application. It wants to know more about some summer employment you mentioned in your résumé—the project you worked on was similar to some of those carried out by Barlow.

   Assume the summer work in question was as "student in training" on one of the projects described in the project sheets in Chapter 2. Write a letter that briefly describes the project and your participation in it. Use information from the project, along with invented details about the activities you completed as an assistant. Even if your tasks were not especially glorified—manual labour or office support, for example—strive to describe learning experiences that would be meaningful to your reader. You are writing to Danielle C. Yates, Barlow Consulting Group, 20 Industrial Avenue, Windsor, ON, N3P 5R7.

5. **Negotiation for entry-level job.** As in assignment 2, pair up with another student. Assume that the letters, résumés, interviews, and follow-up letters from the preceding assignments have resulted in a second interview for one of you. (That is, select one of the positions, with one of you acting as applicant and the other as interviewer.)

The topic of this second interview is the position being offered to you. After talking with your team member about the context of this simulated interview, conduct a negotiation session wherein the two of you discuss one or more aspects of the position being offered (salary, benefits, travel schedule, employee orientation, training arrangement, career development, etc.).

201 Edge Drive
Timmins ON P9T 6R2
March 15, 2006

Mr. James Vernon, Personnel Director
Martin & Koffman
393 University Avenue
Toronto ON M5R 2P9

Dear Mr. Vernon:

My academic adviser, Professor Sam Singleton, informed me about an electronic engineering opening at M&K, where he worked until last year. I am writing to apply for the job.

I understand that M&K is making a major effort to build a full-scale equipment development laboratory. That prospect interests me greatly, because of my academic background in electronic engineering. At Northern College, I took courses in several subjects that might be useful in the lab's work—for example, microprocessor applications, artificial intelligence, and fibre optics.

Also, related work at two firms has given me experience building and developing new electronics systems. In particular, more than two years' work as an assembler taught me the importance of precision and quality control. I'd like the opportunity to apply this knowledge at M&K.

Personal business will take me to Toronto April 8–10. Could you meet with me on one of those days to discuss how M&K might use my skills? Please let me know if an interview would be convenient at that time.

Enclosed is a résumé that highlights my credentials. I hope to be talking with you in April.

Sincerely,

Donald Vizano

Donald Vizano

Enclosure: Résumé

continues

Model 15-1 Job letter and chronological résumé

Donald Vizano
147 Main Street
Timmins, ON
P9T 6R2
(705) 555-7861

OBJECTIVE: A full-time position in electrical engineering, with emphasis on designing new equipment in automation and microprocessing

EDUCATION: 2003–2006 Electronic Engineering Technology
Northern College
3.5 GPA

Major Courses:

Fibre Optics   Artificial Machine Intelligence
Robotic Systems   Communication Control Systems
Microprocessor Control   Microcomputer Applications
Microcomputer Systems   Digital Control Systems
Semiconductor Circuits & Devices

Related Courses:

BASIC Programming   C++
Business Communication   Engineering Economy
Industrial Psychology   Technical Communication

**ACTIVITIES
AND HONOURS:** Institute of Electrical and Electronic Engineering (IEEE)
Dean's List.

EMPLOYMENT:

2001–2006   Electronic Assembler (part-time)
                  Jones Energy & Automation, Inc.
                  Banner, ON

2000–2001   Lab Monitor (part-time)
                  Computer Services
                  Northern College
                  Timmins, ON

1999–2000   Electronic Assembler (part-time)
                  Jones Energy & Automation, Inc.
                  Timmins, ON

1997–1999   Electronic Assembler (full-time)
                  Jones Energy & Automation, Inc.
                  Timmins, ON

PERSONAL: Willing to travel, fluent in French

REFERENCES: Available upon request

Model 15-1 *continued*

15 Park Road
Moncton, NB
E4P 9R9
August 6, 2006

Ms. Wendy Yancy
Director, Automotive Systems
XYZ Motor Company, Product Development Division
1331 Queen Street
Moncton NB E5S 1L8

Dear Ms. Yancy:

Recently I have been researching the leading national companies in automotive computer systems. Your job ad in the July 6 *National Business Employment Weekly* caught my eye because of XYZ's innovations in computer-controlled safety systems. I would like to apply for the automotive computer engineer job.

Your advertisement notes that experience in computer systems for machinery or robotic systems would be a plus. I have had extensive experience in the military with computer systems, ranging from a digital communications computer to an air traffic control training simulator. In addition, my college experience includes courses in computer engineering that have broadened my experience. I am eager to apply what I have learned to your company.

My mechanical knowledge was gained from growing up on my family's dairy farm. After watching and learning from my father, I learned to repair internal combustion engines, diesel engines, and hydraulic systems. Then for five years I managed the entire dairy operation.

With my training and hands-on experience, I believe I can contribute to your company. Please contact me at 506-882-2731 if you wish to arrange an interview.

Sincerely,

James M Sistrunk

James M. Sistrunk

Enclosure: Résumé

continues

Model 15-2 Job letter and chronological résumé

James M. Sistrunk
15 Park Road
Moncton NB E4P 9R9
(506) 882-2731

Professional Objective:

To contribute to the research, design, and development of automotive computer control systems

Education:

B.Sc., Computer Engineering, 2002–2006
University of New Brunswick, Fredericton, NB

Major concentration in Control Systems with minor in Industrial Engineering. Courses included Microcomputer Systems, Digital Control Systems, and several different programming courses.

Computer Repair Technician Certification Training, 1996–2000
RCAF Training, CFB Trenton

General Computer Systems Option with emphasis on mainframe computers. Student leader in charge of processing and orientation for new students from basic training.

Career Development:

Computer Repair Technician, RCAF, 1997–2001
NATO Clearance

Responsibilities and duties included:

- Repair of computer systems
- Documentation of work accomplished
- Preventative maintenance inspections
- Diagnostics and troubleshooting of equipment

Accomplishments included:

- "Excellent" score during skills evaluation
- Award of an Air Force Specialty Code "5" skill level

Assistant Manager, Spring Farm, Shediac, NB, 1992–1997
Responsible for dairy operations on this 500-acre farm. Developed the management and technical skills; learned to repair sophisticated farm equipment.

Special Skills:

Macintosh desktop publishing
IBM—MS DOS
Assembly Language
C++ Programming

References:

Available upon request

Model 15-2 *continued*

8 Cosmic Way, #245
Valleyfield PQ J3E 2L7
September 3, 2006

Ms. Judith R. Gonzalez, Human Resources Consultant
Mercy Hospital
3023 Centre Avenue
Brampton ON L3P 8R4

Dear Ms. Gonzalez:

My placement centre recently informed me about the Management Trainee
opening with Mercy Hospital. As a business major with experience working
in hospitals, I wish to apply for the position.

Your job advertisement notes that you seek candidates with a broad
academic background in business and an interest in hospital management.
At Conestoga College, I've taken extensive coursework in three major areas
in business: finance, marketing, and personnel management. This broad-
based academic curriculum has provided a solid foundation for a wide
variety of management tasks at Mercy Hospital.

My summer and part-time employment also matches the needs of your
position. While attending Conestoga, I worked part-time and summers as
an assistant in the Business Office at Grady Hospital. That experience
acquainted me with the basics of business management within the context
of a mid-sized hospital, much like Mercy.

The enclosed résumé highlights the skills that match your Management
Trainee opening. I would like the opportunity to talk with you in person and
can be reached at 905-555-2642 for an interview.

Sincerely,

Denise Ware Sanborn

Denise Ware Sanborn

continues

Model 15-3 Job letter and functional résumé

Denise Ware Sanborn
8 Cosmic Way, #245
Valleyfield PQ J3E 2L7
905-555-2642

Objective
Entry-level management position in the health care industry. Seek position that includes exposure to a wide variety of management and business-related tasks.

Education
Business Administration, June 2006
Conestoga College
Brampton, ON

Major: Business Administration
Grade Point Average: 3.26 of possible 4.0, with 3.56 in all major courses
All college expenses financed by part-time and summer work at Grady Hospital.

Skills and Experience
Finance
  Helped with research for three fiscal-year budgets
  Developed new spreadsheet for monthly budget reports
  Wrote accounts payable correspondence
  Called on collections from insurance companies
Marketing
  Solicited copy from managers for new brochure
  Designed and edited new brochure
  Participated in team visits to 10 area physicians
  Wrote copy for one-page flyer
Personnel
  Designed new performance appraisal form for secretarial staff
  Interviewed applicants for Maintenance Department jobs
  Coordinated annual training program for nursing staff

Awards
2005 Arden Award for best senior project in the Business Administration Department (paper that examined latest developments in Total Quality Management)

Dean's list for six semesters.

References
Academic and work references available upon request.

Model 15-3 *continued*

2389 Jenson Court
Kamloops BC V5P 7F6
(604) 555-8416
February 17, 2006

Mr. Nigel Pierce, Personnel Director
Structural Systems, Inc.
105 Paisley Way
Vancouver BC V1W 2X3

Dear Mr. Pierce:

I am writing in response to your ad for a technical representative in the February 13 (Sunday) edition of the *Vancouver Province*. I believe my experience and education make me an excellent candidate for this position.

I am very familiar with your products for the wood construction market. The laminated beams and floor joists your company manufactures were specified by many of the architects I worked with during my co-op experience at Pacific College. Work I have done in the residential and small commercial construction industry convinced me of the advantages of your products over nominal lumber.

Enclosed is my résumé, which focuses on the skills gained from my co-op work that would transfer to your firm. I look forward to meeting you and discussing my future with your company.

Sincerely,

Tania Fisher

Tania Fisher

Enclosure: Résumé

continues

Model 15-4 Job letter and functional résumé

Tania Fisher
2389 Jenson Court
Kamloops BC V5P 7F6
(604) 555-8416

PROFESSIONAL OBJECTIVE	Use my education in civil engineering and my construction experience to assume a technical advisory position.
EDUCATION	Civil Engineering Technology Pacific College June 2005, GPA: 3.00 (out of 4.00)
PROFESSIONAL EXPERIENCE	Financed education by working as co-op student for two Vancouver construction firms for 18 months.
Design skills	Assisted with the layout and design of wall panels for Ridge Development condominium project.
	Created layout and design for complete roof and floor systems for numerous churches and small commercial projects.
Computer skills	Introduced computerization to the design offices of a major construction company (HP hardware in HPbasic operating system).
	Designed trusses on Sun workstations in the UNIX operating system. Operated as the system administrator for the office.
	Learned DOS operating system and the Windows environment (on IBM hardware and its clones).
Leadership skills	Instructed new CAD (computer-assisted design) operators on the operation of design software for panel layout and design.
	Designed and implemented management system for tracking jobs in plant.
INTERESTS	Family, gardening, sailing, travel
REFERENCES	References and transcripts available upon request.

Model 15-4 *continued*

SUSAN A. MARTIN

PRESENT ADDRESS
540 Shore Drive
Ottawa ON K3P 061
(613) 555-2222

PERMANENT ADDRESS
12 Yakobusky Drive
Renfrew ON L2C 5L2
(613) 555-6074

PROFESSIONAL OBJECTIVE:	Analyze and solve problems involving natural and pollution control systems as an Environmental Scientist.
EDUCATION:	Environmental Technology Algonquin College May 2006, GPA: 3.15 (out of 4.00)

PROFESSIONAL EXPERIENCE:

Research Skills:
- Worked as lab assistant in a research project to analyze the effect of acid rain on frog reproduction in Lane Lake.
- Designed Algonquin College computer program to analyze data on ozone depletion.

Leadership Skills:
- Taught inventory procedures to new employees of Zane's Office Supply.
- Helped incoming ESL students adjust to Algonquin College.

Organizational Skills:
- Maintained academic department files as student assistant in Environmental Science Department.
- Organized field trips for Algonquin College Mountaineering Club.

HONOURS AND ACTIVITIES:	Dean's List (five semesters) President of Cycling Club
INTERESTS:	Photography, camping, biking, travelling
EMPLOYMENT HISTORY:	Student Tutor, Algonquin College, 2004–2006 Trainer, Zane's Office Supply, Ottawa, ON 2002–2004
REFERENCES:	References and transcripts available upon request

Model 15-5   Combined résumé

Karen S. Patel
237 Alexander Avenue
Toronto ON   M6P 1K3

Home: (416) 555-2112   **Messages:** (416) 555-0111

OBJECTIVE	Position as in-house technical writer and as trainer in communication skills
EDUCATION	**Technical Writer Program, December 2005** Ryerson Polytechnic University **M.A. in English, June 2004** Concordia University **B.A. in English, First Class Honours, June 2000** University of Bombay, India
EMPLOYMENT *Editing/* *Writing*	**Public Relations, Toronto Board of Education,** **2005 to present** *Administrative Assistant:* Write press releases and conduct interviews. Publish news stories in local newspapers. Edit newsletter. **Hawk Newspapers, Montreal, 2003** *Concordia Internship:* Covered and reported special events; conducted interviews; assisted with proofreading, layout, headline count. Scanned newspapers for current events; conducted research for stories. Published feature stories.
Teaching/ *Research*	**Ryerson Polytechnic University, 2004–2005** *Teaching Assistant:* Tutored English at the Writing Centre, answered "Grammar Hotline" phone questions, edited and critiqued student papers, taught English to non-English speakers and helped students prepare for exams. **Concordia University, 2003–2004** *Teaching Assistant:* Taught business writing, supervised peer editing and in-class discussions, held student conferences, and graded student papers. *Research Assistant:* Verified material by checking facts, wrote brief reports related to research, researched information and bibliographies.
COMPUTER SKILLS	WordPerfect, Microsoft Word, Pagemaker, Unix, Excel
REFERENCES	Available upon request

Model 15-6 Combined résumé

Leslie Highland
12 Atlantic Drive
Gander NF A8A 6C5

OBJECTIVE:	A full-time position in architectural design with emphasis on model-making and renderings for future buildings.
EDUCATION:	**Architectural Engineering Technology** School of Architecture Edinburgh University Edinburgh, Scotland June 2006
	Certificate in Advanced Architectural Delineation Harvard University Cambridge, MA August 2000
ACTIVITIES AND HONOURS:	**Winner of Senior Design Project** Edinburgh University Architectural Engineering Technology
	Charter Member of Society of Architectural Perspectives
EMPLOYMENT:	
2000–2004	**Architectural Designer and Delineator** McClelland & McClelland, Architects Halifax, NS
1998–2000	**Architectural Designer and Renderer** Windsor and Associates, Architects Fredericton, NB
1995–1998	**Architectural Renderer and Drafter** Sanders and Associates, Architects Fredericton, NB
1993–1995	**Architectural Drafter** Brown Engineering St. John's, NF
REFERENCES:	References and portfolio available upon request.

Model 15-7   Résumé with innovative format

CHAPTER 16

Style in Technical Writing

This chapter focuses on the last stage of the writing process—revising. As you may already have discovered, revision sometimes gets short shrift during the rush to finish documents on time. That's a big mistake. Your writing must be clear, concise, and correct if you expect the reader to pay attention to your message. Toward that end, this chapter offers a few basic guidelines on style.

After defining style and its importance, this chapter gives suggestions for achieving five main stylistic goals:

- Writing clear sentences
- Being concise
- Being accurate in wording
- Using the active voice
- Using nonsexist language

STYLE OVERVIEW

Just as all writers have distinct personalities, they also display distinct features in their writing. Writing style can be defined in this way:

> **Style:** the features of one's writing that show its individuality and separate it from the writing of another. Style results from the conscious and subconscious decisions each writer makes in matters like word choice, word order, sentence length, and active and passive voice. These decisions are different from the "right and wrong" matters of grammar and mechanics (see the Handbook). Rather, they comprise the *choices* writers make in deciding how to transmit ideas to others.

Style is largely a series of personal decisions you make when you write. As noted in Chapter 1, however, much writing is being done these days by teams of writers. Collaborative writing requires individual writers to combine their efforts to produce a consensus style, which is usually a compromise of the stylistic preferences of the individuals involved. Thus personal style becomes absorbed into a jointly produced product.

Similarly, many companies tend to develop a company style in documents such as reports and proposals. M&K has always encouraged a more informal tone that is readable and reflective of the speech of average readers. You may very well be hired by an organization that is making this same shift toward a more readable style.

Importance of Tone

Tone is a major component of style and thus deserves special mention here. Through tone you express an *attitude* in your writing—for example, neutral objectivity on the one hand, or unbridled enthusiasm on the other. The attitude evident in your tone exerts great influence over the reader. Indeed, it can determine whether your document achieves its objectives. Much like the broader term *style*, *tone* refers to the *way* you say something rather than *what* you say.

The following adjectives and examples show some of the types of tone or "attitude" that can be reflected in your writing:

1. **Casual tone:** Email to three colleagues working with you on a project
2. **Objective tone:** Formal report to a client in which you present data comparing cost information for replacing the company's computer infrastructure
3. **Persuasive tone:** Formal proposal to a client in hopes of winning a contract for goods or services
4. **Enthusiastic tone:** Recommendation letter to a university to accept one of your employees in a master's program
5. **Serious tone:** Memorandum to employees about the need to reduce the workforce and close an office
6. **Authoritative tone:** Memo to an employee in which you reprimand him or her for violations of a policy about documenting absences
7. **Friendly tone:** Letter to long-term clients inviting them to an open house at your new plant location

Although there are almost as many variations in tone as there are occasions to write documents, one guideline always applies: be as positive as you can possibly be, considering the context. Negative writing has little place in technical communication. In particular, avoid a condescending or sarcastic tone. When your tone is positive, you stand the best chance of accomplishing your purpose and gaining the reaction you want from the reader.

Despite the need to make style conform to group or company guidelines, each individual remains the final arbiter of her or his own style in technical writing. Most of us will be our own stylists, even in firms in which in-house editors help "clean up" writing errors. This chapter will help such writers deal with everyday decisions of sentence arrangement, word choice, and the like. But, while style is a personal statement, certain fundamentals are part of all good technical style in the professional world. Let's take a look at these basics.

WRITING CLEAR SENTENCES

As discussed, each writer has his or her own approach to sentence style. Yet everyone has the same tools to work with: words, phrases, and clauses. This section defines some basic terminology in sentence structure. Then it provides simple stylistic guidelines for writing clear sentences.

Sentence Terms

The most important sentence parts are the subject and verb. The *subject* names the person doing the action or the thing being discussed ("*He* completed the study"; "The *figure* shows that . . ."); the *verb* conveys action or state of being ("She *visited* the site"; "He *was* the manager").

Whether they are subjects, verbs, or other parts of speech, words are used in two main units: phrases and clauses. A *phrase* lacks a subject or verb or both; thus it must always relate to or modify another part of the sentence ("She went *to the office*"; "*As project manager,* he had to write the report."). A *clause,* on the other hand, has both a subject and a verb. Either it stands by itself as a *main clause* ("*He talked to the group*"), or it relies on another part of the sentence for its meaning and is thus a *dependent clause* ("*After she left the site*, she went home").

Beyond these basic terms for sentence parts, you also should know the four main types of sentences:

- A *simple sentence* contains one main clause ("*He completed his work*").
- A *compound sentence* contains two or more main clauses connected by conjunctions ("*He completed his work*, but *she stayed at the office to begin another job*").
- A *complex sentence* includes one main clause and at least one dependent clause ("*After he finished the project, he headed for home*").
- A *compound-complex sentence* contains at least two main clauses and at least one dependent clause ("*After they studied the maps, they left the fault line,* but *they were unable to travel much farther that night*").

Guidelines for Sentence Style

Knowing the basic terms of sentence structure makes it easier to apply stylistic guidelines. Following are a few fundamental ones that form the underpinnings of good technical writing. As you review and edit your own writing or that of others, put these principles into practice.

Guideline 1: Place the Main Point Near the Beginning

One way to satisfy this criterion for good style is to avoid excessive use of the passive voice (see the section on "Using the Active Voice" on pages 466–67). Another way is to avoid lengthy introductory phrases or clauses at the beginnings of sentences. Remember that the reader usually wants the most important information first.

Original:	"After reviewing the growth of the Calgary office, it was decided by the corporate staff that an additional lab should be constructed at the Calgary location."
Revision:	"The corporate staff decided to build a new lab in Calgary after reviewing the growth of the office there."

Guideline 2: Focus on One Main Clause in Each Sentence

When you string together too many clauses with *and* or *but*, you dilute the meaning of your text. However, an occasional compound or compound-complex sentence is acceptable, just for variety.

Original:	"The M&K hiring committee planned to interview Jim Steinway today, but bad weather delayed his plane departure, and the committee had to reschedule the interview for tomorrow."
Revision:	"The M&K hiring committee had to change Jim Steinway's interview from today to tomorrow because bad weather delayed his flight."

Guideline 3: Vary Sentence Length but Seek an Average Length of 15 to 20 Words

Of course, you shouldn't inhibit your writing process by counting words while you write. Instead, use your word processor's analysis feature—usually part of the grammar check—to see how you fare. If your sentences are too long, make an effort to shorten them—for example, by making two sentences out of one compound sentence connected by an *and* or a *but*.

You should also vary sentence length to keep your reader's attention. Place important points in short, emphatic sentences. Reserve longer sentences for supporting main points.

Original: "Our field trip for the project required that we conduct research on Pine Island, a wilderness area off the Nova Scotia coast, where we observed a number of species that we had not seen on previous field trips. Porcupines were common in the campgrounds, along with raccoons that were so aggressive that they would come out toward the campfire for a handout while we were still eating. We saw the wild dogs that are fairly common on the island and were introduced there by explorers centuries ago, as well as a few bobcats that were introduced fairly recently in hopes of checking the expanding population of porcupines."

Revision: "Our field trip required that we complete research on Pine Island, a wilderness area off the Nova Scotia coast. There we observed many species we had not seen on previous field trips. Both porcupines and raccoons were common in the campgrounds. Whereas the porcupines were docile, the raccoons were quite aggressive. They would approach the campfire for a handout while we were still eating. We also encountered Pine Island's famous wild dogs, introduced centuries ago by explorers."

BEING CONCISE

Some experts believe that careful attention to conciseness would shorten technical documents by 10%–15%. Reports and proposals would then take less time to read and cost less to produce.

Guidelines for Being Concise

These guidelines for being concise offer several techniques for reducing verbiage without changing meaning.

Guideline 1: Replace Abstract Nouns with Verbs

Concise writing depends more on verbs than it does on nouns. Sentences that contain abstract nouns, especially ones with more than two syllables, can be shortened by focusing on strong verbs instead. By converting abstract nouns to action verbs, you can eliminate wordiness, as the following sentences illustrate:

Wordy: "The *acquisition* of the property was accomplished through long and hard negotiations."

Concise: "We *acquired* the property after long and hard negotiations."

Wordy: "*Confirmation* of the contract occurred yesterday."

Concise: "The contract was *confirmed* yesterday."

Wordy: "*Exploration* of the region had to be effected before the end of the year."

Concise: "The region had to be *explored* before the end of the year."

Wordy: "*Replacement* of the transmission was achieved only three hours before the race."

Concise: "The crew *replaced* the transmission only three hours before the race."

As these examples show, abstract nouns often end with *tion* or *ment* and are often followed by the preposition *of.* These words are not always "bad" words; they cause problems only when they replace the action verbs from which they were derived. The following examples show some noun phrases, along with the preferred verb substitutes:

assessment of	assess
classification of	classify
computation of	compute
delegation of	delegate
development of	develop
disbursement of	disburse
documentation of	document
elimination of	eliminate
establishment of	establish
negotiation of	negotiate
observation of	observe
requirement of	require
verification of	verify

Guideline 2: Shorten Wordy Phrases

Many wordy phrases have become common in business and technical writing. Weighty expressions add unnecessary words and rob prose of clarity. Following are some of the culprits, along with their concise substitutes:

afford an opportunity to	permit
along the lines of	like
an additional	another
at a later date	later
at this point in time	now
by means of	by
come to an end	end
due to the fact that	because
during the course of	during
for the purpose of	for
give consideration to	consider
in advance of	before
in the amount of	for
in the event that	if

in the final analysis	finally
in the proximity of	near
prior to	before
subsequent to	after
with regard to	about

Guideline 3: Replace Long Words with Short Ones

In grade school, most students are taught to experiment with long words. Although this effort helps build vocabularies, it also can lead to a lifelong tendency to use long words when short ones will do. Of course, sometimes you want to use longer words just for variety—for example, using an occasional *approximately* for the preferred *about*. As a rule, however, the following long words in the left column routinely should be replaced by the shorter words in the right column:

advantageous	helpful
alleviate	lessen, lighten
approximately	about
cognizant	aware
commence	start, begin
demonstrate	show
discontinue	end, stop
endeavour	try
finalize	end, complete
implement	carry out
initiate	start, begin
inquire	ask
modification	change
prioritize	rank, rate
procure	buy
terminate	end, fire
transport	move
undertake	try, attempt
utilize	use

Guideline 4: Leave Out Clichés

Clichés are worn-out expressions that add words to your writing. They once were fresh phrases and became clichés only when they stopped conveying their original meaning. You can make writing more concise by replacing clichés with a good adjective or two. Following are some clichés to avoid:

as plain as day
ballpark figure
efficient and effective
few and far between

last but not least

leaps and bounds

needless to say

reinvent the wheel

skyrocketing costs

step in the right direction

Guideline 5: Make Writing More Direct by Reading It Aloud

Wordiness, sometimes called *circumlocution*, arises from the tendency many people have to write indirectly. This stylistic flaw can be avoided by reading passages aloud. Once you hear the passage, the wordiness will be quite obvious and you will be able to condense all kinds of inflated language, including the wordy expressions mentioned earlier. Remember, however, that direct writing must also retain a tactful, diplomatic tone when it conveys negative or sensitive information.

Indirect:	"We would like to suggest that you consider directing your attention toward completing the project before the commencement of the seasonal monsoon rains in the region of the project area."
Direct:	"We suggest you complete the project before the monsoons begin."
Indirect:	"At the close of the last phase of the project, a bill for your services should be expedited to our central office for payment."
Direct:	"After the project ends, please send your bill immediately to our central office."
Indirect:	"It is possible that the well-water samples collected during our investigation of the well on the site of the subdivision could possibly contain some chemicals in concentrations higher than is allowable according to the provincial laws now in effect."
Direct:	"Our samples from the subdivision's well may contain chemical concentrations beyond those permitted by the province."

Guideline 6: Avoid *There Are, It Is,* and Similar Constructions

There are and *it is* should not be substituted for concrete subjects and action verbs, which are preferable in good writing. Such constructions delay the delivery of information about who or what is doing something and tend to make your writing lifeless and abstract. Avoid them by creating (1) main subjects that are concrete nouns and (2) main verbs that are action words. Note that the following revised passages give readers a clear idea of who is doing what in the subject and verb positions.

Original:	"There are many M&K projects that could be considered for design awards."
Revision:	"Many M&K projects could be considered for design awards."
Original:	"It is clear to the hiring committee that writing skills are an important criterion for every technical position."
Revision:	"The hiring committee believes that writing skills are an important criterion for every technical position."
Original:	"There were 15 people who attended the meeting at the client's office in Charlottetown."
Revision:	"Fifteen people attended the meeting at the client's office in Charlottetown."

Guideline 7: Cut Out Extra Words

This guideline covers all wordiness errors not mentioned earlier. You need to watch for any extra words or redundant phrasing. Sometimes the problem is needless connecting words, such as *to be* or *that*. Other times the problem is redundant points— that is, points that have been made earlier in a sentence, paragraph, or section and do not need repeating.

Delete extra words when their use (1) does not add a necessary transition between ideas or (2) does not provide new information to the reader. (One important exception is the intentional repetition of main points for emphasis, as in repeating important conclusions in different parts of a report.) The examples below display a variety of wordy writing, with redundancies shown in italics:

1. Preparing the client's final bill involves *the* checking *of* all *project* invoices for the project.
2. The report examined what the *M&K* project manager considered *to be* a technically acceptable risk.
3. During *the course of* its fieldwork, the *M&K* team will be *engaged in the process of* reviewing *all of* the notes *that have been* accumulated in previous studies.
4. *Because of his position* as head of *the M&K* public relations *group* at M&K, he planned *such that he would be able* to attend the meeting.
5. She believed *that the* recruiting *of* more minorities for the technical staff is essential.
6. The department must determine its *aims and* goals so that they can be included in M&K's *2002 annual strategic* plan *produced by M&K* for *the year of* 2002.
7. Most M&K managers *generally* agree that *all of* their *company's* employees *at all the offices* deserve *at least* some *degree of* training each year *that they work for the firm.*

BEING ACCURATE IN WORDING

Good technical writing also demands accuracy in phrasing. Technical professionals place their reputations and financial futures on the line with every document that goes out the door. You must, therefore, take your time when editing for accuracy of phrasing. Accuracy often demands *more* words, not fewer. The main rule is this:

> Never sacrifice clarity for conciseness.

Guidelines for Being Accurate in Wording

Careful writing helps limit any liability your organization may incur. Your goal is simple: make sure the words convey the meaning you intend—no more, no less. Following are some basic guidelines.

Guideline 1: Distinguish Facts from Opinions

In practice, this guideline means you must identify opinions and judgments as such by using phrases such as *we recommend, we believe, we suggest,* or *in our opinion.* Example: "In our opinion, spread footings would be an acceptable foundation for the building you plan at the site." If you want to avoid repetitious use of such phrases, group your opinions into listings or report sections. Thus, a single lead-in can show the reader that opinions, not facts, are forthcoming. Example: "On the basis of our site visit and our experience at similar sites, we believe that (1) _____, (2) _____, and (3) _____."

Guideline 2: Include Obvious Qualifying Statements When Needed

This guideline does not mean you have to be overly defensive in every part of the report. It does mean that you must be wary of possible misinterpretations. Example: "Our summary of soil conditions is based only on information obtained during a brief visit to the site. We did not drill any soil borings."

Guideline 3: Avoid the Use of Synonyms

When you refer to a part or a process, always use the same term. Unlike in creative writing, the repeated use of a term is necessary because it ensures the reader will not become confused. In other words, sacrifice variety for clarity.

Guideline 4: Use Absolute Words Carefully

Avoid words that convey an absolute meaning or that convey a stronger meaning than you intend. One notable example is *minimize,* which means "to reduce to the lowest possible level or amount." When a report claims that a piece of equipment will "minimize" breakdowns on the assembly line, the reader may well interpret the passage as an absolute commitment. That reader can then consider any breakdown at all to be a violation of the report's implications. If the writer had instead used the verb *limit* or *reduce,* the wording would have been more accurate and less open to misunderstanding.

USING THE ACTIVE VOICE

Striving to use the active voice can greatly improve your technical writing style. This section defines the active and passive voices and then gives examples of each. It also lists some practical guidelines for using both voices.

What Do *Active* and *Passive* Mean?

Active-voice sentences emphasize the person (or thing) *performing* the action—that is, somebody (or something) does something ("Matt completed the field study yesterday"). Passive-voice sentences emphasize the *receiving* of the action—that is, something is being done to something by somebody ("The field study was completed [by Matt] yesterday"). Following are some other examples in first the active and then the passive voice:

- Active-voice sentences:
    1. "We *reviewed* aerial photographs in our initial assessment of possible fault activity at the site."
    2. "The study *revealed* that three underground storage tanks had leaked unleaded gasoline into the soil."

3. "We *recommend* that you use a minimum concrete thickness of 15 cm for residential subdivision streets."

- Passive-voice sentences:
  1. "Aerial photographs *were reviewed* [by us] in our initial assessment of possible fault activity at the site."
  2. "The fact that three underground storage tanks had been leaking unleaded gasoline into the soil *was revealed* in the study."
  3. "*It is recommended* that you use a minimum concrete thickness of 15 cm for residential subdivision streets."

Just reading through these examples shows us that passive constructions are wordier than active ones. Also, passives tend to leave out the person or thing doing the action. Although occasionally this impersonal approach is appropriate, the reader can become frustrated by writing that fails to say who or what is doing something.

When Should You Use Actives and Passives?

Both the active and the passive voice have a place in your writing. Knowing *when* to use each is the key. Following are a few guidelines that will help:

- Use the active voice when you want to:
  1. Emphasize who is responsible for an action ("*We recommend* that you consider . . .")
  2. Stress the name of a company, whether yours or the reader's ("*Pine Hills Contracting has expressed* interest in receiving bids to perform work at . . .")
  3. Rewrite a top-heavy sentence so that the person or thing doing the action is up front ("*Figure 1 shows* the approximate locations of . . .")
  4. Pare down the verbiage in your writing, since the active voice is usually a shorter construction

- Use the passive voice when you want to:
  1. Emphasize the receiver of the action or the action itself rather than the person performing the action ("*Samples will be sent* directly from the site to our laboratory in Montreal")
  2. Avoid the kind of egocentric tone that results from repetitious use of "I," "we," and the name of your company ("*The project will be directed* by two programmers from our Vancouver office")
  3. Break the monotony of writing that relies too heavily on active-voice sentences

Although the passive voice has its place, it is far too common in business and technical writing. This stylistic error results from the common misperception that passive writing is more objective. In fact, excessive use of the passive voice only makes writing more tedious to read. In modern business and technical writing, strive to use the active voice.

USING NONSEXIST LANGUAGE

Language usually *follows* changes in culture, rather than *anticipating* such changes. A case in point is today's shift away from sexist language in business and technical writing—indeed, in all writing and speaking.

This section on style defines sexist and nonsexist language. Then it suggests ways to avoid gender-offensive language in your writing.

Sexism and Language

Sexist language is the use of gender-specific wording, especially masculine pronouns such as *he* or *him*, to represent positions or individuals who could be either men or women. Some examples follow:

- "The operations specialist should check page 5 of his manual before flipping the switch."
- "Every physician was asked to renew his membership in the medical association before next month."
- "Each new student at the military college was asked to leave most of his personal possessions in the front hallway of the administration building."

This inappropriate generic use of the masculine pronoun came under attack for several reasons:

1. Women are well represented in the workplace.
2. Many people believe the use of masculine pronouns in a context that could include both sexes encourages sexism in society as a whole.

Either point is reason enough to avoid sexist language. Many women in positions of responsibility may read your on-the-job writing. If you fail to rid your writing of sexist language, you risk drawing attention to your language rather than your ideas. Common sense argues that you should apply some basic techniques to avoid this problem.

Techniques for Nonsexist Language

This section offers techniques for shifting from sexist to nonsexist language. Not all these strategies will suit your taste in writing style; use the ones that work for you.

Technique 1: Avoid Personal Pronouns Altogether

One easy way to avoid sexist language is to delete or replace unnecessary pronouns:

Example:

> **Sexist language:** "During *his* first day on the job, every new employee in the toxic waste laboratory must report to the company doctor for *his* employment physical."

> **Nonsexist language:** "During *the* first day on the job, every new employee in the toxic waste laboratory must report to the company doctor for *a* physical."

Technique 2: Use Plural Pronouns Instead of Singular

In most contexts you can shift from singular to plural pronouns without altering meaning. The plural usage avoids the problem of using masculine or feminine pronouns.

Example:

> **Sexist language:** "*Each* geologist should submit *his* time sheet by noon on the Thursday before cheques are issued."

> **Nonsexist language:** "*All* geologists should submit *their* time sheets on the Thursday before cheques are issued."

Interestingly, you may sometimes encounter sexist language that uses generic female pronouns inappropriately. For example, "Each nurse should make every effort to complete *her* rounds each hour." As in the preceding case, a shift to plural pronouns is appropriate: "Nurses should make every effort to complete *their* rounds each hour."

Technique 3: Alternate Masculine and Feminine Pronouns

Writers who prefer singular pronouns can avoid sexist language by alternating *he* and *him* with *she* and *her*. When applying this technique, try to avoid switching pronouns too often, which can be unsettling. Instead, switch every few pages, or every section or chapter. This technique is not yet in common use, but its appeal is growing. It gives writers more flexibility than most other techniques. One drawback is that it tends to draw attention to itself. Also, the writer must work to balance the use of masculine and feminine pronouns, to give "equal treatment."

Technique 4: Use Forms Like *He or She, Hers or His,* and *Him or Her*

This solution requires the writer to include pronouns for both sexes.

> *Example:*
>
> > **Sexist language:** "The president made it clear that each M&K branch manager will be responsible for the balance sheet of *his* respective office."
> >
> > **Nonsexist language:** "The president made it clear that each M&K branch manager will be responsible for the balance sheet of *his or her* respective office."

This technique may bother some readers. They feel that the double structure *her or his* is wordy and awkward. Many readers are bothered even more by the slash formations *he/she, his/her,* and *her/him.* Avoid this method.

Technique 5: Shift to Second-Person Pronouns

Consider shifting to "you" and "your" words, which have no sexual bias. This technique is effective only with documents in which it is appropriate to use the instructions-related "command" tone that is associated with the use of *you.*

> *Example:*
>
> > **Sexist language:** "After selecting *her* insurance option in the benefit plan, each new nurse should submit *her* paperwork to the Human Resources Department."
> >
> > **Nonsexist language:** "Submit *your* paperwork to the Human Resources Department after selecting *your* insurance option in the benefit plan."

Technique 6: Be Especially Careful of Titles and Letter Salutations

When you do not know how a woman you are writing prefers to be addressed, use *Ms.* Even better, call the person's employer and ask if the recipient goes by Miss,

Mrs., Ms., or some other title. (When calling, also check on the correct spelling of the person's name and her current job title.) Receptionists and administrative assistants expect to receive such inquiries.

When you do not know who will read your letter, never use "Dear Sir" or "Gentlemen" as a generic greeting. Such a mistake may offend women reading the letter and may even cost you some business. "Dear Sir or Madam" is also inappropriate. It shows you do not know your audience, and it includes the archaic form *madam*. Instead, call the organization for the name of a particular person to whom you can direct your letter. If you must write to a group of people, replace the generic greeting with an Attention line that denotes the name of the group.

> *Examples:*
>
> **Sexist language:** "Dear Miss Finnegan:" [to a single woman for whom you can determine no title preference]
> **Nonsexist language:** "Dear Ms. Finnegan:"
> **Sexist language:** "Dear Sir:" or "Gentlemen:"
> **Nonsexist language:** "Attention: Admissions Committee"

No doubt the coming years will bring additional suggestions for solving the problem of sexist language. Whatever the culture finally settles on, it is clear that good technical writing will no longer tolerate the use of sexist language.

CHAPTER SUMMARY

Style is an important part of technical writing. During the editing process, writers make the kinds of changes that place their personal stamp on a document. Style can also be shaped (1) by a group, in that writing done collaboratively can acquire features of its diverse contributors, or (2) by an organization, in that an organization may require writers to adopt a particular writing style. Even so, the decision-making process of individual writers remains the most important influence on the style of technical documents. In addition, tone is a major component of style, and while there are many variations in author tone, one guideline should always apply: be positive.

This chapter offers five basic suggestions for achieving good technical writing style. First, sentences should be clear, with main ideas at the beginning and with one main clause in most sentences. Although sentences should average only 15 to 20 words, you should vary sentence patterns in every document. Second, technical writing should be concise. You can achieve this by reading prose aloud as you rewrite and edit. Third, wording should be accurate. Fourth, the active voice should be dominant, though the passive voice also has a place in good technical writing. And fifth, the language of technical documents should be free of sexual bias.

ASSIGNMENTS

1. **Conciseness—abstract words.** Make the following sentences more concise by replacing abstract nouns with verbs. Other minor changes in wording may be necessary.

   a. Verification of the agreement was indicated by the signing of the contract by members of the M&K corporate staff.

    b. The inspectors indicated that observation of the site occurred on July 16, 2006.

    c. Negotiation of the final contract was to happen on the day after their arrival.

    d. After three hours of discussion, the branch managers agreed that establishment of a new M&K mission statement should take place in the next fiscal year.

    e. Assessment of the firm's progress will happen during the annual meeting of the M&K board of directors.

    f. The entire company agreed that classification of employees according to level of education was inappropriate.

    g. Documentation of the results of the lab test appeared in the final report.

    h. Unlike the previous year, this year the disbursement of share dividends will occur after the annual meeting.

    i. In analyzing the managerial style of the manager, the outside evaluators determined that delegation of authority appeared to be a problem for her.

    j. The financial statement showed that computation of the annual revenues had been done properly.

2. Conciseness—wordy phrases and long words. Condense the following sentences by replacing long phrases and words with shorter substitutes.

    a. In the final analysis, we decided to place the new pumping station in the proximity of the old one.

    b. Prior to commencing the project, they met to prioritize their objectives.

    c. Endeavouring to complete the study on time, Sheila transported the supplies immediately from the field location to the M&K lab.

    d. During the course of his career, he planned to utilize the experience he had gained in the ambulance business.

    e. His work with the firm terminated due to the fact that he took a job with another competing firm.

    f. In the event that two clients need a crew in Trois-Rivières next week, we can give consideration to using the same crew for both projects and lowering travel costs for both clients.

    g. Jacques Martin was not cognizant of the fact that younger employees felt differently than older employees about the expansion of their office building.

    h. To implement the Phoenix asbestos project, we made adjustments in the workload of two engineers so that they could be available to undertake the project in Phoenix.

    i. Subsequent to the announcement he made, he held a news conference for approximately one hour of time.

    j. At this point in time, she had every hope that her annual bonus would afford her family the opportunity to take an additional family vacation.

3. Conciseness—clichés and *there are/it is* constructions. Rewrite the following sentences by eliminating clichés and the wordy constructions *there are* and *it is*.

    a. They all agreed that the issue had been discussed repeatedly for the past 10 years; thus they did not want to reinvent the wheel during the current study.

    b. There are many examples of skyrocketing equipment costs affecting the final budget for a project.

    c. It is a fact that most employees at M&K believe the company has taken a step in the right direction by adding international offices.

    d. Needless to say, it is clear that Karen is looking forward to the three-week vacation.

    e. She explained to her staff that it was as plain as day that they would have to decrease their labour costs.

    f. The prospective client asked for a ballpark figure of the project costs.

    g. Last but not least, there was the issue of quality control that he wanted to emphasize in his speech.

    h. In these modern times today, there are new approaches that college graduates should take to the job search.

    i. Susan ended the meeting by concluding that there were a number of mutually agreeable solutions that could be explored so that the new departments in conflict could peacefully coexist.

    j. It is a fact that our boss ended the meeting about a loss of profits by noting that we are all in the same boat.

4. **Sentence clarity.** Improve the clarity of the following sentences by changing sentence structures or by splitting long sentences into several shorter ones.

    a. Therefore, to collect a sample from above the water table, and thus to follow the directions provided by the client, the initial boring was abandoned and the drill rig was repositioned about one metre away and a new boring was drilled.

    b. After capping the soil sample ring with PVC end caps and then notifying all members of the project team, we placed it in a cooler for storage on-site and transportation later to a chemical analytical laboratory.

    c. Based on the geotechnical data obtained from the subsurface exploration program, the results of the percolation testing, and the planned plumbing fixtures, the feasibility of installing a leachfield-type on-site sewage-disposal system was evaluated.

    d. Percolation test #1 was performed approximately 15 metres east of the existing pump house and percolation test #2 was performed near the base of the slope approximately 20 metres west of the pump house, and then the results were submitted to the builder.

    e. We appreciate the opportunity to provide our services on this project and look forward to continuing our relationship with XYZ Trading and Transportation Company when we begin the Zanter Project with your Finance Department next spring.

    f. All of the earth materials encountered in our exploration can be used for trench backfill above manhole and pipe bedding, provided they are free of organic material, debris, and other deleterious materials, and they are screened to remove particles greater than 15 centimetres in diameter.

    g. This study was conducted to identify, to the extent possible, based on available information from the city files and the criteria described in our proposal of June 18, 2006, whether activities near the site may have involved the use, storage, disposal, or release of hazardous or potentially hazardous substances to the environment.

    h. The properties consist of approximately 2,000 hectares, including those parcels of Heron Ranch owned by Wild Rose Insurance Company, the unsold Jones Ranch parcels, the village commercial area, the mobile home subdivisions, two condominium complexes, a contractor's storage area, an RV storage area, a sales office, a gatehouse, open space parcels, and the undeveloped areas for future Buildings 1666, 1503, 1990, and 1910.

    i. Having already requested permits for the construction of the bathhouse, medical centre, maintenance building, boat dock, swimming pool, community building, and an addition to the community building, we still need to apply for the storeroom permit.

    j. A report dated May 25, 2006, for the ABC Corporation confirmed that the updated business plan had been completed the previous month, but a new plan had to be submitted by May 25, 2005.

5. **Active- and passive-voice verbs.** Make changes in active- and passive-voice verbs, where appropriate. Refer to the guidelines in the chapter. Be able to supply a rationale for any change you make.

    a. It was recommended by the personnel committee that you consider changing the requirements for promotion.

    b. No formal report about assets was reported by the corporation before it announced the merger.

    c. The graphs showing the differences in depreciation and interest and the net loss on the investment are shown in Appendix A.

    d. It has been noted by the Department of Environmental Services that the laundry business was storing toxic chemicals in an unsafe location.

   e. The samples from Cape Breton will be sent to M&K's engineering lab in Calgary.

   f. The violation of ethical guidelines was reported by the commissioner to the president of the association.

   g. No complete equipment inventory has been made by M&K's Toronto office.

   h. It was concluded by the employee committee that M&K's retirement program needed to be revised.

   i. Dirt brought to the site should be evaluated by the engineer on-site before it is placed in the foundation.

   j. Due to the presence of a good deal of sand at the location, excavations are anticipated by us to be relatively unstable.

6. Sexist language. Revise the following sentences to eliminate sexist language.

   a. The department decided to advertise for a department chairman in three national newspapers.

   b. Although each manager was responsible for his own budget, some managers obviously had better accounting skills than others.

   c. The company policy manual states that each secretary should submit her time card twice a month.

   d. If an hourly worker misses no work for sickness during a calendar year, he will receive a $500 bonus at year's end.

   e. Each flight attendant is required to meet special work standards as long as she is employed by an international airline.

   f. Typically, a new engineer at M&K receives his first promotion after about a year.

   g. Every worker wonders whether he is saving enough for retirement.

   h. If a pilot senses danger, she should abort the takeoff.

   i. Upon arriving at the site, an M&K consultant should make immediate contact with his client representative.

   j. [greeting section of a letter] Gentlemen:

7. Advanced exercise—conciseness. The following sentences contain more words than necessary. Rewrite each passage more concisely, without changing the meaning. If appropriate, make two sentences out of one.

   a. The disbursement of the funds from the estate will occur on the day that the proceedings concerning the estate are finalized in court.

   b. During the course of the project that we conducted for Acme Pipe, several members of our project team were in the unfortunate position of having to perform their field-work at the same time that torrential rains hit the area, totalling 7.5 cm of rain in one afternoon.

   c. At a later date we plan to begin the process of prioritizing our responsibilities on the project so that we will have a clear idea of which activities deserve the most attention from the project personnel.

   d. Needless to say, we do not plan to add our participation to the project if we conclude that the skyrocketing costs of the project will prohibit our earning what could be considered to be a fair profit from the venture.

   e. The government at this point in time plans to discontinue its testing of every item but will undertake to implement testing again in approximately five months.

   f. Hazerd, Inc., will endeavour to finalize the modifications of the blueprints for a ball-park figure of about $850.

   g. For us to supply the additional supplies that the client wishes to procure from us, the client will have to initiate a change order that permits additional funds to be transferred into the project account.

   h. Upon further analysis of the many and varied options that we are cognizant of at this time, it is our opinion that the long-term interests of our firm would be best served by reducing the size of the production staff by 300 workers.

   i. Prior to the implementation of the provincial law with regard to the use of asbestos as a building material, it was common practice to utilize this naturally occurring mineral in all kinds of facilities, some of which became health hazards subsequently.

j. In the event that we are given permission to undertake the research, be sure to make certain to perform an efficient and effective search of available literature in a research facility so that we do not end up, in the final analysis, reinventing the wheel with regard to knowledge of superconductors.

8. Advanced exercise—general rules of style. Revise the following sentences by applying all guidelines mentioned in this chapter. When you change passive verbs to active, you may need to make some assumptions about the agent of the action, since the sentences are taken out of context.

a. Based on our review of the available records, conversations with the various agencies involved, including the Fire Department and the Police Department, and a thorough survey of the site where the spill occurred, it was determined that the site contained chemicals that were hazardous to human health.

b. After seven hours at the negotiation table, the union representatives and management decided that the issues they were discussing could not be resolved that evening, so they met the next day at the hotel complex, at which point they agreed on a new contract that would increase job security and benefits.

c. It is recommended by us that your mainframe computer system be replaced immediately by a newer model.

d. After the study was completed by the research team and the results were published in the company newsletter the following month, the president decided to call a meeting of all senior-level managers to discuss strategies for addressing problems highlighted by the research team.

e. Our project activities can be generally described in this way. The samples were retrieved from the site and then were transported to the testing lab in the containers made especially for this project, and at the lab they were tested to determine their soil properties; the data were analyzed by all the members of the team before findings and conclusions were arrived at.

f. First the old asbestos tile was removed. Then the black adhesive was scraped off. Later the floor was sanded smooth. The wood arrived shortly. Then the floor was installed.

g. The figures on the firm's profit margins in July and August, along with sales commissions for the last six months of the previous year and the top 10 salespersons in the firm, are included in the Appendix.

h. It was suggested by the team that the company needs to invest in modern equipment.

i. It is the opinion of this writer that the company's pension plan is adequate.

j. Shortly after the last change in leadership, and during the time that the board of directors was expressing strong views about the direction that the company was taking, it became clear to me and other members of the senior staff that the company was in trouble.

k. Each manager should complete and submit his monthly report by the second Tuesday of every month.

l. After completing our engineering analysis, it is clear that metal fatigue caused the structure to fail.

m. Upon hearing the captain's signal, each flight attendant should complete her checklist of preflight procedures.

n. Our weed-spraying procedure will have minimal impact on shrubbery that surrounds the building site.

o. It was reported today from the corporate headquarters that the health care plan has been approved by the president.

9. **Editing paper of classmate.** For this assignment, exchange papers with a member of your class. Use either the draft of a current assignment or a paper that was completed earlier in the term. Edit your classmate's work in accordance with this chapter's guidelines on style. Then explain your changes to the writer.

10. **Editing sample memo.** Using the guidelines in this chapter, edit the following memorandum.

DATE: January 12, 2006
TO: All Employees of Calgary
FROM: Leonard Szymanski, Branch Manager
SUBJECT: New Loss-Prevention System

As you may have recently heard, lately we received news from the corporate headquarters of the company that it would be in the best interest of the entire company to pay more attention to matters of preventing accidents and any other safety-related measures that affect the workplace, including both office and field activities related to all types of jobs that we complete. Every single employee in each office at every branch needs to be ever mindful in this regard so that he is most efficient and effective in the daily performance of his everyday tasks that relate to his job responsibilities such that safety is always of paramount concern.

With this goal of safety ever present in our minds, I believe the bottom line of the emphasis on safety could be considered to be the training that each of us receives in his first, initial weeks on the job as well as the training provided on a regular basis throughout each year of our employment with M&K, so that we are always aware of how to operate in a safe manner. The training vehicle gives the company the mechanism to provide each of you with the means to become aware of the elements of safety that relate to the specific needs and requirements of your own particular job. Therefore, at this point in time I have come to the conclusion in the process of contemplating the relevance of the new corporate emphasis on safety to our particular branch that we need, as a branch, to give much greater scrutiny and analysis to the way we can prevent accidents and emphasize the concern of safety at every stage of our operation for every employee. Toward this end, I have asked the training coordinator, Kendra Jones, to assemble a written training program that will involve every single employee and that can be implemented beginning no later than June of this year. When the plan has been written and approved at the various levels within the office, I will conduct a meeting with every department in order to emphasize the major and minor components of this upcoming safety program.

It is my great pleasure to announce to all of you that effective in the next month (February) I will give a monthly safety award of $100 to the individual branch employee at any level of the branch who comes up with the best, most useful suggestion related to safety in any part of the branch activities. Today I will take the action of placing a suggestion box on the wall of the lunchroom so that all of you will have easy access to a way to get your suggestions for safety into the pipeline and to be considered. As an attachment to the memo you are now reading from me I have provided you with a copy of the form that you are to use in making any suggestions that are then to be placed in the suggestion box. On the last day of each month that we work, the box will be emptied of the completed forms for that month, and before the end of the following week a winner will be selected by me for the previous month's suggestion program and an announcement will be placed by me to that effect on the bulletin board in the company workroom.

If you have any questions in regard to the corporate safety program as it affects our branch or about the suggestion program that is being implemented here at our Calgary office, please do not hesitate to make your comments known either in memorandum form or by way of telephonic response to this memorandum.

Handbook

This Handbook includes entries on the basics of writing. Here you will find three main types of information:

1. **Grammar:** the rules by which we edit sentence elements. Examples include rules for the placement of punctuation, the agreement of subjects and verbs, and the placement of modifiers.
2. **Mechanics:** the rules by which we make final proofreading changes. Examples include the rules for abbreviations and the use of numbers. This Handbook also includes a list of commonly misspelled words.
3. **Usage:** information on the correct use of particular words, especially pairs of words that are often confused. Examples include problem words like *affect/effect*, *complement/compliment*, and *who/whom*.

Another editing concern, technical style, was the topic of Chapter 16. That chapter included guidelines for sentence structure, conciseness, accuracy of wording, active and passive voice, and nonsexist language. Together, Chapter 16 and this Handbook will help you turn unedited drafts into final revised documents.

This Handbook is presented in alphabetized form for easy reference. A table of contents follows. Grammar and mechanics entries are in capitals; usage entries are in lower case. Several exercises follow the entries.

A/An

These two words are different forms of the same article. *A* occurs before words that start with consonants or consonant sounds. Examples:

- a three-pronged plug
- a once-in-a-lifetime job (*once* begins with the consonant sound of *w*)
- a historic moment (many speakers and some writers mistakenly use *an* before *historic*)

   An occurs before words that begin with vowels or vowel sounds. Examples:

- an eager new employee
- an hour before closing

A lot/Alot

The correct form is *a lot*. Though acceptable in informal discourse, *a lot* usually should be replaced by more formal diction in technical writing. Example: "They retrieved many [*not* a lot of] soil samples from the construction site."

Abbreviations

Technical writing uses many abbreviations. Without this shorthand form, you would end up writing much longer reports and proposals, without any additional content. Follow these seven basic rules in your use of abbreviations, paying special attention to the first three:

■   *Rule 1: Do Not Use Abbreviations When Confusion May Result*

When you want to use a term just once or twice and you are not certain your readers will understand an abbreviation, write out the term rather than abbreviating it. Example: "They were required to remove formaldehyde from the site, according to the directive from the Workers' Compensation Board." Even though *WCB* is the accepted abbreviation for this provincial agency, you should write out the name in full *if* you are using the term only once to an audience that may not understand it.

■ *Rule 2: Use Parentheses for Clarity*

When you use a term *more* than twice and are not certain that your readers will understand it, write out the term the first time it is used and place the abbreviation in parentheses. Then use the abbreviation in the rest of the document. In long reports or proposals, however, you may need to repeat the full term in key places. Example: "According to the directive from the Workers' Compensation Board (WCB), they were required to remove the formaldehyde from the construction site. Furthermore, the directive indicated that the builders could expect to be visited by WCB inspectors every other week."

■ *Rule 3: Include a Glossary When There Are Many Abbreviations*

When your document contains many abbreviations that may not be understood by all readers, include a well-marked glossary at the beginning or end of the document. A glossary simply collects all the terms and abbreviations and places them in one location, for easy reference.

■ *Rule 4: Use Abbreviations for Units of Measure*

Most technical documents use abbreviations for units of measure. Do not include a period unless the abbreviation could be confused with a word. Examples: km, cm, ml, in., gal., and g. Note that units-of-measurement abbreviations have the same form for both singular and plural amounts. Examples: 0.5 cm, 1 cm, 5 cm.

■ *Rule 5: Avoid Spacing and Periods*

Avoid internal spacing and internal periods in most abbreviations that contain all capital letters. Examples: ASTM, CSA, ASEE. Exceptions include professional titles and degrees, such as P.E., B.Sc., and B.A., and geographical terms such as U.S.A. and U.K.

■ *Rule 6: Be Careful with Company Names*

Abbreviate a company or other organizational name only when you are sure that officials from the organization consider the abbreviation appropriate. IBM (for the company) and CBC (for the public corporation) are two commonly accepted organizational abbreviations. When in doubt, follow Rule 2—write the name in full the first time it is used, followed by the abbreviation in parentheses.

■ *Rule 7: Use These Common Abbreviations*

The following common abbreviations are appropriate for most writing in your technical or business career. They appear here in three main categories: Measurements, Locations, and Titles.

Measurements: Only use the following abbreviations when you place numbers before the measurement.

ac	alternating current	K	Kelvin
amp	ampere	KE	kinetic energy
bbl.	barrel	kg	kilogram
Btu	British thermal unit	km	kilometre
bu.	bushel	km^2	square kilometre
C	Celsius	kW	kilowatt
cal	calorie	kWh	kilowatt-hour
cc	cubic centimetre	l	litre
circ	circumference	lb.	pound
cm	centimetre	lin	linear
cm^2	square centimetre	lm	lumen
cm^3	cubic centimetre	log	logarithm
cos	cosine	m	metre
cot	cotangent	min.	minute
cps	cycles per second	mm	millimetre
cu. ft.	cubic foot (feet)	oz.	ounce
dB	decibel	ppm	parts per million
dc	direct current	psf	pounds per square foot
dm	decimetre	psi	pounds per square inch
doz. or dz	dozen	pt.	pint
F	Fahrenheit	qt.	quart
F	farad	rev	revolution
fbm	foot board measure	rpm	revolutions per minute
fig.	figure	sec.	second
fl. oz.	fluid ounce	sq.	square
FM	frequency modulation	sq. ft.	square foot (feet)
fp	foot pound	t	tonne
ft.	foot (feet)	tan	tangent
g	gram	V	volt
gal.	gallon	VA	volt-ampere
gpm	gallons per minute	W	watt
hp	horsepower	wk.	week
hr.	hour	wl	wavelength
Hz	hertz	yd.	yard
in.	inch	yr.	year
J	joule		

Locations: Use the following common abbreviations for addresses (on envelopes and letters, for example), but write out the words in full in other contexts.

AB	Alberta	NU	Nunavut
BC	British Columbia	ON	Ontario
MB	Manitoba	PE	Prince Edward Island
NB	New Brunswick	PQ	Quebec
NF	Newfoundland and Labrador	SK	Saskatchewan
NT	Northwest Territories	YT	Yukon Territory
NS	Nova Scotia		

AL	Alabama	MO	Missouri
AK	Alaska	MT	Montana
AS	American Samoa	NE	Nebraska
AZ	Arizona	NV	Nevada
AR	Arkansas	NH	New Hampshire
CA	California	NJ	New Jersey
CZ	Canal Zone	NM	New Mexico
CO	Colorado	NY	New York
CT	Connecticut	NC	North Carolina
DE	Delaware	ND	North Dakota
DC	District of Columbia	OH	Ohio
FL	Florida	OK	Oklahoma
GA	Georgia	OR	Oregon
GU	Guam	PA	Pennsylvania
HI	Hawaii	PR	Puerto Rico
ID	Idaho	RI	Rhode Island
IL	Illinois	SC	South Carolina
IN	Indiana	SD	South Dakota
IA	Iowa	TN	Tennessee
KS	Kansas	TX	Texas
KY	Kentucky	UT	Utah
LA	Louisiana	VT	Vermont
ME	Maine	VI	Virgin Islands
MD	Maryland	VA	Virginia
MA	Massachusetts	WA	Washington
MI	Michigan	WV	West Virginia
MN	Minnesota	WI	Wisconsin
MS	Mississippi	WY	Wyoming

Titles: Some of the following abbreviations go before the name (such as *Dr., Ms.,* and *Messrs.*), while others go after the name (such as university degrees, *Jr.*, and *Sr.*).

B.A.	Bachelor of Arts
B.Sc.	Bachelor of Science
Dr.	Doctor (used mainly with medical and dental degrees but also with other doctorates)
Drs.	plural of Dr.
D.V.M.	Doctor of Veterinary Medicine
Hon.	Honourable
Jr.	Junior
LL.D.	Doctor of Laws
M.A.	Master of Arts
M.D.	Doctor of Medicine
Messrs.	Plural of Mr.
Mr.	Mister
Mrs.	used to designate married, widowed, or divorced women. (Note that many women prefer not to be known by their marital status.)
Ms.	used increasingly for all women, especially when the writer is uncertain about a woman's marital status
M.Sc.	Master of Science
Ph.D.	Doctor of Philosophy
Sr.	Senior

Affect/Effect

These two words cause untold grief among many writers. The key to using them correctly is to remember two simple sentences: (1) *affect* with an *a* is a verb meaning "to influence"; (2) *effect* with an *e* is a noun meaning "result." There are some exceptions, however, such as the following: *effect* can be a verb that means "to bring about," as in "He effected considerable change when he became a manager." Examples:

- "His progressive leadership greatly *affected* the company's future."
- "One *effect* of securing the large government contract was the hiring of several more accountants."
- "The president's belief in the future of microcomputers *effected* change in the company's approach to office management." (For a less wordy alternative, substitute *changed* for *effected change in*.)

Agree to/Agree with

In correct usage, *agree to* means that you have consented to an arrangement, an offer, a proposal, etc. *Agree with* is less constraining and only suggests that you are in harmony with a certain statement, idea, person, etc. Examples:

- "Representatives from M&K *agreed to* alter the contract to reflect the new scope of work."
- "We *agree with* you that more study may be needed before the nuclear power plant is built."

All Together/Altogether

All together is used when items or people are being considered in a group or are working in concert. *Altogether* is a synonym for *utterly* or *completely*. Examples:

- "The three firms were *all together* in their support of the agency's plan."
- "There were *altogether* too many pedestrians walking near the dangerous intersection."

Alternately/Alternatively

Because many readers are aware of the distinction between these two words, any misuse can cause embarrassment or even misunderstanding. Follow these guidelines for correct use.

Alternately. As a derivative of *alternate*, *alternately* is best reserved for events or actions that occur in turns. Example: "While digging the trench, he used a backhoe and a hand shovel *alternately* throughout the day."

Alternatively. A derivative of *alternative*, *alternatively* should be used in contexts where two or more choices are being considered. Example: "We suggest that you use deep foundations at the site. *Alternatively,* you could consider spread footings, provided they were carefully installed."

Amount/Number

Amount is used in reference to items that *cannot* be counted, whereas *number* is used to indicate items than *can* be counted. Examples:

- "In the last year, we have greatly increased the *amount* of computer paper ordered for the Montreal office."
- "The last year has seen a huge increase in the *number* [*not* amount] of boxes of computer paper ordered for the Montreal office."

Anticipate/Expect

These two words are *not* synonyms. In fact, their meanings are distinctly different. *Anticipate* is used when you mean to suggest or state that steps have been taken beforehand to prepare for a situation. *Expect* only means you consider something likely to occur. Examples:

- "*Anticipating* that the contract will be successfully negotiated, Jones Engineering is hiring three new hydrologists."
- "We *expect* [*not* anticipate] that you will encounter semicohesive and cohesive soils in your excavations at the Spring Garden Road site."

Assure/Ensure/Insure

Assure is a verb that can mean "to promise." It is used in reference to people, as in "We want to assure you that our crews will strive to complete the project on time." In fact, *assure* and its derivatives (like *assurance*) should be used with care in technical contexts, for these words can be viewed as a guarantee.

The synonyms *ensure* and *insure* are verbs meaning "to make certain." Like *assure*, they imply a level of certainty that is not always appropriate in engineering or the sciences. When their use is deemed appropriate, the preferred word is *ensure;* reserve *insure* for sentences in which the context is insurance. Examples:

- "Be *assured* that our representatives will be on-site to answer questions that the subcontractor may have."
- "To *ensure* that the project stays within schedule, we are building in 10 extra days for bad weather." (An alternative: "So that the project stays within schedule, we are building in 10 extra days for bad weather.")

Augment/Supplement

Augment is a verb that means "to increase" in size, weight, number, or importance. *Supplement* is either (1) a verb that means "to add to" something to make it complete or to make up for a deficiency or (2) a noun that means "the thing that has been added." Examples:

- "The power company supervisor decided to *augment* the line crews in five municipalities."
- "He *supplemented* the audit report by adding the three accounting statements."
- "The three accounting *supplements* helped support the conclusions of the audit report."

Awhile/A While

Awhile means "for a short time." Because *for* is already a part of its definition, it cannot be preceded by the preposition *for*. The noun *while*, however, can be preceded by the two words *for a*, giving it essentially the same meaning as *awhile*. Examples:

- "Kirk waited *awhile* before trying to restart the generator."
- "Kirk waited *for a while* before trying to restart the generator."

Between/Among

The distinction between these two words has become somewhat blurred. However, many readers still prefer to see *between* used with reference to only two items, reserving *among* for three or more items. Examples:

- "The agreement was just *between* my supervisor and me. No one else in the group knew about it."
- "The proposal was circulated *among* all members of the writing team."
- "*Among* Sallie, Todd, and Fran, there was little agreement about the long-term benefits of the project."

Capitalization

As a rule, you should capitalize *specific* names of people, places, and things—sometimes called "proper nouns." For example, capitalize specific streets, towns, trademarks, geological eras, planets, groups of stars, days of the week, months of the year, names of organizations, holidays, and colleges and universities. However, remember that excessive capitalization—as in titles of positions in a company—is inappropriate in technical writing and can appear somewhat pompous.

The following rules cover some frequent uses of capitals:

1. Major words in titles of books and articles. Only capitalize articles when they appear as the first word in titles, and prepositions when they appear as either the first or last words. Examples:
   - *For Whom the Bell Tolls*
   - *In Search of Excellence*
   - *The Power of Positive Thinking*

2. Names of places and geographical locations. Examples:
   - Peace Tower
   - Olympic Stadium
   - Newcastle, New Brunswick
   - Prince Edward County

3. Names of aircraft and ships. Examples:
   - *The Flying Dutchman*
   - HMS *Athabasca*
   - *Nonsuch*

4. Names of specific departments and offices within an organization. Examples:
   - Humanities Department
   - Personnel Department
   - International Division

5. Political, corporate, and other titles that come before names. Examples:
- Chancellor Hairston
- Councilwoman Jones
- Professor Gainesberg
- Prime Minister Pearson

Note, however, that general practice does not call for capitalizing most titles when they are used by themselves or when they follow a person's name. Examples:

- Jane Cannon, a professor in the Business Department
- Jacques Martin, president of Martin & Koffman
- Chris Presley, secretary of the Oil Rig Division

Complement/Compliment

Both words can be nouns and verbs, and both have adjective forms (*complementary, complimentary*).

Complement. This word is used as a noun to mean "that which has made something whole or complete"; as a verb to mean "to make whole, to make complete"; or as an adjective. You may find it easier to remember the word by recalling its mathematical definition: two complementary angles must always equal 90 degrees. Examples:

- (As noun): "The *complement* of five technicians brought our crew strength up to 100%."
- (As verb): "The firm in Ireland served to *complement* ours in that together we won a joint contract."
- (As adjective): "Seeing that project manager and her secretary work so well together made clear their *complementary* relationship in getting the office work done."

Compliment. This word is used as a noun to mean "an act of praise, flattery, or admiration"; as a verb to mean "to praise, to flatter"; or as an adjective to mean "related to praise or flattery, or without charge." Examples:

- (As noun): "He appreciated the verbal *compliments,* but he also hoped they would result in a substantial raise."
- (As verb): "Howard *complimented* the crew for finishing the job on time and within budget."
- (As adjective): "We were fortunate to receive several *complimentary* copies of the new software from the publisher."

Compose/Comprise

These are both acceptable words, with an inverse relationship to each other. *Compose* means "to make up or be included in," whereas *comprise* means "to include or consist of." The easiest way to remember this relationship is to memorize one mnemonic: "The parts compose the whole, but the whole comprises the parts." One more point to remember: the common phrase *is comprised of* is an incorrect, unacceptable replacement for *comprise* or *is composed of.* Careful writers do not use it. Examples:

- "Seven quite discrete layers *compose* the soils that were uncovered at the site."
- "The borings revealed a stratigraphy that *comprises* [*not* is comprised of] seven quite discrete layers."

Continuous/Continual

The technical accuracy of some reports may depend on your understanding of the difference between these two words. *Continuous* and *continuously* should be used in reference to uninterrupted, unceasing activities. However, *continual* and *continually* should be used with activities that are intermittent, or repeated at intervals. If you think your reader may not understand the difference, you should either (1) use synonyms that will be clearer (such as *uninterrupted* for *continuous*, and *intermittent* for *continual*) or (2) define each word at the point you first use it in the document. Examples:

- "We *continually* checked the water pressure for three hours before the equipment arrived, while also using the time to set up the next day's tests."
- "Because it rained *continuously* from 10:00 a.m. until noon, we were unable to move our equipment onto the utility easement."

Data/Datum

Coming as it does from the Latin, the word *data* is the plural form of *datum*. Although most writers now accept *data* as singular or plural, some in the scientific community still consider *data* exclusively a plural form (this textbook, for instance, uses *data* as a plural noun). However, common usage has popularized the use of *data* as singular. To many people, the "correct" use of the word seems odd. Therefore, unless there is a compelling reason to do otherwise, treat *data* as a singular noun. Examples:

Traditional:

- "These *data* show that there is a strong case for building the dam at the other location."
- "This particular *datum* shows that we need to reconsider the recommendations put forth in the original report."

Modern:

- "The data shows . . ."
- "This particular data shows . . ."

Definite/Definitive

Though similar in meaning, these words have slightly different contexts. *Definite* refers to that which is precise, explicit, or final. *Definitive* has the more restrictive meaning of "authoritative" or "final." Examples:

- "It is now *definite* that he will be assigned to the London office for six months."
- "He received the *definitive* study on the effect of the oil spill on the marine ecology."

Discrete/Discreet/Discretion

The adjective *discrete* suggests something that is separate, or something that is made up of many separate parts. The adjective *discreet* is associated with actions that require caution, modesty, or reserve. The noun *discretion* refers to the quality of being discreet or the freedom a person has to act on her or his own. Examples:

- "The orientation program at M&K includes a writing seminar, which is a *discrete* training unit offered for one full day."
- "The orientation program at M&K includes five *discrete* units."

- "As a counsellor in M&K's Human Resources Office, Sharon was *discreet* in her handling of personal information about employees."
- "Every employee in the Human Resources Office was instructed to show *discretion* in handling personal information about employees."
- "In its new flex-time program, M&K will give employees a good deal of *discretion* as to their hours of work."

Disinterested/Uninterested

In contemporary business use, these words have quite different meanings. Because errors can cause confusion for the reader, make sure not to use the words as synonyms. *Disinterested* means "without prejudice or bias," whereas *uninterested* means "showing no interest." Examples:

- "The agency sought a *disinterested* observer who had no stake in the outcome of the trial."
- "They spent several days talking to officials from Iceland, but they still remain *uninterested* in performing work in that country."

Due to/Because of

Besides irritating those who expect proper English, mixing these two phrases can also cause confusion. *Due to* is an adjective phrase meaning "attributable to" and almost always follows a "to be" verb (such as *is, was,* or *were*). *Due to* should not be used in place of prepositional phrases such as *because of, owing to,* or *as a result of.* Examples:

- "The cracked walls were *due to* the lack of proper foundation fill being used during construction."
- "We won the contract *because of* [*not* due to] our thorough understanding of the client's needs."

e.g./i.e.

The abbreviation *e.g.* means "for example," whereas *i.e.* means "that is." These two Latin abbreviations are often confused, a fact that should give you pause before using them. Many writers prefer to write them out, rather than risk confusing the reader. Examples:

- "During the trip, he visited cities where M&K is considering opening offices— e.g., [*or, preferably,* for example] Halifax, Ottawa, and Winnipeg.
- "A spot along the Zayante Fault was the earthquake's epicentre—i.e., [*or, preferably,* that is] the focal point for seismic activity."

Fewer/Less

The adjective *fewer* is used before items that can be counted, whereas the adjective *less* is used before mass quantities. When errors occur, they usually result from *less* being used with countable items, as in this *incorrect* sentence: "We can complete the job with less men at the site." Examples:

- "The newly certified industrial hygienist signed with us because the other firm he was interested in offered *fewer* [*not* less] benefits."
- "There was *less* sand in the sample taken from 15 m than in the one taken from 10 m."

Flammable/Inflammable/Nonflammable

Given the importance of these words in avoiding injury and death, make sure to use them correctly—especially in instructions. *Flammable* means "capable of burning quickly" and is acceptable usage. *Inflammable* has the same meaning, but it is *not* acceptable usage for this reason: some readers confuse it with *nonflammable*. The word *nonflammable*, then, means "not capable of burning" and is accepted usage. Examples:

- "They marked the package *flammable* because its contents could be easily ignited by a spark." (Note that *flammable* is preferred here over its synonym, *inflammable*.)
- "The foreman felt comfortable placing the crates near the heating unit, since all the crates' contents were *nonflammable*."

Fortuitous/Fortunate

The word *fortuitous* is an adjective that refers to an unexpected action, without regard to whether it is desirable or not. The word *fortunate* is an adjective that indicates an action that is clearly desired. The common usage error with this pair is the wrong assumption that "fortuitous" events must also be "fortunate." Examples:

- "Seeing M&K's London manager at the conference was quite *fortuitous,* since I had not been told that he also was attending."
- "It was indeed *fortunate* that I encountered the London manager of M&K for it gave us the chance to talk about an upcoming project involving both our offices."

Generally/Typically/Usually

Words like these can be useful qualifiers in your reports. They indicate to the reader that what you have stated is often, but not always, the case. Make certain to place these adverb modifiers as close as possible to the words they modify. In the following first example, it would be inaccurate to write "were typically sampled," in that the adverb modifies the entire verb phrase *were sampled*. Examples:

- "Cohesionless soils *typically* were sampled by driving a 3 cm diameter, split-barrel sampler." (Active-voice alternative: "*Typically,* we sampled cohesionless soils by driving a 3 cm diameter, split-barrel sampler.")
- "For projects like the one you propose, the technician *usually* will clean the equipment before returning to the office."
- "It is *generally* known that sites for dumping waste should be equipped with appropriate liners."

Good/Well

Though similar in meaning, *good* is used as an adjective and *well* is used as an adverb. A common usage error occurs when writers use the adjective when the adverb is required. Examples:

- "It is *good* practice to submit three-year plans on time."
- "He did *well* to complete the three-year plan on time, considering the many reports he had to finish that same week."

Imply/Infer

Remember that the person doing the speaking or writing implies, whereas the person hearing or reading the words infers. In other words, the word *imply* requires an active role; the word *infer* requires a passive role. When you imply a point, your words suggest rather than state a point. When you infer a point, you form a conclusion or deduce meaning from someone else's words or actions. Examples:

- "The contracts officer *implied* that there would be stiff competition for that $20 million waste treatment project."
- "We *inferred* from her remarks that any firm hoping to secure the work must have completed similar projects recently."

Its/It's

These words are often confused. You can avoid error by remembering that *it's* with the apostrophe is used *only* as a contraction for *it is* or *it has*. The other form—*its*—is a possessive pronoun. Examples:

- "Because of the rain, *it's* [*or* it is] going to be difficult to move the equipment to the site."
- "*It's* [*or* it has] been a long time since we submitted the proposal."
- "The company completed *its* part of the agreement on time."

Loose/Lose

Loose, which rhymes with *goose*, is an adjective that means "unfastened, flexible, or unconfined." *Lose*, which rhymes with *ooze*, is a verb that means "to misplace." Examples:

- "The power failure was linked to a *loose* connection at the switchbox."
- "Because of poor service, the photocopy machine company may *lose* its contract with M&K."

Modifiers: Dangling and Misplaced

This section includes guidelines for avoiding the most common modification errors—dangling modifiers and misplaced modifiers. But first we need to define the term *modifier*. Words, phrases, and even dependent clauses can serve as modifiers. They serve to qualify, or add meaning to, other elements in the sentence. For our purposes here, the most important point is that modifiers need to be clearly connected to what they modify.

Modification errors occur most often with verbal phrases. A phrase is a group of words that lacks either a subject or predicate. The term *verbal* refers to (1) gerunds (*-ing* form of verbs used as nouns, such as "He likes skiing"), (2) participles (*-ing* form of verbs used as adjectives, such as "Skiing down the hill, he lost a glove"), or (3) infinitives (the word *to* plus the verb root, such as "To attend the opera was his favourite pastime"). Now let's look at the two main modification errors.

Dangling modifiers.   When a verbal phrase "dangles," the sentence in which it is used contains no specific word for the phrase to modify. As a result, the meaning of the sentence can be confusing to the reader. For example, "In designing the foundation, several alternatives were discussed." It is not at all clear exactly who is doing the "designing." The phrase dangles because it does not modify a specific word. The modifier does not dangle in this version of the sentence: "In designing the foundation, we discussed several alternatives."

Misplaced modifiers. When a verbal phrase is misplaced, it may appear to refer to a word that it, in fact, does not modify. Example: "Floating peacefully near the oil rig, we saw two humpback whales." Obviously, the whales are doing the floating, and the rig workers are doing the seeing here. Yet because the verbal phrase is placed at the beginning of the sentence, rather than at the end immediately after the word it modifies, the sentence presents some momentary confusion.

Misplaced modifiers can lead to confusion about the agent of action in technical tasks. Example: "Before beginning to dig the observation trenches, we recommend that the contractors submit their proposed excavation program for our review." On quick reading, the reader is not certain about who will be "beginning to dig"—the contractors or the "we" in the sentence. The answer is the contractors. Thus a correct placement of the modifier would be "We recommend the following: before the contractors begin digging observation trenches, they should submit their proposed excavation for our review."

Solving modifier problems. At best, dangling and misplaced modifiers produce a momentary misreading by the audience. At worst, they can lead to confusion that results in disgruntled readers, lost customers, or liability problems. To prevent modification problems, place all verbal phrases—indeed, all modifiers—as close as possible to the word they modify. If you spot a modification error while you are editing, correct it in one of two ways:

1. Leave the modifier as it is and rework the rest of the sentence. Thus you would change "Using an angle of friction of 20 degrees and a vertical weight of 300 tonnes, the sliding resistance would be . . ." to the following: "Using an angle of friction of 20 degrees and a vertical weight of 300 tonnes, we computed a sliding resistance of . . ."
2. Rephrase the modifier as a complete clause. Thus you would change the previous original sentence to "If the angle of friction is 20 degrees and the vertical weight is 300 tonnes, the sliding resistance should be . . ."

In either case, your goal is to link the modifier clearly and smoothly with the word or phrase it modifies.

Numbers

Like rules for abbreviations, those for numbers vary from profession to profession and even from company to company. Most technical writing subscribes to the approach that numbers are best expressed in figures (45) rather than words (forty-five). Note that this style may differ from that used in other types of writing, such as this textbook. Unless the preferences of a particular reader suggest that you do otherwise, follow these common rules for use of numbers in writing your technical documents:

■ *Rule 1: Follow the 10-or-Over Rule*

In general, use figures for numbers of 10 or more, words for numbers below 10. Examples: three technicians at the site/15 reports submitted last month/one rig contracted for the job.

■ *Rule 2: Do Not Start Sentences with Figures*

Begin sentences with the word form of numbers, not with figures. Example: "Forty-five containers were shipped back to the lab."

■ *Rule 3: Use Figures as Modifiers*

Whether above or below 10, numbers are usually expressed as figures when used as modifiers with units of measurement, time, and money, especially when these units are abbreviated. Examples: 4 cm, 7 hr, 17%, $5 per hr. Exceptions can be made when the unit is not abbreviated. Example: five years.

■ *Rule 4: Use Figures in a Group of Mixed Numbers*

Use only figures when the numbers grouped together in a passage (usually *one* sentence) are both above and below 10. Example: "For that project they assembled 15 samplers, 4 rigs, and 25 containers." In other words, this rule argues for consistency within a writing unit.

■ *Rule 5: Use the Figure Form in Illustration Titles*

Use the numeric form when labelling specific tables and figures in your reports. Examples: Figure 3, Table 14-B.

■ *Rule 6: Be Careful with Fractions*

Express fractions as words when they stand alone, but as figures when they are used as a modifier or are joined to whole numbers. Example: "We have completed two-thirds of the project using the $2\frac{1}{2}$-in. pipe."

■ *Rule 7: Use Figures and Words with Numbers in Succession*

When two numbers appear in succession in the same unit, write the first as a word and the second as a figure. Example: "We found fifteen 3 cm pieces of pipe in the machinery."

■ *Rule 8: Only Rarely Use Numbers in Parentheses*

Except in legal documents, avoid the practice of placing figures in parentheses after their word equivalents. Example: "The second party will send the first party forty-five (45) barrels on or before the first of each month." Note that the parenthetical amount is placed immediately after the figure, not after the unit of measurement.

■ *Rule 9: Use Figures with Dollars*

Use figures with all dollar amounts, with the exception of the context noted in Rule 8. Avoid cents columns unless exactness to the penny is necessary.

■ *Rule 10: Use Commas in Four-Digit Figures*

To prevent possible misreading, use commas in figures of four digits or more. Examples: 15,000; 1,247; 6,003.

■   *Rule 11: Use Words for Ordinals*

Usually spell out the ordinal form of numbers. Example: "The government informed all parties of the first, second, and third [not 1st, 2nd, and 3rd] choices in the design competition." A notable exception is tables and figures, where space limitations could argue for the abbreviated form.

Oral/Verbal

Oral refers to words that are spoken, as in "oral presentation." The term *verbal* refers to spoken or written language. To prevent confusion, avoid the word *verbal* and instead specify your meaning with the words *oral* and *written*. Examples:

- "In its international operations, M&K has learned that some countries still rely on *oral* [*not* verbal] contracts."
- "Their *oral* agreement last month was followed by a *written* [*not* verbal] contract this month."

Parts of Speech

This term refers to the eight main groups of words in English grammar. A word's placement in one of these groups is based on its function within the sentence.

Noun.   Words in this group name persons, places, objects, or ideas. The two major categories are (1) proper nouns and (2) common nouns. Proper nouns name specific persons, places, objects, or ideas, and they are capitalized. Examples: *Whitehorse; Ottawa River; M&K; Student Government Association; Susan Jones; Existentialism.* Common nouns name general persons, places, objects, and ideas, and they are not capitalized. Examples: *truck, farmer, engineer, assembly line, philosophy.*

Verb.   A verb expresses action or state of being. Verbs give movement to sentences and form the core of meaning in your writing. Examples: *explore, grasp, write, develop, is, has.*

Pronoun.   A pronoun is a substitute for a noun. Some sample pronoun categories include (1) personal pronouns (*I, we, you, she, he*); (2) relative pronouns (*who, whom, that, which*); (3) reflexive and intensive pronouns (*myself, yourself, itself*); (4) demonstrative pronouns (*this, that, these, those*); and (5) indefinite pronouns (*all, any, each, anyone*).

Adjective.   An adjective modifies a noun. Examples: *horizontal, stationary, green, large, simple.*

Adverb.   An adverb modifies a verb, an adjective, another adverb, or a whole statement. Examples: *soon, generally, well, very, too, greatly.*

Preposition.   A preposition shows the relationship between a noun or pronoun (the object of a preposition) and another element of the sentence. Forming a prepositional phrase, the preposition and its object can reveal relationships such as location ("They went *over the hill*"), time ("He left *after the meeting*"), and direction ("She walked *toward the office*").

Conjunction.   A conjunction is a connecting word that links words, phrases, or clauses. Examples: *and, but, for, nor, although, after, because, since.*

Interjection.   As an expression of emotion, an interjection can stand alone ("Look out!") or can be inserted into another sentence.

Per Cent/Percent/Percentage

Per cent and *percent* have basically the same usage and are used with exact numbers. The one word *percent* is preferred. Even more common in technical writing, however, is the use of the percent sign (%) after numbers. The word *percentage* is only used to express general amounts, not exact numbers. Examples:

- "After completing a marketing survey, M&K discovered that 83 *percent* [*or* 83%] of its current clients have hired M&K for previous projects."
- "A large *percentage* of the defects can be linked to the loss of two experienced quality-control inspectors."

Principal/Principle

When these two words are misused, the careful reader will notice. Keep them straight by remembering this simple distinction: *principle* is always a noun that means "basic truth, belief, or theorem." Example: "He believed in the *principle* of free speech." *Principal* can be either a noun or an adjective and has three basic uses:

- **As a noun meaning "head official" or "person who plays a major role."** Example: "We asked that a *principal* in the firm sign the contract."
- **As a noun meaning "the main portion of a financial account upon which interest is paid."** Example: "If we deposit $5,000 in *principal,* we will earn 9% interest."
- **As an adjective meaning "main or primary."** Example: "We believe that the *principal* reason for contamination at the site is the leaky underground storage tank."

Pronouns: Agreement and Reference

A pronoun is a word that replaces a noun, which is called the *antecedent* of the pronoun. Examples: *this, it, he, she, they.* Pronouns, as such, provide you with a useful strategy for varying your style by avoiding repetition of nouns. Following are some rules to prevent pronoun errors:

■   *Rule 1: Make Pronouns Agree with Antecedents*

Check every pronoun to make certain it agrees with its antecedent in number. That is, both noun and pronoun must be singular, or both must be plural. Of special concern are the pronouns *it* and *they.* Examples:

- Change "M&K plans to complete their Yukon project next month" to this sentence: "M&K plans to complete *its* Yukon project next month."
- Change "The committee released their recommendations to all departments" to this sentence: "The committee released *its* recommendations to all departments."

■   *Rule 2: Be Clear about the Antecedent of Every Pronoun*

There must be no question about which noun a pronoun replaces. Any confusion about the antecedent of a pronoun can change the entire meaning of a sentence. To avoid such reference problems, you may need to rewrite a sentence or even use a noun rather than a pronoun. Do whatever is necessary to prevent misunderstanding by your reader. Example: Change "The gas filters for these tanks are so dirty that they should not be used" to this sentence: "These filters are so dirty that they should not be used."

■   *Rule 3: Avoid Using* **This** *as the Subject Unless a Noun Follows It*

A common stylistic error is the vague use of *this*, especially as the subject of a sentence. Sometimes the reference is not clear at all; sometimes the reference may be clear after several readings. In almost all cases, however, the use of *this* as a pronoun reflects poor technical style and tends to make the reader want to ask, "This what?" Instead, make the subject of your sentences concrete, either by adding a noun after the *this* or by recasting the sentence. Example: Change "He talked constantly about the project to be completed at the Olympics. This made his officemates irritable" to the following: "His constant talk about the Olympics project irritated his officemates."

Punctuation: General

Commas. Most writers struggle with commas, so you are not alone. The problem is threefold. First, the teaching of punctuation has been approached in different, and sometimes quite contradictory, ways. Second, comma rules themselves are subject to various interpretations. And third, problems with comma placement often mask more fundamental problems with the structure of a sentence itself.

You need to start by knowing the basic rules of comma use. The rules that follow are fairly simple. If you learn them now, you will save yourself a good deal of time later in that you will not be constantly questioning usage. In other words, the main benefit of learning the basics of comma use is increased confidence in your own ability to handle the mechanics of editing. (If you do not understand some of the grammatical terms that follow, such as *compound sentence*, refer to the section "Sentence Terms" in Chapter 16.)

■   *Rule 1: Commas in a Series*

Use commas to separate words, phrases, and short clauses written in a series of three or more items. Example: "The samples contained grey sand, sandy clay, and silty sand." According to current usage, a comma always comes before the *and* in a series.

■   *Rule 2: Commas in Compound Sentences*

Use a comma before the conjunction that joins main clauses in a compound sentence. Example: "We completed the drilling at the Smith Industries location, and then we grouted the holes with Sakrete." The comma is needed here to separate two complete clauses, each with its own subject and verb ("we completed" and "we grouted"). If the second *we* had been deleted, there would be only one clause, containing one subject and two verbs ("we completed and grouted"). Thus no comma would be needed. Of course, it may be that a sentence is far too long after this comma rule is applied. Break this rule if doing so will make the sentence clearer.

■ *Rule 3: Commas with Nonessential Modifiers*

Set off nonessential modifiers with commas, either at the beginning, the middle, or the end of sentences. Nonessential modifiers are usually phrases that add more information to a sentence, rather than greatly changing its meaning. When you speak, often there is a pause between this kind of modifier and the main part of the sentence, giving you a clue that a comma break is needed. Example: "The report, which we submitted three weeks ago, indicated that the company would not be responsible for transporting hazardous wastes." But: "The report that we submitted three weeks ago indicated that the company would not be responsible for transporting hazardous wastes." The first example includes a nonessential modifier, would be spoken with pauses, and therefore uses separating commas. The second example includes an *essential* modifier, would be spoken *without* pauses, and therefore includes *no* separating commas.

■ *Rule 4: Commas with Adjectives in a Series*

Use a comma to separate two or more adjectives that modify the same noun. To help you decide if adjectives modify the same noun, use this test: if you can reverse their positions and still retain the same meaning, then the adjectives modify the same word and should be separated by a comma. Example: "Jason opened the two containers in a clean, well-lighted place."

■ *Rule 5: Commas with Introductory Elements*

Use a comma after introductory phrases or clauses of about five words or more. Example: "After completing the topographic survey of the area, the crew returned to headquarters for its weekly project meeting." Commas like the one after *area* help readers separate secondary or modifying points from your main idea, which of course should be in the main clause. Without these commas, readers may have difficulty reading such sentences properly.

■ *Rule 6: Commas in Dates, Titles, Etc.*

Abide by the conventions of comma usage in punctuating dates, titles, geographic place names, and addresses. Examples:

- "May 3, 2006, is the projected date of completion." (But note the change in the "military" form of dates: "We will complete the project on 3 May 2006.")
- "John F. Dunwoody, Ph.D., has been hired to assist on the project."
- "Smithson, Inc., has been selected for the project."
- "He listed Laval, Quebec, as his permanent residence."

Note the need for commas after the year "2006," the title "Ph.D.," the designation "Inc.," and the province name "Quebec." Also note that if the day had not been in the first example, there would have been no comma between the month and year and no comma after the year.

Semicolons. The semicolon is easy to use if you remember that it, like a period, indicates the end of a complete thought. Its most frequent use is in situations where grammar rules would allow you to use a period but where your stylistic preference is for a less abrupt connector. Example: "Five engineers left the convention hotel after dinner; only two had returned by midnight."

One of the most common punctuation errors, the comma splice, occurs when a comma is used instead of a semicolon or period in compound sentences connected by words such as *however, therefore, thus,* and *then.* When you see that these connectors separate two main clauses, make sure either to use a semicolon or to start a new sentence. Example: "We made it to the project site by the agreed-upon time; however, [or " . . . time. However, . . .] the rain forced us to stay in our trucks for two hours."

As noted in the "Punctuation: Lists" entry, there is another instance in which you might use semicolons. Place them after the items in a list when you are treating the list like a sentence and when any one of the items contains internal commas.

Colons. As mentioned in the "Punctuation: Lists" entry, you should place a colon immediately after the last word in the lead-in before a formal list of bulleted or numbered items. Example: "Our field study involved these three steps:" or "In our field study we were asked to:" The colon may come after a complete clause, as in the first example, or it may split a grammatical construction, as in the second example. However, it is preferable to use a complete clause before a formal list.

The colon can also be used in sentences in which you want a formal break before a point of clarification or elaboration. Example: "They were interested in just one result: quality construction." In addition, use the colon in sentences in which you want a formal break before a series that is not part of a listing. Example: "They agreed to perform all on-site work required in these four cities: Moncton, Fredericton, Saint John, and Halifax." But note that there is no colon before a sentence series without a break in thought. Example: "They agreed to perform all the on-site work required in Moncton, Fredericton, Saint John, and Halifax."

Apostrophes. The apostrophe can be used for contractions, for some plurals, and for possessives. Only the latter two uses cause confusion. Use an apostrophe to indicate the plural form of a word *as a word.* Example: "That redundant paragraph contained seven *area*'s and three *factor*'s in only five sentences." Although some writers also use apostrophes to form the plurals of numbers and full-cap abbreviations, the current tendency is to include only the *s.* Examples: 7s, ABCs, PCBs, P.E.s.

As for possessives, you probably already know that the grammar rules seem to vary, depending on the reference book you are reading. Following are some simple guidelines:

■   *Possessive Rule 1*

Form the possessive of singular nouns ending in *s* or an *s* sound by adding an apostrophe plus *s.* Examples: Hoss's horse, Tex's song, the actress's costume, the genius's test score, the boss's progress report.

■   *Possessive Rule 2*

Form the possessive of all plural nouns ending in *s* or an *s* sound by adding just an apostrophe. Examples: the cars' engines, the ducks' flight path, the trees' roots.

■   *Possessive Rule 3*

Form the possessive of all singular and plural nouns not ending in *s* by adding an apostrophe plus *s.* Examples: the man's hat, the men's team, the company's policy.

■   *Possessive Rule 4*

Form the possessive of paired nouns by first determining whether there is joint or individual ownership. For joint ownership, make only the last noun possessive. For individual ownership, make both nouns possessive. Example: "Susan and Terry's project was entered in the science fair; but Tom's and Scott's projects were not."

Quotation marks.   In technical writing, you may want to use this form of punctuation for specific word definitions (the word being defined is usually italicized), to indicate passages taken directly from another source, or to enclose the titles of short documents, such as reports or book chapters. The rule to remember is this: periods and commas go inside quotation marks; semicolons and colons go outside quotation marks.

Parentheses.   Use parentheses carefully, since long parenthetical expressions can cause the reader to lose your train of thought. This form of punctuation can be used when you (1) place an abbreviation after a complete term, (2) add a brief explanation within the text, or (3) include reference citations within the document text (as explained in Chapter 14). The period goes after the closing parenthesis when the parenthetical information is part of the sentence, as in the previous sentence. (However, it goes *inside* the closing parenthesis when the parenthetical information forms its own sentence, as in the sentence you are reading.)

Brackets.   Use a pair of brackets (1) to set off parenthetical material already contained within another parenthetical statement and (2) to draw attention to a comment you are making within a quoted passage. Example: "Two M&K studies have shown that the Colony Dam is up to safety standards. (See Figure 4-3 [Dam Safety Record] for a complete record of our findings.) In addition, the county engineer has a letter on file that will give further assurance to prospective homeowners on the lake. His letter notes that 'After finishing my three-month study [he completed the study in July 1993], I conclude that the Colony Dam meets all safety standards set by the county and state governments.'"

Hyphens.   The hyphen is used to form certain word compounds in English. Although the rules for its use sometimes seem to change from handbook to handbook, those that follow are the most common.

■   *Hyphen Rule 1*

Use hyphens with compound numerals, if you are using spelled-out numbers. Example: twenty-one through ninety-nine.

■   *Hyphen Rule 2*

Use hyphens with most compounds that begin with *self.* Examples: *self-defence, self-image, self-pity.* Some *self* compounds, however, such as *selfhood* and *selfsame*, are written as unhyphenated words. Consult your dictionary when in doubt.

■   *Hyphen Rule 3*

Use hyphens with group modifiers when they precede the noun but not when they follow the noun. Examples: a well-organized paper, a paper that was well organized, twentieth-century geotechnical technology, bluish-grey shale, fire-tested material, thin-bedded limestone.

However, when the first word of the modifier is an adverb ending in *-ly*, place no hyphen between the words. Examples: carefully drawn plate, frightfully ignorant teacher.

■   *Hyphen Rule 4*

Place hyphens between prefixes and root words in the following cases: (a) between a prefix and a proper name (ex-Republican, pre-Sputnik); (b) between some prefixes that end with a vowel and root words beginning with a vowel, particularly if the use of a hyphen would prevent an odd spelling (semi-independent, re-enter, re-elect); and (c) between a prefix and a root when the hyphen helps to prevent confusion (re-sent, not resent; re-form, not reform; re-cover, not recover).

Punctuation: Lists

As noted in Chapter 4 ("Page Design and Web Design"), listings draw attention to parallel pieces of information whose importance would be harder to grasp in paragraph format. In other words, use lists as an attention-getting strategy. Following are some general pointers for punctuating lists. (See Chapter 4 for other rules for lists.)

You have three main options for punctuating a listing. The common denominators for all three are that you (1) always place a colon after the last word of the lead-in and (2) always capitalize the first letter of the first word of each listed item.

Option A: Place no punctuation after listed items. This style is appropriate when the list includes only short phrases. More and more writers are choosing this option, as opposed to Option B. Example:

"In this study, we will develop recommendations that address these six concerns in your project:

- Site preparation
- Foundation design
- Sanitary sewer design
- Storm sewer design
- Geologic surface faulting
- Projections for regional land subsidence"

Option B: Treat the list like a sentence series. In this case, you place commas or semicolons between items and a period at the end of the series. Whether you choose Option A or B largely depends on your own style or that of your employer. Example:

"In this study, we developed recommendations that dealt with four topics:

- Site preparation,
- Foundation design,
- Sewer construction, and
- Geologic surface faulting."

Note that this option requires you to place an *and* after the comma that appears before the last item. Another variation of Option B occurs when you have internal commas within one or more of the items. In this case, you need to change the commas that follow the listed items into semicolons. Yet you still keep the *and* before the last item. Example:

"Last month we completed environmental assessments at three locations:

- A gas refinery in Edmonton, Alberta;
- The site of a former chemical plant in Sarnia, Ontario; and
- A waste pit outside Sydney, Nova Scotia."

Option C: Treat each item like a separate sentence. When items in a list are complete sentences, you may want to punctuate each one like a separate sentence, placing a period at the end of each. You *must* choose this option when one or more of your listed items contain more than one sentence. Example:

"The main conclusions of our preliminary assessment are summarized here:

- At five of the six borehole locations, petroleum hydrocarbons were detected at concentrations greater than a background concentration of 10 mg/kg.
- No PCB concentrations were detected in the subsurface soils we analyzed. We will continue the testing, as discussed in our proposal.
- Sampling and testing should be restarted three weeks from the date of this report."

Sic

Latin for "thus," this word is most often used when a quoted passage contains an error or other point that might be questioned by the reader. Inserted within brackets, *sic* shows the reader that the error was included in the original passage—and that it was not introduced by you. Example: "The customer's letter to our sales department claimed that 'there are too [sic] or three main flaws in the product.'"

Spelling

All writers find at least some words difficult to spell, and some writers have major problems with spelling. Automatic spell-checking software helps solve the problem; even so, you still need to remain vigilant during the proofreading stage. One or more misspelled words in an otherwise well-written document may cause readers to question professionalism in other areas.

This entry includes a list of commonly misspelled words. However, you should keep your own list of words you most frequently have trouble spelling. Like most writers, you probably have a relatively short list of words that give you repeated difficulty.

absence	allotting	calendar	conscious
accessible	analysis	career	controlled
accommodate	analyse	changeable	convenient
accumulate	arctic	channel	definitely
accustomed	athlete	column	dependable
achievement	athletic	commitment	descend
acknowledgment	awful	committee	dilemma
acquaintance	basically	compatible	disappear
admittance	believable	compelled	disappoint
advisable	benefited	conscience	disaster
aisle	bulletin	conscientious	disastrous

efficient	incidentally	miscellaneous	recession
eligible	independence	misspelled	reference
embarrass	indispensable	mortgage	safety
endurance	ingenious	movable	similar
environment	initially	necessary	sincerely
equipment	initiative	noticeable	specifically
equipped	insistence	nuisance	subtle
essential	interfered	numerous	temperament
exaggerate	interference	occasionally	temperature
existence	interrupt	occurred	thorough
experience	irrelevant	occurrence	tolerance
familiar	judgment	omission	transferred
favourite	knowledge	pamphlet	truly
February	later	parallel	undoubtedly
foreign	latter	pastime	unmistakably
foresee	liable	peculiar	until
forfeit	liaison	possess	useful
forty	library	practically	usually
fourth	lightning	preference	valuable
genius	likely	preferred	various
government	loneliness	privilege	vehicle
guarantee	maintenance	profession	wholly
guidance	manageable	professor	writing
handicapped	manoeuvre	pronunciation	written
harass	mathematics	publicly	
height	medieval	quantity	
illogical	mileage	questionnaire	

Writers in Canada may be expected to use either Canadian or American spelling, depending on the audience. For example, American spelling is commonly used in scientific and technical fields. Know your audience, and whichever spelling system you use, make sure you are consistent throughout the document.

Here are some of the most common differences between Canadian and American spelling:

- Canadian spelling uses "-our" endings where American spelling uses "-or" (*colour, labour,* and *neighbour* versus *color, labor,* and *neighbor*).
- The Canadian "-re" in words such as *centre* and *theatre* is "-er" in American spelling (*center, theater*).
- Canadian spelling doubles some final consonants when adding suffixes (*traveller*) while American spelling retains the single consonant (*traveler*).

Other Canadian spelling to be noted include words such as *cheque* (American *check*) and *catalogue* (American *catalog*). The *Canadian Oxford Dictionary* is a useful reference for Canadian spelling.

Subject–Verb Agreement

Subject–verb agreement errors are quite common in technical writing. They occur when writers fail to make the subject of a clause agree in number with the verb.

Example: "The nature of the diverse geological deposits are explained in the report." (The verb should be *is*, since the singular subject is *nature*.)

Writers who tend to make these errors should devote special attention to them. Specifically, isolate the subjects and verbs of all the clauses in a document and make certain that they agree. Following are seven specific rules for making subjects agree with verbs:

■ *Rule 1: Subjects Connected by* **And** *Take Plural Verbs*

This rule applies to two or more words or phrases that, together, form one subject phrase. Example: "The site preparation section and the foundation design portion of the report are to be written by the same person."

■ *Rule 2: Verbs After* **Either/Or** *Agree with the Nearest Subject*

Subject words connected by *either* or *or* confuse many writers, but the rule is clear: your verb choice depends on the subject nearest the verb. Example: "He told his group that neither the three reports nor the proposal was to be sent to the client that week."

■ *Rule 3: Verbs Agree with the Subject, Not with the Subjective Complement*

Sometimes called a predicate noun or adjective, a subjective complement renames the subject and occurs after verbs such as *is, was, are,* and *were.* Example: "The theme of our proposal is our successful projects in that region of the state." But the same rule would permit this usage: "Successful projects in that part of the state are the theme we intend to emphasize in the proposal."

■ *Rule 4: Prepositional Phrases Do Not Affect Matters of Agreement*

As long as, in addition to, as well as, and *along with* are prepositions, not conjunctions. A verb agrees with its subject, not with the object of a prepositional phrase. Example: "The manager of human resources, along with the personnel director, is supposed to meet with the three applicants."

■ *Rule 5: Collective Nouns Usually Take Singular Verbs*

Collective nouns have singular form but usually refer to a group of persons or things (for example, *team, committee,* or *crew*). When a collective noun refers to a group as a whole, use a singular verb. Example: "The project crew was ready to complete the assignment." Occasionally, a collective noun refers to the members of the group acting in their separate capacities. In this case, either use a plural verb or, to avoid awkwardness, reword the sentence. Example: "The crew were not in agreement about the site locations." Or, "Members of the crew were not in agreement about the site locations."

■ *Rule 6: Foreign Plurals Usually Take Plural Verbs*

Although usage is gradually changing, most careful writers still use plural verbs with *data, strata, phenomena, media,* and other irregular plurals. Example: "The data he asked for in the request for proposal are incorporated into the three tables."

■ *Rule 7: Indefinite Pronouns Like* **Each** *and* **Anyone** *Take Singular Verbs*

Writers often fail to follow this rule when they make the verb agree with the object of a prepositional phrase, instead of with the subject. Example: "Each of the committee members are ready to adjourn" (incorrect). "Each of the committee members is ready to adjourn" (correct).

Their/There/They're

Some people have difficulty deciding which of the three versions is correct in a given situation. *Their* is a possessive pronoun. *There* is a place or a direction. *They're* is the contraction for *they are*.

- "All the elephants wash *their* Morris Minis at Joe's Wash 'n Wax."
- "The service *there* is excellent."
- "*They're* impressed by the way Joe removes the footprints from the upholstery."

To/Too/Two

To is either part of the infinitive verb form *or* is a preposition in a prepositional phrase. *Too* is either an adverb that suggests an excessive amount *or* that means "also." *Two* is a noun or an adjective that stands for the numeral 2. Examples:

- "He volunteered *to* go [infinitive verb] *to* Alaska [prepositional phrase] *to* work [another infinitive verb form] on the project."
- "Stephanie explained that the proposed hazardous waste dump would pose *too* many risks *to* the water supply. Scott made this point, *too*."

Utilize/Use

Utilize is simply a long form for the preferred verb *use*. Although some verbs that end in *-ize* are useful words, most are simply wordy substitutes for shorter forms. As some writing teachers say, "Why use *utilize* when you can use *use*?"

Who/Whom

These two words give writers (and speakers) fits, but the importance of their correct use probably has been exaggerated. If you want to be one who uses the two words properly, remember this basic point: *who* is a subjective form that can only be used in the subject slot of a clause; *whom* is an objective form that can only be used as a direct object or other nonsubject noun form of a sentence. Examples:

- "The man *who* you said called me yesterday is a good customer of the firm." (The clause "who . . . called me yesterday" modifies *man*. Within this clause, *who* is the subject of the verb *called*. Note that the subject role of *who* is not affected by the two words *you said*, which interrupt the clause.)
- "They could not remember the name of the person *whom* they interviewed." (The clause "whom they interviewed" modifies *person*. Within this clause, *whom* is the direct object of the verb *interviewed*.)

Exercise 1: Grammar and Mechanics

The following passages contain a variety of grammatical and mechanical errors covered in the Handbook. The major focus is punctuation. Rewrite each passage.

1. Some concerns regarding plumbing design are mentioned in our report, however, no unusual design problems are expected.
2. An estimate of the total charges for an audit and for three site visits are based on our standard fee schedules.
3. The drill bit was efficient cheap and available.
4. The plan unless we have completely misjudged it, will increase sales markedly.
5. Our proposal contains design information for these two parts of the project; Phase 1 (evaluating the 3 computers) and Phase 2 (installing the computer selected).
6. If conditions require the use of all-terrain equipment to reach the construction locations, this will increase the cost of the project slightly.
7. An asbestos survey was beyond the scope of this project, if you want one, we would be happy to submit a proposal.
8. Jones-Simon Company, the owners of the new building, were informed of the problem with the foundation.
9. Also provided is the number and type of tests to be given at the office.
10. Calculating the standard usages by the current purchase order prices result in a downward adjustment of $.065.
11. Data showing the standard uses of the steel, including allowances for scrap, waste and end pieces of the tube rolls, are included for your convenience at the end of this report in Table 7.
12. This equipment has not been in operation for 3 months, and therefore, its condition could not be determined by a quick visual inspection.
13. Arthur Jones Manager of the Calgary branch wrote that three proposals had been accepted.
14. The generator that broke yesterday has been shipped to Corner Brook already by Harry Thompson.
15. The first computer lasted eight years the second two years.
16. He wants one thing out of their work speed.
17. On 25 September 2005 the papers were signed.
18. On March 23 2006 the proposal was accepted.
19. The meeting was held in Fredericton the Capital of New Brunswick.
20. Hanson, Inc. completed its Indonesia project in record time.
21. He decided to write for the brochure then he changed his mind.
22. Interest by the Kettering Hospital staff in the development of a masterplan for the new building wings have been expressed.
23. However much he wants to work for Gasion engineering he will turn the job down if he has to move to another state.
24. 35 computer scientists attended the convention, but only eleven of them were from private industry.
25. Working at a high salary gives him some satisfaction still he would like more emotional satisfaction from his job.

26. His handwriting is almost unreadable therefore his secretary asked him to dictate letters.
27. Any major city especially one that is as large as Toronto is bound to have problems with mass transit.
28. He ended his speech by citing the company motto; "Quality first, last, and always".
29. Montreal situated on the St. Lawrence River is an important international port.
30. The word *effect* is in that student's opinion a difficult one to use.
31. All persons who showed up for the retirement party, told stories about their association with Charlie over the years.
32. The data that was included in the study seems inconclusive.
33. My colleague John handled the presentation for me.
34. Before he arrived failure seemed certain.
35. While evaluating the quality of her job performance a study was made of her writing skills by her supervisor.
36. I shall contribute to the fund for I feel that the cause is worthwhile.
37. James visited the site however he found little work finished.
38. There are three stages cutting grinding and polishing.
39. The three stages are cutting grinding and polishing.
40. Writers occasionally create awkward verbs *prioritize* and *terminate* for example.
41. Either the project engineers or the consulting chemist are planning to visit with the client next week.
42. Besides Gerry Dave worked on the Peru project.
43. The corporation made a large unexpected gift to the university.
44. The reason for his early retirement are the financial incentives given by his employer.
45. Profit, safety and innovation are the factors that affect the design of many foundations.
46. No later than May 2006 the building will be finished.
47. Each of the committee members complete a review of the file submitted by the applicant.
48. The team completed their collaborative writing project on schedule.
49. Both the personnel officers and the one member of the quality team is going to attend the conference in Fargo.
50. He presented a well organized presentation but unfortunately the other speakers on the panel were not well-prepared.

Exercise 2: Usage

For each of the following passages, select the correct word or phrase from the choices within the parentheses. Be ready to explain your choice.

1. John (implied, inferred) in his report that TransAm Oil should reject the bid.
2. Before leaving on vacation, the company president left instructions for the manner in which responsibilities should be split (among, between) the three vice presidents.

3. Harold became (uninterested, disinterested) in the accounting problem after working on it for 18 straight hours.

4. A large (percent, percentage) of the tellers is dissatisfied with the revised work schedule.

5. The typist responded that he would make (less, fewer) errors if the partner would spell words correctly in the draft.

6. From her reading of the annual report, Ms. Jones (inferred, implied) that the company might expand its operations.

7. The president's decision concerning flex-time will be (effected, affected) by the many conversations he is having with employees about scheduling difficulties.

8. His (principal, principle) concern was that the loan's interest and (principle, principal) remain under $500.

9. Throughout the day, his concentration was interrupted (continuously, continually) by phone calls.

10. He jogged (continuously, continually) for 20 minutes.

11. Five thousand books (compose, comprise) his personal library.

12. The clients (who, whom) he considered most important received Christmas gifts from the company.

13. The company decided to expand (its, it's) operations in the hope that (its, it's) the right time to do so.

14. The (nonflammable, flammable, inflammable) liquids were kept in a separate room, because of their danger.

15. They waited for (awhile, a while) before calling the subcontractor.

16. Caution should be taken to (ensure, insure) that the alarm system will not go off accidentally.

17. The new floors (are comprised of, are composed of, comprise) a thick concrete mixture.

18. He (expects, anticipates) that 15 new employees will be hired this year.

19. The main office offered to (augment, supplement) the annual operating budget of the Vancouver office with an additional $100,000 in funds.

20. It was (all together, altogether) too late to make changes in the proposal.

21. The arbitrator made sure that both parties (agreed to, agreed with) the terms and conditions of the contract before it was submitted to the board.

22. Option 1 calls for complete removal of the asbestos. (Alternately, Alternatively), Option 2 would only require that the asbestos material be thoroughly covered.

23. They had not considered the (amount, number) of cement blocks needed for the new addition.

24. (Due to, Because of) the change in weather, they had to reschedule the trip to the project site.

25. The health inspector found (too, to) many violations in that room (to, too).

26. They claimed that the old equipment (used, utilized) too much fuel.

27. Gone are the days when a major construction job gets started with a handshake and (a verbal, an oral) agreement.

28. The complex project has 18 (discreet, discrete) phases; each part deals with confidential information that must be handled (discretely, discreetly).

29. He was (definitive, definite) about the fact that he would not be able to complete the proposal by next Tuesday.
30. He usually received (complementary, complimentary) samples from his main suppliers.
31. To (lose, loose) a client for whom they had worked so hard was devastating.
32. It was (fortunate, fortuitous) he was there at the exact moment the customer needed to order a year's worth of supplies, for the sales commission was huge.
33. Among all the information on the graph, he located the one (data, datum) that shows the price of salmon on the Vancouver market at 5 p.m. on August 7.
34. Each (principle, principal) of the corporation was required to buy stock.
35. He returned to the office to (assure, ensure) that the safe was locked.

APPENDIX

COMMUNICATION CHALLENGE 1

"There Ain't No Justice"

Eddie Gustafson and Fred Gingras were registered in Technical Writing during their second semester at Northern College. Eddie, who had received an A in English in his last year of high school, had managed to acquire an exemption from first-semester English at the College. Fred, a weak English student in high school, had not. In fact, Fred had some problems with English because it was his second language.

Their professor, Miranda Arons, had assigned a report instead of an end-of-semester exam. For the report, students were to inspect and evaluate a process, mechanism, or situation. Based on the results of their inspection/evaluation, they were to write proposals to correct any problems or shortcomings that were identified.

Eddie, who was fascinated by computers, spent a great deal of time researching virus scanners. He did extensive research on the various types of viruses, found out what scanners were available, and did hands-on testing to determine how well each of the scanners functioned. He became very knowledgeable. Then he wrote a report that detailed his findings, taking great care to use language and style that would show his command of language.

For his report, Fred inspected one of the College's labs. He examined the lighting, checked the condition of the furniture, catalogued the equipment and its condition, and determined the level of ambient noise. He also asked hearing-impaired and wheelchair students if they experienced any difficulties in the lab. He then laboriously wrote a report that provided a plan for solving the problems he had found, and provided a cost estimate.

When Professor Arons returned their papers, Eddie received a D grade and Fred received an A–. When the two compared their papers they found that Fred had actually committed more grammatical and spelling errors. The comment on Eddie's paper said that the paper "Lacks focus because the function (purpose) of the report is not defined and a context has not been established."

Eddie was furious. He went to see Professor Arons and complained that his mark was not fair. He said that he had compared his report to those written by others. He felt that he had done as much or more work as anyone and that he had not made as many mistakes as many did. Although Professor Arons refused to discuss the papers of other students, she did admit that Eddie may not have made as many errors as did some others. She said his writing style was not appropriate to a technical report. She also explained that, although she understood he had worked hard, he had failed to address the primary function of the report, which was to propose solutions to a specific problem.

Taken from: *Technical Writing: A Practical Approach*, Third Edition, by William S. Pfeiffer and Jan Boogerd.

Questions for Discussion

1. Did Eddie have a right to be furious?
2. Should the lack of spelling and grammar errors have given Eddie a better grade?
3. Was Fred's grade appropriate? If so, why? If not, why not?
4. Would Eddie's grade have been higher if he had submitted the report in another course? If so, why? If not, why not?
5. Would your attitude change if you knew that Fred had submitted his paper to a local magazine, which had published it as an article? If so, why? If not, why not?

COMMUNICATION CHALLENGE 2

"M&K's Moscow Buyout: Global Dilemmas"

M&K has steadily grown to the point where it now has 15 branches. Though conservative in its approach to growth, the M&K corporate staff is still looking for ways to add international offices so that it can expand its business. Jacques Martin and his staff are considering a recent international opportunity. The following section provides (1) background on the possible buyout of a Moscow firm, (2) issues that the buyout study has raised, and (3) questions and comments for discussion.

Background on the Moscow Buyout

With the break-up of the Soviet Union in December 1991, the 15 republics that made up one of the largest and most powerful empires in the world became a group of separate nations. Actually, economic changes had begun several years earlier with the arrival of *glasnost* (the new openness to other cultures and ideas) and *perestroika* (the economic restructuring of the country). Out of the economic change that followed came many new companies run by a new class of entrepreneurs called *biznesmeny*. One member of this group, Vlad Gorky, joined with some former government engineers and scientists to establish an engineering firm called, in translation, Moscow Technical Services (MTS). By 2000, the firm had grown to 75 employees.

Jacques Martin is interested in the potential for work in Russia and other former Soviet republics, and has met with Vlad Gorky several times, in Canada and in Moscow. The stage has been set for M&K to buy out MTS soon. All government and regulatory requirements have been met in both Canada and Russia. The only remaining obstacle is approval by (1) an M&K committee consisting of high-level corporate staff and representative employees from various levels and offices, and (2) an MTS committee made up of the six principals of that firm. Both groups are meeting this week to discuss important issues relating to the purchase. The thorniest of these issues are summarized below.

Problems with the Buyout

In many ways the buyout appears to be a "win-win" for both firms. M&K wants an avenue into Russia's growing markets—especially for construction expertise and environmental work. MTS, for its part, needs additional capital to expand its operations and wants the stability associated with being part of an international firm. Yet the buyout committees in both firms are struggling with the following issues, among others:

Language

When it started acquiring international offices, M&K adopted a policy that all internal documents would be written in English, to reduce communication barriers within the company. Most external documents, like reports and proposals, are also in English, unless of course clients request otherwise. The only place where this policy is not strictly adhered to is the Montreal branch of Martin & Koffman. Although that office communicates with the head office in English, written communications between office staff in Montreal are in either French or English. All of the staff are bilingual, but people tend to communicate in their first language. With rare exceptions, all of the documents written for clients in Quebec are in French.

The situation in Montreal for M&K is not comparable to the Russian situation. MTS employees do not have the same English skills. In addition, there is the problem of pride. The English-only language policy bothers the MTS committee. MTS sees no reason why it should not continue to write internal memos, reports, procedures, and other documents in Russian. Particularly in light of the practice in the Montreal office of M&K, the MTS committee sees no strong rationale for the English-only policy. To them it smacks of the kind of arbitrary centralized control they remember all too well.

Work rules

Like many new, small entrepreneurial firms around the world, MTS has remained unstructured in its approach to work rules—office hours, lunch breaks, vacation time, job duties, policies and procedures, and so on. The firm was started by a creative, innovative scientist who has attracted many like-minded colleagues. Work rules were not at the top of their list of concerns. M&K, however, has a Human Resources Manual that is quite specific about issues such as work hours (whether regular or flextime), vacation time, office dress, required training, and safety. M&K would want it to be used in the Moscow branch.

Perceptions of undue influence

M&K knows that many of the MTS principals, especially those in the environmental field, were formerly part of the communist technical bureaucracy. They still have strong friendships with present-day officials and do a considerable amount of work for the government. Indeed, MTS continues to hire technical specialists straight from government jobs that pay much less. This "revolving door" practice is considered business as usual by the firm, and provides MTS with well-educated workers who know where the work is. Although no one at M&K is uncomfortable with being friends with clients, some members of the M&K buyout committee are worried about the perception, if not the reality, of undue influence at MTS caused by close associations with, and the "revolving door" hiring of, government officials. At the very least, they worry that the buyout may appear to be an effort by M&K to gain Russian projects through unfair means. Russian officials may hold that perception or it may be held by international competitors of M&K.

Questions and Comments for Discussion

Answer the following questions from your own point of view. Before doing so, however, make sure you have carefully considered the perspective of both M&K and MTS.

1. Is M&K's English-only policy justified? Is there any compromise that would satisfy both groups in this dispute?

2. Elaborate on some of the general language problems multinational firms can face.

3. The use of English does not by itself break down communication barriers with colleagues and customers at global firms. That is, English is spoken around the world by people from many different cultures. Its use does not mean that people necessarily think, write, or speak by the same conventions. Examine this view. Putting aside obvious dialect and vocabulary differences, how can a person's culture and national background affect the use of English in writing and speaking?

4. How can the work rules controversy be solved? How might the way this issue is resolved affect the success of the entire buyout? Give your opinion on the degree to which common work rules and practices are important at M&K's Canadian offices.

5. Discuss the dilemma posed by MTS's close association with the government. What are the real and perceived problems here? Which problems most concern M&K, and why? Is there a solution that would satisfy both sides?

COMMUNICATION CHALLENGE 3

"Telecommuting: The Last Frontier?"

Calling themselves the "Commute Group," five managers at M&K's Montreal office have been meeting to discuss telecommuting (permitting some or all employees to do part of their work at home). Jacques Martin has expressed interest in the group's work. He has asked Angela Koffman to advise the group. Angela suggests that the group use her expertise and their own knowledge of local conditions to write a report proposing a pilot project at the branch. The report would be read by Jacques Martin and by members of M&K's corporate staff in Toronto. Corporate headquarters must approve any change in branch work schedules.

The Commute Group now must decide (1) what to include in its report and (2) how to organize the information for maximum impact. What follows are some details on the audience for the report, the group's reasons for favouring telecommuting, some problems discussed by the group, and questions that remain about the organization of the report. Although the group has made progress in discussing telecommuting, it has been unable to decide on a structure for its report.

Report Audience

The group has spent much time discussing what points would be most persuasive with the primary audience, Angela Koffman and Jacques Martin. Angela has always been open to new ideas. She meets often with all departments in the office and shows a genuine interest in creating a more comfortable workplace. For example, she recently accepted recommendations by department managers to purchase office chairs and desks that will allow employees to work with less physical strain.

Yet Angela knows that Jacques will evaluate the branch largely on the financial performance, not on the comfort level of her staff. Indeed, Jacques keeps a close eye on the "bottom line" of each branch. He is interested in exploring new work practices only if they may improve employee productivity. More than likely, he will be the final decision maker about the pilot project.

Rationale for Pilot Project

The Commute Group spent much time discussing two topics: branch jobs that would be best suited to telecommuting and specific arguments in support of a telecommute policy.

Group members agreed that employees who do much independent work, especially on the computer, would be the best candidates for a pilot project. In particular, members of the technical and scientific staff often spend half their days at personal computers, either performing technical calculations or drafting sections of reports and proposals.

Next, the group discussed reasons for adopting a telecommute pilot project. The group first met to discuss the issue after a series of horrible rush hours over the holiday season in December. Bad weather forced most of the 125 branch employees either to miss some workdays during the period or to arrive up to two hours late several days. Most employees already have a one-way commute of at least one hour, since there is little affordable housing close to the office, which is in downtown Montreal.

In its deliberations, the Commute Group focused mainly on the kind of work that could be done by employees at home. What follows are some of the points discussed by the group, in random order.

- Telecommuting will save time either by eliminating commuting (on days the employee works exclusively at home) or by reducing commuting time (on days the employee comes to the office for part of the day and thus avoids one or both rush-hour periods that day).
- Employees can write and edit reports and proposals at home for several hours at a time, without the usual office interruptions of meetings, phone calls, drop-in visitors, and so on. Some experts claim that writers are most productive during the drafting stage if they have uninterrupted blocks of writing time.
- Morale will improve as long as there is a clear rationale for adopting the policy and selecting participants for the pilot project. Employees chosen should be those who work well independently, whose jobs can be handled through telecommuting, and who have already made a significant contribution to their departments.
- If M&K adopts a telecommuting policy after the pilot project, the firm may attract an additional pool of excellent employees.
- Telecommuting will improve some employees' productivity by allowing them to work while they are recovering from an illness at home or when family members are ill—in other words, when they would normally be on sick leave.
- The company would benefit from the increase in computer literacy among both telecommuters and those who work with them back at the office. The firm would begin to take advantage of the considerable investment it has already made in computer technology—personal computers, networks, e-mail, Internet software, modems, and so on. E-mail in particular would become a way of life. Until now, many employees have been reluctant to replace time-consuming meetings, phone calls, and memos with e-mail.
- If telecommuting were to become a regular way of doing business, it might reduce the amount of work space needed at the office, thereby reducing overhead. For

example, several employees could share the same office space if much of their work time were spent at home.

- Even some noncomputer tasks, such as phone calls to clients, could be done best in the quiet environment of the home, as opposed to the hectic environment of the office, where noise and interruptions are a part of doing business.
- If a telecommuting policy were adopted, M&K would gain public support by showing that it is part of the solution to two central problems: traffic congestion and air pollution. Even some potential clients might be attracted by the firm's progressive policies.

Possible Problems with Telecommuting

The Commute Group also addressed problems that might arise with the pilot project and with telecommuting in general. Group members were unsure how or whether the problems should be woven into the report. Here are some concerns that were discussed:

- The right employees must be selected for the pilot project. Whereas some employees might improve their productivity at home, others might find it difficult to stay on task, either because of their own work habits or because of their home environment. Some kind of appropriate screening device would be in order.
- The branch must determine how to evaluate the pilot project. Perhaps called for here is some combination of (1) self-evaluation by employees, (2) performance evaluations by supervisors, (3) productivity assessment by the corporate office, and (4) surveys of employees who are not part of the pilot project but who deal regularly with those who are telecommuting.
- Good communication is central to the project. Employees must be involved in selecting participants, planning the study, conducting the project on a day-to-day basis, and evaluating its success.

Organization of the Report

The Commute Group has agreed on the audience for the report, the likely qualifications for participants in the pilot study, the advantages of telecommuting, and some possible problems with the study and with telecommuting in general. The group has not resolved two main questions: First, what part of the information assembled should be included in the report? And second, what order should this information assume? In other words, the group must wrestle with matters of *organization*. Indeed, disagreements about these two issues created a stumbling block in the group's work.

Assume that the Commute Group has called you in for help in getting back on track. Answer the following questions, remembering that you are not to be concerned with specific report sections or headings. Rather, your concern will be only with the generic "ABC" structure explained in this chapter.

Questions and Comments for Discussion

1. Briefly, how would you describe an overall ABC structure that would work in this report? Your answer should take into account the intended purpose and audience of the report.

2. More specifically, what points would you suggest be included in the abstract component? What issues need not be addressed? Explain.

3. What points would you suggest be included in the body? Why? In what order? Explain the rationale for the order you suggest. If you have excluded some information discussed by the committee, explain why.

4. Given what you've read so far, what one main purpose should be served by the conclusion component of the group's report? To accomplish this purpose, what information should be included? Why?

5. Should the company or the employee pay the cost (training, hardware, software, etc.) of telecommuting?

6. What issues, if any, remain to be discussed by the Commute Group before it writes its recommendation report?

COMMUNICATION CHALLENGE 4

"The Montreal Format Guide: Trouble in River City"

Frustrated by inconsistency in report formats, Angela Koffman, the branch manager at M&K's Montreal office, decided to take action. After collecting examples of office reports with diverse page designs, she met with her friend and assistant manager, Michelle Tremblay, to complain. "Enough is enough, Michelle," she said as the meeting started. "The technical staff produces all kinds of formats, the word-processing staff doesn't know what designs are approved, and the clients get a fragmented image of the firm. Let's pick one page design for reports and stay with it."

After an hour's talk, Angela and Michelle agreed that the office needed a style sheet to describe the required format for each document type written at the Montreal branch. Busy with many other tasks, Angela told Michelle that she didn't have time to supervise the project. So she gave Michelle the authority to design what she decided would be called the "Format Guide." However, first Michelle had to meet with all department managers and a few other employees about the project. Also, Angela asked that Michelle's first version of the guide be a modest one that covered only brief letter reports. Later the guide could be expanded.

What follows are details about (1) Michelle's process of gathering information, (2) some actual guidelines she decided to include in the Format Guide, and (3) some problems that arose with the project.

Soliciting Opinions from Around the Office

The same morning she met with Angela, Michelle met with all five of her fellow department managers in the Montreal office. Gathering in a meeting room overlooking the St. Lawrence River, they agreed immediately that the format problem needed to be solved. The managers then concurred with the branch manager's idea about starting small—that is, covering only short letter reports now but later adding formal reports, proposals, manuals, letters, and memos, along with suggestions on style and grammar. Knowing that Michelle was one of the best writers and editors in the office, the managers said they were comfortable with her writing the manual herself. She could draw from whatever information she gathered from around the office and whatever guidelines she collected from her research on the subject. When the draft was complete, she would run it by them for their comments. Then it would go to Angela for final approval before distribution to all branch employees.

Michelle could hardly believe it. In one morning, five department managers and the branch manager had reached consensus about the nature of the format problem and its solution. Buoyed by her success, Michelle was almost able to look beyond the fact that she had been given the job of writing the manual. Always the one to get a job done quickly, however, she moved through the following steps in the next few days:

- Notepad in hand, she interviewed all seven word-processing operators and secretaries about their preferences in page design.
- She e-mailed all members of the professional staff, asking them to respond in writing in three days if they had specific preferences about the "look" they wanted to achieve in their letter reports.
- She called a local chapter of the Society for Technical Communication (STC), asking for references on page design.
- She located the four sources she received from STC and read them cover to cover.
- By the end of the following week, Michelle was ready to begin writing the first draft of what would become the Format Guide for M&K's Montreal office.

Michelle's Format for Short Reports

Michelle quickly developed a clear idea of what features should be part of M&K's short reports. To be sure, some of what she heard from department managers and other employees was at odds with her own views. For example, her preference for ragged-right margins in letter reports differed from that of many colleagues. When there were differences of opinion, she made decisions on the basis on her research and the level of response from those employees she surveyed. The following is a summary of the guidelines included in her draft:

1. The font should be 12-point New Century Schoolbook.
2. There should be 3 cm margins on the sides, a 1.25 cm margin on the top, and a 2.5 cm margin on the bottom (except for the first page, where letterhead requires the use of a top margin of 5 cm and a bottom margin of 2.5 cm).
3. Paragraphs should be block style, without indenting of the first line.
4. Text should have ragged-right margins, not right-justified margins.
5. Text should be single spaced, with double spacing between paragraphs.
6. Arrangement of date, inside address, and report title should be the same as that used in Model 9-6 in this text.
7. Every page after the first page should include a header. Placed in the top right-hand corner (see margin guideline above), the header should include three single-spaced items: the company name (M&K Montreal), the project number (e.g., M&K Project #134), and the date (e.g., July 29, 2004).
8. The heading system should follow the pattern shown in example 4 in Figure 4-6 of this chapter.
9. Bulleted and numbered lists should be indented 1.25 cm from the left margin, with double spacing before and after the list and between items in the list.

Once her draft was approved by the branch manager, Michelle had 35 copies printed and distributed to all employees of the Montreal office. In a cover memo with the Format Guide, she indicated that (1) the guide should be considered the new model for all letter reports leaving the office but that (2) it was a pilot draft that the office would review after six months. Further, she noted that the guide would be expanded later to include other documents.

Questions and Comments for Discussion

Having finished her project within deadline, Michelle was pleased. There would be clear guidelines for the staff, and the office would reap the rewards of a more efficient process of producing letter reports. As you look back on Michelle's activities and the guidelines she developed, consider the following questions and comments for discussion:

1. Michelle did a good job of seeking opinions of branch employees before she began her draft. Would it have been useful to consult with M&K customers while the guide was being developed? Explain.

2. Should Michelle have conducted a separate search for opinions regarding format considerations written in French? In other words, are format requirements dependent on the language being used?

3. Should Michelle have "tested" the usefulness of the Format Guide before it was issued to all employees, or was her "pilot draft" approach adequate? If you think further testing was needed, what specifically would you have suggested?

4. Michelle chose to issue the final Format Guide through the office mail, with a cover memo. Was this strategy ideal? If so, why? If not, in what other way might she have introduced the manual?

5. Using Michelle's nine format guidelines, edit the letter report included in Model 9-6 in this textbook. Do you think the revision is in a better format than the original? Why or why not?

6. Michelle's manual provides a fairly rigid set of guidelines, as shown by the guidelines excerpt included in this case. Do you think a company should require employees to follow such a narrowly prescribed format? Explain, both for and against.

7. One engineer called Michelle to complain that the new guidelines did not allow him to use decimal numbered headings and subheadings in his short report. He said that he preferred such headings, and he suspected that his clients did as well. If you were in Michelle's position, how would you respond to this complaint?

8. If you were designing an M&K Format Guide for short reports, what are some of the guidelines you would include, considering your own personal preferences?

COMMUNICATION CHALLENGE 5

Project 3: Managed Construction of Nevada Gold Dome

Client: City of Rondo, Nevada

Brief Project Description

Rondo, Nevada, recently received permission to start a new football team, the Nevada Gamblers. The city is building a domed stadium, called the Gold Dome, for the new franchise. Because of concerns about scheduling the various construction firms and subcontractors involved in the project, the client hired McDuff to manage the entire project—from groundbreaking to occupancy.

Main Technical Tasks

- Established construction schedule that would allow for maximum overlapping of work by different subcontractors
- Held daily coordination meetings with a group of principals that represented every contractor on site that day
- Handled schedule delays by dealing immediately with contractors and subcontractors
- Used M&K's patented "TimeTrack" scheduling software to stay aware of the entire flow of work at site.

Main Findings or Benefits

- Had entire project completed two weeks before the deadline
- Saved client $100,000 by eliminating proposed overtime work that was not needed once scheduling was fine-tuned
- Arranged schedule so that team owners and staff members could complete a walk-through of the facility at key points during the construction process.

"A Dome Gone South: Argument in Action"

When McDuff finished its project of managing construction of the Nevada Gold Dome, all was well. The company more than met its completion deadline and saved its client, the stadium owners, about $100,000. Now, two years later (and a year after the comprehensive warranty expired), a number of problems have surfaced. The following sections (1) present the four main complaints McDuff has heard, (2) analyze the problem from the point of view of both the dome's owners and McDuff, and (3) list questions and comments for you to consider in evaluating this "breakdown." The focus will be on opportunities for using patterns of organization discussed in this chapter.

Problems with the Dome

Over the last few months, the Gold Dome's owners have alerted McDuff to four problems they believe may have resulted from construction or material problems:

1. **Artificial turf:** The turf has pulled up at several spots around the edge of the field. Although dome maintenance staff tried a quick fix, the turf has pulled back up again and again.
2. **Ramp cracks:** Several 2 cm cracks have developed in the concrete ramps that lead from the team locker rooms to the field. Just last week two football players tripped on the cracks as they entered the field in front of TV cameras covering the start of a game. The embarrassment, as well as the possible danger to high-priced players, has the dome management fuming.
3. **Roof leak:** Leaks have developed in the dome roof, caused by the ponding of rainwater on a sunken roof section near one of the spectator decks.

4. Equipment damage: Water has entered one of the dome's control rooms, damaging three TV monitors and causing carpeting to mildew.

What brought the problems to a head was an incident before last Sunday's game. While the team's co-owners, Ted Burner and Jane Honda, were getting settled into their luxury box near the upper deck, a roof panel broke loose near the area of the leak and crashed onto their balcony, spilling wine and cheese on Ted and Jane. Needless to say, that event generated a meeting this week between McDuff and the dome's management.

McDuff and the Dome Management: Different Analyses

With all its training in Total Quality Management, McDuff believes that satisfying the customer is a crucial corporate objective. Besides being the ethical high road, this goal also generally leads to the company getting repeat business from old clients or good recommendations they can use in finding new clients. In either case, good service helps business.

Yet the firm has not reached its current level of success by admitting error every time a client expresses dissatisfaction with a job. Sometimes other parties are at fault. Indeed, at the end of the meeting between McDuff and the dome's management, McDuff's representatives had clear disagreements about the possible causes of the four problems. Here are the main differences that arose from preliminary analyses by both parties.

- **Artificial turf**
  Dome: The dome's managers believe that artificial turf was installed improperly, without adequate drying time allowed for the adhesive.
  McDuff: McDuff expects that the problem was caused wholly or in part by the dome's home team, the Nevada Gamblers. Two years ago the team began practising on the surface before the end of the two-week curing period recommended by the installers.

- **Ramp cracks**
  Dome: The dome's managers remember McDuff's comments on a construction progress report, indicating that several trucks arrived late when concrete was being poured for the ramps. Thus there were longer than usual delays between truck pours for the ramps.
  McDuff: Despite the truck delays, McDuff satisfied the minimum professional standards for timeliness during the concrete pour. Unrelated to this timing problem, McDuff had recommended additional reinforcing bars for the ramp concrete during construction. However, dome management had only approved the minimum amount required by applicable standards.

- **Roof leak**
  Dome: The dome's managers believe that a structural flaw in the roof support system caused water to pool on one small section of the roof, instead of rolling off into the drainage canals.
  McDuff: After observing the roof area, McDuff suspects that a major hailstorm two months ago damaged the roof panels, which caused ponding of rainwater and led to the subsequent leak.

- **Equipment damage**

  Dome: The route of the water suggests that it may have come through wall spacings from the area of the roof leak.

  McDuff: Another possibility is that the damage resulted from a custodial worker failing to turn off a faucet located above the control room in a maintenance area. When the open faucet was discovered, the maintenance room was cleaned up without anyone observing seepage into other rooms or wall space, but such seepage seems just as likely as seepage from the region of the roof leak.

  Although the dome's comprehensive warranty has ended, McDuff and key contractors remain partially liable for five years from construction for problems that can be linked to defects in construction or materials. Even if this warranty were not in force, however, McDuff would want to go above and beyond the call to satisfy the client—if there were some reason for doubt or if corrections were not too expensive. At this point, McDuff has not decided how to proceed.

Questions and Comments for Discussion

In responding to the following questions and comments, use information previously supplied as well as any other rationale you think applies.

1. *Argument:* Cyndy Perlman, a member of McDuff's dome project team, believes that McDuff should correct all four problems. What arguments, from strongest to weakest, should she use to convince her skeptical boss of this path of action?
2. *Argument:* Mason Hunter, another member of the McDuff project team, believes that McDuff should bear no financial responsibility for correcting any of the four problems. What arguments, from strongest to weakest, should he use to convince his skeptical boss of this path of action?
3. *Argument:* In the case presentation, find one example each of what could be considered *non sequitur* and *post hoc ergo propter hoc* argumentative fallacies.
4. *Definition:* Do some research to provide formal sentence definitions for some or all of the following terms mentioned in the Gold Dome case study:

   Warranty

   Dome stadium

   Artificial turf

   Concrete

   TV monitor

   Progress report

   Reinforcing bars

   Hailstorm

5. *Description:* Provide an outline of what you would include in a technical description of a domed athletic stadium.
6. *Classification/Division:* Separate into groups established by your instructor. Then brainstorm to come up with a list of at least 30 additional construction- or materials-related problems that could have occurred with a stadium like the

Gold Dome. Finally, perform a classification exercise like the one presented in this chapter regarding McDuff's safety practices.

7. *Comparison/Contrast:* In the "McDuff and the Dome Management" section of this case study, a comparison/contrast is presented in a "part-by-part" format. Convert it to a "whole-by-whole" format. Which of the two organizational strategies do you consider most effective in this case?

COMMUNICATION CHALLENGE 6

"M&K's Gift of Management: The Sword of Damocles"

Jacques Martin and Angela Koffman had always been active supporters of charities. Personally and as a corporation they made significant monetary contributions. However, they were disturbed by reports that the larger part of their contributions was being used to pay the very high overhead costs—in some cases over 90 percent—incurred by charitable institutions. They decided that M&K would no longer provide money; instead, the company would provide expertise that would enable charities to reduce their overheads.

Project Planning

The process of making "A Gift of Management" a reality began at a meeting attended by Jacques and the branch managers. The group agreed that M&K could more effectively help charitable organizations by providing expertise. The group decided to ask employees to volunteer. Volunteers would be loaned to charitable organizations for a period of one year and receive 75 percent of their salary for that period. Their task would be to reduce the charity's overhead so that more money could be spent where it was needed.

The response from employees was enthusiastic, and the media coverage was positive. All parties agreed that the money spent to pay the volunteers, and their replacements, would result in a greater number of dollars becoming available where they were needed.

Problems

There was an immediate response from charitable organizations. Much of it was negative. Organizations whose overheads were already low felt they were being penalized because they would not be eligible for any help from M&K. Organizations that had moderate overhead costs, and did want help, were afraid they would be denied help because expertise would go to poorly managed or corrupt organizations. Charities with high overheads did not want to be identified and their employees did not want to lose their jobs.

Employee Involvement

The people at M&K were very enthusiastic about participating in the program. Some felt it was the kind of change necessary to reinvigorate them. Others volunteered out of a sense of civic duty. There were, in fact, so many applications that a selection process had to be developed. Peer groups were established to review the submissions from volunteers. Each branch selected one candidate per year.

Community Involvement

M&K was very careful in establishing which charitable groups merited help and which did not. The company did not want to be arbitrary or prejudiced. It therefore formed committees of business people in Toronto, Montreal, Calgary, and Vancouver. These committees were asked to pinpoint the charities that would benefit most from management expertise provided by A Gift of Management.

Implementation

The chairs of the local committees met in Vancouver to decide on the general criteria for deciding which charitable organizations would be eligible. They decided that those whose existing overheads did not exceed 50 percent of their operating budget would be eligible for help. They also decided that help would be offered only if, in the opinion of the local committee, the charity would then be able to offer more to its clients. Finally, in a controversial decision, the chairs decided that missionary work was to be considered overhead, since its primary purpose was to recruit rather than to feed and shelter the needy and improve their health.

In each community the local committees designated a number of eligible charities. Volunteers were required to select a charity from that list and to explain, in writing, how they could help to reduce that charity's overhead. After reviewing the volunteers' documents, each of the workers' committees at the M&K branches selected the individual who would be made available.

When the first volunteers began their work at charitable organizations in January 2004, the company and the charities received a great deal of favourable publicity. There were, however, religious groups in Toronto and Calgary that picketed M&K's offices to protest their exclusion from the program.

Questions and Comments for Discussion

1. The people at the McDuff subsidiary expressed interest in the Canadian model. They have asked the Toronto office for an explanation of the project. Specifically, they want a *process description* for the Gift of Management project. The description will be reviewed by all McDuff branch managers. What major points should be included in this process description? How will it differ from the way information is presented in the case just described?

2. Assume that McDuff's corporate office has actually adopted the model reflected in the Gift of Management project. Now it wants to provide project *instructions* for other urban offices that may want to offer management expertise. What major points will be emphasized in the instructions, and in what order? What particular problems did M&K encounter, and how can the instructions be written to help other offices avoid such problems? In other words, how will the ideal set of instructions differ from the actual process that was performed?

3. What tactical mistakes, if any, were made by M&K's management in the process of promoting, communicating, and running this project? How could the problems have been avoided?

4. Are there any ethical problems revealed in the process described in this case? Specifically, how do you feel about the way employees are encouraged to contribute to such causes?
5. Several large charity groups were disturbed that M&K stopped its financial contributions and instead involved employees in A Gift of Management. Give what you think would be the charities' point of view about the process described in this case.

COMMUNICATION CHALLENGE 7

"Corporate Culture"

Companies in the technology sector have traditionally used a system of individual rewards to motivate their employees. Those rewards included such things as perks, financial compensation, or promotion. While individual rewards did serve M&K well—employees worked hard to obtain the rewards—management came to believe that the interests of the company often suffered when people became too aggressive in the search for personal rewards. In order to develop a more reasonable balance between the interests of the individual and the interests of the company, managers were encouraged to acknowledge contributions to the company as a whole. In addition managers were asked to discourage self-aggrandizement if it occurred at the expense of other employees.

Rapid Reaction

James Mulligan has hired a new employee in his client service group because the demand for service in the IT sector had increased dramatically. The new employee, Suzanne Fortier, was to assume responsibility for a number of clients formerly handled by the most successful seller of service contracts in the group, Gerry Gorbani. James had instructed Suzanne to ask for the files from Gerry and had asked Gerry to give Suzanne all additional background information pertaining to the clients. A day later, Suzanne was in James's office complaining that Gerry had refused to give her the background information.

James suspected that Gerry's refusal resulted from his unwillingness to give up his clients. He assumed that Gerry felt that his bonus would be reduced because the clients were no longer his. James was irritated and, as a manager, felt compelled to follow the new company policy by expressing disapproval. He wrote the following e-mail:

Date: January 28, 2004
To: Gerry Gorbani {Gorbani@M&K.com}
From: James Mulligan {J_Mulligan@M&K.com}
Subject: Your Attitude toward Team Building

Gerry, it has been brought to my attention that you have refused to comply with the instructions that I gave you. I asked you to provide Ms. Fortier with all background information pertinent to the clients who are to be included in her territory. You did not do so when asked. I would like you to provide the information and would like to know why you refused to provide it when asked.

James

After James pressed the "Send" button, he wondered how Gerry would react, but he did believe that the reprimand was warranted.

Twenty minutes later Gerry stormed into James's office. He was furious. He felt insulted by both the tone and content of the e-mail. He said he did e-mail Suzanne the client files but that she failed to arrive in his office at the appointed time. By the time she did arrive he had to go to another meeting and told her that he saw no reason to help her given that she had wasted his time. Gerry was so angry that he demanded a written apology from James and threatened to lodge a complaint against James if he did not receive it.

Questions and Comments for Discussion

1. Who do you feel is to blame for the incident?
2. What, if anything, did James do incorrectly?
3. What, if anything, did Gerry do incorrectly?
4. Do you think that James's e-mail was appropriate or inappropriate?
5. How do you think the situation should be resolved?

COMMUNICATION CHALLENGE 8

"Ethics and Sales Letters"

Technical firms are known for taking a conservative approach to marketing. For the last six months, however, M&K's corporate marketing department has been considering more imaginative marketing strategies. This case study explains their approach, presents the draft of a sales letter that is part of the proposed strategy, and ends with questions and comments for discussion.

The Plan

Traditionally, technical consulting firms have done little if any advertising and have sent out few sales letters. Instead, they have just "been there" when clients needed services like the ones McDuff performs, such as foundation design, construction management, equipment development, and environmental remediation. McDuff has been successful because it has built up a stable of clients that return regularly for continuing services. The Martin & Koffman name is not yet commonly identified with the sort of work McDuff performs. M&K's managers believe that their corporate connection to McDuff must be "sold" so that potential clients will feel that M&K can draw on extensive experience as well as expertise.

Specifically, the marketing staff is proposing a three-stage plan to corporate management and branch managers. The focus will be on governments and private groups who own wetlands that are being considered for commercial or recreational development. Eventually the owners will be told by various government departments that their property must be rigorously evaluated as to the environmental impact of any development. These evaluations will determine how and to what degree (if at all) the land can be used for parks, home building, and so on. M&K would like to write to the owners about this requirement immediately, before the owners officially request environmental studies. In doing so, M&K may beat competitors to the work. Here is the plan they propose:

1. Use public records to identify owners of wetland areas throughout the country.
2. Send a sales letter to all these owners.
3. Follow each letter with phone calls and meetings that will provide a more detailed account of M&K's services.

The marketing staff has decided the sales letter must depart from the predictable, boring letters sent in the past. In fact, the staff has devised a "grabber": Any recipient hiring M&K to perform an environmental study before January 15 will receive a fee reduction of 10 percent, up to a maximum of $1,000. Although the writers do not want their letter to look too commercial, they do want to depart from letters of the past. They believe something is needed to get readers to act; a financial incentive seems appropriate.

The Letter

The marketing staff has just sent out the following letter to M&K's branch managers. They have included with the letter a list of prospective clients and a reference to the three-point marketing strategy noted earlier. Readers are to call or e-mail the marketing staff with their response.

September 15, 2003

Drummond Recreational Development, Inc.
P.O. Box 303
Ajax, ON
L1N 5R3

Reference: 100-Acre Parcel at Star-Gazer Marsh

Dear Mr. Drummond:

Would you like to save up to $1,000 on a study the government requires to evaluate the development potential of Star-Gazer Marsh? For a limited time, M&K can save you this amount on an environmental evaluation of the site.

As you may know, the government requires that you complete an environmental assessment of property that may include wetland areas important for biological diversity. M&K's subsidiary, McDuff, Inc., has completed more than 500 such studies in the last 10 years. In each case, clients have received information they needed to determine (1) possible commercial or recreational development of their property and (2) applicable government restrictions. For making this evaluation, the technical experts we can provide have no equal among consulting firms in Canada.

For a limited time, you have the opportunity to save 10 percent, up to a maximum of $1,000, on an environmental assessment—which will cost you full price for any services contracted after January 15, 2004. Enclosed is a brochure that gives specifics about the features of our assessments and lists our previous clients.

I'll call you in a few days to see if your firm wants to take advantage of our offer for a significant reduction on an evaluation assessment. If you have questions before that time, please give me a call.

Sincerely,

Akira Kariya, Marketing Manager
Enclosure

Questions and Comments for Discussion

1. Explain how M&K's letter does or does not satisfy this chapter's criteria for the content and style of an effective sales letter.
2. What kind of response do you think the marketing staff will get from the M&K managers to whom they sent the draft?
3. Do you believe the financial incentive is ethical? Explain.
4. Do you think the financial incentive would be effective? Explain.
5. Generally speaking, what type of marketing strategy is either ethical or appropriate for technical firms like M&K? Explain your answer. In your view, should marketing techniques for firms like M&K differ from techniques used by retail stores, credit card companies, and other similar organizations? Explain.

COMMUNICATION CHALLENGE 9

"A Nonprofit Job: Good Deed or Questionable Ethics?"

It all started with an innocent conversation. Velora Nescon, a project manager at M&K's McDuff office in Houston, had lunch with her old college friend, Sibyl Sanders. As principal of Houston's Downtown Academy, Sibyl talked about her effort to keep the new private academy financially healthy and academically strong. Now she was busy with an expansion. What follows is a description of a problem she faced with the expansion, the help that Velora tried to offer, and some ethical and procedural questions raised by the situation.

A Working Lunch

Houston's Downtown Academy was established as a private elementary and middle school for bright inner-city kids who couldn't afford other private schools. Five years ago, business leaders had donated a renovated building for the new school and had raised money for a scholarship account. Now the academy had a respectable enrollment, a good academic reputation, and excellent morale among faculty and staff. All in all, the future looked good for the school. Recently a benefactor gave the school a piece of land adjacent to its campus, where a recreational area would be built.

In her conversation with Velora, Sibyl noted that although the school had some money to begin construction, the budget would be tight. At this point, Velora reminded her friend that McDuff, Inc., offered some of the technical services the project might require. She added that she could ask her branch manager if McDuff might handle the job just for cost, as its way of contributing to the growth of the school. Velora genuinely wanted to help her friend with this worthwhile venture, but in truth she also saw an opportunity to keep her technical staff busy during a slack period. By the end of lunch Sibyl and Velora had reached tentative agreement on McDuff's doing the property study that was required before the land could be developed. Then back at the office, Velora got her boss to agree to allowing the job to be done for cost.

Velora's Lucky Find

The project involved a soil and environmental study. McDuff was to drill borings to determine what foundations would be needed for small structures in the recreation area. Also, soil samples would be taken from the site to check for contamination. These tasks were routine.

Before sending out her crew, Velora mentioned the project to a colleague, George Lightfoot, who thought he remembered doing some soil borings at the same location a couple of years ago. On checking his files, George found a report that included two borings paid for by Ace Enterprises, a firm that had considered buying the property. Later Ace backed out of the purchase for reasons unrelated to the report. George loaned Velora the report and suggested she ask Ace for permission to use it, since she was trying to save the Downtown Academy money on the project. Velora thanked George for the report and said she'd call Ace.

Velora wanted to get on this nonprofit job right away, while her crew wasn't busy, so she tried all afternoon to contact Ace Enterprises. There was no listing for the firm in Houston, and the McDuff librarian found no address in a quick search of her regional files. Velora assumed the firm had gone out of business, changed names, or left town. That being the case, she decided to move ahead in using information in the report—thus saving the Downtown Academy money for soil borings that would have been done. She assumed that Ace, if it still existed, would not mind contributing information for a nonprofit job like this one.

McDuff's Fieldwork

The next day the McDuff crew gathered soil samples from the surface and from shallow borings dug with a hand auger. Results of the lab tests on the samples showed there was an underground storage tank on the property. It had been used for kerosene, which had leaked into the surrounding soil. Both the tank and the soil would have to be removed.

Again trying to save her friend some money, Velora had the small tank and soil removed by a McDuff subcontractor working nearby later that week. The crew had been working for another McDuff client most of the day. Because that client had to pay for a full day's use of the crew and crane anyway, Velora didn't charge the Downtown Academy for the two hours it took to remove the tank and soil.

Within a week, Velora handed Sibyl a complete report showing her fieldwork, lab tests, and conclusions. Sibyl was overjoyed that the study had come in even under the zero-profit budget she and Velora had first discussed. In thanking Velora, she assured her that McDuff would be a serious contender for the profit contracts that the Downtown Academy was sure to have in the future.

Questions and Comments for Discussion

1. Do you think there are any ethical problems raised by this case study? If so, what are they and how would you deal with them? If not, explain your views.

2. Specifically, how do Sibyl's and Velora's actions either satisfy or violate the Equal Consideration of Interests principle described in Chapter 2 of this text?

3. Putting aside the ethical issue, do you think Velora followed wise procedures in her handling of the Downtown Academy project? Why or why not?

COMMUNICATION CHALLENGE 10

"The Ethics of Clients Reviewing Report Drafts"

Last week Hank Wallace of M&K completed the draft of its ocean exploration project for the Republic of Cameroon. As is routine with major reports, Hank showed the client a draft before the final draft was submitted. For the first time in his career, he was asked by the client to make changes that he thought were difficult to justify by project data. What follows is an explanation of why M&K shares report drafts with some clients, some background on the ocean exploration project, and questions and comments for discussion.

Sharing Drafts with Clients

In M&K's business, some of the firm's reports must be submitted both to the paying client and to regulatory agencies of the government. This dual audience has created a review procedure common in the industry. Client firms have an opportunity to review a draft and make suggestions before both they and the regulatory agencies are sent final drafts.

For example, an American mining company hired M&K to examine a Siberian site to determine if gold reserves could be mined without damaging the delicate permafrost surface of the tundra. Because the Russian government regulates development in the region, it received a final copy of the report. But before the final copy was submitted to the government, M&K shared a draft with engineers and executives from the mining company. These client representatives questioned several technical assumptions M&K made about the site, but M&K had adequate justifications for its work. In the end, M&K made no change in its original draft recommendation (i.e., that further study is needed before mining is permitted in the permafrost region).

In another case, however, a client's review of a report on a dam in the U.S. Midwest prompted M&K to adjust its report before submission of the final draft to the state's Department of Natural Resources, which regulates high-hazard dams. The owners of the dam—who paid for the study—convinced M&K that the report should emphasize the fact that poor installation of a guardrail over the dam created a drainage problem. When heavy rains came, soil washed out an embankment near the dam's spillway. The first draft had failed to mention that the state's transportation group bore some responsibility for the dam's problems.

The Ocean Exploration Report Review

The draft review of the ocean exploration report did not go as smoothly as the two reviews just described. Major differences of opinion were evident between M&K's project manager and the client, Worldwide Energy, Inc.

M&K engineers developed conclusions and recommendations for the Cameroon coastal site. For the most part, they found that the offshore environment where they did the study would be too environmentally sensitive to drill offshore wells or run pipelines. There were two locations where a pipeline might be safely placed, but even in this case some environmental damage was likely. When Worldwide Energy got the draft report, the company asked for a meeting.

At the meeting the following week, M&K's engineers reviewed their findings, conclusions, and recommendations with the client. Ultimately, M&K managers were asked to change the wording in the report to present a more favourable view of oil exploration at the site because, in the client's opinion, M&K was being too conservative in its conclusions. If M&K would just adjust some wording so as not to emphasize what is only, after all, *possible* environmental damage, then the Cameroon government might be provided the support it needs to develop this potentially rich oil field. Cameroon, the client argued, needs oil revenues to improve its economy and assist poor farmers with the transition to a modern economy. M&K is not being asked to alter the facts—only to adjust the tone of the language.

Back at the office, the M&K project manager met with the branch manager and later with corporate staff via teleconference. The project manager presented the facts of the project and a summary of the meeting. To all present, it was clear that the relationship with a long-term client was at stake.

Questions and Comments for Discussion

1. Should M&K respond to the client's request?
2. Generally, do you think M&K's procedure for reviewing report drafts with clients is ethically sound? Support your answer.
3. a) If you answered "yes" to question 2, do you have any suggestions to improve the procedure for this client report review? That is, how might the process be adjusted to reduce the potential for misunderstandings and abuse?

    b) If you answered "no" to question 2, is there any circumstance in which you would support the review of a report draft by a client before final submission to the client and its regulatory agency?
4. It is often said, in this text and elsewhere, that collaboration is essential in the workplace. Describe the kinds of on-the-job situations where you think collaboration between writer and reader would be useful, appropriate, and ethical.

COMMUNICATION CHALLENGE 11

"The Northern Lights Proposal: Good Marketing or Bad Business?"

To strengthen its proposals, M&K hired a new proposal writer at the head office in Montreal. Ben Sadler came well recommended, having both advertising and marketing experience with technical firms. He finished his first major proposal at M&K; soon after, some disagreements arose when one of the firm's technical experts performed an internal review of his draft. What follows is background information on the project, an overview of decisions Ben made in writing the proposal, and some questions and comments related to the review.

Background on Northern Lights Project

Jacques Martin and his staff hired Ben Sadler for a specific reason. Although business was going fairly well, they felt the company needed new direction and energy in its marketing of construction and environmental projects. Staff members seemed to be taking for granted that clients would always return and that word-of-mouth would keep new clients coming through the doors. Such an attitude was dangerous. They wanted to venture into new types of work and believed the time was right for a new marketing expert. Ben Sadler seemed to be the catalyst the firm needed.

Just after arriving, Ben learned about a request for proposal recently issued for a large construction job—building a new college campus in what would soon be Nunavut. The project's four buildings (total cost: $35 million) were to be the centrepiece of the new campus. M&K had thus far done no major construction work, nor had it done much work at colleges and universities. Yet Ben felt the firm had the technical tools and the personnel to be a contender. After convincing his immediate boss, the manager for business and marketing, that the proposal was worth writing, Ben went to work.

Proposal Strategy

Although Ben had research help from McDuff employees in the United States, he wrote the draft himself. Here are parts of the writing and marketing strategy he planned to use:

- **Experience:** He emphasized the large construction jobs McDuff, M&K's subsidiary company, had done for other types of government-related agencies around the world. Although McDuff itself had done no major college or university construction, Ben felt that work done for government agencies would be an adequate substitute.
- **Technical Experts:** Although M&K offices lacked experts to coordinate large-scale construction, Ben knew the company could bring in experts from the United States. Admittedly, it would be more expensive to import talent, and these high-salary personnel would be able to visit the site only periodically. Yet this arrangement satisfied the minimum technical requirements in the industry. Ben felt comfortable including the experts' résumés in the proposal and highlighting their experience, without mentioning that they did not work out of the Canadian office. To him, that fact was an internal matter.
- **Costs:** When Ben calculated the tentative cost for the project, he was surprised that the figure was so high. The extra personnel costs noted earlier were apparently part of the problem. But Ben also thought some costs might have been overstated because McDuff was not used to bidding on such jobs in Canada. (McDuff's corporate accounting manager had done the tentative cost estimate.) Believing the figures were inflated, Ben cut about 10 percent from the personnel costs mentioned in the draft. He thought M&K would perform more efficiently than the accounting manager had estimated.
- **Proposal Strategy:** Ben wanted to come on strong in the executive summary with what he saw as the benefits M&K could offer. He focused on three main selling points: (a) the availability of a nearby office and lab in Montreal for project coordination, (b) McDuff's experience with large construction jobs, and (c) M&K's history of good working relationships with its clients.
- **Personal Contacts:** Ben happened to have a close friend at a former firm (not a competitor of M&K's) who went to university with an official now on the Northern Lights College board of directors. Ben wanted to use this "friend of a friend" connection to get a meeting with the board member, perhaps to find out more about the project. He might then get the chance to give part of the "M&K story" that was not revealed in the proposal.

Questions and Comments for Discussion

After Ben completed the draft, it was reviewed first by John van Beek, one of the top technical experts at the Calgary branch. Bergin met with Ben and expressed reservations about both the project and the proposal. The questions that follow reflect their conversation, as well as some other concerns about the proposal:

1. Van Beek first wondered why Ben proposed on the job in the first place. Given that such proposals cost $10,000 or $15,000 to write, why did he bother with the Northern Lights job when M&K didn't have experience on large construction jobs? Most current M&K projects are environmental studies. Wouldn't it be a long shot to get the work? And shouldn't M&K managers have some ethical concern about trying to get a job when they know they don't have the experience other competing firms probably have (or at least *should* have)?
   What is your view of the practical and ethical concerns raised by van Beek?

2. Van Beek also questioned whether Ben was being deceptive about the way in which technical experts would be provided for the project. If the résumés are to be included in the proposal, shouldn't M&K also mention that these experts reside in the United States? This matter didn't seem to be an "internal" one, as Ben stated. What's your view of the way Ben handled the issue of outside experts from the United States? How much of this sort of information has to be put forward in a competitive proposal?

3. Ben had an honest disagreement with the accounting manager about how the costs were calculated for bringing American experts into Canada. He may have been right or wrong in his reservations about the estimate. Putting this point aside, was it procedurally correct for him, as project manager, to make changes in the costs submitted by an adviser? Explain. Also, was it ethical?

4. Ben chose a "direct" approach to proposal content; that is, he placed the main selling points first (in the executive summary). Do you think this strategy is appropriate in all cultures? Explain. (If possible, do some research on technical communication in Germany, Japan, or China before answering the question.)

5. As noted earlier, Ben decided to pursue a connection he had on the board of directors of Northern Lights College. Is this strategy ethical? Would it work? What are some possible results of such a strategy?

6. Have two students in the class conduct a role-play of the conversation between van Beek and Sadler. The students can use the information just presented and any additional points that conceivably could be put forward by these two men, considering the sketches provided of them.

COMMUNICATION CHALLENGE 12

"Massaging M&K's Annual Report"

Just about everyone considered M&K's 2002 annual report a boring piece of work. It contained pages of text with only a few tables for visual relief. Wanting to spice up the next annual report, the company hired a graphics firm to create a more appealing design and graphics. GeeWhiz Graphics is completing the 2003 annual report draft for review by M&K's corporate staff. What follows are highlights of the graphical challenge, along with some questions and comments for discussion.

Beth's Part of the Project

When GeeWhiz got the M&K job, Beth Chang and Rick Ford were assigned the account. They were to take text and data provided by M&K's PR department and create a graphically interesting format for readers of the annual report, who are mostly shareholders, M&K employees, or clients of the firm. Beth and Rick have been asked to make data as visually appealing as possible, especially in light of criticism the company received for its previous annual report.

Beth is creating graphics for four pieces of information that M&K wants emphasized in the report:

1. **International sales:** M&K has become a more international firm, with a growing percentage of non-Canadian clients, and in the near future is likely to open additional offices in Eastern Europe, Australia, and Russia. Beth was asked to create one or two graphics to reflect this international shift. In 2002 the international offices accounted for roughly $33 million (i.e., 35 percent) of M&K's $96 million in total sales. Of that amount, the Tokyo office accounted for $12 million in sales and Munich for $10 million. The remaining four international offices split the rest.

2. **Total sales:** Over the last 10 years, total sales for the firm have gone up steadily. Figures for 1994 through 2003 are as follows, in millions: $65, 70, 73, 74, 80, 83.5, 87, 90, 90.5, 96.

3. **Number of employees:** Except for one year, when there was a minor layoff to reduce costs, the number of employees has risen over the last five years, as follows: 1,800 (1998), 1,950 (1999), 1,925 (2000), 2,200 (2001), 2,500 (2002).

4. **Corporate overhead:** The corporate office in Baltimore covered six service areas. The corporate budget was spent as follows: 40 percent on human resources, 20 percent on research, 15 percent on computer operations, 10 percent on training, 10 percent on project management, and 5 percent on marketing. The company wants to emphasize that the employee-related portion of overhead has grown in the past year—for example, training has gone from 5 to 10 percent, and human resources have gone from 35 to 40 percent.

Rick's Part of the Project

Beth's colleague at GeeWhiz Graphics, Rick Ford, was given a similar assignment—that is, to create interesting graphical representations of data about the company. He produced three graphics in his initial work on the report:

1. **Bar chart:** Rick drew a bar chart to reflect the growth of the international offices over the last five years.

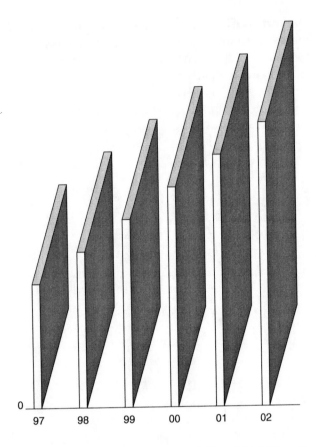

2. Pie chart: To show the investment portfolio of M&K's retirement plan, Rick produced a pie chart.

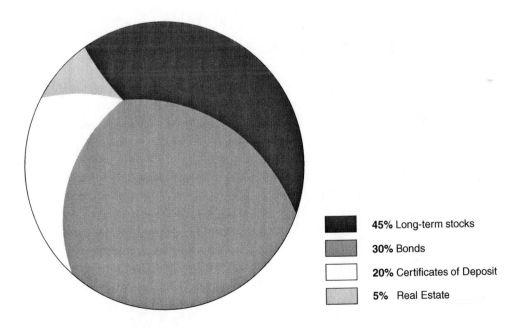

45% Long-term stocks

30% Bonds

20% Certificates of Deposit

5% Real Estate

3. Bar chart without bars: In the past five years, M&K has made a concerted effort to emphasize preventive medical care and "wellness" programs among its employees. A variation on a bar chart was meant to show this progress in a more visually appealing manner than a conventional bar chart.

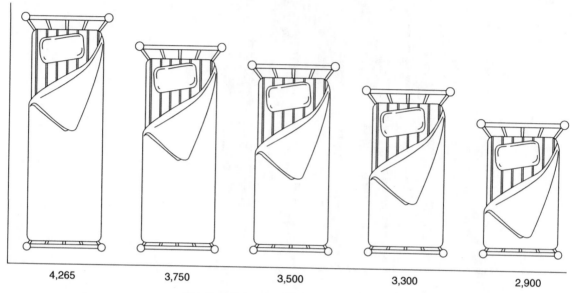

4,265   3,750   3,500   3,300   2,900

Sick Days Taken Last Five Years: M&K, Inc.

Questions and Comments for Discussion

1. Separate into groups and discuss the kinds of graphics that would be most effective, appropriate, and clear for the four assignments given to Beth Chang. Report the results of your discussion to the entire class.

2. Are there any ethical implications Beth should consider in producing her graphics? If so, what are they?

3. Separate into groups and discuss any ethical or clarity issues suggested by the graphics produced by Rick Ford. Should these graphics be included in M&K's annual report? Explain. Also, what if anything would you change? If useful, refer to the ECI (Equal Consideration of Interests) principle discussed in Chapter 2.

COMMUNICATION CHALLENGE 13

"Ethics and the Technical Presentation"

Nuyet Nguyen had been looking forward to attending his first international conference. The Association of Medical Technology invited him to speak at its annual meeting. Now, however, some of his research presents him with an ethical dilemma. The following sections present background on his invitation and some questions and comments for discussion.

An Opportunity in Caracas

Nuyet works as an equipment development specialist in M&K's Baltimore headquarters. For two years he has been helping a large medical equipment firm, MedExcel, Inc., improve its C-2000 electrocardiograph. An electrocardiograph records electrical changes that occur as the human heart beats. One of the most important pieces of equipment in diagnosing heart problems, it is made up of four main parts:

- Electrodes attached to the patient's body
- Electronics that convert and amplify the signal travelling from the electrodes to the computer
- A computer that interprets information provided by the electrodes
- An output screen and printer that provide information to the medical professional.

In his work on the C-2000, Nuyet (1) worked on converting the analog signal from the electrodes to digital, (2) developed the user interface, and (3) developed the database for the information. These refinements, and a host of other ones, have created what he and MedExcel believe is the most user-friendly and accurate electrocardiograph on the market.

Nuyet's work has been recognized in the industry. Next week he will fly from Baltimore to Caracas, Venezuela, to speak at the annual meeting of the Association of Medical Technology (AMT). MedExel, which conveyed the invitation to him from the AMT, will be paying all his expenses for the eight-day trip. He has been asked to speak on "Advances in the Electrocardiogram." As you might expect, MedExcel expects that he will showcase the C-2000 as an example of the most current technological advances.

A Late-Breaking Surprise

Everything has come together for Nuyet. His client is happy, his branch manager is overjoyed that M&K's small Equipment Development group is gaining recognition in a major industry, and a high-visibility professional association is about to showcase his work. The public relations and marketing potential is significant, both for M&K and MedExcel.

Now the other shoe has dropped. Yesterday, just a week before the conference, Nuyet was shocked to learn that Worldwide Medical, the main competitor of MedExcel, just came out with an updated version of its electrocardiograph, the HeartCart 300. According to an article he reviewed in a weekly health-care newspaper, the machine competes with the C-2000 in accuracy of electrode readings and in electronics. In addition, the panel pictured in the article appears to be a significant improvement over the previous HeartCart model. After reading the article, Nuyet went to his computer to find the Web site for Worldwide Medical. From the additional information he found there, it appears the HeartCart 300 will be competitive with the C-2000.

Nuyet has mixed emotions about this finding. On the one hand, he is glad to see that another firm is investing research dollars in this technology, which is crucial to health care throughout the world. On the other, he is understandably concerned that his two years of work may soon be upstaged by the work of a competing company. For the sake of the investment his client has made in this research, he was hoping that the C-2000 would enjoy sales that would justify the research investment.

Questions and Comments for Discussion

More to the immediate point, Nuyet is wondering what effect, if any, this new information should have on his presentation—a presentation that is being underwritten by a $5,000 grant from MedExcel. Here are some questions for you to consider.

1. Do you think Nuyet is obligated to revamp his presentation to include information about the HeartCart 300? If your answer is yes, explain exactly how he should proceed. If your answer is no, give your rationale.
2. Should his association with MedExcel have any bearing on his decision?
3. Should the manner by which Nuyet received this new information have any effect on the answer to question 1?
4. Give what you think the AMT's opinion would be in response to question 1.
5. Explain how your answer to question 1 relates to the Equal Consideration of Interests (ECI) ethical principle discussed in Chapter 2.
6. Generally, do you see any larger concern here in the relationship between professional associations and private enterprise? Explain your answer.

COMMUNICATION CHALLENGE 14

"To Cite or Not to Cite"

Dan Gibbs works as a benefits and finance specialist at M&K's corporate office in Montreal. As the number of M&K employees has grown, he has received many inquiries about ways to save for retirement. Recently he wrote and distributed a four-page flyer on the topic, using materials from print and on-line sources. The response was so positive that his boss wants to send the flyer to clients as a "freebie"—both to help clients' employees and to create "goodwill" in marketing. This use of the flyer has made Dan rethink how he developed the piece. His research process, his results, and some questions for discussion follow.

Background of the Retirement Booklet

Unlike Tanya Grant in the hybrid vehicle project described in this chapter, Dan didn't have time or interest in pursuing a full-scale library search about retirement strategies. Besides, he has personnel magazines in the office with data that would support his points. In addition, he is connected to the Internet, which might provide information directly to him at his office computer.

Like most companies, M&K has a retirement plan largely in the form of a registered retirement savings plan (RRSP). It allows employees to contribute a percentage of their salaries into a retirement plan, a portion of which is matched by the employer. Even though M&K has a generous matching arrangement, many employees do not take full advantage of the program. Therefore, Dan wrote the retirement flyer to remind them that it is never too early to plan for retirement. As it happens, he learned that many workers are failing to put away enough money for their retirement years.

The Research Process

After outlining his goals for the booklet, Dan began "surfing" through related information on the Internet. He made use of four pieces of information from a newspaper article found on an Internet database called "Human Resources Retrieval." Following are three of the themes he stressed, along with related information he used from the newspaper article.

Theme #1: We're living longer past retirement. The following changes occurred in years of life expected after age 65: for men, 12.8 in 1960, 13.1 in 1970, 14.1 in 1980, and 15.1 in 1990; for women, 15.8 in 1960, 17.0 in 1970, 18.3 in 1980, and 18.9 in 1990.

Theme #2: We cannot depend exclusively on the Canada Pension Plan. As many more people retire from the "Baby Boom" generation born between 1946 and 1964, fewer and fewer workers are paying into the Canada Pension Plan. The following numbers are actual and projected number of workers supporting each retiree: 41.9 in 1945, 8.6 in 1955, 4.0 in 1965, 3.2 in 1975, 3.3 in 1985, 3.3 in 1995, 3.1 in 2005, 2.7 in 2015, 2.2 in 2025, and 2.0 in 2035.

Theme #3: We should begin saving when we're young. If at age 25 you start saving $3,000 yearly in an RRSP, with a 9 percent annual return, you'll accumulate $166,971 by age 45, $457,685 by age 55, and $1,170,330 by age 65. If you start at age 35, you'll have $48,378 by 45, $166,971 by 55, and $457,685 by 65. If you start at age 45, you'll have $48,378 by 55 and $166,971 by 65.

Questions and Comments for Discussion

1. If you were presenting the data above in a research report, what format would you choose? Why? (See Chapter 12.)
2. Considering the four data sets Dan took from the newspaper article/Internet sources, which ones need documentation and which, if any, do not? Explain your answer.
3. Does the fact that the flyer will be sent to clients have any effect on your answer to question 2?
4. Complete a "works cited" reference for the data in Theme #1 above. Assume that Dan found the piece on the Internet on March 4, 2004.

COMMUNICATION CHALLENGE 15

"Twenty-Something: Have Degree, Won't Travel"

Zach Lipkowski has been out of Mountain College for almost a year and is still looking for his first real job. In the meantime, he has become a part-time ski instructor and worked in construction. With the help of a cheap apartment and a loan from his parents, he is managing to cover his bills, but he certainly hasn't used his environmental technology diploma from Mountain College. Now he finally has a break, having learned about an opening at M&K's Vancouver office. What follows is a description of Zach's background, along with some questions related to his application letter, résumé, and job interview.

A Checkered College Career

At Mountain College, Zach majored in environmental technology, a field that had interested him since childhood and that he thought promised a good career. His boyhood hobby of studying poison arrow frogs kindled his interest in ecosystems. It also led to a field trip to the Costa Rican rain forest in high school, with a local environmental group. He had even helped a well-known frog expert on a study, providing the researcher with observations about exotic frogs, which Zach kept as pets at home.

Zach considered many career options. Perhaps he could enter veterinary or medical school. Or he might do research for industry or the government in environmental science. Another possibility was graduate school in biology and eventually a teaching career. By the time he was in grade 12, however, it was clear his grades probably were not high enough to get into medical or vet school, or a Ph.D. program in biology. He graduated with a respectable average. Some low grades in subjects like history and English had hurt his average.

Despite some mediocre grades, he had the chance to work on an interesting project in which he studied "microbe digesters," which are organisms used to clean up pollution sites by converting toxins into nontoxic substances through the chemical digestive process. These critters are one of the newest environmental remediation techniques. Though only one member of a six-person team, he helped place microbes and then gather data at the site—a paper mill with toxic water. A team member who was a graduate student actually wrote most of the report, but Zach helped draft the summary of fieldwork. His modest part in the project had further inspired his "hands-on" interest.

Zach Meets the Job Market—Twice

Although Zach did not seem destined to inhabit the ivy-covered walls of graduate school, he thought he would have a good shot at entry-level jobs in environmental science, and he was right. He applied for many environmental science openings and got two good offers, both in Ontario.

After much thought he turned down both offers, wanting to stay in British Columbia because his mother was ill and, frankly, because he had always wanted to work in B.C. for his career. He was confident that an opportunity would open up as the job market improved. In August, when his mother recovered from her illness, Zach started working for a small construction firm as a day labourer, stopping for several months to work at a ski resort. He also took off a month for the trip he had always dreamed about—a fishing and canoeing adventure in Alaska.

By May, a year after graduation, he was regretting not having taken one of the job offers a year earlier. Most of his college friends were working in their fields, even if only at modest jobs, yet he was still doing the same kind of work he had done during summers in college. So Zach decided to reapply for entry-level jobs in environmental consulting firms. These jobs would involve the following main tasks: (1) visiting sites that needed environmental remediation, (2) overseeing lab tests, (3) forming conclusions and recommendations based on these tests, (4) writing reports that summarized activities, and (5) writing proposals and giving presentations to seek new work.

An Offer Brings Self-Assessment

This week the placement centre at Mountain College called Zach about an opening as an environmental scientist at M&K's Vancouver office. He planned to send a job letter and résumé and hoped for a chance to interview.

Taking the advice of a placement specialist at his old school, Zach evaluated his skills, abilities, and experience before writing his new letter and résumé. He jotted down these basic points about his background, some of which were detailed previously:

Positive

- Good work ethic
- Long-time interest in applied biology
- Did well in college in environmental technology courses
- Enjoys outdoors and travel
- Worked on microbe project in college, helping to write report

Neutral or Negative

- Did not take professional position after college
- Had mediocre college grade-point average
- Focused more on straight biology than on applied environmental science
- Got "C" in required technical writing course
- Had no outstanding extracurricular activities—study, part-time work in the dining hall, and "winding down" seemed to take most time

Questions and Comments for Discussion

Put yourself in Zach's shoes. As he prepares for the job application process, what advice would you give him on the following issues? Refer to the guidelines in the chapter in formulating your answers.

1. This chapter cites specific goals for cover letters. What should Zach emphasize in his letter to M&K?
2. Zach plans to submit a one-page résumé with his letter. What format should he select? Why?
3. Reread Zach's list of "positive" and "neutral or negative" features. Do you agree with his self-assessment? What features of his background will be of most concern to M&K? Why? What can Zach do to reduce the impact of negative items in his background during the entire application process?
4. Specifically, how should Zach deal with (a) his mediocre grade point average and (b) the year he has spent doing work unrelated to his intended profession?

5. If his letter and résumé interest M&K, Zach will interview with Mike Patak, an M&K project manager who knows very little about environmental sciences. His field is geology. Yet he manages projects that use the talents of a wide range of scientists, engineers, and technicians. What advice would you give Zach to make the best possible impression during the interview?

COMMUNICATION CHALLENGE 16

"An Editorial Adjustment"

M&K has hired a technical writer/editor at its Vancouver office, the smallest in the company. The office is finally generating enough reports and proposals to justify the addition. Evelyn Tobin started the job a month ago. Some of the Vancouver employees, who were comfortable with the old system, are having trouble adjusting to having an editor. What follows is some background on the hiring of Evelyn, the changes she is making in office writing, and some questions and comments for discussion.

Winds of Change

For years the staff at M&K's Vancouver office handled all their own writing and editing. Managers, engineers, scientists, accountants, trainers, and others had to draft and edit their own copy. Because they could depend on no one else to help, they gave great attention to the process and prided themselves on the quality of their writing. With the aid of several good secretaries, who often corrected grammar while they typed, the documents produced seemed adequate.

The growth of the office, however, increased the number and complexity of the reports and proposals that went out the door. The quality of editing began to decline. Those who observed this trend tied it to the following changes:

- Each writer simply had a higher volume of reports and proposals to complete, to keep the office competitive with similar firms.
- Increasing mobility in the workforce meant that fewer employees had received on-the-job training from old-timers at the office. In fact, more than half the positions requiring a degree or diploma had been filled in the last three years.
- This new workforce came from many different academic backgrounds and from other firms, making it harder than it used to be to impose a set "style" at the office.

The branch manager had observed these changes. Perhaps the last straw came when one long-time client returned a report with corrections made in red ink, along with this note: "You guys used to turn out good reports. What's happened?" With that embarrassment, the branch manager quickly hired an in-house technical writer/editor.

New Editor Takes Charge

When Evelyn Tobin started work a month ago, she met with all the staff to discuss her duties. At that meeting, there was general agreement that Evelyn would (1) provide writing advice, (2) perform a style edit for some reports, (3) be the lead writer for key proposals, (4) help with training in the office, and (5) do a quick grammar edit on as many reports as she had time to review.

With a diploma in technical writing and two years of editing experience with a government agency, Evelyn was used to simplifying writing that was confusing, convoluted, or too technical. Although she had not worked with technical firms like M&K, she assumed all her experience would translate to the new job. As it happened, most of her initial work involved style edits of reports that were to be sent to a mixed readership—some readers had a technical background, but others did not. Following are several changes Evelyn made in the reports, along with the original passages:

1. *Original:* "The purpose of the new well is to allow Tank, Inc., to perform monthly water-level monitoring at three locations at the oil field so that the results can be sent to the Water Quality Control Board."

   Evelyn's revision: "The new well will allow Tank, Inc., to monitor water levels at the oil field. Then the data will be sent to the Water Quality Control Board."

2. *Original:* "During the drilling of the boring, some soil sampling was performed by our technicians for the purpose of determining the exact location of the water table at the site."

   Evelyn's revision: "While drilling the boring, the technicians sampled soils to locate the water table."

3. *Original:* "This letter proposal has been prepared by us for use by whatever attorney you select so that he can present a ballpark figure of costs to the college governing board."

   Evelyn's revision: "We prepared this proposal for whatever lawyer you select. Then she can present a cost estimate to the college governing board."

4. *Original:* "At this point in time, it is our belief that you should give equal consideration to both alternatives, for both can afford you the opportunity to complete expansion of the office complex prior to summer."

   Evelyn's revision: "At this point, we believe you should consider both alternatives. Either one will allow you to expand the office by next summer."

5. *Original:* "There are a total of two ways we are recommending that you consider changing the plans in order to minimize the chance of flood damage."

   Evelyn's revision: "We recommend two changes to reduce the chance of flood damage."

Questions and Comments for Discussion

1. Study the before and after versions carefully.

   - Explain Evelyn's likely rationale for each of the changes she made.
   - Given the audience for the documents, was she right to make the changes?
   - Can you see changes in content that the original writer may find unacceptable?
   - Are there any cases where you need more context surrounding the passage to provide adequate answers to the two previous questions? Explain.

2. Would your answers to any of the previous questions change if the only audience for the report had been a group of technical experts?

3. Are there any alternative revisions that you think would be as effective as, or more effective than, the revisions Evelyn made?

4. Suggest what you think would be the best way for Evelyn to convey her revisions to the writer. Would this method change or stay the same as she gains more experience at the office?

5. One employee has come to Evelyn for advice on some grammar-checking software. He noted that his software stopped at every passive voice sentence and suggested an active voice replacement, and he wondered if he should always make the change. If you were in Evelyn's position, what answer would you give?

6. Discuss the effect that hiring a technical writer/editor might have on an office like M&K's in Vancouver. That is, how might the change affect the "corporate culture" of a such a company, where the professional staff spends from 25 to 50 percent of its time writing and editing documents?

7. If you were working at the Vancouver office, how would you feel about having your documents reviewed for style? for grammar?

Index